MATHEMATICS WORKSHOP

TEST PREPARATION

REVISED EDITION

Annotated Teacher's Edition

GLOBE FEARON EDUCATIONAL PUBLISHER
Upper Saddle River, New Jersey
www.globefearon.com

Developed with the assistance of Royce Editorial Associates, Inc.
Design and production: Electronic Publishing Center, Inc.
Cover design: Marjory Dressler

Printed in the United States of America

1 2 3 4 5 6 7 8 9 10 03 02 01 00 99

ISBN: 0-130-23363-3 (Student Edition)
ISBN: 0-130-23364-1 (Annotated Teacher's Edition)
Formerly titled Exam Preparation

GLOBE FEARON EDUCATIONAL PUBLISHER
Upper Saddle River, New Jersey
www.globefearon.com

TABLE OF CONTENTS

Chapter 3: Fractions and Fraction Computation

Chapter 4: Measurement

Chapter 5: Ratio, Proportion, Percent

Chapter 6: Probability and Statistics

Chapter 7: Geometry

Chapter 8: Perimeter, Area, Volume

Chapter 9: Integers

Chapter 10: Expressions and Equations

Chapter 11: Consumer Topics

TO THE STUDENT

Did you ever notice that your mathematics books always have lots of problems, but very few multiple-choice problems? And did you notice that the tests you have to pass are sometimes multiple-choice tests? Well, we noticed that, and decided to write *Mathematics Workshop: Test Preparation.*

This book has been written to help you do your best on standardized examinations. Every lesson provides multiple-choice problems for you to practice. In this book, you will study the topics that are covered on the exams, and practice solving problems like those given on the exams. In the end, you will have learned the material you need to know to pass the exams.

TO THE TEACHER

Does this situation sound familiar?

> Your students have to take a multiple-choice, standardized examination in mathematics. You feel great pressure to help them do well. The textbooks and workbooks available to you offer no specific guidance in preparing for multiple-choice exams, and little or no multiple-choice problems. Copies of previous standardized exams are either nonexistent or too scarce to fully prepare your students.

Situations like the one above led us to write *Mathematics Workshop: Test Preparation.* Its philosophy is that your students need day-to-day practice in the topics that are covered on standardized exams and day-to-day practice solving multiple-choice problems if they are to gain the confidence they need to succeed on those exams.

Mathematics Workshop: Test Preparation is divided into 11 chapters covering basic skills in arithmetic, measurement, geometry, statistics, and algebra. Each chapter is further divided into the following sections:

Test-Taking Strategies – two-page lessons that teach students special strategies to use on multiple-choice exams. For example, students learn to eliminate incorrect choices, work backwards from the answer choices, and look for key words.

Chapter Pretest – two-page, multiple-choice tests to help you evaluate your students' needs. The first page of each pretest covers prerequisite skills of the chapter; the second page covers the content of the chapter. Thus, you can use the pretest to both assess areas of weakness and judge prior knowledge of the chapter content.

Skills Lessons – two-page and one-page lessons that, first, present the skills, definitions and procedures students need to know, and then present multiple-choice problems for students to solve. Through this approach, students become familiar with the format of standardized exams and gain mastery of the lessons.

Chapter Test – two-page, multiple-choice tests to help you evaluate whether students have mastered the material of each chapter. Chapter tests can also be scored independently by the students, using the Scoring Chart provided on page 243.

In addition, some special features are:

Cumulative Review–four-page, multiple-choice reviews of previous chapters at the end of Chapters 3, 5, 7, 9, and 11. These reviews can be used to help acquaint students with the way diverse topics are typically covered on standardized examinations. Also included are enhanced multiple choice questions which go beyond simple computation, encouraging students to identify the correct answer and explain how they got it. Students will:

- Analyze relationships and patterns in a set of data.
- Use multiple strategies or approaches to determine a solution.
- Identify strategies or approaches to finding the appropriate response.
- Draw logical conclusions from a correct solution.

Problem Solving Lessons – two-page lessons in Chapters 1, 2, 3, and 5 covering multi-step problems, a topic with which students often need extra help.

Name ____ Class ____________ Date ____________

CHAPTER 1: NUMERATION AND WHOLE NUMBER COMPUTATION

TEST-TAKING STRATEGY: LOOK FOR KEY WORDS

Every test question has one or more words that are the key to understanding the question and to finding the answer. If you overlook or miss these words, you're likely to answer the question incorrectly.

Example 1: What is the value of the digit in the hundredths place? 3,895.062

Ⓐ 800 Ⓑ 8 Ⓒ 6 Ⓓ 0.06

There are two key words in this question. One is *hundredths.* It's easy to misread "hundredths" as "hundreds."

The other key word is *value*. The question asks for the *value* of the digit in the *hundredths* place, not simply which digit is in the hundredths place.

Circle these key words, then find the answer.

The digit in the hundredths place is 6. The value of that digit is $\frac{6}{100}$ or 0.06.

Therefore, the correct answer is choice Ⓓ.

Example 2: Judy Bloomberg orders 20 boxes of school tee shirts for $360. Each box contains 12 shirts. What is the price per shirt?

Ⓐ $1.50 Ⓑ $3 Ⓒ $18 Ⓓ $30

The key words here are *price per shirt*. Note that the solution requires two steps. First you have to find the price per box, then find the price per shirt.

Circle the key words and find the answer.

First, find the price per box.	$360 total price	÷	20 boxes	=	$18 price per box
Then, find the price per shirt.	$18 price per box	÷	12 number of shirts in each box	=	$1.50 price per shirt

The price per shirt is $1.50. Therefore, the correct answer is choice Ⓐ.

Circle the key word(s) in each of the following questions. Do not find the answer.

1. Which digit is in the thousandths place?
2. Sandra was born in 1974. Kyle was born two years earlier. How old is Kyle?
3. Which figures are congruent?
4. Laura bowled 145, 106, and 129. What was her average score?
5. What is the product of $3\frac{1}{3}$ and $\frac{1}{2}$ in simplest form?
6. A convertible's engine holds 6 quarts of oil. How many pints is that?

7. What is the sum of 6 and 8?

8. Find the difference between 36 and 48.

9. Round 436 to the nearest hundred.

10. Estimate the product: 321 × 16

11. Find 20% of 100.

12. Eighteen plus some number is twenty-two.

First circle key words to help you understand the question. Then find the answer.

Ⓒ **13.** What is the value of the digit in the tens place? 58,370

Ⓐ 7 Ⓑ 9 Ⓒ 70 Ⓓ 90

Ⓓ **14.** Find the difference between 25 and 17.

Ⓐ 136 Ⓑ 25 Ⓒ 9 Ⓓ 8

Ⓒ **15.** What is the word name for 580?

Ⓐ fifty-eight hundred

Ⓑ fifty-eight thousand

Ⓒ five hundred eighty

Ⓓ five thousand eighty

Ⓑ **16.** Lauren will turn 18 in 2002. In which year was she born?

Ⓐ 1972 Ⓑ 1984 Ⓒ 1992 Ⓓ 2010

Ⓑ **17.** Estimate the difference: 49 – 21

Ⓐ 70 Ⓑ 30 Ⓒ 20 Ⓓ 10

Ⓓ **18.** Estimate the sum: 115 + 63

Ⓐ 0 Ⓑ 100 Ⓒ 150 Ⓓ 180

Ⓑ **19.** Which is the numeral for eighty thousand six?

Ⓐ 8006 Ⓑ 80,006

Ⓒ 80,600 Ⓓ 80,000,006

Ⓓ **20.** Which is the numeral for nine hundred seventy-one?

Ⓐ 90,071 Ⓑ 9701 Ⓒ 997 Ⓓ 971

Ⓒ **21.** Which numbers are listed from least to greatest?

Ⓐ 22, 36, 103, 8 Ⓑ 103, 22, 36, 8

Ⓒ 8, 22, 36, 103 Ⓓ 36, 22, 103, 8

Ⓒ **22.** Which numbers are listed from the greatest to least?

Ⓐ 396, 412, 42, 421 Ⓑ 421, 42, 412, 396

Ⓒ 421, 412, 396, 42 Ⓓ 42, 412, 396, 421

Ⓓ **23.** Round 87,215 to the nearest hundred.

Ⓐ 87,300 Ⓑ 87,210 Ⓒ 87,000 Ⓓ 87,200

Ⓑ **24.** Round 4011 to the nearest ten.

Ⓐ 4100 Ⓑ 4010 Ⓒ 4001 Ⓓ 4000

Ⓐ **25.** What is the quotient of 65 and 5?

Ⓐ 13 Ⓑ 60 Ⓒ 70 Ⓓ 325

Ⓑ **26.** What is the sum of 28 and 13?

Ⓐ 364 Ⓑ 41 Ⓒ 31 Ⓓ 15

Ⓓ **27.** Brian bought 2 CDs on sale for $6.99 each. How much change will he receive from a $20 bill?

Ⓐ $18 Ⓑ $13.98 Ⓒ $13.01 Ⓓ $6.02

Ⓐ **28.** Lori bought 2 tapes on sale. One tape cost $5.49. The other tape cost $4.19. How much did she spend altogether?

Ⓐ $9.68 Ⓑ $9.58 Ⓒ $1.39 Ⓓ $1.30

Ⓒ **29.** Jane bought an airline ticket to Florida for $159. She received a $25 discount. What was the cost of her ticket?

Ⓐ $204 Ⓑ $184 Ⓒ $134 Ⓓ $124

Ⓐ **30.** Marilyn bought 3 scarves. Each scarf cost $1.99. How much did she spend in all?

Ⓐ $5.97 Ⓑ $3.88 Ⓒ $3.77 Ⓓ $2.02

Name ______________________________ Class __________ Date ______________

CHAPTER 1 PRETEST

Fill in the correct circle to answer each question.

Ⓑ **1.** What is the numeral for fifteen?

Ⓐ 10 Ⓑ 15 Ⓒ 50 Ⓓ 55

Ⓒ **2.** What is the numeral for one hundred?

Ⓐ 1 Ⓑ 10 Ⓒ 100 Ⓓ 1000

Ⓒ **3.** What is the numeral for sixty-four?

Ⓐ 4 Ⓑ 60 Ⓒ 64 Ⓓ 604

Ⓑ **4.** What is the numeral for three hundred forty-seven?

Ⓐ 3047 Ⓑ 347 Ⓒ 300 Ⓓ 47

Ⓑ **5.** Continue the sequence: 5, 10, 15, ■ ....

Ⓐ 16 Ⓑ 20 Ⓒ 25 Ⓓ 30

Ⓑ **6.** Continue the sequence: 100, 200, 300, ■ ....

Ⓐ 500 Ⓑ 400 Ⓒ 350 Ⓓ 301

Ⓒ **7.** Continue the sequence: 20, 40, 60, ■ ....

Ⓐ 61 Ⓑ 70 Ⓒ 80 Ⓓ 100

Ⓒ **8.** Continue the sequence: 50, 100, 150, 200, ■ ....

Ⓐ 201 Ⓑ 225 Ⓒ 250 Ⓓ 300

Ⓑ **9.** 68 = 6 tens ■ ones

Ⓐ 10 Ⓑ 8 Ⓒ 6 Ⓓ 0

Ⓒ **10.** 72 = ■ tens 2 ones

Ⓐ 0 Ⓑ 2 Ⓒ 7 Ⓓ 10

Ⓐ **11.** 90 = 9 tens ■ ones

Ⓐ 0 Ⓑ 1 Ⓒ 9 Ⓓ 10

Ⓑ **12.** 51 = ■ tens 1 one

Ⓐ 10 Ⓑ 5 Ⓒ 1 Ⓓ 0

Ⓐ **13.** What is the word name for 483?

Ⓐ four hundred eighty-three
Ⓑ forty eighty-three
Ⓒ eight forty-three
Ⓓ four hundred and eighty-three

Ⓓ **14.** What is the word name for 610?

Ⓐ six-ten
Ⓑ six hundred and ten
Ⓒ sixty-one ten
Ⓓ six hundred ten

Ⓓ **15.** What is the word name for 843?

Ⓐ three hundred forty-eight
Ⓑ eight hundred and forty-three
Ⓒ eight forty-three
Ⓓ eight hundred forty-three

Ⓒ **16.** What is the word name for 632?

Ⓐ sixty thirty-two
Ⓑ six thirty-two
Ⓒ six hundred thirty-two
Ⓓ six hundred and thirty-two

Ⓒ **17.** 7 + 6 = ■

Ⓐ 1 Ⓑ 12 Ⓒ 13 Ⓓ 42

Ⓒ **18.** 16 – 8 = ■

Ⓐ 0 Ⓑ 7 Ⓒ 8 Ⓓ 24

Ⓐ **19.** 54 – 6 = ■

Ⓐ 48 Ⓑ 9 Ⓒ 8 Ⓓ 6

Ⓒ **20.** 5 × 7 = ■

Ⓐ 12 Ⓑ 30 Ⓒ 35 Ⓓ 40

Ⓓ **21.** 7 + 5 = ■

Ⓐ 2 Ⓑ 9 Ⓒ 10 Ⓓ 12

Ⓐ **22.** 17 – ■ = 9

Ⓐ 8 Ⓑ 7 Ⓒ 6 Ⓓ 5

Ⓒ **23.** $8 \times ■ = 48$

Ⓐ 40 Ⓑ 8 Ⓒ 6 Ⓓ 5

Ⓐ **24.** $15 - 6 = ■$

Ⓐ 9 Ⓑ 8 Ⓒ 7 Ⓓ 6

Ⓑ **25.** $8 \times 4 = ■$

Ⓐ 30 Ⓑ 32 Ⓒ 40 Ⓓ 45

Ⓓ **26.** $3\overline{)27} = ■$

Ⓐ 6 Ⓑ 7 Ⓒ 8 Ⓓ 9

Ⓓ **27.** What is the numeral for twenty-three thousand five hundred ten?

Ⓐ 23,000 Ⓑ 23,500

Ⓒ 23,501 Ⓓ 23,510

Ⓑ **28.** What is the *value* of the digit 6 in 206,783?

Ⓐ 60,000 Ⓑ 6000

Ⓒ 600 Ⓓ 60

Ⓐ **29.** Compare: 8433 ■ 8403

Ⓐ $8433 > 8403$ Ⓑ $8433 < 8403$

Ⓒ $8433 = 8403$

Ⓒ **30.** Order from *greatest to least:* 700; 710; 701

Ⓐ 700; 701; 710 Ⓑ 710; 700; 701

Ⓒ 710; 701; 700 Ⓓ 701; 700; 710

Ⓒ **31.** Round 783 to the nearest *ten.*

Ⓐ 800 Ⓑ 790 Ⓒ 780 Ⓓ 700

Ⓓ **32.** Round 925 to the nearest *hundred.*

Ⓐ 1000 Ⓑ 930 Ⓒ 920 Ⓓ 900

Ⓒ **33.** Name the property shown: $7 + 0 = 7$

Ⓐ Commutative Ⓑ Associative

Ⓒ Addition Property of 0 Ⓓ Multiplication Property of 1

Ⓐ **34.** Name the property shown: $8 + 3 = 3 + 8$

Ⓐ Commutative Ⓑ Associative

Ⓒ Distributive Ⓓ Property of 1

Ⓑ **35.** Add:

$$\begin{array}{r} 4322 \\ +7809 \\ \hline \end{array}$$

Ⓐ 12,231 Ⓑ 12,131

Ⓒ 11,131 Ⓓ 11,121

Ⓓ **36.** Subtract:

$$\begin{array}{r} 6215 \\ -3780 \\ \hline \end{array}$$

Ⓐ 9995 Ⓑ 3535 Ⓒ 3335 Ⓓ 2435

Ⓒ **37.** Find the sum: $16 + 854 + 755$

Ⓐ 1515 Ⓑ 1525 Ⓒ 1625 Ⓓ 1769

Ⓑ **38.** Find the difference: $7501 - 488$

Ⓐ 2621 Ⓑ 7013 Ⓒ 7123 Ⓓ 7989

Ⓓ **39.** Multiply:

$$\begin{array}{r} 347 \\ \times 22 \\ \hline \end{array}$$

Ⓐ 1388 Ⓑ 6524 Ⓒ 7534 Ⓓ 7634

Ⓒ **40.** Find the quotient: $4603 \div 35$

Ⓐ 13 R 18 Ⓑ 131

Ⓒ 131 R 18 Ⓓ 137 R 8

Name ______________________ Class __________ Date ______________

1.1 PLACE VALUE

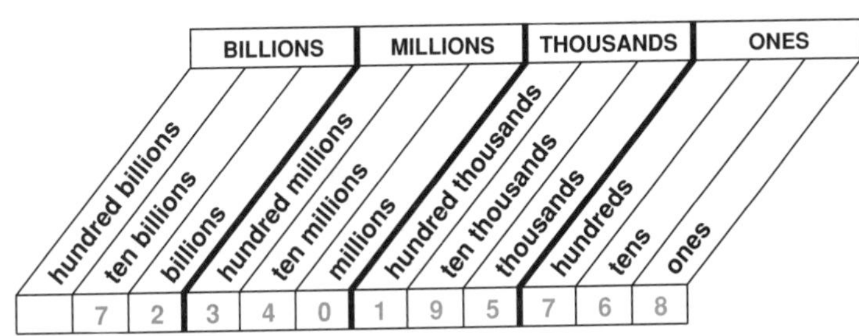

The number shown in the table above is written 72,340,195,768.

Example 1: To read the number, start at the left.

seventy-two billion, three hundred forty million, one hundred ninety-five thousand, seven hundred sixty-eight

Example 2: **A.** Find the *place value* of 3 in the number above.

- 3 is in the hundred millions place.

B. Find the *value* of the digit 3 in the number above.

- Locate the digit 3.
- Replace each digit to the right of 3 with zero.

300,000,000

Fill in the correct circle to answer each question.

(B) **1.** What is the numeral for nine thousand four hundred?

(A) 940 (B) 9400
(C) 90,400 (D) 900,400

(B) **2.** What is the numeral for forty-three thousand thirty?

(A) 43,300 (B) 43,030
(C) 430,030 (D) 43,003

(C) **3.** What is the *place value* of 3 in 48,301?

(A) ones (B) tens
(C) hundreds (D) thousands

(A) **4.** What is the *place value* of 6 in 682,901?

(A) hundred thousands (B) thousands
(C) hundreds (D) ones

(C) **5.** What is the *value* of the digit 7 in 73,891?

(A) 700 (B) 7000
(C) 70,000 (D) 7,000,000

(C) **6.** What is the *value* of the digit 1 in 5,430,016?

(A) 1000 (B) 100
(C) 10 (D) 1

(B) **7.** What is the word name for 5030?

(A) five thousand three hundred
(B) five thousand thirty
(C) five hundred three
(D) fifty-thirty

(D) **8.** What is the *place value* of 3 in 43,200?

(A) ones (B) tens
(C) hundreds (D) thousands

Ⓓ **9.** Which of the following is eight billion six hundred five?

Ⓐ 8,605,000,000 Ⓑ 8,000,605
Ⓒ 8605 Ⓓ 8,000,000,605

Ⓒ **10.** What is the *value* of 3 in 8135?

Ⓐ 3000 Ⓑ 300
Ⓒ 30 Ⓓ 3

Ⓑ **11.** The size of the Pacific Ocean is about 64,000,000 square miles. What is the word name for the underlined number?

Ⓐ six hundred forty million
Ⓑ sixty four million
Ⓒ sixty four thousand
Ⓓ sixty four

Ⓒ **12.** The average depth of the Pacific Ocean is 12,925 feet. What is the word name for the underlined number?

Ⓐ one hundred thousand nine hundred twenty-five
Ⓑ one hundred thousand nine hundred five
Ⓒ twelve thousand nine hundred twenty-five
Ⓓ twelve thousand nine hundred five

Ⓒ **13.** What is the number for thirty thousand sixteen?

Ⓐ 300,016 Ⓑ 30,160
Ⓒ 30,016 Ⓓ 3016

Ⓓ **14.** What is the *value* of 9 in 6019?

Ⓐ 9000 Ⓑ 900
Ⓒ 90 Ⓓ 9

Ⓑ **15.** What is the *place value* of the digit 0 in the number 30,824?

Ⓐ ten thousands Ⓑ thousands
Ⓒ hundreds Ⓓ tens

Ⓓ **16.** What is the *place value* of the digit 7 in 372,045,263?

Ⓐ thousands Ⓑ ten thousands
Ⓒ millions Ⓓ ten millions

Ⓐ **17.** What is the numeral for one thousand five hundred twenty?

Ⓐ 1520 Ⓑ 1500
Ⓒ 1250 Ⓓ 1020

Ⓐ **18.** Which of the following is fifteen thousand nine hundred eighty-nine?

Ⓐ 15,989 Ⓑ 15,998
Ⓒ 150,989 Ⓓ 159,890

Ⓓ **19.** Which of the following is seven thousand fifty-eight?

Ⓐ 70,058 Ⓑ 7580
Ⓒ 7508 Ⓓ 7058

Ⓓ **20.** What is the numeral for forty-three thousand twenty-one?

Ⓐ 430,021 Ⓑ 403,021
Ⓒ 43,210 Ⓓ 43,021

Ⓓ **21.** What digit is in the *hundreds* place in the number 2078?

Ⓐ 8 Ⓑ 7
Ⓒ 2 Ⓓ 0

Ⓑ **22.** Choose the number name for five hundred eighty thousand.

Ⓐ 500,080,000 Ⓑ 580,000
Ⓒ 508,000 Ⓓ 58,000

Ⓒ **23.** What is the *value* of 6 in 36,041?

Ⓐ 60 Ⓑ 600
Ⓒ 6000 Ⓓ 60,000

Ⓑ **24.** What is the *place value* of 5 in 2594?

Ⓐ thousands Ⓑ hundreds
Ⓒ tens Ⓓ ones

Name ________________________ Class ________ Date ____________

1.2 COMPARING AND ORDERING NUMBERS

Example 1: Compare 83,421 and 83,521. Use >, <, or =.

- Line up the digits.
- Start at the left.
- Compare digits until two digits are different.

83,421
83,521 — 4 < 5, therefore 83,421 < 83,521

Since 4 is less than 5, 83,421 is less than 83,521.

Example 2: Order 8502, 8205, and 8225 from *greatest to least*.

- Proceed as in Example 1, to find the greatest number. Since 5 > 2, 8502 is the greatest number.

8502
8205
8225 — 5 > 2, therefore 8502 is the greatest number

- Compare the remaining numbers.

8205
8225 — 2 > 0, therefore 8225 > 8205

The numbers in order from *greatest to least* are 8502; 8225; 8205.

Fill in the correct circle to answer each question.

Ⓒ **1.** Compare: 856 ■ 855

Ⓐ 856 < 855 Ⓑ 856 = 855
Ⓒ 856 > 855

Ⓐ **2.** Compare: 23,204 ■ 23,402

Ⓐ 23,204 < 23,402 Ⓑ 23,204 > 23,402
Ⓒ 23,204 = 23,204

Ⓐ **3.** Which number has the *least* value?
102,358; 120,358; 102,538; 120,538

Ⓐ 102,358 Ⓑ 102,538
Ⓒ 120,358 Ⓓ 120,538

Ⓓ **4.** Which number has the *greatest* value?
17,824; 17,924; 17,294; 20,824

Ⓐ 17,294 Ⓑ 17,824
Ⓒ 17,924 Ⓓ 20,824

Ⓑ **5.** Order from *least to greatest:*
67,021; 67,201; 67,102

Ⓐ 67,021; 67,201; 67,102
Ⓑ 67,021; 67,102; 67,201
Ⓒ 67,201; 67,102; 67,021
Ⓓ 67,201; 67,021; 67,102

Ⓒ **6.** Order from *greatest to least:*
113,845; 113,832; 113,854

Ⓐ 113,832; 113,854; 113,845
Ⓑ 113,854; 113,832; 113,845
Ⓒ 113,854; 113,845; 113,832
Ⓓ 113,845; 113,854; 113,832

Ⓑ **7.** Compare: 23,204 ■ 23,402

Ⓐ 23,204 > 23,402 Ⓑ 23,204 < 23,402
Ⓒ 23,204 = 23,402

Ⓑ **8.** Compare: 598,689 ■ 598,869

Ⓐ 598,689 > 598,869 Ⓑ 598,689 < 598,869
Ⓒ 598,689 = 598,869

Ⓐ **9.** Compare: 710,923 ■ 710,823

Ⓐ 710,923 > 710,823 Ⓑ 710,923 < 710,823
Ⓒ 710,923 = 710,823

Ⓑ **10.** Compare: 52,035 ■ 52,335

Ⓐ 52,035 > 52,335 Ⓑ 52,035 < 52,335
Ⓒ 52,035 = 52,335

(A) **11.** Which statement is *true?*

(A) $9702 > 9700$ (B) $9702 < 9700$

(C) $9702 = 9700$

(B) **12.** Which statement is *true?*

(A) $645 > 645$ (B) $645 = 645$

(C) $645 < 645$

(A) **13.** Which number has the *greatest* value?
8902; 8920; 8209; 2902

(A) 8920 (B) 8902

(C) 8209 (D) 2902

(D) **14.** Which number has the *least* value?
55,892; 55,792; 55,092; 55,192

(A) 55,892 (B) 55,792

(C) 55,192 (D) 55,092

(C) **15.** Order from *greatest to least:* 8936; 8930; 8932

(A) 8936; 8930; 8932

(B) 8930; 8932; 8936

(C) 8936; 8932; 8930

(D) 8930; 8936; 8932

(D) **16.** Order from *least to greatest:*
105,726; 175,726; 125,726

(A) 125,726; 105,726; 175,726

(B) 105,726; 175,726; 125,726

(C) 175,726; 125,726; 105,726

(D) 105,726; 125,726; 175,726

Use the table below to answer questions 17 and 18.

Tallest Skyscrapers in U.S. Cities

Building	Location	Height
World Trade Center	New York	1350 feet
Sears Tower	Chicago	1454 feet
Standard Oil Building	Chicago	1136 feet
Empire State Building	New York	1250 feet
John Hancock Center	Chicago	1127 feet

(B) **17.** Which building is the tallest?

(A) World Trade Center

(B) Sears Tower

(C) Empire State Building

(D) John Hancock Center

(D) **18.** Which of the Chicago skyscrapers is the shortest?

(A) Standard Oil Building

(B) Sears Tower

(C) Empire State Building

(D) John Hancock Center

Find the answer.

(C) **19.** Gwen Baker is figuring her monthly budget. She spends $290 on food, $125 on entertainment, $480 on rent, $160 on gasoline, and $110 on savings. Order her expenses from *greatest to least.*

(A) $480; $160; $290; $125; $110

(B) $290; $480; $160; $125; $110

(C) $480; $290; $160; $125; $110

(D) $480; $290; $125; $160; $110

(D) **20.** Which set of whole numbers shows its elements ordered from *least to greatest?*

(A) {215,453; 215,543; 215,435}

(B) {215,435; 215,543; 215,453}

(C) {215,543; 215,453; 215,435}

(D) {215,435; 215,453; 215,543}

Name ____________________ Class ________ Date ____________

1.3 ROUNDING NUMBERS

To round a number to a given place, find the digit to the right of that place.

If the digit is **less than 5,** round down.

REMEMBER: To round down, do not change the number in the place you are rounding to. Simply, replace each digit to the right of that place with zero.

If the digit is **5 or greater,** round up.

To round up, increase the number in the place you are rounding to by 1. Then, replace each digit to the right of that place with zero.

Example 1: Round 16,853 to the nearest *ten.*

- 3 is to the right of the *tens* place: 16,853
- $3 < 5$. Round down: 16,850

16,853 rounded to the nearest *ten* is 16,850.

Example 2: Round 16,853 to the nearest *hundred.*

- 5 is to the right of the *hundreds* place: 16,853
- $5 = 5$. Round up: 16,900

16,853 rounded to the nearest *hundred* is 16,900.

Example 3: Round 16,853 to the nearest *thousand.*

- 8 is to the right of the *thousands* place: 16,853
- $8 > 5$. Round up: 17,000

16,853 rounded to the nearest *thousand* is 17,000.

Fill in the correct circle for each question.

(B) **1.** Round 582 to the nearest *ten.*

(A) 590 (B) 580 (C) 570 (D) 500

(D) **2.** Round 6021 to the nearest *ten.*

(A) 6000 (B) 6010 (C) 6021 (D) 6020

(D) **3.** Round 758 to the nearest *hundred.*

(A) 700 (B) 750 (C) 760 (D) 800

(A) **4.** Round 74,509 to the nearest *hundred.*

(A) 74,500 (B) 74,600 (C) 75,000 (D) 80,000

(D) **5.** Round 9267 to the nearest *thousand.*

(A) 10,000 (B) 9270 (C) 9200 (D) 9000

(A) **6.** Round 823,619 to the nearest *thousand.*

(A) 824,000 (B) 823,600 (C) 823,000 (D) 820,000

(C) **7.** Round 280 to the nearest *hundred.*

(A) 200 (B) 290 (C) 300 (D) 280

(C) **8.** Round 483,509 to the nearest *thousand.*

(A) 483,000 (B) 483,500 (C) 484,000 (D) 500,000

(C) **9.** What is 8623 rounded to the nearest *ten?*

(A) 9000 (B) 8630 (C) 8620 (D) 8600

(B) **10.** Round 773 to the nearest *hundred.*

(A) 1,000 (B) 800 (C) 780 (D) 700

(B) **11.** Round 469 to the nearest *ten.*

(A) 500 (B) 470 (C) 460 (D) 400

(B) **12.** Round 825,107 to the nearest *hundred.*

(A) 826,000 (B) 825,100 (C) 825,000 (D) 800,000

Ⓐ **13.** The state of Pennsylvania has 347 covered bridges. Round that number to the nearest *hundred.*

Ⓐ 300 Ⓑ 340 Ⓒ 350 Ⓓ 400

Ⓓ **14.** The Evergreen Point Bridge in Washington is 7518 feet long. Round that number to the nearest *thousand.*

Ⓐ 7000 Ⓑ 7500 Ⓒ 7520 Ⓓ 8000

Ⓓ **15.** Round 1496 to the nearest *thousand.*

Ⓐ 1500 Ⓑ 1490 Ⓒ 1400 Ⓓ 1000

Ⓓ **16.** What is 91,208 rounded to the nearest *ten?*

Ⓐ 90,000 Ⓑ 91,000 Ⓒ 91,200 Ⓓ 91,210

Ⓑ **17.** Round 85,710 to the nearest *thousand.*

Ⓐ 90,000 Ⓑ 86,000 Ⓒ 85,000 Ⓓ 80,000

Ⓐ **18.** What is 823 rounded to the nearest *hundred?*

Ⓐ 800 Ⓑ 820 Ⓒ 830 Ⓓ 900

Ⓒ **19.** Round 7064 to the nearest *ten.*

Ⓐ 7100 Ⓑ 7070 Ⓒ 7060 Ⓓ 7000

Ⓒ **20.** Round 17,955 to the nearest *thousand.*

Ⓐ 17,000 Ⓑ 17,900 Ⓒ 18,000 Ⓓ 20,000

Ⓓ **21.** What is 7368 rounded to the nearest *hundred?*

Ⓐ 7000 Ⓑ 7300 Ⓒ 7370 Ⓓ 7400

Ⓒ **22.** Round 458 to the nearest *ten.*

Ⓐ 400 Ⓑ 450 Ⓒ 460 Ⓓ 500

Ⓒ **23.** Round 47,029 to the nearest *thousand.*

Ⓐ 50,000 Ⓑ 48,000 Ⓒ 47,000 Ⓓ 40,000

Ⓒ **24.** What is 37,888 rounded to the nearest *thousand?*

Ⓐ 37,000 Ⓑ 37,900 Ⓒ 38,000 Ⓓ 40,000

Use Table 1.3 to answer questions 25-28.

Table 1.3

Food	Calories
Hamburger	252
Pizza (1 slice)	145
Apple	58
Tuna fish sandwich	278

Ⓐ **25.** Round the number of calories in a hamburger to the nearest *hundred.*

Ⓐ 300 Ⓑ 250 Ⓒ 200 Ⓓ 100

Ⓒ **26.** Round the number of calories in a tuna fish sandwich to the nearest *ten.*

Ⓐ 200 Ⓑ 270 Ⓒ 280 Ⓓ 300

Ⓐ **27.** Round the number of calories in a slice of pizza to the nearest *hundred.*

Ⓐ 100 Ⓑ 140 Ⓒ 150 Ⓓ 200

Ⓑ **28.** Round the number of calories in an apple to the nearest *ten.*

Ⓐ 100 Ⓑ 60 Ⓒ 55 Ⓓ 50

Ⓑ **29.** Round 15,307 to the nearest *hundred.*

Ⓐ 15,000 Ⓑ 15,300 Ⓒ 15,310 Ⓓ 15,400

Ⓐ **30.** What is 6541 rounded to the nearest *thousand?*

Ⓐ 7000 Ⓑ 6540 Ⓒ 6500 Ⓓ 6000

Ⓒ **31.** Round 2085 to the nearest *ten.*

Ⓐ 2000 Ⓑ 2080 Ⓒ 2090 Ⓓ 2100

Ⓒ **32.** Round 54,096 to the nearest *thousand.*

Ⓐ 55,000 Ⓑ 54,100 Ⓒ 54,000 Ⓓ 50,000

Ⓓ **33.** What is 4708 rounded to the nearest *hundred?*

Ⓐ 5000 Ⓑ 4000 Ⓒ 4800 Ⓓ 4700

Ⓒ **34.** Round 158 to the nearest *ten.*

Ⓐ 100 Ⓑ 150 Ⓒ 160 Ⓓ 200

Name ______________________ Class __________ Date __________

1.4 PROPERTIES OF WHOLE NUMBERS

These properties will help you add and multiply.

Properties of Addition

1. **Commutative Property of Addition**

   Changing the order of the addends does *not* change the sum.

   $3 + 5 = 5 + 3$

2. **Associative Property of Addition**

   Changing the grouping of the addends does *not* change the sum.

   $(4 + 2) + 7 = 4 + (2 + 7)$

3. **Addition Property of Zero**

   The sum of any number and 0 is that number.

   $8 + 0 = 8$

Properties of Multiplication

4. **Commutative Property of Multiplication**

   Changing the order of the factors does *not* change the product.

   $4 \times 6 = 6 \times 4$

5. **Associative Property of Multiplication**

   Changing the grouping of the factors does *not* change the product.

   $(2 \times 9) \times 3 = 2 \times (9 \times 3)$

6. **Multiplication Property of One**

   The product of any number and 1 is that number.

   $8 \times 1 = 8$

7. **The Distributive Property**

   This property ties multiplication and addition together.

   $6 \times (7 + 3) = (6 \times 7) + (6 \times 3)$

Fill in the correct circle to answer each question.

Ⓒ **1.** Name the property shown: $7 + 0 = 7$

Ⓐ Commutative
Ⓑ Distributive
Ⓒ Addition Property of 0
Ⓓ Multiplication Property of 1

Ⓐ **2.** Which property is shown?
$2 + 6 = 6 + 2$

Ⓐ Commutative
Ⓑ Associative
Ⓒ Distributive
Ⓓ Multiplication Property of 1

Ⓑ **3.** Which property is shown?
$2 \times (4 + 3) = (2 \times 4) + (2 \times 3)$

Ⓐ Associative
Ⓑ Distributive
Ⓒ Multiplication Property of 1
Ⓓ Addition Property of 0

Ⓓ **4.** Name the property shown: $3 \times 1 = 3$

Ⓐ Commutative
Ⓑ Associative
Ⓒ Addition Property of 0
Ⓓ Multiplication Property of 1

Ⓑ **5.** Name the property shown.
$(2 + 3) + 4 = 2 + (3 + 4)$

Ⓐ Commutative
Ⓑ Associative
Ⓒ Distributive
Ⓓ Multiplication Property of 1

Ⓐ **6.** Which property is shown?
$a + b = b + a$

Ⓐ Commutative
Ⓑ Distributive
Ⓒ Addition Property of 0
Ⓓ Multiplication Property of 1

Ⓐ **7.** Which equation is true?

Ⓐ $70 \times 0 = 0$ Ⓑ $70 \times 0 = 70$

Ⓒ $70 + 0 = 0$ Ⓓ $70 \times 1 = 0$

Ⓓ **8.** Which property is shown? $1 + 0 = 1$

Ⓐ Associative Ⓑ Distributive

Ⓒ Multiplication Property of 1 Ⓓ Addition Property of 0

Ⓑ **9.** Name the property shown.
$(9 + 3) + 4 = 9 + (3 + 4)$

Ⓐ Commutative Ⓑ Associative

Ⓒ Distributive Ⓓ Property of 1

Ⓒ **10.** Name the property shown.
$a \times (b + c) = (a \times b) + (a \times c)$

Ⓐ Associative Ⓑ Commutative

Ⓒ Distributive Ⓓ Property of 0

Ⓒ **11.** Complete: $6 + (2 + 1) = (6 + 2) +$ ■

Ⓐ 6 Ⓑ 2 Ⓒ 1 Ⓓ 0

Ⓒ **12.** Complete: $(3 + 5) + 7 = 3 + ($ ■ $+ 7)$

Ⓐ 0 Ⓑ 3 Ⓒ 5 Ⓓ 7

Ⓐ **13.** Complete: $24 +$ ■ $= 24$

Ⓐ 0 Ⓑ 1 Ⓒ 24 Ⓓ 48

Ⓓ **14.** Complete: $236 + 18 = 18 +$ ■

Ⓐ 0 Ⓑ 1 Ⓒ 18 Ⓓ 236

Ⓓ **15.** Complete: $6395 +$ ■ $= 6395$

Ⓐ 6395 Ⓑ 100 Ⓒ 1 Ⓓ 0

Ⓒ **16.** Complete: $47 \times 1 =$ ■

Ⓐ 0 Ⓑ 1 Ⓒ 47 Ⓓ 471

Ⓐ **17.** Which example shows the Distributive Property?

Ⓐ $4 \times (7 + 2) = (4 \times 7) + (4 \times 2)$

Ⓑ $3 \times 1 = 3$

Ⓒ $8 + 7 = 7 + 8$

Ⓓ $(1 + 3) + 9 = 1 + (3 + 9)$

18. Which example shows the Property of 1?
Ⓐ

Ⓐ $1735 \times 1 = 1735$

Ⓑ $1735 + 0 = 1735$

Ⓒ $(1735 \times 1) = 1$

Ⓓ $1735 + 0 = 0$

Ⓒ **19.** Which property is shown?
$635 \times 1 = 635$

Ⓐ Commutative Ⓑ Associative

Ⓒ Multiplication Property of 1 Ⓓ Addition Property of 0

Ⓐ **20.** Which property is shown?
$a \times 1 = a$

Ⓐ Multiplication Property of 1 Ⓑ Commutative

Ⓒ Addition Property of 1 Ⓓ Distributive

Ⓑ **21.** $3682 \times (371 + 562) =$

Ⓐ $(3682 + 371) \times (3682 + 562)$

Ⓑ $(3682 \times 371) + (3682 \times 562)$

Ⓒ $(371 + 3682) + 562$

Ⓓ $371\ (3682 + 562)$

Ⓒ **22.** Which statement is always true?

Ⓐ $a + b + c = a \times b \times c$

Ⓑ $ab + c = a + bc$

Ⓒ $(a + b) + c = a + (b + c)$

Ⓓ $(a + b) + c = ab + c$

Ⓒ **23.** Name the property shown.
$(18 + 22) + 4 = 18 + (22 + 4)$

Ⓐ Commutative Property of Multiplication

Ⓑ Commutative Property of Addition

Ⓒ Associative Property of Addition

Ⓓ Distributive Property

Ⓒ **24.** Name the property shown.
$2 \times (18 + 37) = (2 \times 18) + (2 \times 37)$

Ⓐ Associative Property of Addition

Ⓑ Associative Property of Multiplication

Ⓒ Distributive Property

Ⓓ Commutative Property of Addition

Name ______________________ Class __________ Date ______________

1.5 ADDING WHOLE NUMBERS

Example 1: Add: 9639 + 604

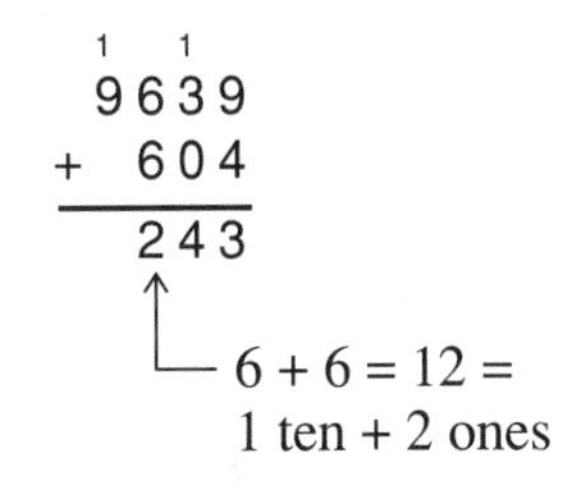

Add the ones. Regroup. Carry.	Add the tens.	Add the hundreds. Regroup. Carry.	Add the thousands. Regroup.
$\begin{array}{r} \scriptstyle 1 \\ 9639 \\ +\ 604 \\ \hline 3 \end{array}$	$\begin{array}{r} \scriptstyle 1 \\ 9639 \\ +\ 604 \\ \hline 43 \end{array}$	$\begin{array}{r} \scriptstyle 1\ \ 1 \\ 9639 \\ +\ 604 \\ \hline 243 \end{array}$	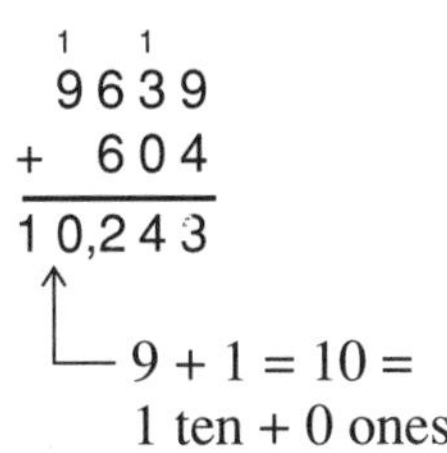 $\begin{array}{r} \scriptstyle 1\ \ 1 \\ 9639 \\ +\ 604 \\ \hline 10{,}243 \end{array}$
9 + 4 = 13 = 1 ten + 3 ones		6 + 6 = 12 = 1 ten + 2 ones	9 + 1 = 10 = 1 ten + 0 ones

REMEMBER: Always **estimate** to see if your answer is **reasonable.**

- Round each addend to the greatest place.

$$\begin{array}{r} 9639 \\ +\ 604 \\ \hline \end{array} \begin{array}{c} \longrightarrow \\ \longrightarrow \\ \end{array} \begin{array}{r} 10{,}000 \\ 600 \\ \hline 10{,}600 \end{array}$$

The estimate and the exact answer are close. Therefore, 10,243 is a reasonable answer.

Fill in the correct circle to answer each question.

Ⓐ **1.** Add: $\begin{array}{r} 33{,}622 \\ +\ 14{,}980 \\ \hline \end{array}$

Ⓐ 48,602 Ⓑ 48,502
Ⓒ 47,602 Ⓓ 47,600

Ⓒ **2.** Add: $\begin{array}{r} 478{,}027 \\ +\ 6992 \\ \hline \end{array}$

Ⓐ 484,019 Ⓑ 484,919
Ⓒ 485,019 Ⓓ 585,019

Ⓑ **3.** Add: 85 + 1352 + 8485

Ⓐ 10,687 Ⓑ 9922 Ⓒ 9912 Ⓓ 9822

Ⓒ **4.** What is the sum of 559 and 321?

Ⓐ 238 Ⓑ 870 Ⓒ 880 Ⓓ 8710

Ⓒ **5.** Estimate the sum by rounding: 942 + 683

Ⓐ 1000 Ⓑ 1200 Ⓒ 1600 Ⓓ 2000

Ⓒ **6.** Estimate the sum by rounding: 2316 + 3692

Ⓐ 10,000 Ⓑ 8000 Ⓒ 6000 Ⓓ 3000

Ⓑ **7.** The Statue of Liberty is 151 feet high. Its base is 65 feet high, and the pedestal is 89 feet high. How tall is the figure altogether?

Ⓐ 205 feet Ⓑ 305 feet
Ⓒ 395 feet Ⓓ 1691 feet

Ⓒ **8.** The Country Bake Shop sold 582 loaves of bread on Friday. They sold 75 more loaves than that on Saturday. How many loaves did they sell on Saturday?

Ⓐ 507 loaves Ⓑ 557 loaves
Ⓒ 657 loaves Ⓓ 1332 loaves

Ⓒ **9.** Add: 7328 + 809

Ⓐ 7127 Ⓑ 8135
Ⓒ 8137 Ⓓ 15,418

Ⓒ **10.** Estimate the sum by rounding: 63,402 + 47,824

Ⓐ 50,000 Ⓑ 80,000
Ⓒ 110,000 Ⓓ 150,000

Ⓑ **11.** 5241 + 28,902 = ■

Ⓐ 81,312 Ⓑ 34,143 Ⓒ 33,143 Ⓓ 24,143

Ⓒ **12.** What is the sum of 492 and 508?

Ⓐ 900 Ⓑ 990 Ⓒ 1000 Ⓓ 9910

Ⓐ **13.** Each day, the Indian Elephant at the Bronx Zoo eats 28 pounds of grain, 16 pounds of fruits and vegetables, and 14 pounds of grass. How much food does the elephant eat altogether?

Ⓐ 58 pounds Ⓑ 57 pounds

Ⓒ 48 pounds Ⓓ 47 pounds

Ⓓ **14.** On Saturday, 329 tickets were sold for the morning Dolphin Show. In the afternoon, 275 tickets were sold. How many tickets were sold for both shows?

Ⓐ 504 tickets Ⓑ 594 tickets

Ⓒ 603 tickets Ⓓ 604 tickets

Ⓑ **15.** Estimate the sum by rounding:
23,692 + 17,480

Ⓐ 20,000 Ⓑ 40,000 Ⓒ 60,000 Ⓓ 80,000

Ⓑ **16.** Estimate the sum by rounding:
895 + 337 + 467

Ⓐ 1000 Ⓑ 1700 Ⓒ 2500 Ⓓ 3000

Ⓒ **17.** Add: 3399 + 47,002

Ⓐ 50,301 Ⓑ 50,391

Ⓒ 50,401 Ⓓ 80,992

Ⓓ **18.** 289,420 + 136,571 = ■

Ⓐ 325,991 Ⓑ 415,991

Ⓒ 423,991 Ⓓ 425,991

Ⓑ **19.** The Allens left St. Louis and drove 1179 miles to Boston. Then they drove 213 miles to New York. The Allens followed the same route home. How many miles did they drive in all?

Ⓐ 1392 miles Ⓑ 2784 miles

Ⓒ 3309 miles Ⓓ 9918 miles

Ⓑ **20.** The Mississippi River is 3872 miles long. The Nile River is 273 miles longer than the Mississippi. How long is the Nile River?

Ⓐ 6602 miles Ⓑ 4145 miles

Ⓒ 3599 miles Ⓓ 3145 miles

Ⓐ **21.** Add:

$$\begin{array}{r} 5689 \\ 48 \\ +\ 713 \\ \hline \end{array}$$

Ⓐ 6450 Ⓑ 6330 Ⓒ 5430 Ⓓ 5350

Ⓑ **22.** Add: 43 + 27 + 19

Ⓐ 79 Ⓑ 89 Ⓒ 97 Ⓓ 98

Ⓑ **23.** 4120 + 682 + 319 = ■

Ⓐ 14,130 Ⓑ 5121 Ⓒ 5011 Ⓓ 4011

Ⓒ **24.** What is the sum of 1526 + 97?

Ⓐ 1513 Ⓑ 1613 Ⓒ 1623 Ⓓ 11,226

Ⓐ **25.** Add:

$$\begin{array}{r} 4923 \\ +\ 8704 \\ \hline \end{array}$$

Ⓐ 13,627 Ⓑ 12,727

Ⓒ 12,627 Ⓓ 12,527

Ⓒ **26.** Estimate the sum by rounding:
9207 + 8802

Ⓐ 10,000 Ⓑ 12,000

Ⓒ 18,000 Ⓓ 22.000

Ⓐ **27.** Add:

$$\begin{array}{r} 27{,}143 \\ 12{,}895 \\ +\ 422 \\ \hline \end{array}$$

Ⓐ 40,460 Ⓑ 40,350

Ⓒ 39,450 Ⓓ 39,350

Ⓑ **28.** Estimate the sum by rounding:
392 + 476 + 220

Ⓐ 900 Ⓑ 1100 Ⓒ 1500 Ⓓ 1800

Name____________________ Class ________ Date __________

1.6 SUBTRACTING WHOLE NUMBERS

Example 1: Subtract: 4702 – 387

Regroup.

```
  6 10
 4 7̸ 0̸ 2
-  3 8 7
 -------
```

Regroup again.

```
     9
  6 1̸0 12
 4 7̸ 0̸ 2̸
-  3 8 7
 -------
```

Subtract.

```
     9
  6 1̸0 12
 4 7̸ 0̸ 2̸
-  3 8 7
 -------
 4 3 1 5
```

REMEMBER: Always **estimate** to see if your answer is **reasonable.**

- Round each number to the greatest place.

```
  4702  →  5000
-  387  →   400
           ----
           4600
```

The estimate and the exact answer are close. Therefore, 4315 is a reasonable answer.

Fill in the correct circle to answer each question.

(B) **1.** Subtract: 27,890 − 14,986

Ⓐ 2904 Ⓑ 12,904 Ⓒ 13,104 Ⓓ 13,904

(D) **2.** Subtract: 923,658 − 14,780

Ⓐ 918,878 Ⓑ 911,138 Ⓒ 908,978 Ⓓ 908,878

(B) **3.** 9452 – 895 = ■

Ⓐ 1520 Ⓑ 8557 Ⓒ 8567 Ⓓ 9557

(C) **4.** Subtract 63 from 802.

Ⓐ 865 Ⓑ 749 Ⓒ 739 Ⓓ 172

(B) **5.** Estimate the difference by rounding: 8621 – 6340

Ⓐ 1000 Ⓑ 3000 Ⓒ 6000 Ⓓ 7500

(C) **6.** Estimate the difference by rounding: 24,863 – 8845

Ⓐ 5000 Ⓑ 11,000 Ⓒ 16,000 Ⓓ 21,000

(A) **7.** A newborn baby has 300 bones. Some of these bones join, forming 206 bones in an adult. How many more bones does a baby have than an adult?

Ⓐ 94 bones Ⓑ 104 bones Ⓒ 194 bones Ⓓ 506 bones

(B) **8.** The Queen Line Cruise Ship booked 1072 passengers for a trip to Australia. There were 196 cancellations. How many people took the cruise?

Ⓐ 112 people Ⓑ 876 people Ⓒ 976 people Ⓓ 1268 people

(D) **9.** Subtract: 34,023 − 14,860

Ⓐ 29,163 Ⓑ 20,843 Ⓒ 19,263 Ⓓ 19,163

(B) **10.** What is the difference between 4875 and 694?

Ⓐ 4161 Ⓑ 4181 Ⓒ 4281 Ⓓ 5569

Ⓒ **11.** Estimate the difference by rounding: 695,821 – 419,788

Ⓐ 1,000,000 Ⓑ 500,000
Ⓒ 300,000 Ⓓ 100,000

Ⓑ **12.** Find the difference: 51,036 – 742

Ⓐ 51,394 Ⓑ 50,294
Ⓒ 50,274 Ⓓ 41,394

Use Table 1.6A to answer questions 13-14.

Table 1.6A

Ocean	Average Depth	
Pacific	12,925	feet
Indian	12,598	feet
Atlantic	11,730	feet
Arctic	3,407	feet

Ⓒ **13.** On the average, about how much deeper is the Pacific Ocean than the Atlantic Ocean?

Ⓐ 24,655 feet Ⓑ 1295 feet
Ⓒ 1195 feet Ⓓ 327 feet

Ⓑ **14.** About how much deeper is the Indian Ocean than the Atlantic Ocean?

Ⓐ 668 feet Ⓑ 868 feet
Ⓒ 1868 feet Ⓓ 24,328 feet

Ⓓ **15.** Subtract: $\begin{array}{r} 3750 \\ -2954 \\ \hline \end{array}$

Ⓐ 1796 Ⓑ 896 Ⓒ 806 Ⓓ 796

Ⓒ **16.** Estimate the difference by rounding: 8730 – 2964

Ⓐ 1000 Ⓑ 3000 Ⓒ 6000 Ⓓ 8000

Table 1.6B

Salaries of New York City Workers in A Recent Year			
	Police Officer	Park Worker	Teacher
Starting Salary	$25,977	$18,003	$21,650
Maximum Salary	$33,273	$24,839	$43,142

Use Table 1.6B to answer questions 17-20.

Ⓑ **17.** What is the difference between the starting salary and the maximum salary for a teacher?

Ⓐ $7296 Ⓑ $21,492
Ⓒ $22,492 Ⓓ $64,792

Ⓐ **18.** What is the difference between the starting salaries for a park worker and a teacher?

Ⓐ $3647 Ⓑ $7000
Ⓒ $13,647 Ⓓ $18,303

Ⓒ **19.** What is the difference between the maximum salaries for a police officer and a teacher?

Ⓐ $76,415 Ⓑ $10,979
Ⓒ $9869 Ⓓ $4327

Ⓐ **20.** What is the difference between the starting salary and maximum salary for a park worker?

Ⓐ $6836 Ⓑ $7296
Ⓒ $16,836 Ⓓ $42,842

Ⓓ **21.** Subtract: $\begin{array}{r} 4825 \\ -1963 \\ \hline \end{array}$

Ⓐ 3952 Ⓑ 3762 Ⓒ 2962 Ⓓ 2862

Ⓑ **22.** Estimate the difference by rounding: 24,193 – 9723

Ⓐ 8000 Ⓑ 14,000
Ⓒ 18,000 Ⓓ 20,000

Name ____________________ Class ________ Date __________

1.7 MULTIPLYING WHOLE NUMBERS

Example 1: Multiply: 824×72

Multiply 824 by 2.

$$\begin{array}{r} 824 \\ \times\ 72 \\ \hline 1648 \end{array}$$

Multiply 824 by 70.

$$\begin{array}{r} {}^{1\,2} \\ 824 \\ \times\ \ 72 \\ \hline 1648 \\ 57680 \end{array}$$

Add.

$$\begin{array}{r} 824 \\ \times\ \ 72 \\ \hline 1648 \\ 57680 \\ \hline 59{,}328 \end{array}$$

REMEMBER: Always **estimate** to see if your answer is **reasonable**.

- Round each number to the greatest place.

$$\begin{array}{rcr} 824 & \longrightarrow & 800 \\ \times\ 72 & \longrightarrow & 70 \\ \hline & & 56{,}000 \end{array}$$

The estimate and the exact answer are close. Therefore, 59,328 is a reasonable answer.

Fill in the correct circle to answer each question.

(C) **1.** Multiply: $\begin{array}{r} 703 \\ \times\ 14 \\ \hline \end{array}$

(A) 98,312 (B) 73,112
(C) 9842 (D) 3515

(B) **2.** Find the product: 629×143

(A) 88,847 (B) 89,947
(C) 116,930 (D) 656,047

(B) **3.** Estimate the product by rounding: 827×78

(A) 64,000,000 (B) 64,000
(C) 6400 (D) 640

(D) **4.** Estimate the product by rounding: 3691×42

(A) 160 (B) 1600
(C) 16,000 (D) 160,000

(C) **5.** A tortoise can travel about 15 feet per minute. At that rate, about how far can a tortoise travel in an hour?

(A) 75 feet (B) 90 feet
(C) 900 feet (D) 9000 feet

(C) **6.** A garden snail has 135 rows of teeth. Each row has 105 teeth. How many teeth does the garden snail have altogether?

(A) 81,000 teeth (B) 15,525 teeth
(C) 14,175 teeth (D) 240 teeth

(C) **7.** Multiply 5253 by 47.

(A) 57,783 (B) 89,301
(C) 246,891 (D) 577,830

(B) **8.** Find the product: 791×824

(A) 1,107,400 (B) 651,784
(C) 640,784 (D) 1615

(C) **9.** Estimate the product: 48×93

(A) 45 (B) 450 (C) 4500 (D) 45,000

(B) **10.** Multiply: $\begin{array}{r} 975 \\ \times\ 26 \\ \hline \end{array}$

(A) 78,000 (B) 25,350 (C) 14,350 (D) 7800

Ⓑ **11.** In 1987, there were 265 babies born in the world every minute. How many children were born every hour?

Ⓐ 159,000 babies Ⓑ 15,900 babies
Ⓒ 15,600 babies Ⓓ 1590 babies

12. Recent statistics show that every American throws Ⓒ out about 1300 pounds of trash a year. About how many pounds of trash would a family of five throw out each year?

Ⓐ 650 pounds Ⓑ 5500 pounds
Ⓒ 6500 pounds Ⓓ 65,000 pounds

Ⓓ **13.** Estimate the product: 348×786

Ⓐ 240 Ⓑ 2400
Ⓒ 24,000 Ⓓ 240,000

Ⓑ **14.** $7029 \times 63 = \blacksquare$

Ⓐ 632,610 Ⓑ 442,827
Ⓒ 442,727 Ⓓ 63,261

Ⓑ **15.** Multiply: $\begin{array}{r} 908 \\ \times\ 52 \\ \hline \end{array}$

Ⓐ 63,560 Ⓑ 47,216 Ⓒ 46,216 Ⓓ 6356

Ⓐ **16.** Estimate the product: 419×88

Ⓐ 36,000 Ⓑ 3600 Ⓒ 3200 Ⓓ 320

Use the chart to answer questions 17-20.

The Home Store, Inc. Week of 1/7		
Item	Price	Number Sold
Stove	$339	16
Dishwasher	289	24
Microwave Oven	163	9
Blender	89	14

Ⓐ **17.** What was the total amount of sales for dishwashers?

Ⓐ $6936 Ⓑ $6836 Ⓒ $5424 Ⓓ $1467

Ⓑ **18.** What was the total amount of sales for microwave ovens?

Ⓐ $2601 Ⓑ $1467 Ⓒ $1447 Ⓓ $1367

Ⓓ **19.** What was the total amount of sales for stoves?

Ⓐ $2373 Ⓑ $5274 Ⓒ $5324 Ⓓ $5424

Ⓐ **20.** What was the total amount of sales for blenders?

Ⓐ $1246 Ⓑ $1146 Ⓒ $445 Ⓓ $103

Ⓐ **21.** $\begin{array}{r} 420 \\ \times\ 67 \\ \hline \end{array}$

Ⓐ 28,140 Ⓑ 27,140 Ⓒ 5460 Ⓓ 487

Ⓓ **22.** Multiply: $\begin{array}{r} 97 \\ \times 82 \\ \hline \end{array}$

Ⓐ 970 Ⓑ 7854 Ⓒ 7944 Ⓓ 7954

Ⓑ **23.** Americans eat about 160 pounds of corn and corn products a year. How many pounds of corn products would you eat in five years?

Ⓐ 8000 pounds Ⓑ 800 pounds
Ⓒ 80 pounds Ⓓ 165 pounds

Ⓓ **24.** A 34-passenger van takes tourists to see rose gardens. The trip costs $5 per person. When the van is full, how much money is earned per trip?

Ⓐ $17 Ⓑ $39 Ⓒ $150 Ⓓ $170

Ⓐ **25.** Estimate the product: 323×674

Ⓐ 210,000 Ⓑ 21,000
Ⓒ 2100 Ⓓ 210

Ⓒ **26.** Estimate the product: 781×34

Ⓐ 240 Ⓑ 2400
Ⓒ 24,000 Ⓓ 240,000

Name________________________________ Class __________ Date ______________

1.8 DIVIDING WHOLE NUMBERS

Example 1: Divide: $24\overline{)2064}$

24 divides 206 eight times, with a remainder of 14.

```
       8
24 )2064
    192
    ---
     14
```

24 divides 144 six times.

```
      86
24 )2064
    192
    ---
     144
     144
     ---
```

2064 ÷ 24 = 86

Example 2: Divide: $36\overline{)7094}$

36 divides 70 once, with a remainder of 34.

```
      1
36 )7094
    36
    --
    34
```

36 divides 349 nine times, with a remainder of 25.

```
      19
36 )7094
    36
    --
    349
    324
    ---
     25
```

36 divides 254 seven times with a remainder of 2.

```
      197  R2
36 )7094
    36
    --
    349
    324
    ---
     254
     252
     ---
       2
```

7094 ÷ 36 = 197 R2

Fill in the correct circle to answer each question.

Ⓑ **1.** Divide: $23\overline{)736}$

Ⓐ 23 Ⓑ 32 Ⓒ 32 R 10 Ⓓ 302

Ⓑ **2.** Divide: $6\overline{)4000}$

Ⓐ 6,666 R 4 Ⓑ 666 R 4 Ⓒ 666 Ⓓ 606 R 4

Ⓑ **3.** Divide: 351 ÷ 4

Ⓐ 87 Ⓑ 87 R 3 Ⓒ 87 R 2 Ⓓ 86 R 7

Ⓒ **4.** Divide 15,832 by 78.

Ⓐ 22 R 76 Ⓑ 202 Ⓒ 202 R 76 Ⓓ 202 R 86

Ⓑ **5.** Lee Allen drove 335 miles from Chicago to Cleveland. He drove about 55 miles per hour. About how many hours did the trip take?

Ⓐ 4 hours Ⓑ 6 hours Ⓒ 50 hours Ⓓ 60 hours

Ⓒ **6.** A charter plane to Paris had 550 seats. There were 11 seats in each row. How many rows of seats were on the plane?

Ⓐ 561 rows Ⓑ 60 rows Ⓒ 50 rows Ⓓ 5 rows

Ⓒ **7.** 6337 ÷ 9 = ■

Ⓐ 74 R 1　　Ⓑ 704

Ⓒ 704 R 1　　Ⓓ 740 R 1

Ⓑ **8.** Divide: $18\overline{)800}$

Ⓐ 444 R 8　　Ⓑ 44 R 8

Ⓒ 44　　Ⓓ 43 R 16

Ⓒ **9.** On Saturday, 105 people sign up for trail rides at the Lazy-K Ranch. Riders can go out on the trails in groups of 15. How many groups will go out on Saturday?

Ⓐ 70 groups　　Ⓑ 8 groups

Ⓒ 7 groups　　Ⓓ 6 groups

Ⓐ **10.** Howard's new car averages 33 miles per gallon of gasoline. He drives 858 miles. How many gallons of gas does he need?

Ⓐ 26 gallons　　Ⓑ 29 gallons

Ⓒ 260 gallons　　Ⓓ 825 gallons

Ⓑ **11.** Divide: 249 ÷ 5

Ⓐ 49　　Ⓑ 49 R 4

Ⓒ 49 R 5　　Ⓓ 48 R 9

Ⓒ **12.** Divide 73,836 by 18.

Ⓐ 412　　Ⓑ 4100 R 6

Ⓒ 4102　　Ⓓ 4120

Ⓓ **13.** A contractor orders 1008 door knobs to be used in 63 apartments. The same number of door knobs is used in each apartment. How many door knobs are in each apartment?

Ⓐ 945 door knobs　　Ⓑ 160 door knobs

Ⓒ 106 door knobs　　Ⓓ 16 door knobs

Ⓑ **14.** Each year, a total of $6750 is collected from 54 apartment owners for use of the Health Club. What are the yearly dues from each apartment owner?

Ⓐ $71　　Ⓑ $125

Ⓒ $127　　Ⓓ $1250

Ⓐ **15.** Divide: $40\overline{)4405}$

Ⓐ 110 R 5　　Ⓑ 110

Ⓒ 101 R 5　　Ⓓ 11 R 5

Ⓐ **16.** Find the quotient: 1407 ÷ 67

Ⓐ 21　　Ⓑ 22 R 33

Ⓒ 201　　Ⓓ 210

Ⓑ **17.** Divide: $35\overline{)490}$

Ⓐ 11 R 5　　Ⓑ 14

Ⓒ 104　　Ⓓ 140

Ⓑ **18.** Divide: 5508 ÷ 54

Ⓐ 12　　Ⓑ 102

Ⓒ 103 R 8　　Ⓓ 120

Ⓑ **19.** Divide: $72\overline{)2088}$

Ⓐ 209　　Ⓑ 29

Ⓒ 28 R 128　　Ⓓ 28

Ⓒ **20.** Find the quotient: $41\overline{)3157}$

Ⓐ 707　　Ⓑ 79 R 18

Ⓒ 77　　Ⓓ 76

Ⓑ **21.** Ellen is 60 inches tall. What is her height in feet?

Ⓐ 6 feet　　Ⓑ 5 feet

Ⓒ 4 feet　　Ⓓ 3 feet

22. 3806 ÷ 17 = ■

Ⓐ

Ⓐ 223 R 15　　Ⓑ 223

Ⓒ 222 R 15　　Ⓓ 22 R 12

Name ______________________ Class __________ Date ______________

1.9 PROBLEM SOLVING

Some problems require more than one step and more than one operation to solve.

Example 1: Joanne Evans works as a babysitter for her neighbor. She works four afternoons a week and earns \$12 each afternoon. How many weeks will Joanne need to work to earn \$288?

- The first step is to calculate Joanne's earnings for one week.

4	×	\$12	=	\$48
afternoons worked		earnings per afternoon		earnings per week

- The second step is to calculate how many weeks Joanne needs to work to earn \$288.

\$288	÷	\$48	=	6
goal		earnings per week		number of weeks to work

Joanne must work 6 weeks to earn \$288.

Example 2: The sophomore class at Jefferson High School needs 250 paper cups for a dance. The class president buys 5 packages with 20 cups in each package. The class treasurer buys 6 packages with 15 cups in each package. How many cups are still needed?

To solve the problem, follow these steps:

- Multiply to find the number of cups the president buys. $5 \times 20 = 100$
- Multiply to find the number of cups the treasurer buys. $6 \times 15 = 90$
- Add to find the total number of cups purchased. $100 + 90 = 190$
- Subtract to find the number of cups still needed. $250 - 190 = 60$

The sophomore class still needs to buy 60 cups for the dance.

Solve.

Ⓒ **1.** The Blue Ridge Diner has 52 tables. Each of 26 tables seats two people. The rest of the tables each seat four people. All of the tables of four are filled. How many people are seated in that section of the diner?

Ⓐ 26 Ⓑ 52 Ⓒ 104 Ⓓ 208

Ⓐ **2.** Kevin Thompson works five afternoons a week at a hardware store. He earns \$16 each afternoon. How many weeks will Kevin need to work to earn \$640?

Ⓐ 8 Ⓑ 40 Ⓒ 80 Ⓓ 560

Ⓑ **3.** The Tidal Waves sold 43,884 copies of their new album in 12 weeks. The album sells for \$8. On an average, how much money did they earn each week?

Ⓐ \$5485.50 Ⓑ \$29,256
Ⓒ \$3657 Ⓓ \$457.13

Ⓒ **4.** Tim Bush is a flight attendant. He is scheduled to fly 80 hours this month. So far, his flights have been 6 hours, 7 hours, 4 hours, 5 hours, and 6 hours. How many hours does he still have to fly this month?

Ⓐ 108 Ⓑ 80 Ⓒ 52 Ⓓ 28

Solve.

(D) **5.** James Madison, the fourth President of the U.S., took office in 1809. He served for 8 years, or 2 terms. James Monroe, our fifth president, also served two terms. In what year did John Quincy Adams, our sixth President, take office?

(A) 1813 (B) 1817 (C) 1819 (D) 1825

(B) **6.** Melanie Fallas opened a savings account in March with a $200 deposit. During the month, she deposited three checks, each for $150. On March 27, she withdrew $235. How much money did she have in the account after her withdrawal?

(A) $115 (B) $415 (C) $885 (D) $435

(A) **7.** There are 12 eggs in one carton. A box contains 16 cartons. A case contains 10 boxes. How many eggs are in one case?

(A) 1920 (B) 192 (C) 120 (D) 38

(C) **8.** An eye doctor can examine one patient every 15 minutes. How many patients can the eye doctor examine in 4 hours?

(A) 11 (B) 15 (C) 16 (D) 60

(C) **9.** The ponies at Open Gate Farm are fed two bales of hay each day. A truck delivers 15 bales at one time. How many deliveries are needed to feed the ponies for 60 days?

(A) 120 (B) 30 (C) 8 (D) 4

(B) **10.** A bakery makes wedding cakes. Each cake contains 8 cups of flour. There are 16 cups in one bag of flour. How many bags will the bakery need to make 22 wedding cakes?

(A) 44 (B) 11 (C) 22 (D) 128

(C) **11.** The Steiner family buys laundry detergent in 64-ounce bottles. Each load of laundry uses 2 ounces of detergent. The Steiners wash 4 loads of clothes a week. How many weeks will one bottle of laundry detergent last?

(A) 2 (B) 4 (C) 8 (D) 16

(A) **12.** The school cafeteria sells apples. On Monday, 250 apples are delivered. On Wednesday, 230 more apples are delivered. On Friday afternoon, there are 94 apples left. How many apples did the cafeteria sell that week?

(A) 386 (B) 324 (C) 156 (D) 136

(D) **13.** The Berkitt family drove 330 miles last weekend. Their car gets 15 miles to the gallon. If gasoline costs $1.20 per gallon, how much did the Berkitt family spend on gasoline last weekend?

(A) $41.25 (B) $18.33 (C) $22 (D) $26.40

14. (A) Joyce Robbins owns a bookstore. She has ordered 900 copies of the latest bestseller. The books come in boxes of 12. So far, she has received 31 boxes of books. How many more boxes does she need for her order to be complete?

(A) 44 (B) 75 (C) 528 (D) 869

(C) **15.** The students at Pioneer High School are selling tee shirts to raise money for the student lounge. Each shirt costs $8. The sophomores have sold 273 shirts. The juniors have sold 319 shirts. How much more money did the junior class bring in than the sophomore class?

(A) $4736 (B) $2552 (C) $368 (D) $46

(B) **16.** Laura Baker is making bouquets of roses for a party. She has 18 white roses, 18 yellow roses, 18 pink roses, and 18 red roses. Each bouquet will have 8 roses. How many bouquets can she make?

(A) 8 (B) 9 (C) 18 (D) 72

(A) **17.** The Orth family plans to drive 7 hours a day on their way to visit Silver Lake, 1155 miles away. They plan to drive at a speed of 55 miles per hour. At that rate, how many days will it take the Orth family to travel 1155 miles?

(A) 3 (B) 21 (C) 30 (D) 165

(C) **18.** Brenda Cheng runs a newsstand. On Monday, she received 125 copies of Celebrity Magazine. She sold 15 copies on Monday, 26 on Tuesday, 38 on Wednesday, 17 on Thursday, and 27 on Friday. How many copies did she have left?

(A) 123 (B) 28 (C) 2 (D) 40

Name ______________________ Class __________ Date __________

CHAPTER 1 TEST

Fill in the correct circle to answer each question.

(B) **1.** Round 7824 to the nearest *hundred.*

(A) 7000 (B) 7800 (C) 7900 (D) 8000

(B) **2.** What is the value of the digit 5 in 25,863?

(A) 50,000 (B) 5000 (C) 500 (D) 50

(A) **3.** Name the property shown: 5 + 8 = 8 + 5

(A) Commutative (B) Associative
(C) Distributive (D) Property of 1

(D) **4.** 425 − 369 = ■

(A) 794 (B) 166 (C) 156 (D) 56

(A) **5.** Compare: 2830 ■ 2803

(A) > (B) < (C) =

(B) **6.** Compare: 816,945 ■ 816,955

(A) > (B) < (C) =

(D) **7.** Multiply: $\begin{array}{r} 852 \\ \times 639 \\ \hline \end{array}$

(A) 524,728 (B) 548,818
(C) 544,418 (D) 544,428

(D) **8.** Add: $\begin{array}{r} 5763 \\ +3098 \\ \hline \end{array}$

(A) 2665 (B) 8851 (C) 8751 (D) 8861

(B) **9.** An Anaconda snake is 37 ft long. A King Cobra is 18 ft long. How much longer is the Anaconda than the King Cobra?

(A) 17 ft (B) 19 ft (C) 29 ft (D) 55 ft

(C) **10.** Experts say that the average American waits in line 30 minutes each day. How many minutes would you spend in line each week?

(A) 2100 minutes (B) 240 minutes
(C) 210 minutes (D) 21 minutes

(D) **11.** Divide: $37\overline{)254}$

(A) 7 (B) 6 (C) 6 R 22 (D) 6 R 32

(B) **12.** What is the *value* of 1 in 8016?

(A) 1 (B) 10 (C) 100 (D) 1000

(B) **13.** Round 7549 to the nearest *ten.*

(A) 8000 (B) 7550 (C) 7540 (D) 7500

(B) **14.** Name the property shown:
(a + b) + c = a + (b + c)

(A) Distributive (B) Associative
(C) Commutative (D) Property of 1

(D) **15.** What is the word name for 81,760?

(A) eighty-one thousand seven hundred six
(B) eighty-one thousand and seven hundred sixty
(C) eighty-one thousand seventy-six
(D) eighty-one thousand seven hundred sixty

(B) **16.** Round 91,266 to the nearest *thousand.*

(A) 90,000 (B) 91,000
(C) 91,300 (D) 92,000

(D) **17.** 845 + 77 = ■

(A) 768 (B) 812 (C) 912 (D) 922

(C) **18.** Divide: 4730 ÷ 8

(A) 603 (B) 591 (C) 591 R 2 (D) 590

(C) **19.** 2802 − 647 = ■

(A) 1155 (B) 2154 (C) 2155 (D) 2165

(B) **20.** What is the numeral for seventy-two thousand four hundred one?

(A) 72,410 (B) 72,401
(C) 72,400 (D) 70,401

Ⓒ **21.** In the United States, a plane is scheduled to take off every six seconds. How many planes are scheduled to take off every minute?

Ⓐ 360 planes Ⓑ 100 planes
Ⓒ 10 planes Ⓓ 5 planes

Ⓓ **22.** The Total Fitness Health Club signed up 48 new members on Saturday. They signed up 19 new members on Sunday. How many new members signed up in all?

Ⓐ 29 people Ⓑ 57 people
Ⓒ 66 people Ⓓ 67 people

Ⓒ **23.** Which property is shown?
$6 \times (5 + 3) = (6 \times 5) + (6 \times 3)$

Ⓐ Property of 1 Ⓑ Commutative
Ⓒ Distributive Ⓓ Associative

Ⓒ **24.** 942 + 2086 + 37 = ■

Ⓐ 2065 Ⓑ 2955
Ⓒ 3065 Ⓓ 15,206

Ⓓ **25.** Find the product: 436×204

Ⓐ 10,364 Ⓑ 10,464
Ⓒ 88,844 Ⓓ 88,944

Ⓑ **26.** Round 20,543 to the nearest *hundred*.

Ⓐ 20,000 Ⓑ 20,500
Ⓒ 20,540 Ⓓ 20,600

Ⓐ **27.** 304 – 235 = ■

Ⓐ 69 Ⓑ 79 Ⓒ 169 Ⓓ 179

Ⓒ **28.** 1701 ÷ 27 = ■

Ⓐ 603 Ⓑ 503 Ⓒ 63 Ⓓ 53

Ⓒ **29.** Order from *least to greatest:* 24,007; 24,700; 24,070

Ⓐ 24,007; 24,700; 24,070
Ⓑ 24,700; 24,070; 24,007
Ⓒ 24,007; 24,070; 24,700
Ⓓ 24,070; 24,007; 24,700

Ⓐ **30.** Order from *greatest to least:* 5620; 5602; 5260

Ⓐ 5620; 5602; 5260
Ⓑ 5602; 5260; 5620
Ⓒ 5260; 5602; 5620
Ⓓ 5602; 5260; 5620

Ⓒ **31.** 1425 + 647 = ■

Ⓐ 1062 Ⓑ 1072 Ⓒ 2072 Ⓓ 7895

Ⓑ **32.** 1608 – 489 = ■

Ⓐ 718 Ⓑ 1119 Ⓒ 1129 Ⓓ 2097

Ⓐ **33.** Round 20,497 to the nearest *thousand.*

Ⓐ 20,000 Ⓑ 20,500 Ⓒ 21,000 Ⓓ 21,500

Name ______________________ Class __________ Date __________

CHAPTER 2: DECIMAL COMPUTATION

TEST-TAKING STRATEGY: *Use Estimation*

Estimating can be helpful on multiple-choice tests.

Before you compute, you can estimate to eliminate answer choices that *are not* reasonable.

After you compute, you can estimate to make sure your answer *is* reasonable.

Here is an example of how you can estimate *before* you compute.

Example 1: $421 \times 32 =$ ■ Ⓐ 8472 Ⓑ 11,872 Ⓒ 13,472 Ⓓ 134,720

- Round each of the factors to the greatest place.

$$\begin{array}{r} 421 \\ \times\ 32 \\ \hline \end{array} \quad \longrightarrow \quad \begin{array}{r} 400 \\ \times\ 30 \\ \hline 12{,}000 \end{array}$$

The answer is close to 12,000. So you can eliminate choices Ⓐ and Ⓓ immediately.

- Compare the numbers in the actual question to the numbers in your estimate.

  In this case, both numbers were rounded down. Therefore, your estimate is *less than* the actual number. You can eliminate choice Ⓑ.

The correct answer must be choice Ⓒ.

Here is an example of how to use estimation *after* you compute.

Example 2: $787 \times 53 =$ ■

- Compute: $\begin{array}{r} 787 \\ \times\ 53 \\ \hline 41{,}711 \end{array}$

- Round each of the factors to the greatest place. $\begin{array}{r} 787 \\ \times\ 53 \\ \hline \end{array} \longrightarrow \begin{array}{r} 800 \\ \times\ 50 \\ \hline 40{,}000 \end{array}$

Your answer is 41,711. Your estimate is 40,000.

Your answer is close to your estimate. Therefore, your answer is reasonable.

Fill in the correct circle to answer each question.

Ⓑ **1.** Round 4325 to the nearest *thousand.*

Ⓐ 5000 Ⓑ 4000 Ⓒ 4400 Ⓓ 4300

Ⓓ **2.** Round 4325 to the nearest *hundred.*

Ⓐ 5000 Ⓑ 4000 Ⓒ 4400 Ⓓ 4300

Ⓐ **3.** Round 882 to the nearest *hundred.*

Ⓐ 900 Ⓑ 880 Ⓒ 800 Ⓓ 700

Ⓐ **4.** Round 5736 to the nearest *thousand.*

Ⓐ 6000 Ⓑ 5740 Ⓒ 5700 Ⓓ 5000

Ⓒ **5.** A good estimate of 57×607 would be

Ⓐ 50×600 Ⓑ 50×700

Ⓒ 60×600 Ⓓ 60×700

Ⓐ **6.** A good estimate of $921 \div 67$ would be

Ⓐ $900 \div 70$ Ⓑ $900 \div 60$

Ⓒ $800 \div 70$ Ⓓ $800 \div 60$

Ⓒ **7.** A good estimate of $614 + 29$ would be

Ⓐ $700 + 30$ Ⓑ $700 + 20$

Ⓒ $600 + 30$ Ⓓ $600 + 20$

Ⓓ **8.** A good estimate of $8319 - 2173$ would be

Ⓐ $9000 - 2000$ Ⓑ $9000 - 3000$

Ⓒ $8000 - 3000$ Ⓓ $8000 - 2000$

Ⓑ **9.** A good estimate of 923×19 would be

Ⓐ 900×10 Ⓑ 900×20
Ⓒ 1000×10 Ⓓ 1000×20

Ⓑ **10.** A good estimate of $4071 \div 369$ would be

Ⓐ $4000 \div 300$ Ⓑ $4000 \div 400$
Ⓒ $5000 \div 300$ Ⓓ $5000 \div 400$

Estimate to help you select the correct answer.

Ⓒ **11.** $245 + 97 =$ ■

Ⓐ 242 Ⓑ 250 Ⓒ 342 Ⓓ 450

Ⓑ **12.** $35 + 89 =$ ■

Ⓐ 114 Ⓑ 124 Ⓒ 214 Ⓓ 224

Ⓐ **13.** $791 - 267 =$ ■

Ⓐ 524 Ⓑ 550 Ⓒ 650 Ⓓ 1058

Ⓑ **14.** $2837 - 315 =$ ■

Ⓐ 3152 Ⓑ 2522 Ⓒ 2122 Ⓓ 1522

Ⓒ **15.** $123 \times 45 =$ ■

Ⓐ 1107 Ⓑ 5000 Ⓒ 5535 Ⓓ 6000

Ⓒ **16.** $543 \times 21 =$ ■

Ⓐ 1629 Ⓑ 10,000 Ⓒ 11,403 Ⓓ 12,000

Ⓐ **17.** $840 \div 21 =$ ■

Ⓐ 40 Ⓑ 400 Ⓒ 819 D. 861

Ⓑ **18.** $2555 \div 73 =$ ■

Ⓐ 3 Ⓑ 35 Ⓒ 40 Ⓓ 300

Ⓒ **19.** $25 + 187 + 412 =$ ■

Ⓐ 514 Ⓑ 524 Ⓒ 624 Ⓓ 849

Ⓑ **20.** $23{,}417 - 3589 =$ ■

Ⓐ 19,000 Ⓑ 19,828 Ⓒ 20,938 Ⓓ 27,006

Ⓐ **21.** $397 \times 42 =$ ■

Ⓐ 16,674 Ⓑ 16,000 Ⓒ 2382 Ⓓ 439

Ⓒ **22.** $4653 \div 47 =$ ■

Ⓐ 990 Ⓑ 909 Ⓒ 99 Ⓓ 98

Ⓒ **23.** $(142 + 973) - 288 =$ ■

Ⓐ 727 Ⓑ 800 Ⓒ 827 Ⓓ 1403

Ⓑ **24.** $(243 \times 121) \div 99 =$ ■

Ⓐ 29,304 Ⓑ 297 Ⓒ 200 Ⓓ 3.7

Ⓑ **25.** $(497 + 376) \div 97 =$ ■

Ⓐ 7 Ⓑ 9 Ⓒ 776 Ⓓ 970

Ⓓ **26.** $(737 - 297) \div 55 =$ ■

Ⓐ 5 Ⓑ 6 Ⓒ 7 Ⓓ 8

Find the answer.

Ⓒ **27.** Bill buys a \$23 book. He pays with a \$50 bill. How much change does he get?

Ⓐ \$37 Ⓑ \$30 Ⓒ \$27 Ⓓ \$20

Ⓒ **28.** Mary drove 327 miles on Monday, 125 miles on Tuesday and 58 miles on Wednesday. How many miles did she drive altogether in those three days?

Ⓐ 410 miles Ⓑ 460 miles
Ⓒ 510 miles Ⓓ 610 miles

Ⓐ **29.** Jose drove 770 miles in 11 hours. On average, how many miles did he drive each hour?

Ⓐ 70 miles per hour
Ⓑ 77 miles per hour
Ⓒ 770 miles per hour
Ⓓ 700 miles per hour

Ⓒ **30.** Maria practices the flute 6.5 hours per week. How many hours does she practice in a 4-week month?

Ⓐ 24 hours Ⓑ 10 hours
Ⓒ 26 hours Ⓓ 30 hours

Name ____________________ Class ________ Date ____________

CHAPTER 2 PRETEST

Fill in the correct circle to answer each question.

(A) **1.** What is the numeral for one hundred fifty thousand five?

(A) 150,005 (B) 155,000 (C) 150,500 (D) 150,000

(D) **2.** What is the numeral for eight hundred thousand twenty-eight?

(A) 828,000 (B) 800,280 (C) 80,028 (D) 800,028

(A) **3.** What is the word name for 250,031?

(A) two hundred fifty thousand thirty-one
(B) twenty-five thousand thirty-one
(C) two hundred fifty thousand and thirty-one
(D) twenty-five hundred thirty-one

(D) **4.** What is the word name for 200,418?

(A) twenty thousand four eighteen
(B) two hundred thousand four hundred and eighteen
(C) two hundred thousand four eighteen
(D) two hundred thousand four hundred eighteen

(A) **5.** What is the *value* of 5 in 152,468?

(A) 50,000 (B) 5000 (C) 500 (D) 5

(D) **6.** What is the *place value* of 2 in 320,175?

(A) tens (B) hundreds (C) thousands (D) ten thousands

(C) **7.** $54 + 18 =$ ■

(A) 972 (B) 92 (C) 72 (D) 62

(A) **8.** Add: $1732 + 829$

(A) 2561 (B) 2551 (C) 2662 (D) 2762

(A) **9.** $24 - 17 =$ ■

(A) 7 (B) 13 (C) 17 (D) 41

(D) **10.** Subtract: $725 - 137$

(A) 698 (B) 688 (C) 589 (D) 588

(B) **11.** $6 \times 9 =$ ■

(A) 36 (B) 54 (C) 56 (D) 63

(B) **12.** $56 \div 7 =$ ■

(A) 63 (B) 8 (C) 9 (D) 6

(D) **13.** Multiply:

$$\begin{array}{r} 13 \\ \times 39 \\ \hline \end{array}$$

(A) 607 (B) 492 (C) 477 (D) 507

(C) **14.** $2189 \times 16 =$ ■

(A) 34,645 (B) 31,024 (C) 35,024 (D) 2205

(C) **15.** $126 \div 9 =$ ■

(A) 12 R 2 (B) 13 (C) 14 (D) 15

(B) **16.** Divide: $250 \div 10$

(A) 20 R 5 (B) 25 (C) 20 (D) 2 R 5

(A) **17.** Round 333 to the nearest *hundred.*

(A) 300 (B) 330 (C) 340 (D) 400

(B) **18.** Round 7635 to the nearest *ten.*

(A) 7630 (B) 7640 (C) 7600 (D) 7000

(C) **19.** $100 \times 100 =$ ■

(A) 200 (B) 1000 (C) 10,000 (D) 100,000

(C) **20.** $4200 \div 100 =$ ■

(A) 4200 (B) 420 (C) 42 (D) 4300

Ⓑ **21.** The difference between 21 and 0.2 is ■.

Ⓐ 19.8 Ⓑ 20.8 Ⓒ 21.2 Ⓓ 19

Ⓒ **22.** What is the *place value* of the 7 in 3.471?

Ⓐ hundreds Ⓑ tenths
Ⓒ hundredths Ⓓ thousandths

Ⓑ **23.** Order from *least to greatest:* 0.7; 0.08; 0.6

Ⓐ 0.7, 0.08, 0.6 Ⓑ 0.08, 0.6, 0.7
Ⓒ 0.08, 0.7, 0.6 Ⓓ 0.7, 0.6, 0.08

Ⓓ **24.** Order from *greatest to least:* 0.9; 1.1; 1.09

Ⓐ 0.9, 1.1, 1.09 Ⓑ 0.9, 1.09, 1.1
Ⓒ 1.09, 1.1, 0.9 Ⓓ 1.1, 1.09, 0.9

Ⓓ **25.** Round 123.454 to the nearest *tenth.*

Ⓐ 123 Ⓑ 123.4 Ⓒ 123.45 Ⓓ 123.5

Ⓐ **26.** Round $123.54 to the nearest *dollar.*

Ⓐ $124 Ⓑ $123
Ⓒ $123.50 Ⓓ $123.54

Ⓑ **27.** 2.123 + 0.08 = ■

Ⓐ 2.231 Ⓑ 2.203 Ⓒ 2.131 Ⓓ 2.103

Ⓒ **28.** Find the sum of *three tenths* and *three and a tenth.*

Ⓐ 3.6 Ⓑ 6.3 Ⓒ 3.4 Ⓓ 0.6

Ⓒ **29.** The next composite number after 4 is ■.

Ⓐ 3 Ⓑ 5 Ⓒ 6 Ⓓ 8

Ⓒ **30.** Find the prime factors of 12.

Ⓐ 1, 2, 3, 4, 6, 12 Ⓑ 1, 3
Ⓒ 2, 3 Ⓓ 1, 2, 3

Ⓒ **31.** Write 3,450,000 in scientific notation.

Ⓐ 235×10^4 Ⓑ 34.5×10^5
Ⓒ 3.45×10^6 Ⓓ 3.45×10^4

Ⓒ **32.** If $x^3 = 27$, then $x =$ ■.

Ⓐ 8 Ⓑ 9 Ⓒ 3 Ⓓ 2.7

Ⓐ **33.** Subtract:

$$\begin{array}{r} 7.2 \\ -0.202 \\ \hline \end{array}$$

Ⓐ 6.998 Ⓑ 7.008 Ⓒ 7.098 Ⓓ 7.404

Ⓑ **34.** $12 \times 1.2 =$ ■

Ⓐ 144 Ⓑ 14.4 Ⓒ 2.4 Ⓓ 1.44

Ⓐ **35.** Multiply: 9.876×10

Ⓐ 98.76 Ⓑ 9.876
Ⓒ 0.9876 Ⓓ 0.09876

Ⓑ **36.** $1.235 \times 100 =$ ■

Ⓐ 1235 Ⓑ 123.5 Ⓒ 12.35 Ⓓ 1.235

Ⓓ **37.** $7.328 \div 100 =$ ■

Ⓐ 732.8 Ⓑ 73.28
Ⓒ 0.7328 Ⓓ 0.07328

Ⓐ **38.** $100 \div 0.01 =$ ■

Ⓐ 10,000 Ⓑ 1000
Ⓒ 0.0001 Ⓓ 1

Ⓑ **39.** Find all the factors of 30.

Ⓐ 2, 3, 5
Ⓑ 1, 2, 3, 5, 6, 10, 15, 30
Ⓒ 5, 6
Ⓓ 2, 3, 5, 6, 10, 15

Ⓓ **40.** 36 = ■

Ⓐ $2^3 \times 3^2$ Ⓑ $2^3 \times 3$
Ⓒ $2^2 \times 3^3$ Ⓓ $2^2 \times 3^2$

Name ____________________ Class __________ Date __________

2.1 PLACE VALUE OF DECIMALS

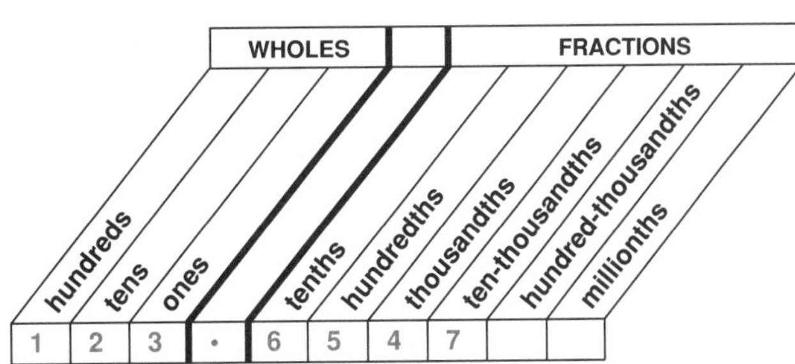

The number shown in the table above is written 123.6547.

Example 1: To read the number, start at the left.

one hundred twenty-three **and** six thousand five hundred forty-seven ten-thousandths

REMEMBER: When writing word names for decimal numerals, the word **and** takes the place of the decimal point.

Example 2:

A. Find the *place value* of 5 in the number above.

- 5 is in the hundredths place.

B. Find the *value* of the digit 5 in the number above.

- Locate the digit 5.
- Replace each digit except 5 with zero.

000.0500 = 0.05

Fill in the correct circle to answer each question.

Ⓒ **1.** What is the numeral for six thousandths?

Ⓐ 6000 Ⓑ 0.06 Ⓒ 0.006 Ⓓ 0.0006

Ⓐ **2.** What is the numeral for twenty-three millionths?

Ⓐ 0.000023 Ⓑ 0.00023
Ⓒ 23.000000 Ⓓ 23,000,000

Ⓒ **3.** What is the *place value* of 4 in 3.2945?

Ⓐ tenths Ⓑ hundredths
Ⓒ thousandths Ⓓ ten-thousandths

Ⓑ **4.** What is the *place value* of 5 in 0.1537?

Ⓐ thousandths Ⓑ hundredths
Ⓒ tenths Ⓓ five

Ⓒ **5.** What is the *value* of the digit 2 in 33.2975?

Ⓐ 0.002 Ⓑ 0.02 Ⓒ 0.2 Ⓓ 2

Ⓒ **6.** What is the *value* of the digit 1 in 8.7155?

Ⓐ 1 Ⓑ 0.1 Ⓒ 0.01 Ⓓ 0.001

Ⓑ **7.** What is the numeral for one thousandth?

Ⓐ 0.0001 Ⓑ 0.001 Ⓒ 1.000 Ⓓ 1000

Ⓒ **8.** What is the *place value* of the digit 4 in 0.123456?

Ⓐ hundredths Ⓑ thousandths
Ⓒ ten-thousandths Ⓓ millionths

Ⓐ **9.** Find the *place value* of the digit 6 in 91.6142.

Ⓐ tenths Ⓑ hundredths
Ⓒ thousandths Ⓓ millionths

Ⓑ **10.** Which digit is in the *hundredths* place in the numeral 759.348?

Ⓐ 3 Ⓑ 4 Ⓒ 7 Ⓓ 8

Ⓒ **11.** What is the *value* of the digit 2 in 45.91288?

Ⓐ 0.2 Ⓑ 0.02 Ⓒ 0.002 Ⓓ 0.0002

Ⓒ **12.** What is the *place value* of 5 in 0.15873?

Ⓐ fifths Ⓑ tenths
Ⓒ hundredths Ⓓ thousandths

Ⓓ **13.** What is the numeral for two thousand twenty-five ten-thousandths?

Ⓐ 2025 Ⓑ 2000.0025
Ⓒ 2000.25 Ⓓ 0.2025

Ⓑ **14.** Alex ran six and four tenths miles. What is the underlined number?

Ⓐ 64 Ⓑ 6.4 Ⓒ 6.04 Ⓓ 6.004

Ⓓ **15.** What digit is in the *hundredths* place in the numeral 372.086?

Ⓐ 0 Ⓑ 3 Ⓒ 6 Ⓓ 8

Ⓐ **16.** In the number 96.35, which digit is in the *tenths* place?

Ⓐ 3 Ⓑ 5 Ⓒ 6 Ⓓ 9

Ⓑ **17.** Which means the same as three hundred seventy dollars and four cents?

Ⓐ \$307.04 Ⓑ \$370.04
Ⓒ \$370.40 Ⓓ 370.04¢

Ⓒ **18.** Which means the same as seven and forty-six ten-thousandths?

Ⓐ 70.046 Ⓑ 7.046
Ⓒ 7.0046 Ⓓ 7.00046

Ⓑ **19.** What is the word name for 42.0623?

Ⓐ forty-two and six hundred twenty-three
Ⓑ forty-two and six hundred twenty-three ten-thousandths
Ⓒ forty two and six hundred twenty-three thousandths
Ⓓ forty-two and six hundred twenty-three tenths

Ⓓ **20.** What is the word name for 71.352?

Ⓐ seventy-one thousand and three hundred fifty-two
Ⓑ seventy-one thousand and three hundred fifty-two thousandths
Ⓒ seventy-one and three hundred fifty-two
Ⓓ seventy-one and three hundred fifty-two thousandths

Ⓒ **21.** What is the numeral for five hundred thirty-three thousandths?

Ⓐ 500.33 Ⓑ 500.033
Ⓒ 0.533 Ⓓ 0.0533

Ⓑ **22.** What is the numeral for five hundred and thirty-three thousandths?

Ⓐ 500.33 Ⓑ 500.033
Ⓒ 0.533 Ⓓ 0.0533

Ⓒ **23.** In the number 23.019, which digit is in the *hundredths* place?

Ⓐ 9 Ⓑ 3 Ⓒ 1 Ⓓ 0

Ⓑ **24.** What is the *value* of the digit 3 in 47.385?

Ⓐ 3 Ⓑ 0.3 Ⓒ 0.03 Ⓓ 0.003

Ⓐ **25.** What is the numeral for three hundred five ten-thousandths?

Ⓐ 0.0305 Ⓑ 0.305
Ⓒ 300.005 Ⓓ 300.0005

Ⓓ **26.** What is the numeral for three hundred and five ten-thousandths?

Ⓐ 0.0305 Ⓑ 0.305
Ⓒ 300.005 Ⓓ 300.0005

Name ________________________________ Class __________ Date ______________

2.2 COMPARING AND ORDERING DECIMALS

Example 1: Compare 2.451 and 2.473. Use >, <, or =.

- Line up the decimal points.
- Start at the left.
- Compare digits until two digits are different.

2.451
2.473
5 < 7, therefore 2.451 < 2.473

Since 5 is less than 7, 2.451 is less than 2.473.

Example 2: Order 0.5, 0.07, and 0.009 from *greatest to least.*

- Proceed as in Example 1, to find the greatest number. Since 5 > 0, 0.5 is the greatest number.

0.5
0.07
0.009
5 > 0, therefore 0.5 is the greatest number

- Compare the remaining numbers.

0.07
0.009
7 > 0, therefore 0.07 > 0.009

The numbers in order from *greatest to least* are 0.5, 0.07, 0.009.

Fill in the correct circle to answer each question.

(A) **1.** Compare: 2.3579 ■ 2.3468

(A) 2.3579 > 2.3468 (B) 2.3579 < 2.3468 (C) 2.3579 = 2.3468

(A) **2.** Compare: 4.359 ■ 4.801

(A) 4.359 < 4.801 (B) 4.359 > 4.801 (C) 4.359 = 4.801

(D) **3.** Which number has the *least* value?
0.4, 0.45, 0.54, 0.5

(A) 0.54 (B) 0.5 (C) 0.45 (D) 0.4

(A) **4.** Which number has the *greatest* value?
0.9, 9.0, 0.09, 0.009

(A) 9.0 (B) 0.9 (C) 0.09 (D) 0.009

(C) **5.** Order from *greatest to least:* 0.17, 0.16, 0.67

(A) 0.17, 0.16, 0.67 (B) 0.16, 0.17, 0.67 (C) 0.67, 0.17, 0.16 (D) 0.67, 0.16, 0.17

(D) **6.** Order from *least to greatest:* 2.71, 2.61, 2.76

(A) 2.71, 2.61, 2.76 (B) 2.76, 2.61, 2.71 (C) 2.61, 2.76, 2.71 (D) 2.61, 2.71, 2.76

(A) **7.** Compare: 4.76 ■ 4.706

(A) 4.76 > 4.706 (B) 4.76 < 4.706 (C) 4.76 = 4.706

(C) **8.** Compare: 63.24 ■ 63.240

(A) 63.24 > 63.240 (B) 63.24 < 63.240 (C) 63.24 = 63.240

(A) **9.** Which statement is *true?*

(A) 24.83 > 14.75 (B) 24.83 < 14.75 (C) 24.83 = 14.75 (D) 14.75 > 24.83

(B) **10.** Compare: 74.005 ■ 74.026

(A) 74.005 > 74.026 (B) 74.005 < 74.026 (C) 74.005 = 74.026

(A) **11.** Which number has the *greatest* value?
6.302; 6.3; 6.32; 6.3002

(A) 6.32 (B) 6.302 (C) 6.3002 (D) 6.3

(D) **12.** Which number has the *least* value?
5.839; 58.39; 5.8; 583.9

(A) 583.9 (B) 58.39 (C) 5.839 (D) 5.8

(B) **13.** Compare: 0.1234 ■ 0.1254

Ⓐ 0.1234 > 0.1254 Ⓑ 0.1234 < 0.1254

Ⓒ 0.1234 = 0.1254

(B) **14.** Which statement is *true?*

Ⓐ 1.4 > 1.40 Ⓑ 1.4 = 1.40

Ⓒ 1.4 < 1.40

(C) **15.** Order from *least to greatest:* 0.2, 0.04, 0.008

Ⓐ 0.2, 0.04, 0.008

Ⓑ 0.04, 0.2, 0.008

Ⓒ 0.008, 0.04, 0.2

Ⓓ 0.008, 0.2, 0.04

(D) **16.** Order from *greatest to least:* 33.29, 33.209, 33.92

Ⓐ 33.29, 33.209, 33.92

Ⓑ 33.92, 33.209, 33.29

Ⓒ 33.209, 33.92, 33.29

Ⓓ 33.92, 33.29, 33.209

(A) **17.** Which is between 0.06 and 0.50 in value?

Ⓐ 0.07 Ⓑ 0.056 Ⓒ 0.055 Ⓓ 0.7

(B) **18.** Compare: 1.23 ■ 2.13

Ⓐ 1.23 > 2.13 Ⓑ 1.23 < 2.13

Ⓒ 1.23 = 2.13

Use Table 2.2 to answer questions 19-22.

Table 2.2

Number of Teenagers Who Played Team Sports In a Recent Year (in millions)	
Baseball	7.7
Basketball	10.1
Football	6.2
Soccer	6.3
Softball	6.5
Volleyball	6.3

(B) **19.** Which sport had more than ten million players?

Ⓐ baseball Ⓑ basketball

Ⓒ soccer Ⓓ volleyball

(C) **20.** Which sport had the least number of players?

Ⓐ volleyball Ⓑ softball

Ⓒ football Ⓓ soccer

(A) **21.** Which sport had the same number of players as soccer?

Ⓐ volleyball Ⓑ football

Ⓒ softball Ⓓ baseball

(B) **22.** Which sport had the greatest number of players?

Ⓐ baseball Ⓑ basketball

Ⓒ softball Ⓓ soccer

(C) **23.** Which is between 0.5 and 0.80 in value?

Ⓐ 5.8 Ⓑ 0.9 Ⓒ 0.6 Ⓓ 0.06

(A) **24.** Which statement is *true?*

Ⓐ 14.8 > 1.48 Ⓑ 14.8 = 1.48

Ⓒ 14.8 < 1.48

(C) **25.** Which number has the *greatest* value?
8.5; 8.05; 80.5; 80.05

Ⓐ 8.05 Ⓑ 8.5 Ⓒ 80.5 Ⓓ 80.05

(D) **26.** Which number has the *least* value?
6.03; 0.063; 0.0063; 6.3

Ⓐ 6.3 Ⓑ 6.03 Ⓒ 0.063 Ⓓ 0.0063

(A) **27.** Compare: 4.31 ■ 4.031

Ⓐ 4.31 > 4.031 Ⓑ 4.31 < 4.031

Ⓒ 4.31 = 4.031

(B) **28.** Compare: 50.02 ■ 500.02

Ⓐ 50.02 > 500.02 Ⓑ 50.02 < 500.02

Ⓒ 50.02 = 500.02

Name ______________________ Class __________ Date __________

2.3 ROUNDING DECIMALS

Example 1: Round 4.3572 to the nearest *whole number.*

- 3 is to the right of the *ones* place: 4.3572
- $3 < 5$, so round down: 4.0000

4.3572 rounded to the nearest *whole number* is 4.

Example 2: Round 4.3572 to the nearest *tenth.*

- 5 is to the right of the *tenths* place: 4.3572
- $5 = 5$, so round up: 4.4000

4.3572 rounded to the nearest *tenth* is 4.4.

Example 3: Round 4.3572 to the nearest *hundredth.*

- 7 is to the right of the *hundreths* place: 4.3572
- $7 > 5$, so round up: 4.3600

4.3572 rounded to the nearest *hundredth* is 4.36.

Fill in the correct circle for each question.

(D) **1.** Round 341.652 to the nearest *whole number.*

(A) 300 (B) 340 (C) 340.7 (D) 342

(A) **2.** Round 1.256 to the nearest *whole number.*

(A) 1 (B) 1.2 (C) 1.3 (D) 2

(C) **3.** Round 20.652 to the nearest *tenth.*

(A) 20 (B) 20.6 (C) 20.7 (D) 21

(B) **4.** Round 341.256 to the nearest *tenth.*

(A) 341.2 (B) 341.3 (C) 340 (D) 341

(C) **5.** Round 479.125 to the nearest *hundredth.*

(A) 479.1 (B) 479.12 (C) 479.13 (D) 500

(A) **6.** Round $18.72 to the nearest *dollar.*

(A) $19.00 (B) $18.70 (C) $18.75 (D) $18.00

(C) **7.** Round 56.7 to the nearest *whole number.*

(A) 50 (B) 56 (C) 57 (D) 60

(D) **8.** Round 0.6785 to the nearest *whole number.*

(A) 0 (B) 0.678 (C) 0.679 (D) 1

(D) **9.** Round 0.6785 to the nearest *hundredth.*

(A) 0.670 (B) 0.678 (C) 0.679 (D) 0.680

(C) **10.** Round $27.49 to the nearest *dollar.*

(A) $30.00 (B) $28.00 (C) $27.00 (D) $20.00

(C) **11.** Students in France receive an average of 7.9 hours of homework each week. Round that number to the nearest *whole number.*

(A) 6 (B) 7 (C) 8 (D) 9

(C) **12.** Students in the United States receive an average of 4.6 hours of homework each week. Round that number to the nearest *whole number.*

(A) 7 (B) 6 (C) 5 (D) 4

(A) **13.** Round 7.142857 to the nearest *tenth.*

(A) 7.1 (B) 7.14 (C) 7.15 (D) 7.2

(C) **14.** Round 1.4142 to the nearest *hundredth.*

(A) 1 (B) 1.414 (C) 1.41 (D) 1.4

(D) **15.** Round $99.99 to the nearest *dollar.*

(A) $90.00 (B) $99.00 (C) $99.90 (D) $100.00

(D) **16.** Round 123.456 to the nearest *tenth.*

(A) 123.4 (B) 123.45 (C) 123.46 (D) 123.5

Ⓐ **17.** Round 1.0049 to the nearest *hundredth.*

Ⓐ 1.00 Ⓑ 1.004 Ⓒ 1.005 Ⓓ 1.01

Ⓑ **18.** Round 9.67 to the nearest *tenth.*

Ⓐ 9.6 Ⓑ 9.7 Ⓒ 10 Ⓓ 10.67

Ⓒ **19.** In a recent year, 41.5 million Americans walked for exercise. Round that number to the nearest *million.*

Ⓐ 40 million Ⓑ 41 million
Ⓒ 42 million Ⓓ 50 million

Ⓑ **20.** In a recent year, 73.3 million Americans swam for exercise. Round that number to the nearest *million.*

Ⓐ 70 million Ⓑ 73 million
Ⓒ 74 million Ⓓ 80 million

Ⓒ **21.** Round $163.72 to the nearest *dollar.*

Ⓐ $160.00 Ⓑ $163.00
Ⓒ $164.00 Ⓓ $200.00

Ⓒ **22.** Round $85.21 to the nearest *dollar.*

Ⓐ $90.00 Ⓑ $86.00 Ⓒ $85.00 Ⓓ $85.20

Ⓓ **23.** Round 206.489 to the nearest *tenth.*

Ⓐ 206 Ⓑ 206.4 Ⓒ 206.49 Ⓓ 206.5

Ⓑ **24.** Round 52.114 to the nearest *hundredth.*

Ⓐ 52.12 Ⓑ 52.11 Ⓒ 52.1 Ⓓ 52

Ⓒ **25.** Recently Americans redeemed 8.75 billion coupons. Round that number to the nearest *tenth of a billion.*

Ⓐ 8 billion Ⓑ 8.7 billion
Ⓒ 8.8 billion Ⓓ 9 billion

Ⓒ **26.** Americans redeemed 19.6 billion coupons for frozen foods. Round that number to the nearest *billion.*

Ⓐ 10 billion Ⓑ 19 billion
Ⓒ 20 billion Ⓓ 200 billion

Ⓐ **27.** Round 193.463 to the nearest *hundredth.*

Ⓐ 193.46 Ⓑ 193.47 Ⓒ 193.5 Ⓓ 200

Ⓒ **28.** Round $37.24 to the nearest *dollar.*

Ⓐ $40.00 Ⓑ $38.00 Ⓒ $37.00 Ⓓ $30.00

Ⓑ **29.** Round 10.162 to the nearest *tenth.*

Ⓐ 10 Ⓑ 10.2 Ⓒ 10.16 Ⓓ 10.1

Ⓓ **30.** Round 28.407 to the nearest *whole number.*

Ⓐ 30 Ⓑ 29 Ⓒ 28.4 Ⓓ 28

Ⓒ **31.** Round $391.02 to the nearest *dollar.*

Ⓐ $400 Ⓑ $395 Ⓒ $391 Ⓓ $390

Ⓒ **32.** Round 435.976 to the nearest *hundredth.*

Ⓐ 436 Ⓑ 400 Ⓒ 435.98 Ⓓ 435.97

Ⓑ **33.** Round 351.7 to the nearest *whole number.*

Ⓐ 400 Ⓑ 352 Ⓒ 35 Ⓓ 300

Ⓑ **34.** Round 17.2198 to the nearest *tenth.*

Ⓐ 20 Ⓑ 17.2 Ⓒ 17.1 Ⓓ 17

Ⓑ **35.** Round $500.98 to the nearest *dollar.*

Ⓐ $600 Ⓑ $501 Ⓒ $500 Ⓓ $400

Ⓑ **36.** Round 87.016 to the nearest *hundredth.*

Ⓐ 87.01 Ⓑ 87.02 Ⓒ 90 Ⓓ 100

Ⓒ **37.** Round 1.242 to the nearest *whole number.*

Ⓐ 0.2 Ⓑ 0.24 Ⓒ 1 Ⓓ 2

Ⓒ **38.** Round 89.0846 to the nearest *tenth.*

Ⓐ 89 Ⓑ 89.08 Ⓒ 89.1 Ⓓ 90

Ⓓ **39.** Round $19.95 to the nearest *dollar.*

Ⓐ $10 Ⓑ $19 Ⓒ $19.90 Ⓓ $20

Ⓒ **40.** Round 101.7392 to the nearest *hundredth.*

Ⓐ 102 Ⓑ 100 Ⓒ 101.74 Ⓓ 101.73

Name____________________ Class ________ Date ____________

2.4 ADDING DECIMALS

Example 1: Add: 2.92 + 3.1 + 5

- Line up the decimal points.
- 5 can be written as 5.0.
- Add as with whole numbers.
- Place the decimal point in the answer.

$$\begin{array}{r} \scriptstyle 1 \\ 2.92 \\ 3.1 \\ +5.0 \\ \hline 11.02 \end{array}$$

REMEMBER: Always **estimate** to see if your answer is **reasonable**.

- Round each addend to the greatest place.

$$\begin{array}{rcr} 2.92 & \longrightarrow & 3 \\ 3.1 & \longrightarrow & 3 \\ +5.0 & \longrightarrow & +5 \\ \hline & & 11 \end{array}$$

The estimate and the exact answer are close. Therefore, 11.02 is a reasonable answer.

Fill in the correct circle to answer each question.

Ⓒ **1.** Add: 2.12 + 3.22

Ⓐ 534 Ⓑ 53.4 Ⓒ 5.34 Ⓓ 0.534

Ⓓ **2.** Find the sum of 10.49 and 11.2

Ⓐ 11.51 Ⓑ 11.61 Ⓒ 21.51 Ⓓ 21.69

Ⓑ **3.** Add 2, 0.2, and 0.002.

Ⓐ 2.222 Ⓑ 2.202 Ⓒ 2.022 Ⓓ 0.006

Ⓒ **4.** 0.2345 + 0.7655 = ■

Ⓐ 0.9990 Ⓑ 0.9999 Ⓒ 1 Ⓓ 1.01

Ⓓ **5.** Add:

$$\begin{array}{r} \$543.89 \\ 124.50 \\ 86.97 \\ +\ \ 111.74 \\ \hline \end{array}$$

Ⓐ $864.10 Ⓑ $867.00

Ⓒ 867 Ⓓ $867.10

Ⓐ **6.** Add:

$$\begin{array}{l} 1.111 \\ 2.222 \\ 3.33 \\ +4 \\ \hline \end{array}$$

Ⓐ 10.663 Ⓑ 11.6631

Ⓒ 13.7 Ⓓ 106,633

Ⓒ **7.** Alex uses a bicycle odometer to keep track of how far he travels. When he left home, the odometer read 14.6 kilometers. He rode 2.3 kilometers to the library. What did the odometer read when he got to the library?

Ⓐ 169 kilometers Ⓑ 37.6 kilometers

Ⓒ 16.9 kilometers Ⓓ 12.3 kilometers

Ⓒ **8.** Jean is training for a long bike trip. She keeps a log of how far she rides each day. She rode 6.8 kilometers on Saturday and 9.2 kilometers on Sunday. How far did she ride, in all?

Ⓐ 2.4 kilometers Ⓑ 15 kilometers

Ⓒ 16 kilometers Ⓓ 160 kilometers

Ⓐ **9.** Add:

$$\begin{array}{r} 24.51 \\ 19.19 \\ +37.83 \\ \hline \end{array}$$

Ⓐ 81.53 Ⓑ 81.43 Ⓒ 71.53 Ⓓ 71.43

Ⓐ **10.** Find the sum:

$$\begin{array}{r} 44.98 \\ 101 \\ +\ \ 8.33 \\ \hline \end{array}$$

Ⓐ 154.31 Ⓑ 154.211 Ⓒ 143.21 Ⓓ 138.38

(C) **11.** Find the sum: four tenths plus four and one tenth

(A) 4.14 (B) 4.1 (C) 4.5 (D) 8.1

(A) **12.** Find the sum: seven hundredths plus seven and one hundredth

(A) 7.08 (B) 7.071 (C) 7.017 (D) 0.14

Use Table 2.4 to answer questions 13-15.

Table 2.4

January Clearance	
Sweaters	$23.95
Scarves	10.98
Skirts	24.00
Dresses	49.99

(A) **13.** Janet bought a scarf, a sweater, and a dress. Round the cost of each item to the nearest *dollar*. Then find the total cost of Janet's purchase.

(A) $85.00 (B) $84.92

(C) $82.00 (D) $59.00

(B) **14.** Suzanne bought two skirts and a sweater. What was the cost of these items?

(A) $24.43 (B) $71.95 (C) $79.95 (D) $91.95

(C) **15.** Alice bought three scarves. What was the total cost?

(A) $72.00 (B) $71.85 (C) $32.94 (D) $30.74

(D) **16.** Add:

$$\begin{array}{r} 24.000 \\ 24.159 \\ 39.876 \\ +41.299 \\ \hline \end{array}$$

(A) 119.234 (B) 119.334

(C) 129.234 (D) 129.334

(D) **17.** Add:

$$\begin{array}{r} 1.11 \\ 0.222 \\ 33.3 \\ +989 \\ \hline \end{array}$$

(A) 1012.632 (B) 1013.632

(C) 1022.632 (D) 1023.632

(B) **18.** Find the sum of 3 tenths and 7 hundredths:

(A) 10 (B) 0.37 (C) 0.10 (D) 0.010

(C) **19.** 1.011 + 0.98 = ■

(A) 1.109 (B) 1.99 (C) 1.991 (D) 11.09

(C) **20.** Find the sum: 24.15 + 3.475

(A) 5.89 (B) 27.525 (C) 27.625 (D) 58.9

(C) **21.** Round to the nearest *dollar*, then find the sum: $5.56 + $8.98 + $11.23

(A) $25.00 (B) $24.00 (C) $26.00 (D) $30.00

(C) **22.** Add:

$$\begin{array}{l} 1.6 \\ 1.338 \\ +1.19 \\ \hline \end{array}$$

(A) 41.28 (B) 31.28 (C) 4.128 (D) 3.028

(A) **23.** Add:

$$\begin{array}{r} 43.47 \\ +\ \ 9.32 \\ \hline \end{array}$$

(A) 52.79 (B) 42.79 (C) 5.279 (D) 4.279

(D) **24.** Find the sum of 4.12 and 36.9.

(A) 4.102 (B) 7.81 (C) 31.07 (D) 41.02

(A) **25.** Add: 9 + 6.11

(A) 15.11 (B) 14.11 (C) 1.511 (D) 1.411

(B) **26.** Add 27.6 and 9.58.

(A) 123.4 (B) 37.18 (C) 27.18 (D) 2.718

(A) **27.** $42.13 + 39.17 = ■

(A) $81.30 (B) $81.20 (C) $71.20 (D) $2.96

(C) **28.** Find the sum of 0.408 and 23.72.

(A) 2.4128 (B) 2.780 (C) 24.128 (D) 27.80

(B) **29.** 29.5 + 7.08 = ■

(A) 3658 (B) 36.58 (C) 10.03 (D) 1.003

Name ____________________ Class __________ Date __________

2.5 SUBTRACTING DECIMALS

Example 1: Subtract: 1.75 – 0.283

- Line up the decimal points.
- 1.75 can be written as 1.750.
- Subtract as with whole numbers.
- Place the decimal point in the answer.

$$\begin{array}{r} 1.750 \\ -0.283 \\ \hline \end{array} \qquad \begin{array}{r} {\scriptstyle 6\,\overset{14}{\not 4}\,10} \\ 1.\not 7\not 5\not 0 \\ -0.283 \\ \hline 1.467 \end{array}$$

REMEMBER: Always **estimate** to see if your answer is **reasonable**.

- Round each number to the greatest place.

$$\begin{array}{r} 1.75 \\ -0.283 \\ \hline \end{array} \begin{array}{c} \longrightarrow \\ \longrightarrow \end{array} \begin{array}{r} 2.0 \\ -0.3 \\ \hline 1.7 \end{array}$$

The estimate and the exact answer are close. Therefore, 1.467 is a reasonable answer.

Fill in the correct circle to answer each question.

(B) **1.** Subtract: $\begin{array}{r} 2.375 \\ -1.125 \\ \hline \end{array}$

Ⓐ 0.250 Ⓑ 1.25 Ⓒ 2.75 Ⓓ 3.5

(A) **2.** Subtract: $\begin{array}{r} 2.12 \\ -0.875 \\ \hline \end{array}$

Ⓐ 1.245 Ⓑ 1.255 Ⓒ 2.355 Ⓓ 2.995

(D) **3.** Subtract: 2 – 0.125

Ⓐ 2.125 Ⓑ 1.985 Ⓒ 1.975 Ⓓ 1.875

(B) **4.** Subtract 13.66 from 23.66.

Ⓐ 1 Ⓑ 10 Ⓒ 37.32 Ⓓ 1,000

(D) **5.** Find the difference: 7.8910 – 1.2345

Ⓐ 9.1246 Ⓑ 6.6666
Ⓒ 6.6656 Ⓓ 6.6565

(B) **6.** From 1.5 subtract 0.5 .

Ⓐ 10 Ⓑ 1 Ⓒ 0.5 Ⓓ 0.01

(D) **7.** Sam gave the clerk \$45. His purchases totalled \$37.02. What was his change?

Ⓐ \$82.02 Ⓑ \$18.08 Ⓒ \$8.98 Ⓓ \$7.98

(A) **8.** A handknit sweater cost \$79. Jill bought the sweater on sale for \$59.95. How much did she save?

Ⓐ \$19.05 Ⓑ \$20.05 Ⓒ \$20.15 Ⓓ \$138.95

(D) **9.** Round to the nearest *dollar*, then find the difference: \$542.99 – \$69.15

Ⓐ \$430 Ⓑ \$470 Ⓒ \$473.84 Ⓓ \$474

(A) **10.** Round to the nearest *dollar*, then find the difference: \$789.36 – \$53.60

Ⓐ \$735 Ⓑ \$736 Ⓒ \$740 Ⓓ \$735.76

(C) **11.** Find the difference: 3 – 0.012

Ⓐ 29.88 Ⓑ 3.012
Ⓒ 2.988 Ⓓ 2.098

(B) **12.** Subtract: $\begin{array}{r} 7.009 \\ -0.011 \\ \hline \end{array}$

Ⓐ 6.098 Ⓑ 6.998
Ⓒ 7.018 Ⓓ 7.098

(C) **13.** Will received \$17.02 change from a \$20 bill when he bought a notebook. What was the total cost of the notebook?

Ⓐ \$3.98 Ⓑ \$3.08 Ⓒ \$2.98 Ⓓ \$2.08

(A) **14.** If 6.75 is added to a number, the sum is 10. What is the number?

Ⓐ 3.25 Ⓑ 4.35 Ⓒ 13.25 Ⓓ 16.75

Ⓓ **15.** Subtract 345.12 from 500.

Ⓐ 845.12 Ⓑ 340.88 Ⓒ 254.88 Ⓓ 154.88

Ⓐ **16.** 8.5 – 6.85 = ■

Ⓐ 1.65 Ⓑ 2.35 Ⓒ 2.65 Ⓓ 6

Use Table 2.5A to answer questions 17-20.

Table 2.5A

Precipitaton of Selected Cities in a Recent Year		
City	Rainfall (inches)	Snowfall (inches)
Caribou, Maine	35.6	122.2
Chicago, Illinois	34	38.1
Dallas, Texas	33.89	0
New York, New York	57.03	29.3

Ⓒ **17.** How much more snowfall did Chicago have than New York?

Ⓐ 67.4 inches Ⓑ 23.03 inches
Ⓒ 8.8 inches Ⓓ 8.1 inches

Ⓓ **18.** How much more rainfall did Chicago have than Dallas?

Ⓐ 67.89 inches Ⓑ 38.1 inches
Ⓒ 1.11 inches Ⓓ 0.11 inches

Ⓑ **19.** How much more snowfall than rainfall was there in Caribou?

Ⓐ 4.1 inches Ⓑ 86.6 inches
Ⓒ 157.8 inches Ⓓ 233.8 inches

Ⓓ **20.** How much more rainfall than snowfall was there in New York?

Ⓐ 86.33 inches Ⓑ 38.73 inches
Ⓒ 28 inches Ⓓ 27.73 inches

Ⓓ **21.** Subtract: 3.1 – 0.125

Ⓐ 3.225 Ⓑ 3.075 Ⓒ 3.025 Ⓓ 2.975

Ⓓ **22.** Find the difference: 1.71 – 1.31

Ⓐ 3.02 Ⓑ 2.1 Ⓒ 2.02 Ⓓ 0.40

Ⓒ **23.** Jill saved $13. Karen saved $7.12. How much more money did Jill save?

Ⓐ $6.78 Ⓑ $5.98 Ⓒ $5.88 Ⓓ $5.78

Ⓓ **24.** Round to the nearest *dollar*, then find the difference: $97.03 – $24.68

Ⓐ $30 Ⓑ $50 Ⓒ $60 Ⓓ $72

Use Table 2.5B to answer questions 25-28.

Table 2.5B

Country Kitchen Lunch Specials	
Chili	$2.50
Garden Salad	3.75
Turkey Sandwich	2.25
Chicken Soup	1.65
Omelet	2.75

Ⓒ **25.** How much more does the garden salad cost than the chili?

Ⓐ $6.25 Ⓑ $1.50 Ⓒ $1.25 Ⓓ $0.25

Ⓑ **26.** Richard bought chicken soup. He gave the cashier a $5 bill. What was his change?

Ⓐ $2.75 Ⓑ $3.35 Ⓒ $4.45 Ⓓ $6.65

Ⓒ **27.** How much more does the omelet cost than the chicken soup?

Ⓐ $4.40 Ⓑ $1.20 Ⓒ $1.10 Ⓓ $0.10

Ⓐ **28.** Stephanie bought a turkey sandwich. She gave the cashier $3.00. What was her change?

Ⓐ $.75 Ⓑ $1.75 Ⓒ $2.25 Ⓓ $5.25

Ⓓ **29.** From 18.75 subtract 15.95.

Ⓐ 12.80 Ⓑ 3.80 Ⓒ 3.20 Ⓓ 2.80

Ⓐ **30.** Find the difference: 8.920 – 6.893

Ⓐ 2.027 Ⓑ 2.127 Ⓒ 2.133 Ⓓ 2.037

Name ______________________ Class ________ Date ____________

2.6 MULTIPLYING DECIMALS

Example 1: Multiply: 42.75×5.2

Line up the digits along the right.

$$\begin{array}{r} 42.75 \\ \times \quad 5.2 \\ \hline \end{array}$$

Multiply as with whole numbers.

$$\begin{array}{r} 4275 \\ \times \quad 52 \\ \hline 8550 \\ 213750 \\ \hline 222300 \end{array}$$

Add the number of decimal places in the multipliers to get the number of decimal places in the product.

$$\begin{array}{rl} 42.75 & \text{2 places} \\ \times \quad 5.2 & \text{1 place} \\ \hline 8550 & \\ 213750 & \\ \hline 222.300 & \text{3 places} \end{array}$$

REMEMBER: Always **estimate** to see if your answer is **reasonable**.

- Round each factor to the greatest place.

$$\begin{array}{r} 42.75 \\ \times \quad 5.2 \\ \hline \end{array} \longrightarrow \begin{array}{r} 40 \\ \times \quad 5 \\ \hline 200 \end{array}$$

The estimate and the answer are close. Therefore, 222.3 is a reasonable answer.

Fill in the correct circle to answer each question.

Ⓓ **1.** Multiply: $\begin{array}{r} 234 \\ \times \ 0.5 \\ \hline \end{array}$

Ⓐ 1170 Ⓑ 1150 Ⓒ 1070 Ⓓ 117

Ⓒ **2.** Multiply: $\begin{array}{r} 0.687 \\ \times \ 987 \\ \hline \end{array}$

Ⓐ 67806.9 Ⓑ 6780.69
Ⓒ 678.069 Ⓓ 67.8069

Ⓑ **3.** Multiply 24.15 by 1.5.

Ⓐ 3.6225 Ⓑ 36.225
Ⓒ 362.25 Ⓓ 3622.5

Ⓒ **4.** $12.175 \times 1.5 =$ ■

Ⓐ 182.625 Ⓑ 73.05
Ⓒ 18.2625 Ⓓ 7.305

Ⓒ **5.** Find the cost of 13 pencils at $0.35 each.

Ⓐ $1.30 Ⓑ $1.40 Ⓒ $4.55 Ⓓ $45.50

Ⓐ **6.** Find the cost of three notebooks at $4.60 each.

Ⓐ $13.80 Ⓑ $12.80 Ⓒ $12.18 Ⓓ $1.38

Ⓐ **7.** Multiply: 68.7×987

Ⓐ 67,806.9 Ⓑ 6780.69
Ⓒ 678.069 Ⓓ 67.8069

Ⓒ **8.** $134.7 \times 2.29 =$ ■

Ⓐ 17.511 Ⓑ 297.463
Ⓒ 308.463 Ⓓ 3084.63

Ⓑ **9.** Multiply: 174×0.2

Ⓐ 24.8 Ⓑ 34.8 Ⓒ 248 Ⓓ 348

Ⓑ **10.** Multiply: 1.483×0.9

Ⓐ 0.9627 Ⓑ 1.3347
Ⓒ 9.627 Ⓓ 13.347

Ⓒ **11.** $44.44 \times 3.3 =$ ■

Ⓐ 1466.52 Ⓑ 266.64
Ⓒ 146.652 Ⓓ 26.664

Ⓑ **12.** What is the product of 24.24 and 0.0011?

Ⓐ 0.004848 Ⓑ 0.026664
Ⓒ 0.2664 Ⓓ 4848

Use Table 2.6 to answer questions 13-15.

Table 2.6

Occupation	Miles Walked in a Work Day
Hospital Nurse	4.9
Banker	2.8
Security Officer	5.1
Secretary	2.3
Teacher	1.7

Ⓑ **13.** How many miles would a secretary walk in a five-day work week?

Ⓐ 115 miles Ⓑ 11.5 miles Ⓒ 10.5 miles Ⓓ 8.5 miles

Ⓒ **14.** How many miles would a nurse walk in a 20-day work month?

Ⓐ 9.8 miles Ⓑ 88 miles Ⓒ 98 miles Ⓓ 980 miles

Ⓒ **15.** How many miles would a teacher walk in a 180-day school year?

Ⓐ 144 miles Ⓑ 206 miles Ⓒ 306 miles Ⓓ 3,060 miles

Ⓐ **16.** $19.98 × 24 = ■

Ⓐ $479.52 Ⓑ $478.52 Ⓒ $368.52 Ⓓ $119.88

Ⓐ **17.** Multiply 1.7 by 30.

Ⓐ 51 Ⓑ 31 Ⓒ 5.1 Ⓓ 3.1

Ⓒ **18.** Find the product: 1.3×7.7

Ⓐ 1.82 Ⓑ 7.8 Ⓒ 10.01 Ⓓ 91.01

Ⓓ **19.** A **great gross** is a dozen times a dozen times a dozen. What would a great gross of pencils cost at $0.22 each?

Ⓐ $17.28 Ⓑ $31.68 Ⓒ $379.16 Ⓓ $380.16

Ⓑ **20.** Anthony Orlando works 40 hours each week. He earns $10.50 an hour. What is his weekly pay?

Ⓐ $400.50 Ⓑ $420.00 Ⓒ $424.00 Ⓓ $440.00

Ⓑ **21.** Suzanne's car travels 18.6 miles on a gallon of gasoline. The car tank holds 20 gallons. How far can she travel on a full tank of gas?

Ⓐ 262 miles Ⓑ 372 miles Ⓒ 2620 miles Ⓓ 3720 miles

Ⓒ **22.** Round to the nearest ten, then find the product: 362×24

Ⓐ 8690 Ⓑ 8688 Ⓒ 7200 Ⓓ 8000

Ⓑ **23.** What is the cost of 3.5 dozen cookies if they cost $0.70 per dozen?

Ⓐ $2.35 Ⓑ $2.45 Ⓒ $2.55 Ⓓ $12.25

Ⓒ **24.** Kim had three rolls of film developed. It cost $3.15 to develop each roll. What was the total cost?

Ⓐ $94.50 Ⓑ $93.50 Ⓒ $9.45 Ⓓ $9.35

Ⓐ **25.** Multiply:

$$\begin{array}{r} 8.4 \\ \times 62 \\ \hline \end{array}$$

Ⓐ 520.8 Ⓑ 67.2 Ⓒ 52.08 Ⓓ 6.72

Ⓒ **26.** Multiply:

$$\begin{array}{r} 8.52 \\ \times 0.65 \\ \hline \end{array}$$

Ⓐ 55.38 Ⓑ 9.17 Ⓒ 5.538 Ⓓ 0.9382

Name ________________ Class ________ Date ________

2.7 DIVIDING DECIMALS

Example 1: Divide: $2.94 \div 6$

2.94 is the dividend.
6 is the divisor.
0.49 is the quotient.

- To divide a decimal by a whole number, first write the decimal point in the quotient directly above the decimal point in the dividend.
- Then divide as with whole numbers.

$$\begin{array}{r} 0.49 \\ 6\overline{)\,2.94} \\ \underline{24} \\ 54 \\ \underline{54} \\ 0 \end{array}$$

Example 2: Find the quotient of 100.1 and 9.1

100.1 is the dividend.
9.1 is the divisor.
11 is the quotient.

- The divisor, 9.1, is not a whole number. Therefore, move the decimal point one place to the right in the divisor and in the dividend to make the divisor a whole number.
- Then proceed as in Example 1.

$$\begin{array}{r} 11. \\ 9.1.\overline{)\,100.1.} \\ \underline{91} \\ 91 \\ \underline{91} \\ 0 \end{array}$$

REMEMBER: Moving the decimal point one place to the right is is the same as multiplying by 10.

Example 3: Divide 0.02 into 6.

6 is the dividend.
0.02 is the divisor.
300 is the quotient.

- Write zeros in the dividend so that you can move the decimal points in the divisor and in the dividend 2 places to the right.
- Then proceed as in Example 1.

$$\begin{array}{r} 300. \\ 0.02.\overline{)\,6.00.} \end{array}$$

REMEMBER: Moving the decimal point 2 places to the right is is the same as multiplying by 100.

Fill in the correct circle to answer each question.

Ⓒ **1.** Divide: $3.7\overline{)\,1.11}$

Ⓐ 30 Ⓑ 3 Ⓒ 0.3 Ⓓ 0.03

Ⓒ **2.** Find the quotient: $3.5 \div 5$

Ⓐ 7 Ⓑ 6 Ⓒ 0.7 Ⓓ 0.07

Ⓓ **3.** Divide 80 by 0.04.

Ⓐ 2 Ⓑ 20 Ⓒ 200 Ⓓ 2000

Ⓑ **4.** Seven people contributed for a gift for a friend. The total cost of the gift was $28.56. How much did each person contribute?

Ⓐ $3.08 Ⓑ $4.08 Ⓒ $40.80 Ⓓ $408

Ⓐ **5.** Divide: $0.18 \div 0.45$

Ⓐ 0.4 Ⓑ 2.5 Ⓒ 4 Ⓓ 25

Ⓓ **6.** Find the quotient: $350 \div 0.25$

Ⓐ 0.14 Ⓑ 14 Ⓒ 140 Ⓓ 1400

Ⓑ **7.** What is the quotient of 0.1728 and 6?

Ⓐ 0.0101 Ⓑ 0.0288

Ⓒ 0.2713 Ⓓ 0.288

Ⓒ **8.** $4\overline{)44.884}$

Ⓐ 11221 Ⓑ 112.21

Ⓒ 11.221 Ⓓ 1.1221

Ⓑ **9.** Big Dan's Record Shop is selling three video tapes for $29.85. What is the price of each video tape?

Ⓐ $89.55 Ⓑ $9.95 Ⓒ $9.93 Ⓓ $9.89

Ⓑ **10.** Ned bought four pounds of hamburger for $4.36. What is the price of hamburger per pound?

Ⓐ $0.19 Ⓑ $1.09 Ⓒ $1.90 Ⓓ $17.44

Ⓒ **11.** $2.5 \div 0.5 = \blacksquare$

Ⓐ 0.2 Ⓑ 2 Ⓒ 5 Ⓓ 50

Ⓐ **12.** Divide: $0.11\overline{)242}$

Ⓐ 2200 Ⓑ 220 Ⓒ 22 Ⓓ 2.2

Ⓓ **13.** Divide: $1000 \div 0.001$

Ⓐ 1 Ⓑ 1000

Ⓒ 100,000 Ⓓ 1,000,000

Ⓒ **14.** Find the quotient: $1.4 \div 0.4$

Ⓐ 0.035 Ⓑ 0.35 Ⓒ 3.5 Ⓓ 35

Ⓑ **15.** Divide, then round the quotient to the nearest *tenth*: $7.4 \div 2.6$

Ⓐ 2.7 Ⓑ 2.8 Ⓒ 2.84 Ⓓ 284

Ⓑ **16.** Divide, then round the quotient to the nearest *hundredth*: $8\overline{)0.49}$

Ⓐ 0.05 Ⓑ 0.06 Ⓒ 0.07 Ⓓ 0.6

Ⓐ **17.** Chris saved $36.00 in two weeks. At this rate, how much will she save in nine weeks?

Ⓐ $162 Ⓑ $324 Ⓒ $342 Ⓓ $648

Ⓒ **18.** John and Jack spent $8.16 on lunch. They decided to share the cost equally. How much did they each pay?

Ⓐ $40.20 Ⓑ $10.10 Ⓒ $4.08 Ⓓ $1.01

Ⓓ **19.** Divide: $50.25 \div 25$

Ⓐ 201 Ⓑ 21 Ⓒ 2.1 Ⓓ 2.01

Ⓒ **20.** Divide: $0.8 \div 40$

Ⓐ 2 Ⓑ 20 Ⓒ 0.02 Ⓓ 0.002

Ⓒ **21.** Divide, then round the quotient to the nearest *tenth*: $8.41\overline{)18.5}$

Ⓐ 0.2 Ⓑ 0.02 Ⓒ 2.2 Ⓓ 0.5

Ⓑ **22.** Divide, then round the quotient to the nearest *hundredth*: $7.5\overline{)62.91}$

Ⓐ 8.38 Ⓑ 8.39 Ⓒ 8.4 Ⓓ 8

Ⓒ **23.** Divide: $4.1\overline{)123}$

Ⓐ 0.03 Ⓑ 3 Ⓒ 30 Ⓓ 40

Ⓑ **24.** $2.5 \div 0.5 = \blacksquare$

Ⓐ 0.2 Ⓑ 5 Ⓒ 0.5 Ⓓ 50

Ⓓ **25.** What is the quotient of 4.24 and 0.8?

Ⓐ 0.053 Ⓑ 0.53 Ⓒ 53 Ⓓ 5.3

Ⓐ **26.** Divide: $34.04 \div 0.37$

Ⓐ 92 Ⓑ 9.2 Ⓒ 0.92 Ⓓ 0.092

Name ______________________ Class ________ Date ____________

2.8 MULTIPLYING AND DIVIDING BY POWERS OF 10

Example 1: **Multiply** 14.57 by 10, by 100, and by 1,000.

14.57×10

- 10 has 1 zero.
- Move the decimal point 1 place to the *right*.

$14.57 \times 10 = 145.7$

14.57×100

- 100 has 2 zeros.
- Move the decimal point 2 places to the *right*.

$14.57 \times 100 = 1457.$

14.57×1000

- 1000 has 3 zeros.
- Move the decimal point 3 places to the *right*.

$14.57 \times 1000 = 14570.$

Example 2: **Divide** 14.57 by 10, by 100, and by 1000.

$14.57 \div 10$

- 10 has 1 zero.
- Move the decimal point 1 place to the *left*.

$14.57 \div 10 = 1.457$

$14.57 \div 100$

- 100 has 2 zeros.
- Move the decimal point 2 places to the *left*.

$14.57 \div 100 = 0.1457$

$14.57 \div 1000$

- 1,000 has 3 zeros.
- Move the decimal point 3 places to the *left*.

$14.57 \div 1000 = 0.01457$

Fill in the correct circle to answer each question.

Ⓓ **1.** Multiply 1.4 by 10.
Ⓐ 0.14 Ⓑ 1.04 Ⓒ 1.4 Ⓓ 14

Ⓒ **2.** Divide 1.4 by 10.
Ⓐ 14 Ⓑ 1.4 Ⓒ 0.14 Ⓓ 1.04

Ⓓ **3.** $3.12 \times 100 = ■$
Ⓐ 0.0312 Ⓑ 3.12 Ⓒ 31.2 Ⓓ 312

Ⓐ **4.** $3.12 \div 100 = ■$
Ⓐ 0.0312 Ⓑ 3.12 Ⓒ 31.2 Ⓓ 312

Ⓓ **5.** Multiply: 6.91×1000
Ⓐ 0.00691 Ⓑ 0.0691
Ⓒ 691 Ⓓ 6910

Ⓐ **6.** Divide: $6.91 \div 1000$
Ⓐ 0.00691 Ⓑ 0.0691
Ⓒ 691 Ⓓ 6910

Ⓑ **7.** Multiply 0.873 by 10.
Ⓐ 873 Ⓑ 8.73
Ⓒ 0.873 Ⓓ 0.0873

Ⓐ **8.** $0.002 \div 1000 = ■$
Ⓐ 0.000002 Ⓑ 0.02
Ⓒ 0.2 Ⓓ 2

Ⓐ **9.** $17.825 \times 100 = ■$
Ⓐ 1782.5 Ⓑ 17.825
Ⓒ 1.7825 Ⓓ 0.17825

Ⓒ **10.** Find the product: 2.67×1000
Ⓐ 0.00267 Ⓑ 26.7
Ⓒ 2670 Ⓓ 267

Ⓑ **11.** $10.492 \div 100 = ■$
Ⓐ 104.92 Ⓑ 0.10492
Ⓒ 1.0492 Ⓓ 1.492

Ⓐ **12.** Divide 3.1416 by 10.
Ⓐ 0.31416 Ⓑ 3.1416
Ⓒ 3.142 Ⓓ 31.416

Name ____________________ Class ________ Date __________

2.9 EXPONENTS

Example 1: Write $4 \times 4 \times 4$ in exponential form.

- The base is 4.
  4 is multiplied by itself 3 times.

$4 \times 4 \times 4 = 4^3$

Example 2: Write 3^4 in expanded form.

3^4 ← exponent
↑ base

- 3 is multiplied by itself 4 times.

$3^4 = 3 \times 3 \times 3 \times 3 = 81$

Fill in the correct circle to answer each question.

(A) **1.** Write in exponential form: $2 \times 2 \times 2 \times 2$

(A) 2^4 (B) 4^2 (C) 16 (D) 8

(B) **2.** Write in exponential form: $10 \times 10 \times 10 \times 10 \times 10$

(A) 5^{10} (B) 10^5 (C) 100,000 (D) $100{,}000^5$

(B) **3.** Complete: If $4^x = 16$, $x =$ ■ .

(A) 1 (B) 2 (C) 3 (D) 4

(B) **4.** Find the missing exponent: $5^x = 125$

(A) 4 (B) 3 (C) 2 (D) 1

(C) **5.** Write in expanded form: 10^2

(A) 20 (B) 2×10 (C) 100 (D) 200

(C) **6.** Write in expanded form: 7^2

(A) 77 (B) 72 (C) 49 (D) 14

(A) **7.** Write in exponential form: $14 \times 14 \times 14 \times 14$

(A) 14^4 (B) 4^{14} (C) 56 (D) 38,416

(B) **8.** Express as a product of factors: 8^2

(A) $8 + 2$ (B) 8×8 (C) 8×2 (D) $8 + 8$

(D) **9.** If $2^x = 64$, then $x =$ ■ .

(A) 32 (B) 4 (C) 5 (D) 6

(A) **10.** Write in expanded form: 9^4

(A) 6561 (B) 9×4 (C) $9 \times 9 \times 9$ (D) 36

(B) **11.** If $10^x = 10{,}000$, then $x =$ ■ .

(A) 3 (B) 4 (C) 5 (D) 6

(C) **12.** Find the missing exponent: $2^x = 8$

(A) 0 (B) 2 (C) 3 (D) 4

(B) **13.** Write in exponential form: $3 \times 3 \times 3 \times 3$

(A) 4^3 (B) 3^4 (C) 27 (D) 81

(D) **14.** Write in expanded form: 5^4

(A) 20 (B) 5×4 (C) $4 \times 4 \times 4 \times 4 \times 4$ (D) 625

(A) **15.** Find the missing exponent: $3^x = 81$

(A) 4 (B) 3 (C) 1 (D) 0

(B) **16.** Write in exponential form: $12 \times 12 \times 12$

(A) 12×3 (B) 12^3 (C) 3^{12} (D) 1728

(C) **17.** Write 6^2 in expanded form.

(A) 6 (B) 12 (C) 36 (D) 216

(B) **18.** Write in exponential form: $20 \times 20 \times 20$

(A) 20×3 (B) 20^3 (C) 60 (D) 8000

(A) **19.** Complete: $4^3 =$ ■

(A) 64 (B) 4×3 (C) 12 (D) 36

(D) **20.** Write 7^3 in expanded form.

(A) 0 (B) 7×3 (C) 21 (D) 343

Name ______________________ Class __________ Date __________

2.10 SCIENTIFIC NOTATION

A number is in **scientific notation** when it is written as the product of a number between 1 and 10 and a power of 10. For example, 23,700 is written as 2.37×10^4 in scientific notation.

Example 1: Write 4.76×10^3 in standard form.

- $4.76 \times 10^3 = 4.76 \times 1000$
  $= 4.760$
  $= 4760$

Example 2: Write 364,000 in scientific notation.

- $364{,}000 = 3.64000 \times 10^5$
  5 places
  $= 3.64 \times 10^5$

Fill in the correct circle to answer each question.

(B) **1.** Write the missing exponent: $687 = 6.87 \times 10^{\square}$

Ⓐ 1 Ⓑ 2 Ⓒ 3 Ⓓ 4

(B) **2.** Write the missing exponent: $800{,}000 = 8 \times 10^{\square}$

Ⓐ 6 Ⓑ 5 Ⓒ 4 Ⓓ 3

(C) **3.** Write in scientific notation: 564,000

Ⓐ 564×10^5 Ⓑ 564×10^3
Ⓒ 5.64×10^5 Ⓓ 5.64×10^3

(B) **4.** Write in standard form: 3.217×10^3

Ⓐ 321,700 Ⓑ 3217
Ⓒ 3.217 Ⓓ 3.217000

(C) **5.** Write in scientific notation: 1989

Ⓐ 198.9×10 Ⓑ 19.89×10^2
Ⓒ 1.989×10^3 Ⓓ 0.1989×10^4

(D) **6.** Write in standard form: 2.5×10^4

Ⓐ 0.0025 Ⓑ 250
Ⓒ 2500 Ⓓ 25,000

(C) **7.** Write in scientific notation: 84,000,000

Ⓐ 84×10^6 Ⓑ 84×10^8
Ⓒ 8.4×10^7 Ⓓ $84{,}000 \times 10^3$

(C) **8.** Write in scientific notation: 5600

Ⓐ 56×10^3 Ⓑ 56×10^2
Ⓒ 5.6×10^3 Ⓓ 5.6×10^2

(B) **9.** The Earth is about 93 million miles from the Sun. Write the underlined number in scientific notation.

Ⓐ 9.3×10^6 Ⓑ 9.3×10^7
Ⓒ 93×10^6 Ⓓ 93×10^7

10. (C) The planet Mars is about 1.42×10^8 miles from the Sun. Write the underlined number in standard form.

Ⓐ 142 Ⓑ 142,000
Ⓒ 142,000,000 Ⓓ 14,200,000,000

(B) **11.** Write in scientific notation: 40,000

Ⓐ 0.4×10^4 Ⓑ 4×10^4
Ⓒ 40×10^4 Ⓓ 40×10^3

(C) **12.** Write in standard form: 8.26×10^5

Ⓐ 826 Ⓑ 82,600
Ⓒ 826,000 Ⓓ 82,600,000

(C) **13.** Write the missing exponent: $4566 = 4.566 \times 10^{\square}$

Ⓐ 1 Ⓑ 2 Ⓒ 3 Ⓓ 4

14. (B) Write the missing exponent: $28 = 2.8 \times 10^{\square}$

Ⓐ 0 Ⓑ 1 Ⓒ 2 Ⓓ 3

Ⓓ **15.** The population of North America is about 382,000,000 people. Write that number in scientific notation.

Ⓐ 382×10^8 Ⓑ 3.82×10^9

Ⓒ 3.82×10^6 Ⓓ 3.82×10^8

Ⓓ **16.** The population of Canada is about 24,620,000 people. Write that number in scientific notation.

Ⓐ $24{,}620 \times 10^8$ Ⓑ $24{,}620 \times 10^4$

Ⓒ 2.462×10^8 Ⓓ 2.462×10^7

Ⓒ **17.** Write in standard form: 8.4×10^4

Ⓐ 84 Ⓑ 8400

Ⓒ 84,000 Ⓓ 840,000

Ⓑ **18.** Write in scientific notation: 700

Ⓐ 7×10^1 Ⓑ 7×10^2

Ⓒ 7×10^3 Ⓓ 0.7×10^2

Ⓓ **19.** Write the missing exponent: $75{,}000 = 7.5 \times 10^{\blacksquare}$

Ⓐ 1 Ⓑ 2 Ⓒ 3 Ⓓ 4

Ⓑ **20.** Write the missing exponent: $30{,}000{,}000 = 3 \times 10^{\blacksquare}$

Ⓐ 8 Ⓑ 7 Ⓒ 6 Ⓓ 5

Ⓓ **21.** Write in standard form: 4.5×10^1

Ⓐ 450,000 Ⓑ 45,000

Ⓒ 4500 Ⓓ 45

Ⓐ **22.** Write in scientific notation: 370,000

Ⓐ 3.7×10^5 Ⓑ 3.7×10^4

Ⓒ 37×10^2 Ⓓ 37×10^1

Ⓑ **23.** Write the missing exponent: $50{,}000 = 5 \times 10^{\blacksquare}$

Ⓐ 5 Ⓑ 4 Ⓒ 3 Ⓓ 2

Ⓑ **24.** Write the missing exponent: $750 = 7.5 \times 10^{\blacksquare}$

Ⓐ 3 Ⓑ 2 Ⓒ 1 Ⓓ 0

Ⓒ **25.** Write in scientific notation: 300

Ⓐ 30×10 Ⓑ 3×10^1

Ⓒ 3×10^2 Ⓓ 3×10^3

Ⓒ **26.** Write in scientific notation: 400,000

Ⓐ 400×1000 Ⓑ 4×10^4

Ⓒ 4×10^5 Ⓓ 4×10^6

Ⓒ **27.** Write in standard form: 2.1×10^4

Ⓐ 210 Ⓑ 2100

Ⓒ 21,000 Ⓓ 21,100

Ⓑ **28.** Write in standard form: 5.7×10^2

Ⓐ 0.57 Ⓑ 570

Ⓒ 5700 Ⓓ 57,000

Ⓓ **29.** Write the missing exponent: $6500 = 6.5 \times 10^{\blacksquare}$

Ⓐ 0 Ⓑ 1 Ⓒ 2 Ⓓ 3

Ⓑ **30.** Write the missing exponent: $145{,}000 = 1.45 \times 10^{\blacksquare}$

Ⓐ 6 Ⓑ 5 Ⓒ 4 Ⓓ 3

Ⓒ **31.** Write 25 million in scientific notation.

Ⓐ 25×10^7 Ⓑ 2.5×10^6

Ⓒ 2.5×10^7 Ⓓ 2.5×10^8

Ⓐ **32.** Write 6.42×10^4 in standard form.

Ⓐ 64,200 Ⓑ 642,000

Ⓒ 6420 Ⓓ 642×10

Ⓓ **33.** Write in scientific notation: 30,500,000

Ⓐ 3.05×10^6 Ⓑ 305×10^6

Ⓒ 305×10^7 Ⓓ 3.05×10^7

Ⓐ **34.** Write the missing exponent: $62{,}000 = 6.2 \times 10^{\blacksquare}$

Ⓐ 4 Ⓑ 3 Ⓒ 2 Ⓓ 1

Ⓑ **35.** Write in standard form: 9.07×10^5

Ⓐ 90,700 Ⓑ 907,000

Ⓒ 9,070,000 Ⓓ 90,700,000

Ⓒ **36.** Write in scientific notation: 543,000,000

Ⓐ 5.43×10^6 Ⓑ 5.43×10^7

Ⓒ 5.43×10^8 Ⓓ 5.43×10^9

Name ________________________________ Class __________ Date ______________

2.11 PRIME AND COMPOSITE NUMBERS

When two or more numbers are multiplied, each number is called a **factor**.

A **prime number** is any whole number greater than 1 that has exactly two factors: 1 and the number itself.

A **composite number** is any whole number greater than 1 that has more than two factors.

Example 1: List all the factors of 12.

$$\left.\begin{array}{l} 1 \times 12 \\ 2 \times 6 \\ 3 \times 4 \\ 4 \times 3 \end{array}\right\} = 12$$

(Once factors repeat, you have found all possiblities.)

The factors of 12 are 1, 2, 3, 4, 6, 12.

Example 2: List all the factors of 36.

$$\left.\begin{array}{l} 1 \times 36 \\ 2 \times 18 \\ 3 \times 12 \\ 4 \times 9 \\ 6 \times 6 \\ 9 \times 4 \end{array}\right\} = 36$$

(Repeated factors. Stop!)

The factors of 36 are 1, 2, 3, 4, 6, 9, 12, 18, 36.

Example 3: Is 15 a prime number or a composite number?

- List all the factors of 15: 1, 3, 5, 15
- 15 has more than 2 factors.

Therefore, 15 is a composite number.

Example 4: Is 29 a prime number or a composite number?

- List all the factors of 29: 1, 29
- 29 has only 2 factors: 1 and itself.

Therefore, 29 is a prime number.

Fill in the correct circle to answer each question.

Ⓓ **1.** What is the next prime number after 7?

Ⓐ 8 Ⓑ 9 Ⓒ 10 Ⓓ 11

Ⓐ **2.** What is the next composite number after 8?

Ⓐ 9 Ⓑ 10 Ⓒ 11 Ⓓ 12

Ⓑ **3.** Which number is a *prime* number?

Ⓐ 1 Ⓑ 2 Ⓒ 6 Ⓓ 8

Ⓒ **4.** Which number is a *composite* number?

Ⓐ 3 Ⓑ 11 Ⓒ 12 Ⓓ 13

Ⓒ **5.** List all the factors of 50.

Ⓐ 2, 5, 10, 25

Ⓑ 1, 2, 5, 10, 25

Ⓒ 1, 2, 5, 10, 25, 50

Ⓓ 1, 2, 4, 5, 10, 25, 50

Ⓓ **6.** The next four prime numbers after 13 are:

Ⓐ 15, 17, 19, 21

Ⓑ 17, 19, 21, 23

Ⓒ 17, 19, 23, 25

Ⓓ 17, 19, 23, 29

Ⓒ **7.** Which number is a *prime* number?

Ⓐ 0 Ⓑ 1 Ⓒ 13 Ⓓ 21

Ⓐ **8.** Which number is a *composite* number?

Ⓐ 6 Ⓑ 13 Ⓒ 7 Ⓓ 11

Ⓓ **9.** Which number is a *composite* number?

Ⓐ 0 Ⓑ 7 Ⓒ 11 Ⓓ 35

Ⓐ **10.** Which number is a *prime* number?

Ⓐ 43 Ⓑ 22 Ⓒ 14 Ⓓ 10

Name ____________________ Class __________ Date __________

2.12 PRIME FACTORIZATION

A composite number can be expressed as a product of prime factors.

Example 1: Find the prime factorization of 24.
Use a factor tree. There are many factor trees that represent the prime factorization of 24. Here are a few.

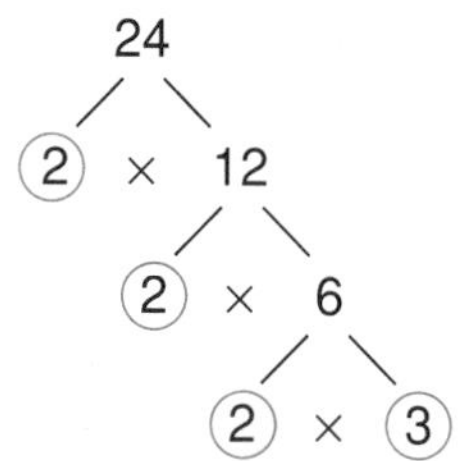

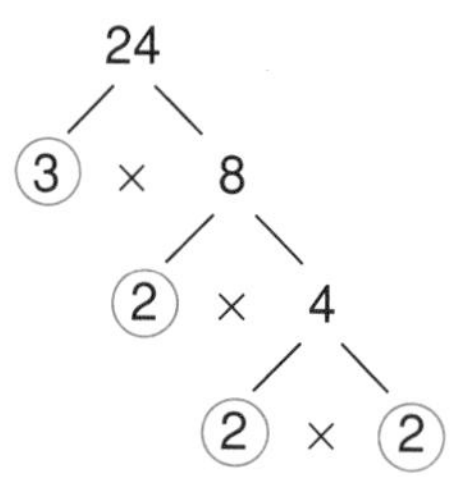

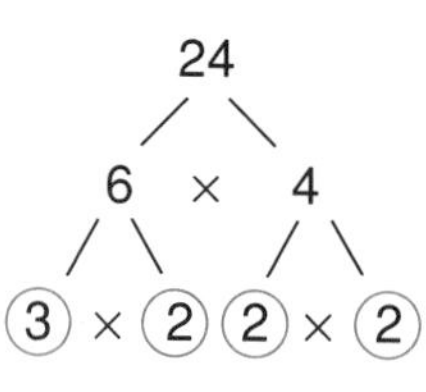

- Start with any two factors of 24.
- When you get to a prime number, end that branch and circle the prime.
- Repeat until each branch of the factor tree has a prime on its tip.

The prime factorization is: $24 = 2 \times 2 \times 2 \times 3$
$= 2^3 \times 3$

Fill in the correct circle to answer each question.

Ⓒ **1.** Which factor tree shows the prime factorization for 28?

Ⓐ 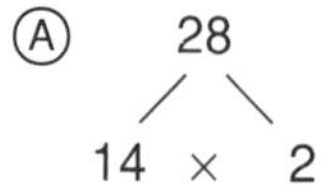

Ⓑ 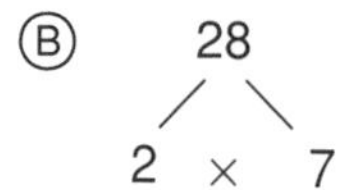

Ⓒ 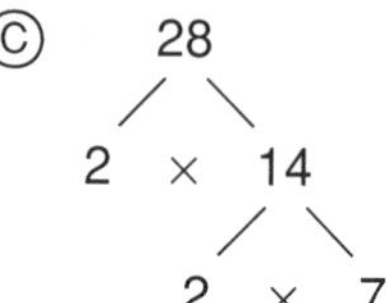

Ⓓ 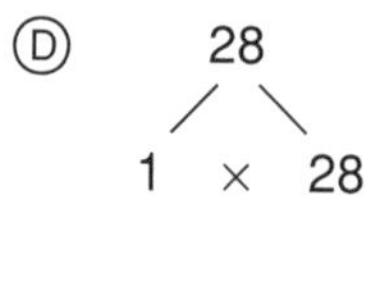

Ⓑ **2.** Find the prime factorization of 18.

Ⓐ 2×9 Ⓑ $2 \times 3 \times 3$
Ⓒ $2 \times 9 \times 3 \times 3$ Ⓓ 3×3

Ⓓ **3.** Find the prime factorization of 36.

Ⓐ $2 \times 3 \times 3 \times 3$ Ⓑ $9 \times 2 \times 2$
Ⓒ 9×4 Ⓓ $2 \times 2 \times 3 \times 3$

Ⓐ **4.** Find the prime factorization of 20.

Ⓐ $2^2 \times 5$ Ⓑ 10×2
Ⓒ $4 \times 2^2 \times 5$ Ⓓ 2^2

Ⓑ **5.** Find the prime factorization of 96.

Ⓐ $2^4 \times 3$ Ⓑ $2^5 \times 3$
Ⓒ 2×48 Ⓓ 2×3^5

Ⓒ **6.** Find the prime factorization of 54.

Ⓐ 6×9 Ⓑ $2 \times 3 \times 3$
Ⓒ $2 \times 3 \times 3 \times 3$ Ⓓ $2 \times 2 \times 3 \times 3$

Ⓓ **7.** Find the prime factorization of 48.

Ⓐ $2 \times 2 \times 3$ Ⓑ $2 \times 2 \times 2 \times 3$
Ⓒ $2 \times 2 \times 2 \times 2$ Ⓓ $2 \times 2 \times 2 \times 2 \times 3$

Ⓓ **8.** Find the prime factorization of 27.

Ⓐ 3^2 Ⓑ 9×3
Ⓒ 27×1 Ⓓ 3^3

Ⓐ **9.** Find the prime factorization of 40.

Ⓐ $2^3 \times 5$ Ⓑ 8×5
Ⓒ $2 \times 4 \times 5$ Ⓓ $2^4 \times 5$

Name ______________________ Class __________ Date ______________

2.13 PROBLEM SOLVING

Many standardized tests have word problems that require more than one step and more than one operation to solve. Before you calculate the answer, the first step is to recognize which operations are needed to find the answer.

Example 1: A parking lot attendant earns $0.60 for every car he parks. Before lunch, he parks 23 cars. He parks a total of 92 cars during the day. How much money did he earn parking cars in the afternoon?

Which steps would you follow to solve the problem above?

The quickest way to solve this problem is to subtract and then multiply.

- First, find the number of cars parked in the afternoon.

92	−	23	=	69
total number of cars parked		number of cars parked before lunch		number of cars parked in the afternoon

- Then, find the amount of money earned in the afternoon.

69	×	$0.60	=	$41.40
number of cars parked in the afternoon		amount earned per car		amount earned in the afternoon

The attendant earned $41.40 parking cars in the afternoon.

Example 2: Lockers are being installed along a wall that is 40 feet long. Each locker is 1.25 feet wide. Two students will share a locker. How many students will be able to use the new lockers?

To solve this problem, you should divide and then multiply.

- First, find the number of lockers that are being installed.

40 ft	÷	1.25 ft	=	32
length of wall		length of one locker		number of lockers being installed

- Then, calculate the number of students that will use the new lockers.

2	×	32	=	64
students per locker		number of new lockers		number of students using new lockers

64 students will be able to use the new lockers.

Solve.

Ⓓ **1.** A plumber orders copper tubing for a sink. Tubing comes in lengths of 10.5 feet. He orders 2 lengths and uses all but 3.7 feet. How many feet of tubing did the plumber use?

Ⓐ 6.8 ft Ⓑ 7.4 ft
Ⓒ 8.8 ft Ⓓ 17.3 ft

Ⓑ **2.** Gloves are packed 12 pairs to a box. A box of gloves costs $63.00. How much do 5 pairs of gloves cost?

Ⓐ $12.60 Ⓑ $26.25
Ⓒ $52.50 Ⓓ $115.50

(A) **3.** Pencils at the school bookstore cost 8 cents each. Stacy Loudon buys 3 pencils and her brother buys 4 pencils. What is the total cost of the pencils?

(A) $0.56 (B) $0.96
(C) $0.24 (D) $0.32

(D) **4.** A corsage costs $4.25. The Garden Club wants to purchase a corsage for each of its 48 members. They have $216 to spend. How much money will be left after the corsages are paid for?

(A) $211.75 (B) $204.00
(C) $168.00 (D) $12.00

(B) **5.** A ream of paper is 3.2 centimeters thick. A bundle of reams is 16 centimeters thick. How many reams do 7 bundles contain?

(A) 51.2 (B) 35 (C) 22.4 (D) 5

(B) **6.** On Friday, about 2800 people went to Sunnyside Beach. On Saturday, 2.5 times that number went to the beach. About how many more people went to the beach on Saturday?

(A) 1120 (B) 4200 (C) 7000 (D) 9800

(D) **7.** A grocer weighs a shipment of apples, pears, and oranges. The total weight is 159 pounds. The oranges weigh 62.4 pounds. The weight of the apples is equal to the weight of the pears. How many pounds of apples are in the shipment?

(A) 110.7 (B) 96.6 (C) 53 (D) 48.3

(A) **8.** Cub Scout Den 215 is selling boxes of notecards to raise money. There are 25 club members. The goal is for each member to sell 8 boxes at $1.50 per box. How much money will the club earn if each member meets the goal?

(A) $300.00 (B) $200.00
(C) $37.50 (D) $12.00

(B) **9.** To clean up a yard, Valerie Tocco charges $7.00 an hour. It takes her about 5 hours to clean up a yard. She takes care of 8 yards a week. How much more money could she earn each week if she charged $40.00 per yard?

(A) $5.00 (B) $40.00
(C) $280.00 (D) $320.00

10. (C) Lucille Chandler receives an allowance of $10.00 a week. She spends $7.50 on lunches and bus fare. She saves the rest. How many weeks will it take her to save $20?

(A) 2 (B) 2.5 (C) 8 (D) 10

(B) **11.** Jason Greene was training for a race. He ran 4.5 miles the first week, 6.25 miles the second, and 8 miles the third. On the average, how many miles did he run per week?

(A) 6 (B) 6.25 (C) 18.75 (D) 24

(C) **12.** Six pounds of bananas cost $2.94. What is the cost of a single banana if there are 7 bananas in one pound?

(A) $2.52 (B) $0.42 (C) $0.07 (D) $0.06

(D) **13.** Shelly Wong saves $2.50 a week for college. How much money will she save in 5 years? (52 weeks = 1 year)

(A) $12.50 (B) $130.00
(C) $600.00 (D) $650.00

(D) **14.** Todd Britt finds a total of $28.75 in loose change in his desk. He counts $12.75 in quarters, $9.00 in dimes, and the rest in nickels. How many nickels does he find?

(A) $7.00 (B) 14 (C) 35 (D) 140

(D) **15.** Envelopes cost $40.95 per 1000 if you buy 1000, and $38.95 per 1000 if you buy 2000. How much less expensive is each envelope, if you buy the larger quantity?

(A) $0.13 (B) $0.20
(C) $0.02 (D) $0.002

(A) **16.** Tickets for the school dance cost $1.25 each. The tickets are printed in rolls of 200. 8 rolls were sold. How much money was earned from ticket sales?

(A) $2000 (B) $1600
(C) $250 (D) $209.25

Name ______________________ Class ________ Date ____________

CHAPTER 2 TEST

Fill in the correct circle to answer each question.

Ⓑ **1.** Write the numeral for 492 *thousandths.*

Ⓐ 492.000 Ⓑ 0.492
Ⓒ 0.0492 Ⓓ 0.00492

Ⓓ **2.** 0.7 + 0.08 + 1.002 = ■

Ⓐ 1.8 Ⓑ 1.7 Ⓒ 2.7 Ⓓ 1.782

Ⓐ **3.** Compare: 2.374 ■ 2.364

Ⓐ > Ⓑ < Ⓒ =

Ⓓ **4.** Which number has the *least* value?

Ⓐ 5.304 Ⓑ 5.043 Ⓒ 4.304 Ⓓ 4.043

Ⓑ **5.** The price of a sign is $1.39. What will 10 signs cost?

Ⓐ $13 Ⓑ $13.90
Ⓒ $13.95 Ⓓ $14

Ⓓ **6.** Round 123.564 to the nearest *tenth.*

Ⓐ 123.56 Ⓑ 123.5
Ⓒ 123.57 Ⓓ 123.6

Ⓑ **7.** The total cost of a $145.23 suit and a $10 hat is ■.

Ⓐ $245.23 Ⓑ $155.23
Ⓒ $145.33 Ⓓ $155

Ⓒ **8.** 11 + 0.11 + 1.1 + 0.011 = ■

Ⓐ 11.111 Ⓑ 12.121
Ⓒ 12.221 Ⓓ 44

Ⓓ **9.** Subtract 1.11 from 7.

Ⓐ 6.99 Ⓑ 6.89 Ⓒ 5.99 Ⓓ 5.89

Ⓑ **10.** Subtract: 12.5 – 0.31

Ⓐ 0.94 Ⓑ 12.19 Ⓒ 9.4 Ⓓ 11.19

Ⓑ **11.** Multiply: 5.12×51.2

Ⓐ 26.2144 Ⓑ 262.144
Ⓒ 2621.44 Ⓓ 26,214.4

Ⓑ **12.** Multiply: 12.3×36.9

Ⓐ 4538.7 Ⓑ 453.87
Ⓒ 45.387 Ⓓ 4.5387

Ⓓ **13.** $54 \div 0.02$ = ■

Ⓐ 0.27 Ⓑ 27 Ⓒ 270 Ⓓ 2700

Ⓓ **14.** Divide: $2.48 \div 0.8$

Ⓐ 0.0031 Ⓑ 0.031
Ⓒ 0.31 Ⓓ 3.1

Ⓓ **15.** Multiply 7.12 by 100.

Ⓐ 0.0712 Ⓑ 7.1200
Ⓒ 71.200 Ⓓ 712

Ⓒ **16.** A total of 7.15 pounds of spice was divided into 100 equal packages. How much spice was in each package?

Ⓐ 715 pounds Ⓑ 0.715 pounds
Ⓒ 0.0715 pounds Ⓓ 0.00715 pounds

Ⓒ **17.** Write 1991 in scientific notation.

Ⓐ 199.1×10 Ⓑ 19.91×10^2
Ⓒ 1.991×10^3 Ⓓ 0.1991×10^4

Ⓓ **18.** 2^9 is the same as ■.

Ⓐ 18 Ⓑ 11 Ⓒ 256 Ⓓ 512

Ⓒ **19.** 9.7×10^6 is the same as ▩.

Ⓐ 97,000,000 Ⓑ 970,000

Ⓒ 9,700,000 Ⓓ 97,106

Ⓑ **21.** Select the factor tree showing the prime factorization of 24.

Ⓐ
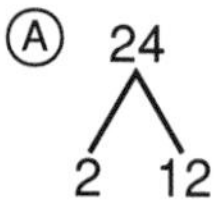

Ⓑ
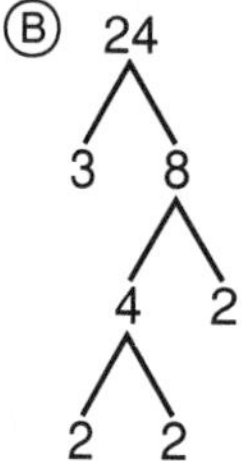

Ⓒ
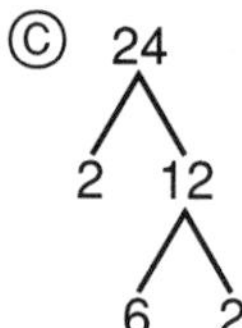

Ⓓ
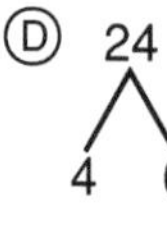

Ⓑ **25.** Add:

$$\begin{array}{r} 1.75 \\ 0.0175 \\ +17.5 \\ \hline \end{array}$$

Ⓐ 18.2675 Ⓑ 19.2675

Ⓒ 18.5225 Ⓓ 19.5225

Ⓒ **27.** Find the difference in weight between 2.4 grams and 0.24 grams.

Ⓐ 0 grams Ⓑ 0.216 grams

Ⓒ 2.16 grams Ⓓ 0.226 grams

Ⓓ **29.** Five friends shared the cost of a meal. The total cost was \$9.45. How much did each person contribute?

Ⓐ \$47.25 Ⓑ \$2.30 Ⓒ \$2.16 Ⓓ \$1.89

Ⓑ **31.** Round 0.9752 to the nearest *thousandth.*

Ⓐ 0.1 Ⓑ 0.975 Ⓒ 0.98 Ⓓ 1

Ⓒ **33.** Divide: $18.23 \div 100$

Ⓐ 1823 Ⓑ 1.823

Ⓒ 0.1823 Ⓓ 0.01823

Ⓓ **20.** List the next three prime numbers after 23.

Ⓐ 25, 27 and 29 Ⓑ 29, 31 and 41

Ⓒ 27, 29 and 31 Ⓓ 29, 31 and 37

Ⓓ **22.** If 0.2 oz of a mixture made up of 0.25 oz of gasoline and 0.25 oz of turpentine is spilled, how much of the mixture is left?

Ⓐ 0.75 oz Ⓑ 0.5 oz

Ⓒ 0.70 oz Ⓓ 0.3 oz

Ⓐ **23.** Which statement is *true?*

Ⓐ $2.63 > 2.6$ Ⓑ $2.63 < 2.6$

Ⓒ $2.63 = 2.6$

Ⓐ **24.** Find the value of 3.1412×10^4 rounded to the nearest *hundred.*

Ⓐ 31,400 Ⓑ 34,120

Ⓒ 31,412 Ⓓ 30,000

Ⓑ **26.** What are the prime factors of 36?

Ⓐ 1, 2, 3, 4, 6, 9, 12, 18, 36

Ⓑ 2, 3

Ⓒ 1, 2, 3

Ⓓ 2, 3, 4, 6, 9, 12, 18, 36

Ⓑ **28.** Emma buys 8 pairs of socks at \$2.10 a pair. What is the total cost?

Ⓐ \$1.68 Ⓑ \$16.80 Ⓒ \$18.80 Ⓓ \$0.26

Ⓐ **30.** What is the *place value* of the 5 in 25.873?

Ⓐ ones Ⓑ tens

Ⓒ tenths Ⓓ hundredths

Ⓐ **32.** Round 67.023 to the nearest *whole number.*

Ⓐ 67 Ⓑ 67.1 Ⓒ 68 Ⓓ 68.1

Name ______________________ Class ________ Date ____________

CHAPTER 3: FRACTIONS AND FRACTION COMPUTATION

TEST-TAKING STRATEGY: *Should You Guess?*

The odds of guessing a correct answer on a test question are against you! For example, if there are four answer choices, the chance that you will choose the right answer is 1 out of 4.

If you don't know the answer to a question, try this plan before guessing.

- Read the problem carefully.
- Look for key words to use as clues.
- Use your "number sense" to rule out answers.

Example 1: $1\frac{2}{3} \times 4\frac{1}{4} = ■$ Ⓐ $1\frac{5}{6}$ Ⓑ $4\frac{1}{6}$ Ⓒ $6\frac{1}{12}$ Ⓓ $7\frac{1}{12}$

If you don't remember how to multiply mixed numbers, examine each answer choice first, instead of making a guess.

- Choice Ⓐ is much too low. The answer must be greater than 4, since you are multiplying a number greater than 4 by a number greater than 1.
- Choice Ⓑ also seems low.
- Now you can choose between choices Ⓒ and Ⓓ. You have increased your chances of guessing the correct answer.

The correct answer is choice Ⓓ.

Example 2: What is the value of the digit 6 in 23.02631? Ⓐ 6000 Ⓑ 600 Ⓒ $\frac{6}{100}$ Ⓓ $\frac{6}{1000}$

- Suppose you are confused by this problem. Even if you don't know exactly what to do, you would recall that a digit to the right of a decimal point must have a value less than 1. This observation would allow you to eliminate choices Ⓐ and Ⓑ.
- Now you must choose between choices Ⓒ and Ⓓ. You have increased your chance of guessing the correct answer.

The correct answer is choice Ⓓ.

Fill in the correct circle to answer each question. If you don't know how to solve the problem, use the plan described above.

Ⓒ **1.** 323 + 419 = ■

Ⓐ 842 Ⓑ 752 Ⓒ 742 Ⓓ 96

Ⓑ **2.** Compare: 21.019 ■ 21.03

Ⓐ > Ⓑ < Ⓒ =

Ⓒ **3.** Round $19.09 to the nearest *dollar.*

Ⓐ $20.00 Ⓑ $19.10 Ⓒ $19.00 Ⓓ $18.00

Ⓓ **4.** 169 × 22 = ■

Ⓐ 191 Ⓑ 3398 Ⓒ 3696 Ⓓ 3718

Ⓑ **5.** Estimate: 949 – 435

Ⓐ 50 Ⓑ 500 Ⓒ 800 Ⓓ 1300

Ⓒ **6.** Find the quotient of 19 and 5.

Ⓐ 24 Ⓑ 4 Ⓒ 3 R 4 Ⓓ 3 R 3

Ⓑ **7.** $\begin{array}{r} 26 \\ -\ 4.0189 \\ \hline \end{array}$

Ⓐ 30.0189 Ⓑ 21.9811
Ⓒ 21.9921 Ⓓ 22.0189

Ⓓ **8.** What is the *value* of the digit 3 in 0.00635?

Ⓐ 30,000 Ⓑ 30
Ⓒ 0.003 Ⓓ 0.0003

Ⓒ **9.** $400 \times 1000 =$ ■

Ⓐ 1400 Ⓑ 40,000
Ⓒ 400,000 Ⓓ 4,000,000

Ⓑ **10.** $4 + 1.409 + 0.78 + 6.1136 =$ ■

Ⓐ 6.2627 Ⓑ 12.3026
Ⓒ 12.3035 Ⓓ 89.5226

Ⓓ **11.** Order from *least to greatest:*
1.21, 2.11, 1.12

Ⓐ 2.11, 1.21, 1.12 Ⓑ 2.11, 1.12, 1.21
Ⓒ 1.21, 1.12, 2.11 Ⓓ 1.12, 1.21, 2.11

Ⓓ **12.**
$$\begin{array}{r} 3560 \\ +9190 \\ \hline \end{array}$$

Ⓐ 13,650 Ⓑ 12,850
Ⓒ 12,760 Ⓓ 12,750

Ⓒ **13.** Vicki is 190 months old. What is her age to the nearest year?

Ⓐ 57 years Ⓑ 32 years
Ⓒ 16 years Ⓓ 6 years

Ⓒ **14.** Round $89.95 to the nearest *dollar.*

Ⓐ $80.00 Ⓑ $89.00
Ⓒ $90.00 Ⓓ $100.00

Ⓑ **15.** In August 1997, Carl earned $4.75 an hour as a dishwasher. In September 1997, when the minimum wage was increased, he earned $5.15 an hour. What was the increase in his hourly rate?

Ⓐ $0.84 Ⓑ 0.40 Ⓒ $1.94 Ⓓ $7.64

Ⓑ **16.** A study showed that it cost $4595 to drive a car 15,000 miles in 1989. What is the approximate cost per mile?

Ⓐ $0.03 Ⓑ $0.33 Ⓒ $3.00 Ⓓ $30.00

Ⓑ **17.** Which number is a prime number?

Ⓐ 6 Ⓑ 11 Ⓒ 18 Ⓓ 39

Ⓑ **18.** What is the *value* of the digit 2 in 1293?

Ⓐ 2000 Ⓑ 200 Ⓒ 20 Ⓓ 2

Ⓑ **19.** $3^4 =$ ■

Ⓐ 87 Ⓑ 81 Ⓒ 12 Ⓓ 7

Ⓑ **20.** Find the sum: $87 + 104$

Ⓐ 291 Ⓑ 191 Ⓒ 181 Ⓓ 17

Use Table 1 to answer questions 21-23.

Table 1

Activity	Calories Used Per Hour
Writing postcards	156
Cleaning windows	222
Waterskiing	480
Housepainting	210
Waiting in line	156

Ⓒ **21.** Richard writes postcards for two hours. How many calories does he use?

Ⓐ 468 calories
Ⓑ 444 calories
Ⓒ 312 calories
Ⓓ 202 calories

Ⓒ **22.** John waits in line for 1.5 hours to ride the Screaming Demon roller coaster. How many calories does he use?

Ⓐ 2340 calories Ⓑ 963 calories
Ⓒ 234 calories Ⓓ 111 calories

Ⓑ **23.** Rhoda paints her room for an hour and cleans her windows for thirty minutes. How many calories does she use?

Ⓐ 160 calories Ⓑ 321 calories
Ⓒ 327 calories Ⓓ 432 calories

Ⓓ **24.** In 1950 there were 3.9 million households with television sets. In 1989 there were 90.4 million households with television sets. How many more households had television sets in 1989?

Ⓐ 865 million Ⓑ 94.3 million
Ⓒ 87.5 million Ⓓ 86.5 million

Ⓐ **25.** The sophomore class needs 500 cups for a dance. They have 120 cups. Paper cups come in packages of 20. How many packages should they buy?

Ⓐ 19 Ⓑ 38 Ⓒ 120 Ⓓ 380

Name ____________________ Class ________ Date ____________

CHAPTER 3 PRETEST

Fill in the correct circle to answer each question.

Ⓐ **1.** Compare: 98 ■ 100

Ⓐ < Ⓑ > Ⓒ =

Ⓒ **2.** Which number is between 169 and 196?

Ⓐ 75 Ⓑ 166 Ⓒ 173 Ⓓ 197

Ⓓ **3.** Order 14, 9, 32, and 29 from *least to greatest:*

Ⓐ 32, 29, 14, 9 Ⓑ 29, 32, 14, 9
Ⓒ 9, 29, 14, 32 Ⓓ 9, 14, 29, 32

Ⓓ **4.** Which number is *least:*

Ⓐ 1700 Ⓑ 1619
Ⓒ 1211 Ⓓ 1102

Ⓑ **5.** Compare: 15,666 ■ 15.666

Ⓐ < Ⓑ > Ⓒ =

Ⓒ **6.** 9 + 8 = ■

Ⓐ 19 Ⓑ 18 Ⓒ 17 Ⓓ 1

Ⓑ **7.** Add: $\begin{array}{r} 43 \\ +26 \\ \hline \end{array}$

Ⓐ 67 Ⓑ 69 Ⓒ 79 Ⓓ 96

Ⓓ **8.** Find the sum: $\begin{array}{r} 106 \\ +\ \ 15 \\ \hline \end{array}$

Ⓐ 91 Ⓑ 110 Ⓒ 111 Ⓓ 121

Ⓒ **9.** 19 + 36 + 5 = ■

Ⓐ 105 Ⓑ 70 Ⓒ 60 Ⓓ 59

Ⓑ **10.** 314 + 711 = ■

Ⓐ 1250 Ⓑ 1025 Ⓒ 1015 Ⓓ 915

Ⓒ **11.** 29 + 29 = ■

Ⓐ 48 Ⓑ 56 Ⓒ 58 Ⓓ 59

Ⓑ **12.** 15 − 7 = ■

Ⓐ 9 Ⓑ 8 Ⓒ 7 Ⓓ 6

Ⓐ **13.** Subtract: $\begin{array}{r} 93 \\ -88 \\ \hline \end{array}$

Ⓐ 5 Ⓑ 11 Ⓒ 15 Ⓓ 181

Ⓒ **14.** Find the difference: $\begin{array}{r} 52 \\ -16 \\ \hline \end{array}$

Ⓐ 46 Ⓑ 44 Ⓒ 36 Ⓓ 34

Ⓓ **15.** What is the difference between 500 and 250?

Ⓐ 750 Ⓑ 350 Ⓒ 300 Ⓓ 250

Ⓑ **16.** Subtract 2 from 5.

Ⓐ 2 Ⓑ 3 Ⓒ 4 Ⓓ 7

Ⓑ **17.** 845 − 292 = ■

Ⓐ 543 Ⓑ 553 Ⓒ 643 Ⓓ 653

Ⓓ **18.** 7 × 6 = ■

Ⓐ 54 Ⓑ 49 Ⓒ 48 Ⓓ 42

Ⓐ **19.** Find the product: 30 × 4

Ⓐ 120 Ⓑ 100 Ⓒ 34 Ⓓ 70

Ⓒ **20.** Multiply: 15 × 12

Ⓐ 45 Ⓑ 170 Ⓒ 180 Ⓓ 267

Ⓓ **21.** 108 × 8 = ■

Ⓐ 144 Ⓑ 849 Ⓒ 863 Ⓓ 864

Ⓒ **22.** 333 × 41 = ■

Ⓐ 1665 Ⓑ 8103 Ⓒ 13,653 Ⓓ 22,553

Ⓐ **23.** 16 × 6 = ■

Ⓐ 96 Ⓑ 86 Ⓒ 72 Ⓓ 22

Ⓒ **24.** Find the quotient: $3\overline{)90}$

Ⓐ 12 Ⓑ 60 Ⓒ 30 Ⓓ 3

Ⓓ **25.** 84 ÷ 6 = ■

Ⓐ 9 Ⓑ 12 R 2 Ⓒ 13 Ⓓ 14

Ⓓ **26.** 75 ÷ 15 = ■

Ⓐ 6 Ⓑ 5 R 10 Ⓒ 5 R 5 Ⓓ 5

Ⓑ **27.** 810 ÷ 90 = ■

Ⓐ 90 Ⓑ 9 Ⓒ 8 R 8 Ⓓ 8

Ⓒ **28.** 660 ÷ 33 = ■

Ⓐ 110 Ⓑ 200 Ⓒ 20 Ⓓ 22

Ⓓ **29.** What fraction of diamonds is red?

Ⓐ $\frac{4}{9}$ Ⓑ $\frac{2}{5}$ Ⓒ $\frac{4}{11}$ Ⓓ $\frac{3}{5}$

Ⓐ **30.** What fraction of the boxes is black?

Ⓐ $\frac{3}{4}$ Ⓑ $\frac{1}{2}$ Ⓒ $\frac{1}{4}$ Ⓓ $\frac{6}{8}$

Ⓑ **31.** Compare: $\frac{3}{5}$ ■ $\frac{1}{5}$

Ⓐ < Ⓑ > Ⓒ =

Ⓒ **32.** What fraction is between $\frac{3}{10}$ and $\frac{7}{10}$?

Ⓐ $\frac{1}{10}$ Ⓑ $\frac{1}{5}$ Ⓒ $\frac{1}{2}$ Ⓓ $\frac{9}{10}$

Ⓒ **33.** Compare: $\frac{1}{3}$ ■ $\frac{3}{9}$

Ⓐ < Ⓑ > Ⓒ =

Ⓓ **34.** $\frac{3}{4} \times \frac{1}{2}$ = ■

Ⓐ $1\frac{1}{2}$ Ⓑ $\frac{2}{3}$ Ⓒ $\frac{1}{2}$ Ⓓ $\frac{3}{8}$

Ⓑ **35.** $6 \times \frac{5}{6}$ = ■

Ⓐ $\frac{5}{36}$ Ⓑ 5 Ⓒ $5\frac{1}{6}$ Ⓓ $6\frac{5}{6}$

Ⓐ **36.** $\frac{8}{9} \div \frac{1}{9}$ = ■

Ⓐ 8 Ⓑ 7 Ⓒ $\frac{1}{8}$ Ⓓ $\frac{8}{81}$

Ⓓ **37.** $3\frac{1}{2} \div \frac{1}{4}$ = ■

Ⓐ $\frac{7}{8}$ Ⓑ $3\frac{3}{4}$ Ⓒ 12 Ⓓ 14

Ⓓ **38.** $\frac{7}{8} + \frac{1}{2}$ = ■

Ⓐ $\frac{7}{10}$ Ⓑ $\frac{4}{5}$ Ⓒ $1\frac{1}{4}$ Ⓓ $1\frac{3}{8}$

Ⓑ **39.** Add: $2\frac{1}{6} + 1\frac{5}{6}$

Ⓐ $4\frac{1}{3}$ Ⓑ 4 Ⓒ $3\frac{1}{2}$ Ⓓ 3

Ⓒ **40.** Subtract: $\frac{11}{12} - \frac{7}{12}$

Ⓐ $1\frac{1}{2}$ Ⓑ $\frac{5}{12}$ Ⓒ $\frac{1}{3}$ Ⓓ $\frac{1}{4}$

Ⓓ **41.** $7 - 1\frac{2}{3}$ = ■

Ⓐ $8\frac{2}{3}$ Ⓑ $6\frac{2}{3}$ Ⓒ $6\frac{1}{3}$ Ⓓ $5\frac{1}{3}$

Ⓓ **42.** $\frac{6}{7} + \frac{2}{7} + \frac{1}{7}$ = ■

Ⓐ $\frac{3}{7}$ Ⓑ $\frac{4}{7}$ Ⓒ $1\frac{1}{7}$ Ⓓ $1\frac{2}{7}$

Ⓓ **43.** $\frac{9}{10} + \frac{1}{5} - \frac{3}{4}$ = ■

Ⓐ $\frac{7}{11}$ Ⓑ $\frac{9}{20}$ Ⓒ $\frac{2}{5}$ Ⓓ $\frac{7}{20}$

Ⓒ **44.** Find the least common multiple (LCM) of 4 and 8.

Ⓐ 1 Ⓑ 4 Ⓒ 8 Ⓓ 32

Ⓑ **45.** What is the greatest common factor (GCF) of 4 and 6?

Ⓐ 1 Ⓑ 2 Ⓒ 6 Ⓓ 12

Ⓑ **46.** Find *n*: $\frac{4}{5} = \frac{24}{n}$

Ⓐ 35 Ⓑ 30 Ⓒ 25 Ⓓ 20

Ⓒ **47.** $4\frac{5}{6} \times 1\frac{1}{3}$ = ■

Ⓐ $3\frac{2}{9}$ Ⓑ $4\frac{5}{18}$ Ⓒ $6\frac{4}{9}$ Ⓓ $9\frac{2}{3}$

Ⓓ **48.** $7 \div \frac{3}{4}$ = ■

Ⓐ $\frac{3}{28}$ Ⓑ $5\frac{1}{4}$ Ⓒ $7\frac{3}{4}$ Ⓓ $9\frac{1}{3}$

Ⓒ **49.** $5 + 2\frac{1}{10}$ = ■

Ⓐ $2\frac{9}{10}$ Ⓑ $6\frac{1}{10}$ Ⓒ $7\frac{1}{10}$ Ⓓ $7\frac{9}{10}$

Ⓐ **50.** $6\frac{7}{9} - 2\frac{4}{9}$ = ■

Ⓐ $4\frac{1}{3}$ Ⓑ $4\frac{2}{9}$ Ⓒ $3\frac{1}{3}$ Ⓓ $3\frac{2}{9}$

Name ____________________ Class __________ Date __________

3.1 FRACTIONS AND MIXED NUMBERS

Example 1: Write the fraction for the red part in each square below.

- Find the numerator and the denominator. $\frac{\text{Numerator}}{\text{Denominator}} = \frac{\text{Number of shaded parts}}{\text{Total number of parts}}$

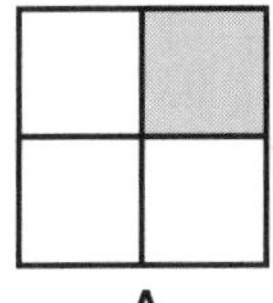
A

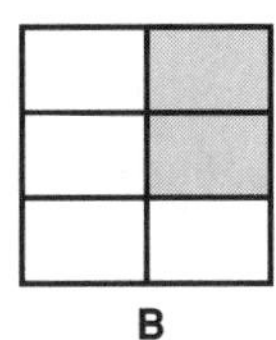
B

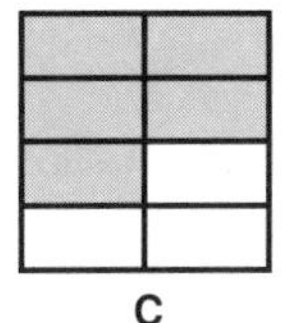
C

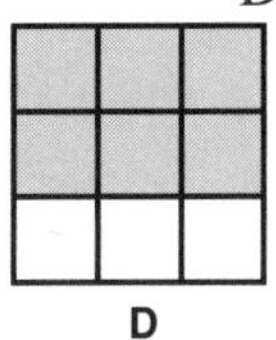
D

Square A is divided into 4 equal parts. One part out of 4 is red, so we write $\frac{1}{4}$.

Square B is divided into 6 equal parts. Two parts out of 6 are red, so we write $\frac{2}{6}$.

Square C is divided into 8 equal parts. Five parts out of 8 are red, so we write $\frac{5}{8}$.

Square D is divided into 9 equal parts. Six parts out of 9 are red, so we write $\frac{6}{9}$.

Example 2: **A.** Write $\frac{19}{8}$ as a mixed number.

- Divide the numerator by the denominator. Write the remainder as a fraction.

$$\frac{19}{8} = 8\overline{)19} \text{ (2 R3; } 19 - 16 = 3) = 2\frac{3}{8}$$

The mixed number is $2\frac{3}{8}$.

B. Write $3\frac{2}{5}$ as an improper fraction.

- Multiply the denominator by the whole number. $5 \times 3 = 15$
- Add the numerator to this product to get a new numerator. $15 + 2 = 17$
- The denominator remains the same: 5
- The improper fraction is $\frac{17}{5}$.

Fill in the correct circle to answer each question.

Ⓐ **1.** Which fraction represents the part of Square A that is *not* shaded?

Ⓐ $\frac{3}{4}$ Ⓑ $\frac{4}{3}$ Ⓒ $\frac{1}{4}$ Ⓓ $\frac{4}{1}$

Ⓐ **2.** Which fraction represents the part of Square D that is *not* shaded?

Ⓐ $\frac{3}{9}$ Ⓑ $\frac{6}{9}$ Ⓒ $\frac{9}{3}$ Ⓓ $\frac{4}{1}$

Ⓐ **3.** $2\frac{5}{8}$ = ■

Ⓐ $\frac{21}{8}$ Ⓑ $\frac{19}{8}$ Ⓒ $\frac{18}{8}$ Ⓓ $\frac{13}{8}$

Ⓒ **4.** $\frac{13}{3}$ = ■

Ⓐ $5\frac{1}{3}$ Ⓑ $4\frac{2}{3}$ Ⓒ $4\frac{1}{3}$ Ⓓ $3\frac{2}{3}$

Ⓓ **5.** Which fraction represents the part of Square B that is *not* shaded?

Ⓐ $\frac{6}{4}$ Ⓑ $\frac{6}{2}$ Ⓒ $\frac{2}{6}$ Ⓓ $\frac{4}{6}$

Ⓐ **6.** Which fraction represents the part of Square C that is *not* shaded?

Ⓐ $\frac{3}{8}$ Ⓑ $\frac{8}{3}$ Ⓒ $\frac{5}{8}$ Ⓓ $\frac{8}{5}$

Ⓒ **7.** $\frac{13}{6}$ = ■

Ⓐ $2\frac{4}{6}$ Ⓑ $2\frac{1}{3}$ Ⓒ $2\frac{1}{6}$ Ⓓ $1\frac{1}{6}$

Ⓒ **8.** $\frac{28}{25}$ = ■

Ⓐ $1\frac{1}{25}$ Ⓑ $1\frac{2}{25}$ Ⓒ $1\frac{3}{25}$ Ⓓ $1\frac{1}{5}$

Use the circles below to answer questions 9-14.

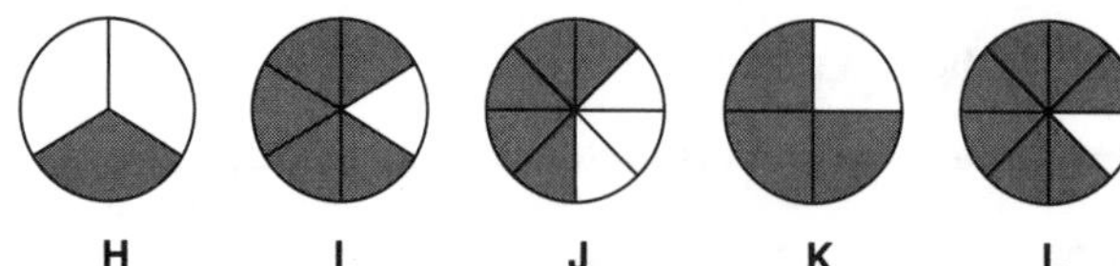

(A) **9.** Which circle represents $\frac{5}{6}$?

(A) I (B) J (C) L (D) K

(B) **10.** Which fraction represents the part of Circle J that is shaded?

(A) $\frac{5}{6}$ (B) $\frac{5}{8}$ (C) $\frac{7}{8}$ (D) $\frac{8}{5}$

(A) **11.** Which circle represents $\frac{5}{8}$?

(A) J (B) L (C) K (D) I

(C) **12.** Which fraction represents the part of Circle H that is *not* shaded?

(A) $\frac{3}{2}$ (B) $\frac{1}{3}$ (C) $\frac{2}{3}$ (D) $\frac{3}{1}$

(C) **13.** Which circle represents $\frac{3}{4}$?

(A) H (B) J (C) K (D) I

(D) **14.** Which fraction represents the part of Circle L that is *not* shaded?

(A) $\frac{7}{8}$ (B) $\frac{8}{7}$ (C) $\frac{8}{1}$ (D) $\frac{1}{8}$

(D) **15.** $16\frac{1}{2}$ = ■

(A) $\frac{19}{2}$ (B) $\frac{23}{2}$ (C) $\frac{32}{2}$ (D) $\frac{33}{2}$

(C) **16.** $\frac{13}{9}$ = ■

(A) $1\frac{2}{9}$ (B) $1\frac{1}{3}$ (C) $1\frac{4}{9}$ (D) $1\frac{5}{9}$

(B) **17.** $6\frac{3}{10}$ = ■

(A) $\frac{19}{10}$ (B) $\frac{63}{10}$ (C) $\frac{90}{10}$ (D) $\frac{180}{10}$

(C) **18.** $\frac{12}{7}$ = ■

(A) $2\frac{5}{7}$ (B) $1\frac{2}{7}$ (C) $1\frac{5}{7}$ (D) $2\frac{2}{7}$

(C) **19.** $2\frac{4}{5}$ = ■

(A) $\frac{40}{5}$ (B) $\frac{28}{5}$ (C) $\frac{14}{5}$ (D) $\frac{13}{5}$

(A) **20.** $\frac{7}{2}$ = ■

(A) $3\frac{1}{2}$ (B) $3\frac{1}{7}$ (C) $2\frac{1}{2}$ (D) $2\frac{1}{7}$

(D) **21.** $10\frac{1}{3}$ = ■

(A) $\frac{3}{30}$ (B) $\frac{3}{31}$ (C) $\frac{30}{3}$ (D) $\frac{31}{3}$

(C) **22.** $\frac{12}{5}$ = ■

(A) 3 (B) $2\frac{3}{5}$ (C) $2\frac{2}{5}$ (D) $2\frac{1}{5}$

(C) **23.** $\frac{16}{9}$ = ■

(A) $1\frac{5}{9}$ (B) $1\frac{8}{9}$ (C) $1\frac{7}{9}$ (D) $1\frac{1}{2}$

(D) **24.** $7\frac{3}{4}$ = ■

(A) $\frac{14}{4}$ (B) $\frac{28}{4}$ (C) $\frac{30}{4}$ (D) $\frac{31}{4}$

Name______________________ Class ________ Date ____________

3.2 GREATEST COMMON FACTOR

The **greatest common factor (GCF)** of two or more numbers is the largest number that divides each of those numbers.

Example 1: Find the greatest common factor (GCF) of 6 and 9.

- List the factors of 6: 1, 2, 3, 6
- List the factors of 9: 1, 3, 9
- List the common factors: 1, 3

The greatest common factor (GCF) of 6 and 9 is 3.

Example 2: Find the greatest common factor (GCF) of 18, 24, and 36.

- List the factors of 18: 1, 2, 3, 6, 9, 18
- List the factors of 24: 1, 2, 3, 4, 6, 8, 12, 24
- List the factors of 36: 1, 2, 3, 4, 6, 9, 12, 18, 36
- List the common factors: 1, 2, 3, 6

The greatest common factor (GCF) of 18, 24, and 36 is 6.

Fill in the correct circle to answer each question.

Ⓓ **1.** List the factors of 12.

Ⓐ 2, 3, 4, 6 Ⓑ 0, 1, 2, 3, 4, 6
Ⓒ 0, 1, 2, 3, 4, 6, 12 Ⓓ 1, 2, 3, 4, 6, 12

Ⓐ **2.** List the factors of 16.

Ⓐ 1, 2, 4, 8, 16 Ⓑ 0, 1, 2, 4, 8
Ⓒ 0, 1, 2, 4, 8, 16 Ⓓ 1, 2, 4, 8

Ⓒ **3.** List the factors of 9.

Ⓐ 0, 1, 3 Ⓑ 0, 1, 3, 9
Ⓒ 1, 3, 9 Ⓓ 1, 3, 9, 18

Ⓓ **4.** List the factors of 18.

Ⓐ 0, 1, 2, 3, 6, 9 Ⓑ 1, 2, 3, 6, 9
Ⓒ 0, 1, 2, 3, 6, 9, 18 Ⓓ 1, 2, 3, 6, 9, 18

Ⓐ **5.** Find the greatest common factor (GCF) of 5 and 8.

Ⓐ 1 Ⓑ 2 Ⓒ 5 Ⓓ 8

Ⓒ **6.** Find the greatest common factor (GCF) of 6 and 15.

Ⓐ 1 Ⓑ 2 Ⓒ 3 Ⓓ 5

Ⓑ **7.** Find the GCF of 4, 10, and 12.

Ⓐ 1 Ⓑ 2 Ⓒ 4 Ⓓ 5

Ⓓ **8.** Find the GCF of 7, 21, and 42.

Ⓐ 1 Ⓑ 3 Ⓒ 6 Ⓓ 7

Ⓓ **9.** Find the GCF of 54 and 81.

Ⓐ 1 Ⓑ 3 Ⓒ 9 Ⓓ 27

Ⓑ **10.** Find the GCF of 25, 45, and 75.

Ⓐ 3 Ⓑ 5 Ⓒ 15 Ⓓ 25

Ⓑ **11.** What is the GCF of 12 and 14?

Ⓐ 1 Ⓑ 2 Ⓒ 6 Ⓓ 7

Ⓐ **12.** What is the GCF of 24 and 32?

Ⓐ 8 Ⓑ 6 Ⓒ 4 Ⓓ 2

Ⓓ **13.** What is the GCF of 54 and 72?

Ⓐ 1 Ⓑ 6 Ⓒ 9 Ⓓ 18

Ⓒ **14.** Find the GCF of 20 and 80.

Ⓐ 1 Ⓑ 10 Ⓒ 20 Ⓓ 40

Name ______________________ Class __________ Date __________

3.3 LEAST COMMON MULTIPLE

The **least common multiple (LCM)** of two or more numbers is the smallest number greater than zero that is divisible by each of those numbers.

Example 1: Find the least common multiple (LCM) of 2 and 5.

- List multiples of 2: 2, 4, 6, 8, 10, 12, 14, 16, 18, 20, ...
- List multiples of 5: 5, 10, 15, 20, 25, 30, 35, ...
- List the common multiples: 10, 20, ...

The least common multiple (LCM) of 2 and 5 is 10.

Example 2: Find the least common multiple (LCM) of 3, 4, and 6.

- List multiples of 3: 3, 6, 9, 12, 15, 18, ...
- List multiples of 4: 4, 8, 12, 16, 20, 24, ...
- List multiples of 6: 6, 12, 18, 24, 30, 36, ...

The least common multiple (LCM) of 3, 4, and 6 is 12.

Fill in the correct circle to answer each question.

(D) **1.** Find the least common multiple (LCM) of 2 and 7.

(A) 1 (B) 2 (C) 7 (D) 14

(A) **2.** Find the least common multiple (LCM) of 2, 4, and 9.

(A) 36 (B) 18 (C) 4 (D) 2

(C) **3.** Find the LCM of 4 and 8.

(A) 32 (B) 16 (C) 8 (D) 4

(D) **4.** Find the LCM of 3, 7, and 9.

(A) 0 (B) 1 (C) 45 (D) 63

(D) **5.** Find the LCM of 15 and 18.

(A) 3 (B) 180 (C) 270 (D) 90

(B) **6.** Find the LCM of 5 and 10.

(A) 5 (B) 10 (C) 50 (D) 100

(C) **7.** Find the LCM of 6, 11, and 12.

(A) 66 (B) 72 (C) 132 (D) 220

(D) **8.** Find the LCM of 12 and 16.

(A) 4 (B) 24 (C) 32 (D) 48

(C) **9.** Find the LCM of 12 and 15.

(A) 3 (B) 30 (C) 60 (D) 120

(B) **10.** Find the LCM of 9 and 12.

(A) 60 (B) 36 (C) 12 (D) 3

(D) **11.** Find the LCM of 3, 5, and 12.

(A) 1 (B) 12 (C) 30 (D) 60

(B) **12.** Find the LCM of 25 and 20.

(A) 200 (B) 100 (C) 50 (D) 5

(B) **13.** What is the LCM of 4 and 5?

(A) 10 (B) 20 (C) 50 (D) 100

(C) **14.** What is the LCM of 12 and 18?

(A) 6 (B) 18 (C) 36 (D) 72

(C) **15.** Find the LCM of 6 and 8?

(A) 2 (B) 14 (C) 24 (D) 48

(A) **16.** What is the LCM of 3, 6, and 7?

(A) 42 (B) 35 (C) 28 (D) 21

Name__________ Class ______ Date ________

3.4 EQUIVALENT FRACTIONS

Equivalent fractions are fractions that have the same value. For example, $\frac{2}{3}$ and $\frac{4}{6}$ are equivalent fractions.

Example 1: Find three fractions that are equivalent to $\frac{3}{9}$.

- Multiply or divide the numerator and denominator by the same nonzero whole number.

$\frac{3}{9} = \frac{3 \times 3}{9 \times 3} = \frac{9}{27}$ $\quad\quad$ $\frac{3}{9} = \frac{3 \div 3}{9 \div 3} = \frac{1}{3}$ $\quad\quad$ $\frac{3}{9} = \frac{3 \times 5}{9 \times 5} = \frac{15}{45}$

$\frac{9}{27}$, $\frac{1}{3}$ and $\frac{15}{45}$ are equivalent to $\frac{3}{9}$.

Example 2: Write $\frac{3}{9}$ in simplest form.

$\frac{3}{9} = \frac{3 \div 3}{9 \div 3}$

$= \frac{1}{3}$

- Divide the numerator and the denominator by the GCF: 3.

$\frac{3}{9}$, in simplest form, is $\frac{1}{3}$.

Fill in the correct circle to answer each question.

(B) **1.** $\frac{1}{2} = \frac{\blacksquare}{10}$

(A) 4 (B) 5 (C) 6 (D) 20

(A) **2.** $\frac{4}{6} = \frac{\blacksquare}{3}$

(A) 2 (B) 7 (C) 8 (D) 12

(C) **3.** $\frac{2}{5} = \frac{\blacksquare}{20}$

(A) 10 (B) 9 (C) 8 (D) 6

(D) **4.** $\frac{8}{24} = \frac{\blacksquare}{3}$

(A) 64 (B) 16 (C) 2 (D) 1

(B) **5.** What is $\frac{9}{18}$ in simplest form?

(A) $\frac{3}{6}$ (B) $\frac{1}{2}$ (C) $\frac{18}{36}$ (D) $\frac{27}{54}$

(A) **6.** What is $\frac{10}{25}$ in simplest form?

(A) $\frac{2}{5}$ (B) $\frac{20}{50}$ (C) $\frac{1}{3}$ (D) $\frac{1}{5}$

(D) **7.** $\frac{5}{8} = \frac{\blacksquare}{64}$

(A) 5 (B) 25 (C) 35 (D) 40

(B) **8.** $\frac{48}{54} = \frac{\blacksquare}{9}$

(A) 48 (B) 8 (C) 7 (D) 6

(C) **9.** What is $\frac{16}{40}$ in simplest form?

(A) $\frac{1}{2}$ (B) $\frac{4}{10}$ (C) $\frac{2}{5}$ (D) $\frac{8}{20}$

(B) **10.** $\frac{3}{7} = \frac{\blacksquare}{42}$

(A) 15 (B) 18 (C) 21 (D) 38

(D) **11.** Which fraction is equivalent to $\frac{3}{12}$?

(A) $\frac{9}{12}$ (B) $\frac{3}{4}$ (C) $\frac{1}{3}$ (D) $\frac{1}{4}$

(B) **12.** Which fraction is equivalent to $\frac{6}{8}$?

(A) $\frac{8}{6}$ (B) $\frac{3}{4}$ (C) $\frac{1}{2}$ (D) $\frac{1}{4}$

Ⓒ **13.** What is $\frac{8}{40}$ in simplest form?

Ⓐ $\frac{40}{8}$ Ⓑ $\frac{2}{10}$ Ⓒ $\frac{1}{5}$ Ⓓ $\frac{4}{20}$

Ⓓ **14.** $\frac{3}{6} = \frac{■}{12}$

Ⓐ 2 Ⓑ 3 Ⓒ 4 Ⓓ 6

Ⓑ **15.** Sam cut a pizza into 8 equal pieces. He gave $\frac{1}{4}$ of the pizza to his brother. How many eighths of the pizza did he give to his brother?

Ⓐ $\frac{1}{8}$ Ⓑ $\frac{2}{8}$ Ⓒ $\frac{4}{8}$ Ⓓ $\frac{6}{8}$

Ⓑ **16.** Jeannie divided a submarine sandwich into 6 equal parts. She ate $\frac{1}{3}$ of the sandwich. How many sixths of the sandwich did she eat?

Ⓐ $\frac{1}{6}$ Ⓑ $\frac{2}{6}$ Ⓒ $\frac{3}{6}$ Ⓓ $\frac{4}{6}$

Ⓐ **17.** $\frac{3}{18} = \frac{■}{6}$

Ⓐ 1 Ⓑ 2 Ⓒ 3 Ⓓ 8

Ⓑ **18.** Give the next equivalent fraction: $\frac{1}{2}, \frac{2}{4}, \frac{3}{6}$, ■

Ⓐ $\frac{4}{7}$ Ⓑ $\frac{4}{8}$ Ⓒ $\frac{5}{7}$ Ⓓ $\frac{5}{10}$

Ⓒ **19.** $\frac{3}{4} = \frac{■}{12}$

Ⓐ 6 Ⓑ 8 Ⓒ 9 Ⓓ 10

Ⓒ **20.** What is $\frac{12}{16}$ in simplest form?

Ⓐ $1\frac{1}{4}$ Ⓑ $\frac{4}{5}$ Ⓒ $\frac{3}{4}$ Ⓓ $\frac{6}{8}$

Ⓐ **21.** Which fraction is *not* equivalent to $\frac{8}{48}$?

Ⓐ $\frac{1}{2}$ Ⓑ $\frac{1}{6}$ Ⓒ $\frac{4}{24}$ Ⓓ $\frac{2}{12}$

Ⓑ **22.** $\frac{16}{32} = \frac{■}{8}$

Ⓐ 5 Ⓑ 4 Ⓒ 3 Ⓓ 2

Ⓑ **23.** What is $\frac{20}{30}$ in simplest form?

Ⓐ $\frac{10}{15}$ Ⓑ $\frac{2}{3}$ Ⓒ $\frac{4}{6}$ Ⓓ $\frac{1}{3}$

Ⓑ **24.** $\frac{12}{42} = \frac{■}{14}$

Ⓐ 3 Ⓑ 4 Ⓒ 5 Ⓓ 6

Ⓐ **25.** $\frac{24}{30} = \frac{■}{15}$

Ⓐ 12 Ⓑ 8 Ⓒ 6 Ⓓ 3

Ⓑ **26.** What is $\frac{9}{15}$ in simplest form?

Ⓐ $\frac{1}{2}$ Ⓑ $\frac{3}{5}$ Ⓒ $\frac{2}{5}$ Ⓓ $\frac{1}{3}$

Ⓒ **27.** Tom bought eight new shirts. One-half of the shirts were blue. What fraction of the shirts was blue?

Ⓐ $\frac{3}{4}$ Ⓑ $\frac{2}{3}$ Ⓒ $\frac{4}{8}$ Ⓓ $\frac{1}{3}$

Ⓑ **28.** Sarah took 12 rolls of film on her vacation. Three rolls were of slide film. Which fraction of the rolls of film was of slide film?

Ⓐ $\frac{1}{8}$ Ⓑ $\frac{1}{4}$ Ⓒ $\frac{1}{3}$ Ⓓ $\frac{1}{2}$

Ⓑ **29.** What is $\frac{20}{24}$ in simplest form?

Ⓐ $\frac{10}{12}$ Ⓑ $\frac{5}{6}$ Ⓒ $\frac{3}{4}$ Ⓓ $\frac{2}{3}$

Ⓓ **30.** $\frac{2}{3} = \frac{■}{9}$

Ⓐ 1 Ⓑ 3 Ⓒ 8 Ⓓ 6

Ⓑ **31.** Give the next equivalent fraction: $\frac{1}{3}, \frac{2}{6}, \frac{3}{9}$, ■

Ⓐ $\frac{4}{10}$ Ⓑ $\frac{4}{12}$ Ⓒ $\frac{6}{9}$ Ⓓ $\frac{9}{12}$

Ⓒ **32.** Which fraction is *not* equivalent to $\frac{12}{36}$?

Ⓐ $\frac{1}{3}$ Ⓑ $\frac{2}{6}$ Ⓒ $\frac{2}{3}$ Ⓓ $\frac{3}{9}$

Name________________________________ Class __________ Date ______________

3.5 COMPARING AND ORDERING FRACTIONS

Example 1: Compare the fractions.

A. $\frac{3}{8}$ ■ $\frac{7}{8}$

- If the denominators are the same, just compare the numerators: $3 < 7$

So, $\frac{3}{8} < \frac{7}{8}$

B. $\frac{3}{8}$ ■ $\frac{1}{2}$

- If the denominators are different, first find the least common denominator (LCD).

Multiples of 8: 8, 16, 24, . . .
Multiples of 2: 2, 4, 6, 8, . . .

The LCD of 2 and 8 is 8.

- Then, write each fraction as an equivalent fraction using the LCD.

$\frac{3}{8} = \frac{3}{8}$; $\frac{1}{2} = \frac{1 \times 4}{2 \times 4} = \frac{4}{8}$

- Compare the numerators: $3 < 4$

So, $\frac{3}{8} < \frac{1}{2}$

Example 2: Order the following fractions from *greatest to least:* $\frac{2}{5}, \frac{1}{3}, \frac{5}{6}, \frac{9}{10}$

- Find the least common denominator: The LCD of 5, 3, 6, and 10 is 30.
- Find equivalent fractions using the LCD. $\frac{2}{5} = \frac{12}{30}, \frac{1}{3} = \frac{10}{30}, \frac{5}{6} = \frac{25}{30}, \frac{9}{10} = \frac{27}{30}$
- Order the equivalent fractions from *greatest to least.* $\frac{27}{30}, \frac{25}{30}, \frac{12}{30}, \frac{10}{30}$
- Write the original fractions in order from *greatest to least.* $\frac{9}{10}, \frac{5}{6}, \frac{2}{5}, \frac{1}{3}$

Fill in the correct circle to answer each question.

Ⓑ **1.** $\frac{1}{3}$ ■ $\frac{1}{2}$

Ⓐ > Ⓑ < Ⓒ =

Ⓑ **2.** $\frac{1}{4}$ ■ $\frac{3}{4}$

Ⓐ > Ⓑ < Ⓒ =

Ⓐ **3.** $\frac{4}{7}$ ■ $\frac{3}{14}$

Ⓐ > Ⓑ < Ⓒ =

Ⓑ **4.** $\frac{2}{9}$ ■ $\frac{5}{8}$

Ⓐ > Ⓑ < Ⓒ =

Ⓓ **5.** Order $\frac{3}{13}, \frac{11}{13}, \frac{5}{13}, \frac{9}{13}$ from *least to greatest.*

Ⓐ $\frac{11}{13}, \frac{9}{13}, \frac{5}{13}, \frac{3}{13}$ Ⓑ $\frac{9}{13}, \frac{5}{13}, \frac{3}{13}, \frac{11}{13}$

Ⓒ $\frac{5}{13}, \frac{3}{13}, \frac{11}{13}, \frac{9}{13}$ Ⓓ $\frac{3}{13}, \frac{5}{13}, \frac{9}{13}, \frac{11}{13}$

Ⓐ **6.** Order $\frac{1}{3}, \frac{1}{2}, \frac{1}{4}$ from *greatest to least.*

Ⓐ $\frac{1}{2}, \frac{1}{3}, \frac{1}{4}$ Ⓑ $\frac{1}{3}, \frac{1}{2}, \frac{1}{4}$

Ⓒ $\frac{1}{3}, \frac{1}{4}, \frac{1}{2}$ Ⓓ $\frac{1}{4}, \frac{1}{3}, \frac{1}{2}$

(A) **7.** Order from *least to greatest:* $\frac{5}{7}, \frac{7}{10}, \frac{3}{5}$

(A) $\frac{3}{5}, \frac{7}{10}, \frac{5}{7}$ (B) $\frac{5}{7}, \frac{3}{5}, \frac{7}{10}$

(C) $\frac{7}{10}, \frac{3}{5}, \frac{5}{7}$ (D) $\frac{7}{10}, \frac{5}{7}, \frac{3}{5}$

(D) **8.** Find the *greatest* fraction: $\frac{17}{30}, \frac{8}{15}, \frac{2}{3}, \frac{1}{5}$

(A) $\frac{1}{5}$ (B) $\frac{8}{15}$

(C) $\frac{17}{30}$ (D) $\frac{2}{3}$

(C) **9.** What fraction is between $\frac{2}{3}$ and $\frac{8}{9}$?

(A) $\frac{5}{9}$ (B) $\frac{16}{27}$ (C) $\frac{7}{9}$ (D) $\frac{17}{18}$

(B) **10.** $\frac{7}{11}$ ■ $\frac{3}{4}$

(A) > (B) < (C) =

(A) **11.** Order from *greatest to least:* $\frac{3}{20}, \frac{3}{10}, \frac{3}{50}$

(A) $\frac{3}{10}, \frac{3}{20}, \frac{3}{50}$ (B) $\frac{3}{10}, \frac{3}{50}, \frac{3}{20}$

(C) $\frac{3}{20}, \frac{3}{10}, \frac{3}{50}$ (D) $\frac{3}{50}, \frac{3}{20}, \frac{3}{10}$

(A) **12.** Order from *least to greatest:* $\frac{89}{100}, \frac{19}{100}, \frac{3}{100}, \frac{87}{100}$

(A) $\frac{3}{100}, \frac{19}{100}, \frac{87}{100}, \frac{89}{100}$ (B) $\frac{3}{100}, \frac{19}{100}, \frac{89}{100}, \frac{87}{100}$

(C) $\frac{19}{100}, \frac{87}{100}, \frac{89}{100}, \frac{3}{100}$ (D) $\frac{89}{100}, \frac{87}{100}, \frac{19}{100}, \frac{3}{100}$

(A) **13.** What fraction is between $\frac{1}{4}$ and $\frac{17}{32}$?

(A) $\frac{1}{2}$ (B) $\frac{9}{16}$ (C) $\frac{5}{8}$ (D) $\frac{3}{4}$

(B) **14.** What fraction is between $\frac{4}{9}$ and $\frac{41}{45}$?

(A) $\frac{43}{45}$ (B) $\frac{4}{5}$ (C) $\frac{12}{36}$ (D) $\frac{2}{9}$

(A) **15.** $\frac{2}{11}$ ■ $\frac{2}{15}$

(A) > (B) < (C) =

(A) **16.** Which fraction is *least?*

(A) $\frac{1}{36}$ (B) $\frac{1}{18}$ (C) $\frac{1}{9}$ (D) $\frac{1}{6}$

(B) **17.** $\frac{13}{25}$ ■ $\frac{3}{5}$

(A) > (B) < (C) =

(A) **18.** Which fraction is *least?*

(A) $\frac{2}{9}$ (B) $\frac{1}{3}$ (C) $\frac{5}{12}$ (D) $\frac{5}{6}$

(C) **19.** What fraction is between $\frac{2}{3}$ and $\frac{8}{9}$?

(A) $\frac{5}{9}$ (B) $\frac{16}{27}$ (C) $\frac{7}{9}$ (D) $\frac{17}{18}$

(D) **20.** Which fraction is *greatest?*

(A) $\frac{2}{9}$ (B) $\frac{1}{3}$ (C) $\frac{5}{12}$ (D) $\frac{5}{6}$

(A) **21.** $\frac{2}{5}$ ■ $\frac{1}{4}$

(A) > (B) < (C) =

(B) **22.** $\frac{7}{8}$ ■ $\frac{8}{9}$

(A) > (B) < (C) =

(A) **23.** Find the *greatest* fraction: $\frac{2}{3}, \frac{5}{6}, \frac{9}{12}, \frac{1}{2}$

(A) $\frac{5}{6}$ (B) $\frac{9}{12}$ (C) $\frac{2}{3}$ (D) $\frac{1}{2}$

(B) **24.** Compare: $\frac{3}{4}$ ■ $\frac{7}{8}$

(A) > (B) < (C) =

(C) **25.** Compare: $\frac{2}{3}$ ■ $\frac{4}{6}$

(A) > (B) < (C) =

(D) **26.** Find the *least* fraction: $\frac{2}{3}, \frac{7}{15}, \frac{2}{5}, \frac{1}{3}$

(A) $\frac{2}{3}$ (B) $\frac{7}{15}$ (C) $\frac{2}{5}$ (D) $\frac{1}{3}$

Name ____________________ Class ________ Date ____________

3.6 MULTIPLYING FRACTIONS

Example 1: Multiply: $\frac{1}{3} \times \frac{3}{8}$

$\frac{1}{3} \times \frac{3}{8} = \frac{1 \times 3}{3 \times 8}$ • Multiply the numerators. • Multiply the denominators.

$= \frac{3}{24}$

$= \frac{1}{8}$ • Write the product in simplest form.

Example 2: Multiply: $\frac{3}{4} \times 6$

$\frac{3}{4} \times 6 = \frac{3}{4} \times \frac{6}{1}$ • Write the whole number as a fraction.

$= \frac{3 \times 6}{4 \times 1}$ • Multiply the numerators. • Multiply the denominators.

$= \frac{18}{4}$

$= 4\frac{1}{2}$ • Write the product as a mixed number in simplest form.

Fill in the correct circle to answer each question.

Ⓓ **1.** Multiply: $\frac{2}{5} \times \frac{1}{2}$

Ⓐ $\frac{4}{5}$ Ⓑ $\frac{3}{7}$ Ⓒ $\frac{3}{10}$ Ⓓ $\frac{1}{5}$

Ⓓ **2.** $\frac{4}{9} \times \frac{5}{6} =$ ■

Ⓐ $1\frac{1}{3}$ Ⓑ $\frac{3}{5}$ Ⓒ $\frac{4}{9}$ Ⓓ $\frac{10}{27}$

Ⓐ **3.** Multiply: $\frac{5}{8} \times 4$

Ⓐ $2\frac{1}{2}$ Ⓑ $1\frac{1}{8}$ Ⓒ $\frac{5}{8}$ Ⓓ $\frac{5}{32}$

Ⓒ **4.** $9 \times \frac{2}{7} =$ ■

Ⓐ $\frac{2}{63}$ Ⓑ $2\frac{3}{7}$ Ⓒ $2\frac{4}{7}$ Ⓓ $9\frac{2}{7}$

Ⓓ **5.** What is $\frac{3}{4}$ of 12?

Ⓐ $\frac{1}{16}$ Ⓑ $\frac{36}{48}$ Ⓒ $3\frac{3}{4}$ Ⓓ 9

Ⓒ **6.** Multiply 8 by $\frac{1}{3}$.

Ⓐ $8\frac{1}{3}$ Ⓑ 3 Ⓒ $2\frac{2}{3}$ Ⓓ $\frac{1}{24}$

Ⓐ **7.** Multiply $\frac{3}{10}$ by $\frac{2}{3}$.

Ⓐ $\frac{1}{5}$ Ⓑ $\frac{1}{6}$ Ⓒ $\frac{5}{13}$ Ⓓ $\frac{6}{13}$

Ⓓ **8.** What is $\frac{5}{8}$ of $\frac{7}{9}$?

Ⓐ $\frac{45}{56}$ Ⓑ $\frac{12}{17}$ Ⓒ $\frac{1}{2}$ Ⓓ $\frac{35}{72}$

Ⓑ **9.** $\frac{6}{11} \times \frac{4}{5} =$ ■

Ⓐ $\frac{10}{55}$ Ⓑ $\frac{24}{55}$ Ⓒ $\frac{5}{8}$ Ⓓ $1\frac{1}{2}$

Ⓒ **10.** What is $\frac{9}{10}$ of 15?

Ⓐ 15 Ⓑ $14\frac{1}{2}$ Ⓒ $13\frac{1}{2}$ Ⓓ $\frac{3}{50}$

Ⓐ **11.** Multiply: $\frac{3}{14} \times \frac{1}{3}$

Ⓐ $\frac{1}{14}$ Ⓑ $\frac{3}{17}$ Ⓒ $\frac{4}{17}$ Ⓓ $\frac{9}{14}$

Ⓐ **12.** Find the product: $\frac{1}{2} \times \frac{27}{50}$

Ⓐ $\frac{27}{100}$ Ⓑ $\frac{14}{50}$ Ⓒ $\frac{27}{52}$ Ⓓ $1\frac{2}{25}$

Ⓒ **13.** What is $\frac{6}{7}$ of 13?

Ⓐ $\frac{6}{91}$ Ⓑ $9\frac{5}{7}$ Ⓒ $11\frac{1}{7}$ Ⓓ $12\frac{3}{7}$

Ⓑ **14.** $10 \times \frac{5}{12} =$ ■

Ⓐ $\frac{5}{120}$ Ⓑ $4\frac{1}{6}$ Ⓒ $4\frac{1}{4}$ Ⓓ $4\frac{1}{3}$

Ⓓ **15.** $\frac{1}{4} \times \frac{1}{2} =$ ■

Ⓐ $\frac{1}{2}$ Ⓑ $\frac{1}{5}$ Ⓒ $\frac{1}{6}$ Ⓓ $\frac{1}{8}$

Ⓒ **16.** Multiply: $\frac{3}{8} \times \frac{4}{6}$

Ⓐ $\frac{1}{2}$ Ⓑ $\frac{1}{3}$ Ⓒ $\frac{1}{4}$ Ⓓ $\frac{1}{5}$

Ⓓ **17.** What is $\frac{6}{7}$ of 20?

Ⓐ $\frac{3}{70}$ Ⓑ $3\frac{5}{7}$ Ⓒ $16\frac{2}{7}$ Ⓓ $17\frac{1}{7}$

Ⓐ **18.** $\frac{4}{5} \times 100 =$ ■

Ⓐ 80 Ⓑ 90 Ⓒ $100\frac{4}{5}$ Ⓓ 125

Ⓓ **19.** Multiply: $\frac{1}{6} \times \frac{1}{8}$

Ⓐ $\frac{3}{4}$ Ⓑ $\frac{1}{7}$ Ⓒ $\frac{1}{24}$ Ⓓ $\frac{1}{48}$

Ⓐ **20.** What is $\frac{7}{10}$ of 3?

Ⓐ $2\frac{1}{10}$ Ⓑ 2 Ⓒ $\frac{7}{13}$ Ⓓ $\frac{7}{30}$

Ⓓ **21.** $\frac{3}{10} \times \frac{5}{6} =$ ■

Ⓐ $\frac{15}{16}$ Ⓑ $\frac{8}{16}$ Ⓒ $\frac{1}{2}$ Ⓓ $\frac{1}{4}$

Ⓑ **22.** $30 \times \frac{1}{4} =$ ■

Ⓐ $8\frac{1}{2}$ Ⓑ $7\frac{1}{2}$ Ⓒ $6\frac{1}{5}$ Ⓓ $\frac{1}{120}$

Ⓒ **23.** Jane has 80 compact disks in her collection. One-fifth of the disks are jazz. How many jazz disks does she have?

Ⓐ 400 Ⓑ 20 Ⓒ 16 Ⓓ 15

Ⓒ **24.** Doug earns $240 a week. $\frac{1}{4}$ of his salary is deducted for taxes. How much is deducted for taxes?

Ⓐ $40 Ⓑ $50 Ⓒ $60 Ⓓ $80

Ⓒ **25.** Multiply: $\frac{3}{4} \times \frac{8}{9}$

Ⓐ $1\frac{1}{2}$ Ⓑ $\frac{11}{13}$ Ⓒ $\frac{2}{3}$ Ⓓ $\frac{27}{32}$

Ⓓ **26.** $\frac{1}{4} \times \frac{3}{4} =$ ■

Ⓐ $\frac{4}{8}$ Ⓑ $\frac{1}{2}$ Ⓒ $\frac{3}{4}$ Ⓓ $\frac{3}{16}$

Ⓓ **27.** What is $\frac{3}{4}$ of 60?

Ⓐ $\frac{1}{80}$ Ⓑ $12\frac{3}{5}$ Ⓒ 36 Ⓓ 45

Ⓓ **28.** $\frac{3}{8} \times \frac{1}{6} =$ ■

Ⓐ $\frac{4}{14}$ Ⓑ $\frac{2}{7}$ Ⓒ $\frac{3}{45}$ Ⓓ $\frac{1}{16}$

Ⓒ **29.** What is $\frac{3}{4}$ of 36?

Ⓐ $\frac{1}{27}$ Ⓑ 24 Ⓒ 27 Ⓓ 48

Ⓒ **30.** $\frac{2}{9} \times \frac{7}{8} =$ ■

Ⓐ $5\frac{1}{7}$ Ⓑ $\frac{7}{32}$ Ⓒ $\frac{7}{36}$ Ⓓ $\frac{16}{63}$

Ⓑ **31.** See-the-World Travel Agency booked 90 people on the 5-day cruise. One sixth of the people received discount tickets. How many people received discounts?

Ⓐ 10 people Ⓑ 15 people
Ⓒ 18 people Ⓓ 20 people

Ⓒ **32.** There are 20 men and 16 women in the Seaville Chorus. One-fourth of the members are sopranos. How many people are sopranos?

Ⓐ 4 people Ⓑ 5 people
Ⓒ 9 people Ⓓ 12 people

Name ______________________ Class ________ Date ____________

3.7 MULTIPLYING MIXED NUMBERS

Example 1: Multiply: $2\frac{1}{2} \times \frac{3}{4}$

$2\frac{1}{2} \times \frac{3}{4} = \frac{5}{2} \times \frac{3}{4}$ • Write the mixed number as an improper fraction.

$= \frac{5 \times 3}{2 \times 4}$ • Multiply the numerators. • Multiply the denominators.

$= \frac{15}{8}$

$= 1\frac{7}{8}$ • Write the product as a mixed number in simplest form.

Example 2: Multiply: $5\frac{2}{3} \times 6$

$5\frac{2}{3} \times 6 = \frac{17}{3} \times \frac{6}{1}$ • Write the mixed number and the whole number as improper fractions.

$= \frac{17}{\cancel{3}_1} \times \frac{\cancel{6}^2}{1}$ • Divide the numerator and the denominator by a common factor: 3.

$= \frac{17 \times 2}{1 \times 1}$ • Multiply the numerators. • Multiply the denominators.

$= \frac{34}{1}$

$= 34$ • Write the product as a mixed number in simplest form.

Fill in the correct circle to answer each question.

Ⓒ **1.** Multiply: $3\frac{3}{8} \times \frac{1}{3}$

Ⓐ $1\frac{3}{11}$ Ⓑ $\frac{3}{8}$ Ⓒ $1\frac{1}{8}$ Ⓓ $\frac{1}{8}$

Ⓒ **2.** $\frac{4}{7} \times 6\frac{1}{2} =$ ■

Ⓐ $1\frac{8}{9}$ Ⓑ $2\frac{2}{7}$ Ⓒ $3\frac{5}{7}$ Ⓓ $6\frac{2}{7}$

Ⓐ **3.** $2\frac{4}{9} \times 9 =$ ■

Ⓐ 22 Ⓑ 20 Ⓒ 15 Ⓓ $\frac{22}{81}$

Ⓓ **4.** Multiply: $2 \times 5\frac{9}{10}$

Ⓐ $2\frac{19}{20}$ Ⓑ $6\frac{1}{10}$ Ⓒ $10\frac{9}{10}$ Ⓓ $11\frac{4}{5}$

Ⓐ **5.** Find the product: $1\frac{1}{4} \times 1\frac{1}{2}$

Ⓐ $1\frac{7}{8}$ Ⓑ $1\frac{1}{4}$ Ⓒ $1\frac{1}{8}$ Ⓓ $7\frac{1}{2}$

Ⓐ **6.** Multiply $7\frac{1}{7}$ by $4\frac{2}{3}$.

Ⓐ $33\frac{1}{3}$ Ⓑ $32\frac{2}{3}$ Ⓒ $28\frac{2}{21}$ Ⓓ $6\frac{2}{5}$

Ⓑ **7.** $10\frac{5}{6} \times \frac{7}{10} =$ ■

Ⓐ $10\frac{7}{12}$ Ⓑ $7\frac{7}{12}$ Ⓒ $6\frac{1}{2}$ Ⓓ $2\frac{9}{20}$

Ⓒ **8.** What is $2\frac{2}{3}$ of 3 ?

Ⓐ $\frac{8}{9}$ Ⓑ $2\frac{3}{4}$ Ⓒ 8 Ⓓ $6\frac{2}{3}$

Ⓑ **9.** $5 \times 5\frac{5}{6} =$ ■

Ⓐ $29\frac{1}{3}$ Ⓑ $29\frac{1}{6}$ Ⓒ $29\frac{5}{6}$ Ⓓ $1\frac{1}{6}$

Ⓓ **10.** What is $\frac{1}{3}$ of $8\frac{1}{2}$?

Ⓐ $25\frac{1}{2}$ Ⓑ $8\frac{1}{6}$ Ⓒ $3\frac{1}{6}$ Ⓓ $2\frac{5}{6}$

Ⓒ **11.** The Donut Hole Bake Shop had $10\frac{1}{2}$ dozen donuts. They sold $\frac{2}{3}$ of the donuts. How many donuts did they sell?

Ⓐ 126 donuts Ⓑ 120 donuts
Ⓒ 84 donuts Ⓓ 7 donuts

Ⓐ **12.** Jeff works $8\frac{1}{4}$ hours a day at the bakery. He spends $\frac{1}{4}$ of his day baking bread. How much time does he spend baking bread?

Ⓐ $2\frac{1}{16}$ hours Ⓑ 2 hours
Ⓒ $2\frac{1}{8}$ hours Ⓓ $2\frac{1}{4}$ hours

Ⓑ **13.** Multiply: $2 \times 1\frac{1}{2}$

Ⓐ $\frac{3}{4}$ Ⓑ 3 Ⓒ $2\frac{1}{2}$ Ⓓ 4

Ⓓ **14.** $\frac{3}{4} \times 3\frac{3}{4} = \blacksquare$

Ⓐ $6\frac{3}{4}$ Ⓑ $4\frac{1}{2}$ Ⓒ $3\frac{9}{16}$ Ⓓ $2\frac{13}{16}$

Ⓒ **15.** Multiply: $1\frac{2}{3} \times 1\frac{2}{3}$

Ⓐ 16 Ⓑ 1 Ⓒ $2\frac{7}{9}$ Ⓓ $1\frac{4}{9}$

Ⓑ **16.** $\frac{3}{10} \times 4\frac{5}{6} = \blacksquare$

Ⓐ $\frac{29}{30}$ Ⓑ $1\frac{9}{20}$ Ⓒ $2\frac{5}{12}$ Ⓓ $4\frac{1}{4}$

Ⓓ **17.** Multiply: $5\frac{1}{2} \times 4$

Ⓐ 16 Ⓑ 8 Ⓒ $20\frac{1}{2}$ Ⓓ 22

Ⓑ **18.** What is $3\frac{1}{4} \times \frac{8}{9}$?

Ⓐ $3\frac{2}{9}$ Ⓑ $2\frac{8}{9}$ Ⓒ $2\frac{2}{3}$ Ⓓ $1\frac{7}{9}$

Ⓐ **19.** $1\frac{1}{3} \times 5 = \blacksquare$

Ⓐ $6\frac{2}{3}$ Ⓑ $6\frac{1}{3}$ Ⓒ $5\frac{1}{3}$ Ⓓ $\frac{4}{15}$

Ⓓ **20.** Find the product: $3\frac{1}{6} \times 2\frac{3}{4}$

Ⓐ $6\frac{3}{24}$ Ⓑ $6\frac{1}{8}$ Ⓒ $8\frac{1}{3}$ Ⓓ $8\frac{17}{24}$

Ⓓ **21.** Multiply: $6 \times 5\frac{1}{3}$

Ⓐ 18 Ⓑ 30 Ⓒ $30\frac{1}{3}$ Ⓓ 32

Ⓑ **22.** What is $1\frac{3}{4}$ of 12 ?

Ⓐ 24 Ⓑ 21 Ⓒ $12\frac{3}{4}$ Ⓓ $\frac{7}{48}$

Ⓐ **23.** $4 \times 4\frac{1}{3} = \blacksquare$

Ⓐ $17\frac{1}{3}$ Ⓑ $16\frac{1}{3}$ Ⓒ $17\frac{2}{3}$ Ⓓ $1\frac{1}{12}$

Ⓒ **24.** Multiply: $1\frac{1}{5} \times 1\frac{1}{2}$

Ⓐ 1 Ⓑ $1\frac{1}{10}$ Ⓒ $1\frac{4}{5}$ Ⓓ 2

Use table 3.7 to answer Exercises 25-26.

Ⓓ **25.** Jen wants to make four coffee cakes. How many cups of milk does she need?

Ⓐ $\frac{5}{8}$ cups Ⓑ $6\frac{1}{2}$ cups
Ⓒ $8\frac{1}{2}$ cups Ⓓ 10 cups

Ⓐ **26.** Bob wants to make three coffee cakes. How many cups of butter does he need?

Ⓐ $4\frac{1}{2}$ cups Ⓑ 4 cups
Ⓒ 2 cups Ⓓ $\frac{1}{2}$ cup

Table 3.7

Norwegian Coffee Cake	
$1\frac{1}{2}$ cups butter	2 T yeast
$1\frac{1}{2}$ cups brown sugar	4 eggs
$2\frac{1}{2}$ cups milk	1 t salt
	10 cups flour

Name ______________________________ Class __________ Date ______________

3.8 DIVIDING FRACTIONS

Reciprocals are two fractions whose product is 1.
To divide fractions, multiply the dividend by the reciprocal of the divisor.

$$\frac{6}{1} \times \frac{1}{6} = \frac{6}{6} = 1$$

Reciprocals

Example 1: Divide: $\frac{3}{4} \div \frac{1}{3}$

$\frac{3}{4} \div \frac{1}{3} = \frac{3}{4} \times \frac{3}{1}$ • Multiply by the reciprocal of the divisor.

$= \frac{3 \times 3}{4 \times 1}$ • Multiply the numerators. • Multiply the denominators.

$= \frac{9}{4}$

$= 2\frac{1}{4}$ • Write the answer as a mixed number in simplest form.

Example 2: Divide 4 by $\frac{1}{8}$.

$4 \div \frac{1}{8} = \frac{4}{1} \div \frac{1}{8}$ • Write the whole number as an improper fraction.

$= \frac{4}{1} \times \frac{8}{1}$ • Multiply by the reciprocal of the divisor.

$= \frac{4 \times 8}{1 \times 1}$ • Multiply the numerator. • Multiply the demonimator.

$= \frac{32}{1}$

$= 32$ • Write the answer in simplest form.

Fill in the correct circle to answer each question.

Ⓓ **1.** What is the reciprocal of 2?

Ⓐ $\frac{2}{1}$ Ⓑ 1 Ⓒ $\frac{2}{2}$ Ⓓ $\frac{1}{2}$

Ⓑ **2.** What is the reciprocal of $\frac{5}{6}$?

Ⓐ $\frac{3}{2}$ Ⓑ $\frac{6}{5}$ Ⓒ $\frac{5}{6}$ Ⓓ $\frac{1}{6}$

Ⓒ **3.** Divide: $\frac{1}{4} \div \frac{1}{2}$

Ⓐ 2 Ⓑ $\frac{3}{5}$ Ⓒ $\frac{1}{2}$ Ⓓ $\frac{1}{8}$

Ⓒ **4.** What is $\frac{4}{7}$ divided by $\frac{2}{3}$?

Ⓐ $\frac{8}{21}$ Ⓑ $\frac{7}{6}$ Ⓒ $\frac{6}{7}$ Ⓓ $\frac{7}{9}$

Ⓐ **5.** $\frac{8}{9} \div 3 =$ ■

Ⓐ $\frac{8}{27}$ Ⓑ $\frac{3}{8}$ Ⓒ $2\frac{2}{3}$ Ⓓ $3\frac{3}{8}$

Ⓓ **6.** Divide 6 by $\frac{3}{8}$.

Ⓐ $\frac{1}{16}$ Ⓑ $\frac{4}{9}$ Ⓒ $2\frac{1}{4}$ Ⓓ 16

Ⓑ **7.** $\frac{3}{10} \div \frac{2}{5} =$ ■

Ⓐ $\frac{4}{3}$ Ⓑ $\frac{3}{4}$ Ⓒ $\frac{1}{3}$ Ⓓ $\frac{3}{25}$

Ⓐ **8.** Divide: $12 \div \frac{1}{3}$

Ⓐ 36 Ⓑ 5 Ⓒ 4 Ⓓ $\frac{1}{36}$

Ⓒ **9.** What is the reciprocal of $\frac{4}{3}$?

Ⓐ $\frac{4}{4}$ Ⓑ $\frac{3}{3}$ Ⓒ $\frac{3}{4}$ Ⓓ 0

Ⓐ **10.** $10 \div \frac{3}{5} =$ ■

Ⓐ $16\frac{2}{3}$ Ⓑ $10\frac{3}{5}$ Ⓒ 6 Ⓓ 5

Ⓒ **11.** There is $\frac{7}{8}$ of a pecan pie left at the Shady Lane Cafe. A serving is $\frac{1}{16}$ of the pie. How many servings of pie are left?

Ⓐ $\frac{7}{128}$ servings Ⓑ 12 servings

Ⓒ 14 servings Ⓓ 128 servings

12. The Cafe serves fresh pineapple. A serving is $\frac{1}{4}$ of a pineapple. How many servings can be made from 5 pineapples?
Ⓐ

Ⓐ 20 servings Ⓑ 18 servings

Ⓒ 16 servings Ⓓ $1\frac{1}{4}$ servings

Ⓐ **13.** $\frac{7}{8} \div \frac{1}{4} = \blacksquare$

Ⓐ $3\frac{1}{2}$ Ⓑ $3\frac{3}{8}$ Ⓒ $\frac{2}{7}$ Ⓓ $\frac{7}{32}$

Ⓓ **14.** What is the reciprocal of 19?

Ⓐ 1 Ⓑ 0 Ⓒ $\frac{19}{1}$ Ⓓ $\frac{1}{19}$

Ⓑ **15.** $\frac{3}{4} \div \frac{3}{4} = \blacksquare$

Ⓐ 9 Ⓑ 1 Ⓒ $\frac{6}{8}$ Ⓓ $\frac{9}{16}$

Ⓓ **16.** Divide: $5 \div \frac{1}{2}$

Ⓐ $\frac{1}{10}$ Ⓑ $2\frac{1}{2}$ Ⓒ $5\frac{1}{2}$ Ⓓ 10

Ⓐ **17.** Divide $\frac{1}{9}$ by 9.

Ⓐ $\frac{1}{81}$ Ⓑ 1 Ⓒ $9\frac{1}{9}$ Ⓓ 81

Ⓑ **18.** $\frac{5}{10} \times \blacksquare = 1$

Ⓐ $\frac{5}{10}$ Ⓑ $\frac{10}{5}$ Ⓒ 1 Ⓓ $\frac{1}{2}$

Ⓐ **19.** $\frac{4}{5} \div \frac{3}{5} = \blacksquare$

Ⓐ $1\frac{1}{3}$ Ⓑ $1\frac{1}{8}$ Ⓒ $\frac{3}{4}$ Ⓓ $\frac{12}{25}$

Ⓓ **20.** Divide: $\frac{2}{3} \div \frac{1}{3}$

Ⓐ $\frac{2}{9}$ Ⓑ $\frac{1}{3}$ Ⓒ $\frac{1}{2}$ Ⓓ 2

Ⓓ **21.** What is the reciprocal of $\frac{19}{100}$?

Ⓐ 100 Ⓑ 81 Ⓒ 19 Ⓓ $\frac{100}{19}$

Ⓑ **22.** $2 \div \frac{6}{7} = \blacksquare$

Ⓐ $2\frac{2}{3}$ Ⓑ $2\frac{1}{3}$ Ⓒ $1\frac{2}{7}$ Ⓓ $1\frac{5}{7}$

Ⓓ **23.** Maria swims laps $\frac{1}{8}$ of a mile long. She swims for two miles. How many laps does she swim?

Ⓐ $\frac{1}{4}$ lap Ⓑ $\frac{1}{16}$ lap Ⓒ 4 laps Ⓓ 16 laps

Ⓓ **24.** John buys six pounds of hamburger. He makes quarter-pound hamburgers. How many hamburgers does he make?

Ⓐ $1\frac{1}{2}$ hamburgers Ⓑ 6 hamburgers

Ⓒ 12 hamburgers Ⓓ 24 hamburgers

Ⓐ **25.** Divide: $\frac{4}{6} \div 10$

Ⓐ $\frac{1}{15}$ Ⓑ $\frac{2}{35}$ Ⓒ $6\frac{2}{3}$ Ⓓ 15

Ⓒ **26.** What is the reciprocal of 8?

Ⓐ $\frac{8}{1}$ Ⓑ 1 Ⓒ $\frac{1}{8}$ Ⓓ 0

Ⓒ **27.** $\frac{1}{6} \div \frac{7}{9} = \blacksquare$

Ⓐ $4\frac{2}{3}$ Ⓑ $1\frac{1}{6}$ Ⓒ $\frac{3}{14}$ Ⓓ $\frac{7}{54}$

Ⓐ **28.** Divide: $8 \div \frac{2}{5}$

Ⓐ 20 Ⓑ 15 Ⓒ $3\frac{4}{5}$ Ⓓ $3\frac{1}{5}$

Ⓐ **29.** $10 \div \frac{7}{10} = \blacksquare$

Ⓐ $14\frac{2}{7}$ Ⓑ $14\frac{5}{7}$ Ⓒ 7 Ⓓ $\frac{1}{7}$

Ⓓ **30.** What is the reciprocal of $\frac{4}{5}$?

Ⓐ $\frac{4}{5}$ Ⓑ 0 Ⓒ 1 Ⓓ $\frac{5}{4}$

Name ____________________ Class ________ Date ____________

3.9 DIVIDING MIXED NUMBERS

To **divide mixed numbers,** first write each mixed number as an improper fraction. Then multiply the dividend by the reciprocal of the divisor.

Example 1: Divide: $\frac{1}{2} \div 3\frac{1}{4}$

$$\frac{1}{2} \div 3\frac{1}{4} = \frac{1}{2} \div \frac{13}{4}$$
- Write the mixed number as an improper fraction.

$$= \frac{1}{2} \times \frac{4}{13}$$
- Multiply by the reciprocal of the divisor.

$4 \div 2 = 2$
$2 \div 2 = 1$

$$= \frac{1}{\not{2}_{1}} \times \frac{\not{4}^{2}}{13}$$
- Divide the numerator and the denominator by a common factor.

$$= \frac{1 \times 2}{1 \times 13}$$
- Multiply the numerators.
- Multiply the denominators.

$$= \frac{2}{13}$$

Example 2: Divide 3 by $1\frac{2}{3}$.

$$3 \div 1\frac{2}{3} = \frac{3}{1} \div \frac{5}{3}$$
- Write the whole number and the mixed number as improper fractions.

$$= \frac{3}{1} \times \frac{3}{5}$$
- Multiply by the reciprocal of the divisor.

$$= \frac{3 \times 3}{1 \times 5}$$
- Multiply the numerators.
- Multiply the denominators.

$$= \frac{9}{5}$$

$$= 1\frac{4}{5}$$
- Write the product as a mixed number in simplest form.

Fill in the correct circle to answer each question.

Ⓓ **1.** Divide: $\frac{3}{4} \div 1\frac{3}{4}$

Ⓐ 5 Ⓑ $\frac{4}{7}$ Ⓒ $1\frac{5}{16}$ Ⓓ $\frac{3}{7}$

Ⓓ **2.** $3\frac{1}{3} \div \frac{1}{9} = $ ■

Ⓐ $3\frac{1}{3}$ Ⓑ $\frac{10}{27}$ Ⓒ $\frac{1}{30}$ Ⓓ 30

Ⓒ **3.** $5 \div 2\frac{1}{8} = $ ■

Ⓐ $10\frac{5}{8}$ Ⓑ $10\frac{3}{8}$ Ⓒ $2\frac{6}{17}$ Ⓓ $2\frac{4}{17}$

Ⓒ **4.** Divide: $4\frac{1}{4} \div 2$

Ⓐ $\frac{8}{17}$ Ⓑ $1\frac{1}{8}$ Ⓒ $2\frac{1}{8}$ Ⓓ $2\frac{7}{8}$

Ⓑ **5.** Divide: $6\frac{1}{9} \div 1\frac{1}{3}$

Ⓐ $1\frac{1}{3}$ Ⓑ $4\frac{7}{12}$ Ⓒ $4\frac{5}{12}$ Ⓓ $\frac{27}{220}$

Ⓐ **6.** $5\frac{3}{10} \div 2\frac{1}{2} = $ ■

Ⓐ $2\frac{3}{25}$ Ⓑ $13\frac{1}{4}$ Ⓒ $\frac{18}{25}$ Ⓓ $4\frac{1}{2}$

Ⓑ **7.** What is 1 divided by $1\frac{1}{8}$?

Ⓐ $1\frac{1}{8}$ Ⓑ $\frac{8}{9}$ Ⓒ $\frac{9}{8}$ Ⓓ 1

Ⓒ **8.** $3\frac{3}{4} \div 1\frac{4}{5} = ■$

Ⓐ $1\frac{7}{18}$ Ⓑ $4\frac{1}{2}$ Ⓒ $2\frac{1}{12}$ Ⓓ $6\frac{3}{4}$

Ⓓ **9.** Harry has a box of books that weighs $18\frac{3}{4}$ lb. He wants to distribute the books evenly in two boxes. How much will each box weigh?

Ⓐ $37\frac{1}{2}$ lb Ⓑ $12\frac{1}{2}$ lb

Ⓒ $3\frac{1}{8}$ lb Ⓓ $9\frac{3}{8}$ lb

Ⓐ **10.** Joseph has $4\frac{1}{2}$ lb of hamburger. He wants to pack the meat evenly in $\frac{1}{2}$ lb packages. How many packages can he make?

Ⓐ 9 packages Ⓑ 8 packages

Ⓒ $2\frac{1}{4}$ packages Ⓓ 2 packages

Ⓑ **11.** $10 \div 4\frac{2}{3} = ■$

Ⓐ 30 Ⓑ $2\frac{1}{7}$ Ⓒ $3\frac{1}{3}$ Ⓓ $46\frac{2}{3}$

Ⓓ **12.** Divide $7\frac{1}{2}$ pears equally among 3 people. How many pears does each person get?

Ⓐ $1\frac{1}{3}$ pear Ⓑ $1\frac{2}{3}$ pears

Ⓒ $2\frac{1}{3}$ pears Ⓓ $2\frac{1}{2}$ pears

Ⓒ **13.** Divide: $\frac{7}{8} \div 1\frac{7}{8}$

Ⓐ 11 Ⓑ $1\frac{41}{64}$ Ⓒ $\frac{7}{15}$ Ⓓ $\frac{1}{9}$

Ⓓ **14.** $1\frac{2}{9} \div 2\frac{1}{6} = ■$

Ⓐ $2\frac{26}{27}$ Ⓑ $2\frac{35}{54}$ Ⓒ $1\frac{17}{22}$ Ⓓ $\frac{22}{39}$

Ⓓ **15.** $7\frac{1}{2} \div \frac{3}{4} = ■$

Ⓐ $5\frac{5}{8}$ Ⓑ $6\frac{1}{3}$ Ⓒ $6\frac{2}{3}$ Ⓓ 10

Ⓒ **16.** Divide 5 by $3\frac{1}{8}$.

Ⓐ $15\frac{5}{8}$ Ⓑ $7\frac{1}{2}$ Ⓒ $1\frac{3}{5}$ Ⓓ $3\frac{1}{3}$

Ⓒ **17.** $1\frac{7}{10} \div 10 = ■$

Ⓐ 17 Ⓑ $\frac{7}{10}$ Ⓒ $\frac{17}{100}$ Ⓓ $\frac{1}{7}$

Ⓓ **18.** Divide: $\frac{2}{3} \div 3\frac{1}{3}$

Ⓐ $1\frac{5}{9}$ Ⓑ $2\frac{2}{9}$ Ⓒ $\frac{2}{7}$ Ⓓ $\frac{1}{5}$

Ⓒ **19.** $6\frac{1}{5} \div 2\frac{3}{4} = ■$

Ⓐ $1\frac{1}{15}$ Ⓑ $2\frac{3}{16}$ Ⓒ $2\frac{14}{55}$ Ⓓ $17\frac{1}{20}$

Ⓐ **20.** $4\frac{1}{4} \div \frac{5}{8} = ■$

Ⓐ $6\frac{4}{5}$ Ⓑ $3\frac{3}{5}$ Ⓒ $2\frac{21}{32}$ Ⓓ $1\frac{13}{32}$

Use Table 3.9 to answer questions 21-22.

Ⓓ **21.** How many haircuts can be done in three hours?

Ⓐ $\frac{1}{4}$ haircut Ⓑ $2\frac{1}{4}$ haircuts

Ⓒ 3 haircuts Ⓓ 4 haircuts

Ⓑ **22.** How many permanents can be finished in 7 hours?

Ⓐ $3\frac{1}{2}$ permanents Ⓑ 3 permanents

Ⓒ 14 permanents Ⓓ $16\frac{1}{3}$ permanents

Table 3.9

Total Look Hair Care	
Service	Time
Hair Cut	$\frac{3}{4}$ hour
Permanent	$2\frac{1}{3}$ hours
Manicure	$\frac{1}{2}$ hour
Hair Color	$1\frac{1}{2}$ hour

Name ______________________ Class __________ Date __________

3.10 ADDING FRACTIONS

Example 1:

$$\begin{array}{r} \frac{1}{10} \\ +\ \frac{7}{10} \\ \hline \end{array}$$

$\frac{1}{10} + \frac{7}{10} = \frac{8}{10}$

$= \frac{4}{5}$

- Since the denominators are equal, add the numerators.
- Write the sum in simplest form.

Example 2: Add $\frac{3}{4}$, $\frac{2}{3}$, and $\frac{1}{2}$.

Multiples of 4: 4, 8, 12, 16, ...
Multiples of 3: 3, 6, 9, 12, 15, ...
Multiples of 2: 2, 4, 6, 8, 10, 12, ...

- Find the LCD.

The LCD is 12.

$$\begin{array}{r} \frac{3}{4} = \frac{9}{12} \\ \frac{2}{3} = \frac{8}{12} \\ +\ \frac{1}{2} = \frac{6}{12} \\ \hline \frac{23}{12} \end{array}$$

- Write equivalent fractions using the LCD.
- Add the numerators.

$\frac{23}{12} = 1\frac{11}{12}$

- Write the sum as a mixed number.

Fill in the correct circle to answer each question.

Ⓒ **1.** $\frac{3}{5} + \frac{1}{5} = ■$

Ⓐ 4 Ⓑ $\frac{3}{5}$ Ⓒ $\frac{4}{5}$ Ⓓ $\frac{2}{5}$

Ⓓ **2.** What is the sum of $\frac{6}{7}$ and $\frac{4}{7}$?

Ⓐ $\frac{3}{7}$ Ⓑ $\frac{5}{7}$ Ⓒ $1\frac{2}{7}$ Ⓓ $1\frac{3}{7}$

Ⓐ **3.** Add: $\frac{3}{5} + \frac{1}{3}$

Ⓐ $\frac{14}{15}$ Ⓑ $\frac{13}{15}$ Ⓒ $\frac{1}{2}$ Ⓓ $\frac{1}{5}$

Ⓒ **4.** Add $\frac{1}{6}$, $\frac{1}{3}$ and $\frac{9}{10}$.

Ⓐ $\frac{11}{19}$ Ⓑ $\frac{5}{16}$ Ⓒ $1\frac{2}{5}$ Ⓓ $1\frac{1}{6}$

Ⓑ **5.** $$\begin{array}{r} \frac{11}{12} \\ +\ \frac{7}{12} \\ \hline \end{array}$$

Ⓐ $1\frac{7}{12}$ Ⓑ $1\frac{1}{2}$ Ⓒ $\frac{3}{4}$ Ⓓ $\frac{1}{3}$

Ⓒ **6.** $$\begin{array}{r} \frac{5}{8} \\ +\ \frac{3}{4} \\ \hline \end{array}$$

Ⓐ $\frac{2}{3}$ Ⓑ $1\frac{1}{4}$ Ⓒ $1\frac{3}{8}$ Ⓓ $3\frac{3}{4}$

Ⓓ **7.** $\frac{19}{100} + \frac{4}{25} + \frac{3}{10} = ■$

Ⓐ $\frac{26}{135}$ Ⓑ $\frac{33}{50}$ Ⓒ $\frac{57}{100}$ Ⓓ $\frac{13}{20}$

Ⓑ **8.** What is the sum of $\frac{11}{16}$ and $\frac{7}{8}$?

Ⓐ $2\frac{3}{16}$ Ⓑ $1\frac{9}{16}$ Ⓒ $1\frac{11}{16}$ Ⓓ $\frac{3}{4}$

(B) **9.** $\begin{array}{r} \frac{2}{3} \\ + \frac{2}{3} \\ \hline \end{array}$

Ⓐ $1\frac{2}{3}$ Ⓑ $1\frac{1}{3}$ Ⓒ 1 Ⓓ $\frac{2}{3}$

(A) **10.** $\begin{array}{r} \frac{1}{3} \\ + \frac{3}{7} \\ \hline \end{array}$

Ⓐ $\frac{16}{21}$ Ⓑ $\frac{4}{7}$ Ⓒ $\frac{13}{21}$ Ⓓ $\frac{2}{5}$

(B) **11.** Add: $\frac{4}{9} + \frac{5}{12}$

Ⓐ $\frac{23}{36}$ Ⓑ $\frac{31}{36}$ Ⓒ $\frac{5}{6}$ Ⓓ $\frac{3}{7}$

(C) **12.** Find the sum of $\frac{1}{4}$, $\frac{5}{7}$ and $\frac{1}{2}$.

Ⓐ $1\frac{23}{28}$ Ⓑ $1\frac{7}{12}$ Ⓒ $1\frac{13}{28}$ Ⓓ $\frac{7}{13}$

(C) **13.** $\frac{13}{36} + \frac{5}{36} + \frac{7}{36} =$

Ⓐ $1\frac{11}{15}$ Ⓑ $\frac{25}{108}$ Ⓒ $\frac{25}{36}$ Ⓓ $\frac{27}{36}$

(B) **14.** $\frac{7}{10} + \frac{7}{10} + \frac{7}{10} =$

Ⓐ $2\frac{3}{10}$ Ⓑ $2\frac{1}{10}$ Ⓒ $1\frac{2}{5}$ Ⓓ $\frac{21}{30}$

(B) **15.** On a wilderness hike, Stephanie walked $\frac{5}{8}$ of a mile to Eagle Point. Then she walked $\frac{1}{16}$ of a mile to Lookout Cove. How far did she walk altogether?

Ⓐ $\frac{3}{4}$ mile Ⓑ $\frac{11}{16}$ mile

Ⓒ $\frac{9}{16}$ mile Ⓓ $\frac{3}{8}$ mile

(C) **16.** Jason planned a vacation. He earned $\frac{1}{5}$ of the money he needs by raking leaves. He earned $\frac{3}{5}$ of the money he needs by babysitting. What part of the money has he earned?

Ⓐ $\frac{2}{5}$ Ⓑ $\frac{3}{5}$ Ⓒ $\frac{4}{5}$ Ⓓ $\frac{1}{5}$

(B) **17.** What is the sum of $\frac{1}{6}$ and $\frac{1}{3}$?

Ⓐ $\frac{2}{3}$ Ⓑ $\frac{1}{2}$ Ⓒ $\frac{2}{9}$ Ⓓ $\frac{1}{18}$

(C) **18.** $\frac{9}{25} + \frac{6}{25} =$ ■

Ⓐ $2\frac{4}{25}$ Ⓑ $\frac{16}{25}$ Ⓒ $\frac{3}{5}$ Ⓓ $\frac{3}{10}$

(C) **19.** Add: $\frac{3}{9} + \frac{5}{10}$
Write the answer in simplest form.

Ⓐ $\frac{8}{19}$ Ⓑ $\frac{75}{90}$ Ⓒ $\frac{5}{6}$ Ⓓ $\frac{15}{18}$

(B) **20.** Add: $\frac{7}{16} + \frac{5}{16}$
Write the answer in simplest form.

Ⓐ $\frac{12}{32}$ Ⓑ $\frac{3}{4}$ Ⓒ $\frac{3}{8}$ Ⓓ $\frac{12}{16}$

(A) **21.** $\begin{array}{r} \frac{5}{6} \\ + \frac{2}{9} \\ \hline \end{array}$

Ⓐ $1\frac{1}{18}$ Ⓑ $1\frac{1}{9}$ Ⓒ $\frac{2}{3}$ Ⓓ $\frac{7}{15}$

(B) **22.** $\begin{array}{r} \frac{1}{4} \\ + \frac{5}{9} \\ \hline \end{array}$

Ⓐ $\frac{18}{36}$ Ⓑ $\frac{29}{36}$ Ⓒ $\frac{29}{32}$ Ⓓ $\frac{6}{13}$

(A) **23.** $\frac{7}{15} + \frac{3}{15} =$ ■

Ⓐ $\frac{2}{3}$ Ⓑ $\frac{1}{2}$ Ⓒ $1\frac{2}{5}$ Ⓓ $\frac{1}{3}$

(D) **24.** $\frac{5}{9} + \frac{1}{6} + \frac{1}{3} =$ ■

Ⓐ $\frac{7}{18}$ Ⓑ $\frac{1}{18}$ Ⓒ $1\frac{1}{6}$ Ⓓ $1\frac{1}{18}$

(D) **25.** Add: $\frac{4}{5} + \frac{3}{4}$

Ⓐ $1\frac{9}{20}$ Ⓑ $\frac{3}{5}$ Ⓒ $\frac{7}{9}$ Ⓓ $1\frac{11}{20}$

(C) **26.** Add: $\frac{7}{24} + \frac{3}{8}$

Ⓐ $\frac{17}{24}$ Ⓑ $\frac{5}{16}$ Ⓒ $\frac{2}{3}$ Ⓓ $\frac{13}{24}$

Name ______________________ Class __________ Date __________

3.11 ADDING MIXED NUMBERS

Example 1: $3\frac{1}{5} + 2\frac{2}{5} = ■$

$$\begin{array}{r} 3\frac{1}{5} \\ +\ 2\frac{2}{5} \\ \hline 5\frac{3}{5} \end{array}$$

Add the whole numbers. ↑ ↑ Add the fractions.

Example 2: $\begin{array}{r} 1\frac{1}{2} \\ +\ 4\frac{3}{4} \\ \hline \end{array}$

- Find the LCD.
  Multiples of 2: 2, 4, 6, ...
  Multiples of 4: 4, 8, ...
  The LCD is 4.

$$\begin{array}{rcl} 1\frac{1}{2} & = & 1\frac{2}{4} \\ +\ 4\frac{3}{4} & = & 4\frac{3}{4} \\ \hline & & 5\frac{5}{4} \end{array}$$

- Write equivalent fractions using the LCD.
- Add the fractions.
  Add the whole numbers.
- Write the sum in simplest form.

$$5\frac{5}{4} = 5 + \frac{5}{4} = 5 + 1\frac{1}{4} = 6\frac{1}{4}$$

Fill in the correct circle to answer each question.

Ⓑ **1.** $6\frac{1}{9} + 2\frac{7}{9} = ■$

Ⓐ 9 Ⓑ $8\frac{8}{9}$ Ⓒ $8\frac{2}{3}$ Ⓓ $1\frac{2}{3}$

Ⓒ **2.** Add: $4\frac{1}{3} + 1\frac{5}{6}$

Ⓐ $5\frac{2}{3}$ Ⓑ $5\frac{1}{3}$ Ⓒ $6\frac{1}{6}$ Ⓓ $6\frac{1}{3}$

Ⓐ **3.** $\begin{array}{r} 2\frac{1}{4} \\ +2\frac{1}{4} \\ \hline \end{array}$

Ⓐ $4\frac{1}{2}$ Ⓑ $4\frac{1}{4}$ Ⓒ $4\frac{1}{8}$ Ⓓ $4\frac{1}{16}$

Ⓒ **4.** $\begin{array}{r} 1\frac{2}{7} \\ +3\frac{1}{2} \\ \hline \end{array}$

Ⓐ $4\frac{3}{14}$ Ⓑ $4\frac{1}{3}$ Ⓒ $4\frac{11}{14}$ Ⓓ $4\frac{6}{7}$

Ⓑ **5.** Find the sum of $2\frac{2}{3}$ and $3\frac{1}{3}$.

Ⓐ 5 Ⓑ 6 Ⓒ $5\frac{1}{2}$ Ⓓ $5\frac{1}{3}$

Ⓒ **6.** Add $1\frac{3}{10}$ and $4\frac{2}{5}$.

Ⓐ $5\frac{1}{3}$ Ⓑ $5\frac{3}{5}$ Ⓒ $5\frac{7}{10}$ Ⓓ $5\frac{1}{2}$

Ⓓ **7.** $6\frac{1}{4} + 3\frac{2}{3} = ■$

Ⓐ $9\frac{1}{4}$ Ⓑ $9\frac{3}{7}$ Ⓒ $9\frac{5}{6}$ Ⓓ $9\frac{11}{12}$

Ⓐ **8.** What is the sum of $4\frac{3}{8}$ and $1\frac{5}{6}$?

Ⓐ $6\frac{5}{24}$ Ⓑ $5\frac{3}{4}$ Ⓒ $6\frac{1}{12}$ Ⓓ $5\frac{4}{7}$

Ⓒ **9.** Find the sum of $3\frac{7}{18}$ and $2\frac{1}{6}$.

Ⓐ $6\frac{5}{9}$ Ⓑ $5\frac{1}{3}$ Ⓒ $5\frac{5}{9}$ Ⓓ $6\frac{1}{6}$

Ⓒ **10.** $4\frac{8}{11} + 4\frac{2}{11} =$ ■

Ⓐ $16\frac{10}{11}$ Ⓑ $8\frac{5}{11}$ Ⓒ $8\frac{10}{11}$ Ⓓ $9\frac{5}{11}$

Ⓒ **11.** Jim drove from Morris to Centerville. Then he drove to Southton. How many miles did he drive altogether?

Ⓐ $9\frac{1}{2}$ miles Ⓑ $8\frac{2}{3}$ miles

Ⓒ $9\frac{1}{4}$ miles Ⓓ 10 miles

Ⓑ **12.** Laurie drove from Southton to Centerville. Then she drove to Waterville. How many miles did she drive in all?

Ⓐ $10\frac{1}{2}$ miles Ⓑ 10 miles

Ⓒ $9\frac{1}{2}$ miles Ⓓ 9 miles

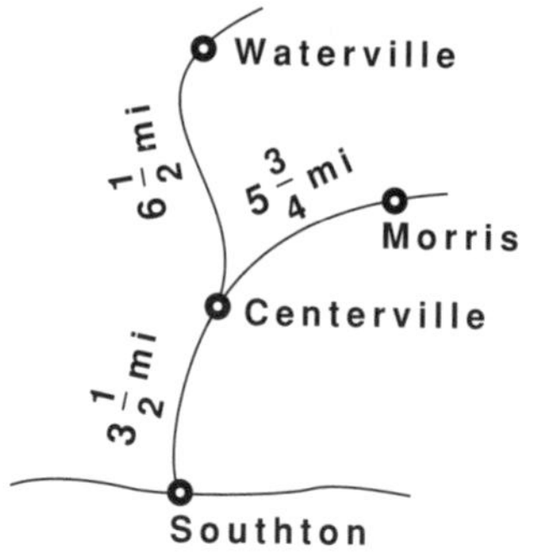

Ⓑ **13.** $2\frac{1}{6} + 1\frac{5}{6}$

Ⓐ 3 Ⓑ 4 Ⓒ $3\frac{5}{6}$ Ⓓ $3\frac{1}{2}$

Ⓓ **14.** $10\frac{5}{7} + 7\frac{3}{4}$

Ⓐ $17\frac{8}{11}$ Ⓑ $17\frac{15}{28}$ Ⓒ $17\frac{13}{28}$ Ⓓ $18\frac{13}{28}$

Ⓐ **15.** Add: $6\frac{1}{2} + 5\frac{7}{8}$

Ⓐ $12\frac{3}{8}$ Ⓑ $11\frac{1}{2}$ Ⓒ $11\frac{4}{5}$ Ⓓ $11\frac{3}{8}$

Ⓑ **16.** $16\frac{7}{12} + 10\frac{5}{12} =$ ■

Ⓐ $27\frac{1}{6}$ Ⓑ 27 Ⓒ 26 Ⓓ $26\frac{1}{2}$

Ⓒ **17.** $2\frac{3}{16} + 4\frac{1}{4}$

Ⓐ $8\frac{7}{16}$ Ⓑ $6\frac{1}{5}$ Ⓒ $6\frac{7}{16}$ Ⓓ $6\frac{1}{2}$

Ⓐ **18.** $13\frac{3}{5} + 3\frac{1}{5}$

Ⓐ $16\frac{4}{5}$ Ⓑ $16\frac{3}{5}$ Ⓒ $16\frac{2}{5}$ Ⓓ $10\frac{4}{5}$

Ⓒ **19.** What is the sum of $9\frac{2}{27} + 2\frac{2}{9}$?

Ⓐ $18\frac{8}{27}$ Ⓑ $11\frac{7}{27}$ Ⓒ $11\frac{8}{27}$ Ⓓ $11\frac{1}{9}$

Ⓑ **20.** $7\frac{1}{2} + 1\frac{1}{2} =$ ■

Ⓐ 10 Ⓑ 9 Ⓒ $8\frac{1}{2}$ Ⓓ 8

Ⓓ **21.** $2\frac{7}{20} + 5\frac{7}{8}$

Ⓐ $7\frac{1}{2}$ Ⓑ $7\frac{9}{40}$ Ⓒ $8\frac{1}{4}$ Ⓓ $8\frac{9}{40}$

Ⓒ **22.** $12\frac{3}{4} + 9\frac{3}{25}$

Ⓐ $22\frac{87}{100}$ Ⓑ $21\frac{9}{29}$ Ⓒ $21\frac{87}{100}$ Ⓓ $21\frac{6}{29}$

Name ____________ Class ________ Date ________

3.12 SUBTRACTING FRACTIONS

Example 1: Subtract $\frac{2}{9}$ from $\frac{8}{9}$.

$\frac{8}{9} - \frac{2}{9} = \frac{6}{9}$

$= \frac{2}{3}$

- Since the denominators are equal, subtract the numerators.
- Write the answer in simplest form.

Example 2: $\frac{9}{10} - \frac{1}{2}$

$\frac{9}{10} = \frac{9}{10}$

$-\frac{1}{2} = \frac{5}{10}$

$\frac{4}{10} = \frac{2}{5}$

- Find the LCD.

  Multiples of 10: 10, 20, ...
  Multiples of 2: 2, 4, 6, 8, 10, 12, ...

  The LCD is 10.

- Write equivalent fractions using the LCD.
- Subtract the numerators.
- Write the answer in simplest form.

Fill in the circle to answer each question.

Ⓒ **1.** $\frac{3}{4} - \frac{1}{4} = \blacksquare$

Ⓐ 3 Ⓑ 2 Ⓒ $\frac{1}{2}$ Ⓓ $\frac{1}{4}$

Ⓒ **2.** What is $\frac{3}{8}$ subtracted from $\frac{7}{8}$?

Ⓐ $1\frac{19}{24}$ Ⓑ $\frac{5}{8}$ Ⓒ $\frac{1}{2}$ Ⓓ $\frac{3}{8}$

Ⓓ **3.** Subtract: $\frac{4}{5} - \frac{1}{2}$

Ⓐ $1\frac{3}{10}$ Ⓑ 1 Ⓒ $\frac{2}{5}$ Ⓓ $\frac{3}{10}$

Ⓓ **4.** Subtract: $\frac{2}{3} - \frac{2}{7}$

Ⓐ $\frac{10}{21}$ Ⓑ $\frac{3}{7}$ Ⓒ $\frac{2}{5}$ Ⓓ $\frac{8}{21}$

Ⓒ **5.** $\frac{19}{20} - \frac{9}{20}$

Ⓐ $1\frac{2}{5}$ Ⓑ $\frac{11}{20}$ Ⓒ $\frac{1}{2}$ Ⓓ $\frac{9}{20}$

Ⓐ **6.** $\frac{4}{15} - \frac{1}{5}$

Ⓐ $\frac{1}{15}$ Ⓑ $\frac{1}{5}$ Ⓒ $\frac{1}{4}$ Ⓓ $\frac{3}{5}$

Ⓑ **7.** Subtract $\frac{1}{12}$ from $\frac{5}{6}$.

Ⓐ $\frac{11}{12}$ Ⓑ $\frac{3}{4}$ Ⓒ $\frac{2}{3}$ Ⓓ $\frac{1}{2}$

Ⓓ **8.** $\frac{15}{16} - \frac{3}{4} = \blacksquare$

Ⓐ $\frac{12}{12}$ Ⓑ $\frac{1}{2}$ Ⓒ $\frac{1}{4}$ Ⓓ $\frac{3}{16}$

Ⓐ **9.** George lives $\frac{2}{3}$ of a mile from Johnson High School. Wendell lives $\frac{3}{4}$ of a mile from the high school. How much farther from Johnson High School does Wendell live than George?

Ⓐ $\frac{1}{12}$ of a mile Ⓑ $\frac{5}{7}$ of a mile

Ⓒ 1 mile Ⓓ $1\frac{5}{12}$ miles

Ⓓ **10.** Vicki swam for $\frac{5}{6}$ of an hour before school. Madeline swam for $\frac{2}{3}$ of an hour. How much longer did Vicki swim than Madeline?

Ⓐ $1\frac{1}{2}$ hours Ⓑ 1 hour

Ⓒ $\frac{7}{9}$ of an hour Ⓓ $\frac{1}{6}$ of an hour

(B) **11.** $$\begin{array}{r} \frac{5}{6} \\ -\ \frac{1}{6} \\ \hline \end{array}$$

Ⓐ 1 Ⓑ $\frac{2}{3}$ Ⓒ $\frac{1}{2}$ Ⓓ $\frac{1}{3}$

(B) **12.** $$\begin{array}{r} \frac{7}{10} \\ -\ \frac{4}{15} \\ \hline \end{array}$$

Ⓐ $\frac{29}{30}$ Ⓑ $\frac{13}{30}$ Ⓒ $\frac{4}{5}$ Ⓓ $\frac{2}{15}$

(A) **13.** What is $\frac{13}{20}$ subtracted from $\frac{19}{20}$?

Ⓐ $\frac{3}{10}$ Ⓑ $\frac{1}{4}$ Ⓒ $\frac{7}{10}$ Ⓓ $1\frac{3}{10}$

(C) **14.** Subtract $\frac{51}{100}$ from $\frac{97}{100}$.

Ⓐ $\frac{9}{25}$ Ⓑ $\frac{9}{20}$ Ⓒ $\frac{23}{50}$ Ⓓ $\frac{49}{100}$

(D) **15.** $$\begin{array}{r} \frac{10}{11} \\ -\ \frac{3}{11} \\ \hline \end{array}$$

Ⓐ 7 Ⓑ $1\frac{2}{11}$ Ⓒ $\frac{8}{11}$ Ⓓ $\frac{7}{11}$

(B) **16.** $$\begin{array}{r} \frac{2}{3} \\ -\ \frac{4}{9} \\ \hline \end{array}$$

Ⓐ $\frac{1}{9}$ Ⓑ $\frac{2}{9}$ Ⓒ $\frac{1}{3}$ Ⓓ $\frac{4}{9}$

(D) **17.** $\frac{6}{7} - \frac{1}{2} =$ ■

Ⓐ $1\frac{5}{14}$ Ⓑ 1 Ⓒ $\frac{4}{7}$ Ⓓ $\frac{5}{14}$

(B) **18.** Subtract $\frac{3}{35}$ from $\frac{31}{35}$.

Ⓐ $\frac{6}{7}$ Ⓑ $\frac{4}{5}$ Ⓒ $\frac{33}{35}$ Ⓓ $\frac{34}{35}$

(C) **19.** $$\begin{array}{r} \frac{39}{40} \\ -\ \frac{19}{40} \\ \hline \end{array}$$

Ⓐ $\frac{3}{4}$ Ⓑ $\frac{29}{40}$ Ⓒ $\frac{1}{2}$ Ⓓ $\frac{1}{4}$

(C) **20.** $$\begin{array}{r} \frac{5}{8} \\ -\ \frac{1}{6} \\ \hline \end{array}$$

Ⓐ $\frac{1}{3}$ Ⓑ $\frac{1}{2}$ Ⓒ $\frac{11}{24}$ Ⓓ $\frac{3}{8}$

(C) **21.** Joan spends $\frac{1}{2}$ of an hour reading. She spends $\frac{3}{4}$ of an hour practicing the flute. How much longer does she spend practicing the flute?

Ⓐ $\frac{1}{2}$ of an hour Ⓑ $\frac{1}{3}$ of an hour

Ⓒ $\frac{1}{4}$ of an hour Ⓓ $\frac{1}{8}$ of an hour

22. (C) One-fourth of the students at Emerson High School belong to the school band. One-eighth of the students belong to the school chorus. How many more students belong to the band?

Ⓐ $\frac{3}{8}$ of the students Ⓑ $\frac{1}{4}$ of the students

Ⓒ $\frac{1}{8}$ of the students Ⓓ $\frac{1}{32}$ of the students

(B) **23.** Subtract $\frac{1}{4}$ from $\frac{11}{12}$.
Write the answer in simplest form.

Ⓐ $\frac{8}{12}$ Ⓑ $\frac{2}{3}$ Ⓒ $\frac{3}{4}$ Ⓓ $1\frac{1}{8}$

(B) **24.** Subtract $\frac{1}{3}$ from $\frac{5}{6}$.
Write the answer in simplest form.

Ⓐ $1\frac{1}{3}$ Ⓑ $\frac{1}{2}$ Ⓒ $\frac{3}{6}$ Ⓓ $\frac{1}{3}$

(A) **25.** Last month, $\frac{9}{10}$ of the sophomores attended the class meeting. This month, $\frac{3}{4}$ of the sophomores attended the meeting. How many more of the sophomore class attended last month's meeting?

Ⓐ $\frac{3}{20}$ Ⓑ $\frac{12}{14}$ Ⓒ $\frac{7}{6}$ Ⓓ $1\frac{13}{20}$

26. (D) In last year's Scholarship Run, $\frac{5}{8}$ of the runners finished the race. This year, $\frac{7}{8}$ of the runners finished the race. Which fraction shows the increase in the number of runners who finished this year's race?

Ⓐ 1 Ⓑ $1\frac{1}{2}$ Ⓒ $\frac{12}{16}$ Ⓓ $\frac{1}{4}$

Name ______________________ Class ________ Date ____________

3.13 SUBTRACTING MIXED NUMBERS

Example 1: Subtract $2\frac{2}{3}$ from $5\frac{1}{3}$.

$$\begin{array}{r} 5\frac{1}{3} \\ -\,2\frac{2}{3} \\ \hline \end{array}$$

- You can't subtract $\frac{2}{3}$ from $\frac{1}{3}$. Therefore, rename:

$$\begin{aligned} 5\frac{1}{3} &= 5 + \frac{1}{3} \\ &= 4 + 1 + \frac{1}{3} \\ &= 4 + \frac{3}{3} + \frac{1}{3} \\ &= 4\frac{4}{3} \end{aligned}$$

$$\begin{array}{rcr} 5\frac{1}{3} & = & 4\frac{4}{3} \\ -\,2\frac{2}{3} & = & 2\frac{2}{3} \\ \hline & & 2\frac{2}{3} \end{array}$$

- Subtract fraction from fraction, whole number from whole number.

Example 2: Subtract $1\frac{1}{4}$ from $3\frac{5}{8}$.

$$\begin{array}{r} 3\frac{5}{8} \\ -\,1\frac{1}{4} \\ \hline \end{array}$$

- Find the LCD.
  Multiples of 8: 8, 16, 24, ...
  Multiples of 4: 4, 8, 12, ...

  The LCD is 8.

$$\begin{array}{rcr} 3\frac{5}{8} & = & 3\frac{5}{8} \\ -\,1\frac{1}{4} & = & 1\frac{2}{8} \\ \hline & & 2\frac{3}{8} \end{array}$$

- Write equivalent fractions using the LCD.
- Subtract.

Fill in the correct circle to answer each question.

Ⓑ **1.** $9\frac{5}{6} - 4\frac{1}{6} = \blacksquare$

Ⓐ 14 Ⓑ $5\frac{2}{3}$ Ⓒ $5\frac{1}{2}$ Ⓓ $4\frac{2}{3}$

Ⓓ **2.** Subtract $2\frac{4}{5}$ from $4\frac{2}{5}$.

Ⓐ $2\frac{2}{5}$ Ⓑ $2\frac{3}{5}$ Ⓒ $1\frac{2}{5}$ Ⓓ $1\frac{3}{5}$

Ⓑ **3.** $$\begin{array}{r} 6\frac{7}{10} \\ -\,2\frac{1}{5} \\ \hline \end{array}$$

Ⓐ $5\frac{1}{5}$ Ⓑ $4\frac{1}{2}$ Ⓒ $4\frac{1}{5}$ Ⓓ $3\frac{1}{2}$

Ⓓ **4.** $$\begin{array}{r} 8\frac{2}{9} \\ -\,7\frac{2}{3} \\ \hline \end{array}$$

Ⓐ $1\frac{5}{9}$ Ⓑ $1\frac{1}{6}$ Ⓒ $\frac{2}{3}$ Ⓓ $\frac{5}{9}$

(D) **5.** $\frac{1}{5} + \frac{1}{2} - \frac{1}{4} = \blacksquare$

(A) $\frac{19}{20}$ (B) $\frac{1}{3}$ (C) $\frac{3}{10}$ (D) $\frac{9}{20}$

(B) **6.** $1\frac{2}{3} - \frac{2}{9} + 1\frac{5}{6} = \blacksquare$

(A) $2\frac{5}{18}$ (B) $3\frac{5}{18}$ (C) $3\frac{5}{16}$ (D) $3\frac{13}{18}$

(A) **7.** $10 - 6\frac{1}{2} = \blacksquare$

(A) $3\frac{1}{2}$ (B) $2\frac{1}{2}$ (C) $4\frac{1}{2}$ (D) $5\frac{1}{2}$

(D) **8.** Subtract: $5\frac{8}{9} - 4$

(A) $\frac{1}{9}$ (B) $\frac{8}{9}$ (C) $1\frac{1}{9}$ (D) $1\frac{8}{9}$

(A) **9.** $15\frac{5}{8} - 5\frac{7}{8}$

(A) $9\frac{3}{4}$ (B) $10\frac{1}{4}$ (C) $10\frac{3}{4}$ (D) $11\frac{1}{2}$

(C) **10.** $9\frac{3}{4} - 2\frac{1}{2}$

(A) 7 (B) 8 (C) $7\frac{1}{4}$ (D) $6\frac{1}{4}$

(C) **11.** $\frac{2}{15} + \frac{4}{5} - \frac{1}{3} = \blacksquare$

(A) $1\frac{4}{15}$ (B) $\frac{5}{17}$ (C) $\frac{3}{5}$ (D) $\frac{2}{3}$

(B) **12.** Subtract $4\frac{3}{7}$ from $9\frac{6}{7}$.

(A) $5\frac{4}{7}$ (B) $5\frac{3}{7}$ (C) $5\frac{2}{7}$ (D) $4\frac{3}{7}$

(A) **13.** $24\frac{5}{12} - 12\frac{3}{4}$

(A) $11\frac{2}{3}$ (B) $11\frac{3}{4}$ (C) $12\frac{1}{4}$ (D) $12\frac{3}{4}$

(D) **14.** $5 - 2\frac{5}{6}$

(A) $7\frac{5}{6}$ (B) $3\frac{5}{6}$ (C) $3\frac{1}{6}$ (D) $2\frac{1}{6}$

(C) **15.** Alex weighed 95 pounds. He went on a diet and lost $4\frac{1}{2}$ pounds. How much did he weigh after the diet?

(A) $99\frac{1}{2}$ pounds (B) $91\frac{1}{2}$ pounds

(C) $90\frac{1}{2}$ pounds (D) $89\frac{1}{2}$ pounds

16. (A) Ken caught a perch that weighed $1\frac{1}{4}$ pounds. Lois caught a perch that weighed $1\frac{1}{2}$ pounds. How much more did Lois's fish weigh?

(A) $\frac{1}{4}$ pound (B) $\frac{1}{8}$ pound

(C) $1\frac{1}{4}$ pounds (D) $2\frac{3}{4}$ pounds

(B) **17.** Subtract $10\frac{3}{16}$ from $18\frac{1}{2}$.

(A) $8\frac{11}{16}$ (B) $8\frac{5}{16}$ (C) $8\frac{1}{7}$ (D) $7\frac{5}{16}$

(C) **18.** $\frac{95}{100} + \frac{3}{10} - \frac{3}{5} = \blacksquare$

(A) $\frac{95}{105}$ (B) $\frac{75}{100}$ (C) $\frac{13}{20}$ (D) $\frac{11}{20}$

(B) **19.** $13\frac{1}{4} - 5$

(A) $7\frac{1}{4}$ (B) $8\frac{1}{4}$ (C) $8\frac{3}{4}$ (D) $9\frac{1}{4}$

(C) **20.** $29\frac{3}{8} - 9\frac{3}{4}$

(A) $9\frac{5}{8}$ (B) $18\frac{5}{8}$ (C) $19\frac{5}{8}$ (D) $20\frac{1}{2}$

(A) **21.** Subtract $4\frac{9}{10}$ from $12\frac{3}{10}$.

(A) $7\frac{2}{5}$ (B) $7\frac{3}{10}$ (C) $8\frac{2}{5}$ (D) $8\frac{3}{5}$

(C) **22.** Subtract: $15\frac{1}{4} - 7\frac{1}{3}$

(A) $8\frac{11}{12}$ (B) $8\frac{3}{4}$ (C) $7\frac{11}{12}$ (D) $7\frac{3}{4}$

Name _______________ Class _______ Date _______

3.14 PROBLEM SOLVING

Following directions correctly is very important on a standardized test.

Example 1: Here is a set of directions from a standardized test.

> Answer all 20 questions in this part. Write your answers on the lines provided in Part A on the separate answer sheet. Use only a black lead pencil on the answer sheet.

According to these instructions, you should:

Ⓐ Write your answers on the line below each question.

Ⓒ Use a red pen to mark your answers.

Ⓑ Write your answers on Part B of the answer sheet.

Ⓓ Use a black lead pencil to mark your answers.

- You may know the correct answer immediately. If not, read the directions again to find that the correct answer is choice Ⓓ.

Some test questions involve following a set of directions to find the answer.

Example 2: What is the sum of 10 consecutive odd numbers if 5 is the first odd number?

> To find the sum of 10 consecutive odd numbers:
>
> 1. Subtract 1 from the first number.
> 2. Multiply the result by 10.
> 3. Add 100.

Ⓐ 130 Ⓑ 140

Ⓒ 130 Ⓓ 160

- Follow the given steps.

1. The first number is 5. $5 - 1 = 4$
2. Multiply the result by 10. $4 \times 10 = 40$
3. Add 100. $40 + 100 = 140$

The correct answer is choice Ⓑ.

TEST DIRECTIONS

Work carefully and try to get as many questions right as you can. Do not spend too much time on any one question. If you do not know an answer, make the best choice you can and then go on to the next question.

Mark all of your answers on your answer sheet. Make your answer marks heavy and dark. Mark only one answer for each question. If you make a mistake or wish to change an answer, erase your first choice completely.

Whenever you come to a STOP sign in your test booklet, do not go any further until you are given directions. You may go back and check your work on that part of the test only. Make sure that the question number on the test and the answer number on your answer sheet are the same.

Use the directions above to answer the following questions.

Ⓑ **1.** Where should you mark your answers?

Ⓐ On a separate sheet of paper
Ⓑ On the answer sheet
Ⓒ To the left of each question
Ⓓ On the line under each question

Ⓓ **2.** What should you do if you do not know an answer?

Ⓐ Keep trying until you get the answer.
Ⓑ Ask for help.
Ⓒ Skip the question.
Ⓓ Make the best choice you can and go on.

Ⓐ **3.** If you make a mistake, you should

Ⓐ erase your first choice completely.
Ⓑ draw an × through your first choice.
Ⓒ ask for a new answer sheet.
Ⓓ use a red pencil to show your new answer.

Ⓒ **4.** Which of the following should you *not* do when you see a STOP sign?

Ⓐ Go back and check your work on that part of the test.
Ⓑ Wait for further directions.
Ⓒ Look at the next section.
Ⓓ Make sure that you have marked your answer sheet correctly.

Follow the instructions in the box at the right to answer the following questions.

1. Choose a number between 1 and 10.
2. Add 10 to the number.
3. If the sum is an even number, go to step 5.
   If the sum is an odd number, go to step 4.
4. Multiply by 3.
5. Divide the result by 2.
6. Write the answer.

Ⓒ **5.** Start with 5. What is the result?

Ⓐ 5 Ⓑ 7.5 Ⓒ 22.5 Ⓓ 45

Ⓑ **6.** Start with 8. What is the result?

Ⓐ 54 Ⓑ 9 Ⓒ 18 Ⓓ 27

Ⓒ **7.** Start with 2. What is the result?

Ⓐ 36 Ⓑ 18 Ⓒ 6 Ⓓ 2

Ⓑ **8.** Start with 9. What is the result?

Ⓐ 57 Ⓑ 28.5 Ⓒ 19 Ⓓ 9.5

Follow the directions in the box at the right for the following groups of numbers.

1. If the fraction is less than $\frac{1}{2}$, go to step 2.
   If the fraction is greater than $\frac{1}{2}$, go to step 3.
2. Multiply the fraction by its reciprocal. Go to step 4.
3. Divide the fraction by $\frac{1}{4}$. Go to step 5.
4. Add 4 to your answer.
5. Write the answer in lowest terms.

Ⓓ **9.** $\frac{1}{3}$

Ⓐ $\frac{1}{12}$ Ⓑ 4 Ⓒ $1\frac{1}{3}$ Ⓓ 5

Ⓒ **10.** $\frac{5}{6}$

Ⓐ 5 Ⓑ $\frac{5}{24}$ Ⓒ $3\frac{1}{3}$ Ⓓ 1

Ⓒ **11.** $\frac{3}{4}$

Ⓐ $\frac{3}{16}$ Ⓑ 1 Ⓒ 3 Ⓓ 5

Ⓐ **12.** $\frac{3}{8}$

Ⓐ 5 Ⓑ $\frac{3}{32}$ Ⓒ $1\frac{1}{2}$ Ⓓ 8

Name ______________________ Class ________ Date ____________

CHAPTER 3 TEST

Fill in the correct circle to answer each question.

(C) **1.** $\frac{3}{8} \times 6 =$

Ⓐ $6\frac{3}{8}$ Ⓑ 3 Ⓒ $2\frac{1}{4}$ Ⓓ $\frac{1}{16}$

(D) **2.** What is the mixed number for $\frac{19}{5}$?

Ⓐ $\frac{5}{19}$ Ⓑ $2\frac{4}{5}$ Ⓒ $3\frac{3}{5}$ Ⓓ $3\frac{4}{5}$

(A) **3.** $\frac{17}{100} + \frac{93}{100}$

Ⓐ $1\frac{1}{10}$ Ⓑ $1\frac{1}{100}$ Ⓒ 1 Ⓓ $\frac{11}{20}$

(D) **4.** $5\frac{3}{4} - 2\frac{5}{6}$

Ⓐ $8\frac{7}{12}$ Ⓑ $3\frac{11}{12}$ Ⓒ $2\frac{1}{12}$ Ⓓ $2\frac{11}{12}$

(D) **5.** The reciprocal of $\frac{3}{6}$ is

Ⓐ $\frac{1}{2}$ Ⓑ $\frac{3}{6}$ Ⓒ 18 Ⓓ $\frac{6}{3}$

(A) **6.** Which fraction is between $\frac{1}{4}$ and $\frac{1}{2}$?

Ⓐ $\frac{1}{3}$ Ⓑ $\frac{2}{3}$ Ⓒ $\frac{1}{6}$ Ⓓ $\frac{1}{8}$

(A) **7.** $8 \div \frac{3}{8} =$

Ⓐ $21\frac{1}{3}$ Ⓑ 18 Ⓒ 3 Ⓓ $\frac{3}{64}$

(C) **8.** Compare: $\frac{1}{4}$ ■ $\frac{16}{24}$

Ⓐ = Ⓑ > Ⓒ <

(C) **9.** $1\frac{1}{2} \times 2\frac{1}{4} =$

Ⓐ $2\frac{1}{8}$ Ⓑ $3\frac{1}{3}$ Ⓒ $3\frac{3}{8}$ Ⓓ $3\frac{3}{4}$

(D) **10.** $4\frac{2}{3} + 4\frac{2}{3} =$ ■

Ⓐ 0 Ⓑ $8\frac{1}{3}$ Ⓒ $8\frac{2}{3}$ Ⓓ $9\frac{1}{3}$

(A) **11.** Order $\frac{7}{10}$, $\frac{1}{2}$, and $\frac{3}{4}$ from *greatest to least.*

Ⓐ $\frac{3}{4}, \frac{7}{10}, \frac{1}{2}$ Ⓑ $\frac{3}{4}, \frac{1}{2}, \frac{7}{10}$

Ⓒ $\frac{7}{10}, \frac{3}{4}, \frac{1}{2}$ Ⓓ $\frac{1}{2}, \frac{7}{10}, \frac{3}{4}$

(D) **12.** What is the difference between $9\frac{7}{11}$ and $6\frac{3}{11}$?

Ⓐ $15\frac{10}{11}$ Ⓑ $15\frac{5}{11}$ Ⓒ $4\frac{4}{11}$ Ⓓ $3\frac{4}{11}$

(D) **13.** What is $\frac{3}{10}$ of 60?

Ⓐ $\frac{1}{200}$ Ⓑ $\frac{1}{20}$

Ⓒ $6\frac{3}{10}$ Ⓓ 18

(C) **14.** $\frac{2}{9}$ and $\frac{6}{27}$ are ■.

Ⓐ reciprocals Ⓑ mixed numbers

Ⓒ equivalent fractions Ⓓ improper fractions

(C) **15.** $\frac{5}{6} + \frac{1}{4} + \frac{4}{9} =$

Ⓐ $\frac{10}{19}$ Ⓑ $1\frac{1}{2}$ Ⓒ $1\frac{19}{36}$ Ⓓ $1\frac{5}{9}$

(C) **16.** $\frac{5}{6} + \frac{1}{4} - \frac{4}{9} =$ ■

Ⓐ 2 Ⓑ $\frac{1}{2}$ Ⓒ $\frac{23}{36}$ Ⓓ $\frac{4}{9}$

(D) **17.** $5\frac{2}{5} \div \frac{2}{5} =$

Ⓐ $\frac{2}{27}$ Ⓑ $5\frac{2}{5}$ Ⓒ $2\frac{4}{25}$ Ⓓ $13\frac{1}{2}$

(B) **18.** Subtract $\frac{2}{7}$ from $\frac{6}{7}$.

Ⓐ $\frac{3}{7}$ Ⓑ $\frac{4}{7}$ Ⓒ $\frac{5}{7}$ Ⓓ $1\frac{1}{7}$

Ⓐ **19.** What is the least common multiple (LCM) of 3, 6, and 9?

Ⓐ 18 Ⓑ 9 Ⓒ 6 Ⓓ 3

Ⓒ **20.** $6 \times \frac{4}{9} = ■$

Ⓐ $6\frac{4}{9}$ Ⓑ $3\frac{1}{3}$ Ⓒ $2\frac{2}{3}$ Ⓓ $\frac{2}{27}$

Ⓑ **21.** The greatest common factor (GCF) of 15 and 60 is ■.

Ⓐ 60 Ⓑ 15 Ⓒ 5 Ⓓ 3

Ⓒ **22.** $\frac{2}{9} \div \frac{8}{15} =$

Ⓐ $\frac{135}{16}$ Ⓑ $\frac{12}{5}$ Ⓒ $\frac{5}{12}$ Ⓓ $\frac{16}{135}$

Ⓒ **23.** Derek is making a picket fence to border his garden. Each picket will be $1\frac{1}{2}$ ft long. How many pickets can Derek cut from a board that is 9 ft long?

Ⓐ $13\frac{1}{2}$ Ⓑ 8 Ⓒ 6 Ⓓ $5\frac{1}{3}$

Ⓑ **24.** There are $8\frac{5}{8}$ yd of red velvet. Ada measures and then cuts $4\frac{1}{2}$ yd of the velvet. How many yards of red velvet are left?

Ⓐ $3\frac{1}{8}$ yd Ⓑ $4\frac{1}{8}$ yd Ⓒ $4\frac{1}{2}$ yd Ⓓ $13\frac{1}{8}$ yd

Ⓑ **25.** A turkey weighs $18\frac{1}{2}$ lb. It will need to be cooked $\frac{1}{3}$ h for each pound. For how many hours should the turkey be cooked?

Ⓐ $5\frac{5}{6}$ Ⓑ $6\frac{1}{6}$ Ⓒ $6\frac{1}{3}$ Ⓓ $13\frac{7}{8}$

Ⓐ **26.** Bella plans to make 2 cakes. The carrot cake calls for $3\frac{3}{4}$ c of flour. The chocolate cake needs $2\frac{1}{2}$ c flour. What is the total amount of flour Bella will need?

Ⓐ $6\frac{1}{4}$ c Ⓑ 6 c Ⓒ $5\frac{1}{4}$ c Ⓒ $1\frac{1}{4}$ c

Ⓑ **27.** Solve for *n*: $\frac{n}{49} = \frac{5}{7}$

Ⓐ 47 Ⓑ 35 Ⓒ 30 Ⓓ 25

Ⓐ **28.** $\frac{1}{2}$ ■ $\frac{7}{15}$

Ⓐ > Ⓑ < Ⓒ =

Ⓓ **29.** Subtract: $5 - 4\frac{8}{9}$

Ⓐ $9\frac{8}{9}$ Ⓑ $1\frac{8}{9}$ Ⓒ $1\frac{1}{9}$ Ⓓ $\frac{1}{9}$

Ⓒ **30.** $2\frac{3}{8} \div 4\frac{3}{4} =$

Ⓐ 2 Ⓑ $\frac{13}{22}$ Ⓒ $\frac{1}{2}$ Ⓓ $\frac{32}{361}$

Ⓒ **31.** $\frac{21}{50} + \frac{8}{35}$

Ⓐ $\frac{29}{85}$ Ⓑ $\frac{207}{350}$ Ⓒ $\frac{227}{350}$ Ⓓ $\frac{22}{25}$

Ⓑ **32.** $\frac{9}{10} - \frac{1}{6}$

Ⓐ $\frac{2}{15}$ Ⓑ $\frac{11}{15}$ Ⓒ $\frac{7}{10}$ Ⓓ 2

Use Table 1 to answer question 33.

Ⓐ **33.** Who ran the greatest distance?

Ⓐ Judy Ⓑ Doug

Ⓒ Leon Ⓓ Lee

Table 1

River City Run	
Leon: $2\frac{5}{8}$ mi	Judy: $2\frac{4}{5}$ mi
Doug: $2\frac{6}{10}$ mi	Lee: $2\frac{2}{3}$ mi

Name______________________ Class ________ Date ____________

CHAPTERS 1-3 CUMULATIVE REVIEW

Fill in the correct circle to answer each question.

(C) **1.** What is the *place value* of 3 in 278,310?

Ⓐ ten thousands Ⓑ thousands
Ⓒ hundreds Ⓓ tens

(B) **2.** What is the difference between 7069 and 6178?

Ⓐ 991 Ⓑ 891
Ⓒ 881 Ⓓ 871

(C) **3.** 0.783 + 27.91 = ■

Ⓐ 25.74 Ⓑ 28.692
Ⓒ 28.693 Ⓓ 28.703

(D) **4.** 17,821 ÷ 100 = ■

Ⓐ 1,782,100 Ⓑ 178,210
Ⓒ 1782.1 Ⓓ 178.21

(C) **5.** Write $5\frac{3}{4}$ as an improper fraction.

Ⓐ $\frac{15}{4}$ Ⓑ $\frac{20}{4}$ Ⓒ $\frac{23}{4}$ Ⓓ $\frac{20}{3}$

(A) **6.** Add $7\frac{1}{4}$ and $2\frac{3}{4}$.

Ⓐ 10 Ⓑ $9\frac{3}{4}$ Ⓒ $9\frac{1}{4}$ Ⓓ $\frac{38}{4}$

(A) **7.** What property is shown?
$12 \times (1 + 3) = (12 \times 1) + (12 \times 3)$

Ⓐ Distributive Ⓑ Associative
Ⓒ Commutative Ⓓ Property of 1

(A) **8.** $678 \times 239 =$ ■

Ⓐ 162,042 Ⓑ 162,012
Ⓒ 161,042 Ⓓ 41,802

(A) **9.** Steven bought a new tennis racquet, shoes, and a can of tennis balls. The items cost $59.95, $20.00 and $4.95. What was the total cost?

Ⓐ $84.90 Ⓑ $85.90 Ⓒ $129.45 Ⓓ $129.50

(B) **10.** Jennifer bought 3 pairs of socks for $4.95. How much did one pair cost?

Ⓐ $1.68 Ⓑ $1.65 Ⓒ $0.93 Ⓓ $0.83

(A) **11.** Order from *least to greatest:* $\frac{3}{7}, \frac{5}{12}, \frac{1}{3}$

Ⓐ $\frac{1}{3}, \frac{5}{12}, \frac{3}{7}$ Ⓑ $\frac{1}{3}, \frac{3}{7}, \frac{5}{12}$
Ⓒ $\frac{3}{7}, \frac{1}{3}, \frac{5}{12}$ Ⓓ $\frac{3}{7}, \frac{5}{12}, \frac{1}{3}$

(B) **12.** Multiply: 46.31×7.2

Ⓐ 324.432 Ⓑ 333.432
Ⓒ 333.442 Ⓓ 334.432

(C) **13.** Round 738,750 to the nearest *hundred.*

Ⓐ 800,000 Ⓑ 739,000
Ⓒ 738,800 Ⓓ 738,700

(B) **14.** 28,910 ÷ 11 = ■

Ⓐ $2629\frac{2}{11}$ Ⓑ 2628 R 2
Ⓒ 262 R 8 Ⓓ $255\frac{4}{11}$

(D) **15.** What is the *value* of 5 in 5328.071?

Ⓐ 50,000 Ⓑ thousands
Ⓒ thousandths Ⓓ 5000

(A) **16.** Find the difference: 1.0782 – 0.9835

Ⓐ 0.0947 Ⓑ 0.0957 Ⓒ 0.1047 Ⓓ 8.7568

(B) **17.** Estimate the sum: 2681 + 72,445 + 9369.

Ⓐ 18,000 Ⓑ 84,000 Ⓒ 96,000 Ⓓ 165,000

(C) **18.** Find the quotient of 795 and 5.

Ⓐ 157 Ⓑ 158 Ⓒ 159 Ⓓ 179

(B) **19.** Add: 7.39 + 25.6 + 0.031

Ⓐ 10.26 Ⓑ 33.021 Ⓒ 33.30 Ⓓ 99.81

(D) **20.** Add $\frac{3}{7}$ and $\frac{5}{8}$.

Ⓐ $\frac{29}{28}$ Ⓑ 1 Ⓒ $\frac{58}{56}$ Ⓓ $1\frac{3}{56}$

Use Table 1 to answer questions 21–24.

Table 1

Annual Per Capita Consumption of Selected Foods			
Meat	Pounds	Poultry	Pounds
Beef	79.1	Fish	15.2
Veal	1.6	Eggs	33.8
Lamb	1.5	Chicken	57.1
Pork	59.7	Turkey	12.0

(B) **21.** How many pounds of meat would ten people eat in one year?

(A) 141.9 (B) 1419 (C) 1571 (D) 2600

(C) **22.** In one year, how much more chicken than fish would one person eat?

(A) 2.6 lb (B) 31.9 lb (C) 41.9 lb (D) 72.3 lb

(A) **23.** List from *least to greatest* the annual per capita consumption of beef, fish, chicken, and turkey.

(A) 12.0, 15.2, 57.1, 79.1

(B) 79.1, 59.7, 15.2, 12.0

(C) 12.0, 15.2, 57.1, 141.9

(D) 15.2, 33.8, 57.1, 79.1

(B) **24.** Rounded to the nearest *pound*, what is the total annual per capita consumption of the four types of meat?

(A) 140 lb (B) 142 lb (C) 145 lb (D) 150 lb

(C) **25.** Which fraction is equivalent to $\frac{2}{3}$?

(A) $\frac{7}{22}$ (B) $\frac{8}{24}$ (C) $\frac{18}{27}$ (D) $\frac{6}{12}$

(D) **26.** $\frac{3}{2} + \frac{1}{6} - \frac{2}{3} = \blacksquare$

(A) $\frac{2}{5}$ (B) $2\frac{1}{3}$ (C) $\frac{14}{12}$ (D) 1

(D) **27.** What is $\frac{2}{5}$ of 65?

(A) $\frac{325}{2}$ (B) 25 (C) $\frac{120}{5}$ (D) 26

(A) **28.** Subtract $\frac{7}{8}$ from $\frac{13}{10}$.

(A) $\frac{17}{40}$ (B) $\frac{27}{40}$ (C) $\frac{3}{10}$ (D) $\frac{91}{80}$

(C) **29.** Add:

$$\begin{array}{r} 728{,}916 \\ 52{,}783 \\ +154{,}030 \\ \hline \end{array}$$

(A) 934,729 (B) 935,629 (C) 935,729 (D) 935,739

(B) **30.** Subtract:

$$\begin{array}{r} 98{,}003 \\ -\quad 786 \\ \hline \end{array}$$

(A) 97,216 (B) 97,217 (C) 97,227 (D) 98.217

(D) **31.** What is the *place value* of 3 in 2.013?

(A) thousands (B) hundredths

(C) 0.003 (D) thousandths

(C) **32.** What is the quotient of 44.984 and 2.0?

(A) 32.76 (B) 26.0 (C) 22.492 (D) 2.276

(A) **33.** Compare: $\frac{11}{16} \blacksquare \frac{13}{16}$

(A) < (B) > (C) =

(D) **34.** Divide: $3\frac{1}{3} \div \frac{7}{9}$

(A) 3 (B) $\frac{70}{27}$ (C) $\frac{30}{8}$ (D) $4\frac{2}{7}$

(C) **35.** Nathan was considering buying a used car. The price was $2750. It needed two new tires that cost $35 each, and a tune-up costing $85. How much should Nathan plan on spending?

(A) $2630 (B) $2870 (C) $2905 (D) $2595

(B) **36.** Mrs. Saunders had $50. She wanted to buy some new tools. A hammer cost $12, a set of screwdrivers was $7, and an electric drill was on sale for $24. How much money would she have left if she bought the drill?

(A) $7 (B) $26 (C) $24 (D) $43

(C) **37.** $3^2 \times 1^4 = \blacksquare$

(A) 24 (B) 10 (C) 9 (D) 36

(A) **38.** $7\frac{2}{3} \times 1 = \blacksquare$

(A) $7\frac{2}{3}$ (B) $8\frac{2}{3}$ (C) $\frac{25}{3}$ (D) 1

Name ______________________ Class __________ Date __________

(D) **39.** What is the sum of $\frac{17}{3}$ and 1?

Ⓐ $\frac{17}{3}$ Ⓑ $\frac{21}{3}$ Ⓒ 6 Ⓓ $6\frac{2}{3}$

(C) **40.** Compare: 721,983 ■ 1,112,924

Ⓐ = Ⓑ $>$ Ⓒ $<$

(A) **41.** Estimate the product of 2798 and 49.

Ⓐ 150,000 Ⓑ 3050
Ⓒ 1500 Ⓓ 60

(D) **42.** The numeral for three hundred thousand five hundred seventy.

Ⓐ 305,070 Ⓑ 305,470
Ⓒ 375,400 Ⓓ 300,570

(B) **43.** What are the factors of 21?

Ⓐ 1,2,3,7 Ⓑ 1,3,7,21
Ⓒ 0,1,3,7,21 Ⓓ 3,7

(B) **44.** What is the least common multiple of 4 and 6?

Ⓐ 2 Ⓑ 12
Ⓒ 16 Ⓓ 24

(A) **45.** Subtract: $\frac{7}{15} - \frac{1}{5}$

Ⓐ $\frac{4}{15}$ Ⓑ $\frac{1}{3}$ Ⓒ $\frac{6}{15}$ Ⓓ $\frac{3}{5}$

(C) **46.** Which one of the following statements is *true*?

Ⓐ $38.1 > 111.0$ Ⓑ $67.1 < 9.795$
Ⓒ $0.215 > 0.099$ Ⓓ $99.9 > 222$

Use the temperature data to complete Table 2. (For example, at 2 P.M. it was 23° + 14° = 37°.) Then answer questions 47–50.

(D) **47.** What is the difference between the highest and lowest temperatures for the period?

Ⓐ 10° Ⓑ 14° Ⓒ 16° Ⓓ 20°

Table 2

Temperature Chart		
Time	Temp.	Change from Previous Temp.
12 P.M.	23°	
2 P.M.	**37°**	+14°
4 P.M.		+6°
6 P.M.	43°	
8 P.M.		−10°
10 P.M.	39°	

(B) **48.** Between 4 P.M. and 6 P.M. the temperature:

Ⓐ fell for the first time. Ⓑ stayed the same.
Ⓒ rose 6°. Ⓓ reached a high.

(D) **49.** Give the best plan for finding the average for the period.

Ⓐ Order temperatures to find a median (middle) value.

Ⓑ Combine high and low temperatures; divide by 2.

Ⓒ Add temperatures after 12 P.M.; divide by 5.

Ⓓ Add all 6 temperatures; divide by 6.

(C) **50.** When was the temperature lower than it was at 2 P.M.?

Ⓐ 12 P.M. only Ⓑ 12 P.M. and 4 P.M.
Ⓒ 12 P.M. and 8 P.M. Ⓓ 12 P.M., 4 P.M., and 8 P.M.

(D) **51.** What is the reciprocal of $\frac{20}{3}$?

Ⓐ $\frac{60}{9}$ Ⓑ 1 Ⓒ $6\frac{2}{3}$ Ⓓ $\frac{3}{20}$

(A) **52.** $\frac{3}{4} + \frac{2}{5} =$ ■

Ⓐ $1\frac{3}{20}$ Ⓑ $1\frac{1}{10}$ Ⓒ $\frac{5}{9}$ Ⓓ $\frac{6}{20}$

(B) **53.** What is the word name for 70,617?

Ⓐ seventy thousand six hundred seventy

Ⓑ seventy thousand six hundred seventeen

Ⓒ seventy thousand and six hundred seventeen

Ⓓ seventy thousand sixty one seven

(B) **54.** Estimate the difference between 9850 and 7059.

Ⓐ 17,000

Ⓑ 3000

Ⓒ 2000

Ⓓ 1000

Ⓒ **55.** Round 489.075 to the nearest *hundredth*.

Ⓐ 490 Ⓑ 489.07 Ⓒ 489.08 Ⓓ 500

Ⓑ **56.** Find ■: 4 + ■ = 16

Ⓐ 64 Ⓑ 12 Ⓒ 4 Ⓓ 2

Ⓒ **57.** $29.83 \times 0.19 =$ ■

Ⓐ 56.677 Ⓑ 29.849
Ⓒ 5.6677 Ⓓ 5.6657

Ⓑ **58.** $5\frac{3}{4} + 3\frac{1}{4} =$ ■

Ⓐ 9 Ⓑ $8\frac{3}{4}$ Ⓒ $2\frac{1}{2}$ Ⓓ $1\frac{1}{2}$

Ⓑ **59.** Compare: $\frac{7}{11}$ ■ $\frac{5}{8}$

Ⓐ < Ⓑ > Ⓒ =

Ⓐ **60.** $17 \div \frac{1}{2} =$ ■

Ⓐ 34 Ⓑ $9\frac{1}{2}$ Ⓒ 8 R 2 Ⓓ $8\frac{1}{2}$

Ⓐ **61.** What property is shown? $a + b = b + a$

Ⓐ Commutative Ⓑ Associative
Ⓒ Distributive Ⓓ Property of 1

Ⓒ **62.** $377 \div 13 =$ ■

Ⓐ 4901 Ⓑ 31 R 4
Ⓒ 29 Ⓓ 29 R 6

Ⓐ **63.** Mr. Woodsum ordered a hamburger and fries for $3.15 and a cup of coffee for 65¢. How much was his bill?

Ⓐ $3.80 Ⓑ $3.70 Ⓒ $3.22 Ⓓ $2.50

Ⓓ **64.** $52.755 \div 1.5 =$ ■

Ⓐ 3.511 Ⓑ 3.517
Ⓒ 35.11 Ⓓ 35.17

Ⓒ **65.** $2\frac{2}{5} \div \frac{2}{7} =$ ■

Ⓐ $6\frac{3}{10}$ Ⓑ $\frac{24}{35}$ Ⓒ $8\frac{2}{5}$ Ⓓ $\frac{5}{42}$

Ⓐ **66.** Which fraction is between $\frac{1}{3}$ and $\frac{2}{5}$?

Ⓐ $\frac{3}{8}$ Ⓑ $\frac{3}{15}$ Ⓒ $\frac{1}{5}$ Ⓓ $\frac{2}{3}$

Ⓑ **67.** Write 278,900 in scientific notation.

Ⓐ 278×900
Ⓑ 2.789×10^5
Ⓒ 2.78×10^5
Ⓓ 2.789×10^6

Ⓑ **68.** Which expression demonstrates the Multiplication Property of 1?

Ⓐ $3 + 1 = 1 + 3$
Ⓑ $3 \times 1 = 3$
Ⓒ $(3 + 2) \times 1 = (3 \times 1) + (2 \times 1)$
Ⓓ $(3 \times 2) \times 1 = 3 \times (2 \times 1)$

Ⓑ **69.** $9444 \div 12 =$ ■

Ⓐ 78 R 8 Ⓑ 787
Ⓒ 793 R 8 Ⓓ 837

Ⓑ **70.** What is the *value* of 3 in 701.23?

Ⓐ hundredths Ⓑ 0.03
Ⓒ tenths Ⓓ 0.01

Ⓒ **71.** Find the product: 2.1×783

Ⓐ 165.43 Ⓑ 234.9 Ⓒ 1644.3 Ⓓ 1664.3

Ⓒ **72.** $80 \times \frac{3}{4} =$ ■

Ⓐ 78 Ⓑ 66 Ⓒ 60 Ⓓ $\frac{1}{60}$

Ⓐ **73.** $5\frac{1}{4} - 2\frac{3}{4} =$ ■

Ⓐ $2\frac{1}{2}$ Ⓑ $2\frac{3}{4}$ Ⓒ $3\frac{1}{2}$ Ⓓ 8

Ⓑ **74.** Samatha Jones had 12 pencils at the start of school year. She had 2 left in June. How many pencils did she use?

Ⓐ 2 pencils Ⓑ 10 pencils
Ⓒ 12 pencils Ⓓ 14 pencils

Name ______________________ Class __________ Date __________

CHAPTER 4: MEASUREMENT

TEST-TAKING STRATEGY: *Use Your Time Efficiently*

To get your best test score, you must answer correctly as many questions as you can. To do this you must use your time efficiently. You can use this plan.

1. Read each question and work on those you **know** you can do first.
2. Next, do each question you **think** you can do.
3. With the time that is left, try the **most difficult** questions.

You can budget your time by finding how long each problem should take, on average.

Caution: If a question takes much longer than the time it should, and it is giving you trouble, stop work on it until you have finished the rest of the test.

You can get good at "using your time efficiently" by taking practice tests and timing yourself.

Example 1: A 30-minute test has 60 questions. How much time can you spend on each question?

$$\frac{\text{time}}{\text{question}} = \frac{\text{total time for test}}{\text{number of questions}} = \frac{30}{60} = \frac{1}{2}$$

You should spend about $\frac{1}{2}$ minute on each question.

How much time should you spend on each test item? Fill in the correct circle to answer each question.

Ⓑ **1.** A 6 item test is to take 18 minutes.

Ⓐ $\frac{1}{3}$ minute Ⓑ 3 minutes

Ⓒ 6 minutes Ⓓ 18 minutes

Ⓒ **2.** A 25-minute test has 20 items.

Ⓐ 48 seconds Ⓑ 1 minute

Ⓒ 1.25 minutes Ⓓ 5 minutes

Ⓐ **3.** A 20-minute test has 50 items.

Ⓐ 24 seconds Ⓑ 2 minutes

Ⓒ $2\frac{1}{2}$ minutes Ⓓ 10 minutes

Ⓐ **4.** A 30-item test is to last 20 minutes.

Ⓐ 40 seconds Ⓑ $1\frac{1}{2}$ minutes

Ⓒ 2 minutes Ⓓ 3 minutes

Time yourself. Answer the following 20 questions in 24 minutes.

Ⓒ **5.** How much time should you spend on each question?

Ⓐ 24 minutes Ⓑ 6 minutes

Ⓒ 1 minute 12 seconds Ⓓ 50 seconds

Ⓒ **6.** The number named by 0.008 is ▇ .

Ⓐ eight Ⓑ thousandths

Ⓒ eight thousandths Ⓓ eight hundredths

(C) **7.** Order 0.27, 0.26 and 0.62 from *greatest to least.*

(A) 0.26; 0.27; 0.62 (B) 0.27; 0.26; 0.62

(C) 0.62, 0.27; 0.26 (D) 0.62; 0.26; 0.27

(B) **8.** Round 247.469 to the nearest *whole number.*

(A) 200 (B) 247

(C) 248 (D) 250

(C) **9.** 67.31 + 316.7 = ■

(A) 9.898 (B) 98.98 (C) 384.01 (D) 989.8

(D) **10.** 54.37 – 26.37 = ■

(A) 80.74 (B) 80.64 (C) 32 (D) 28

(C) **11.** $12.175 \times 2.5 =$ ■

(A) 3.04375 (B) 14.675

(C) 30.4375 (D) 304.375

(B) **12.** $1.26 \div 0.18 =$ ■

(A) 0.7 (B) 7

(C) 70 (D) 700

(A) **13.** Divide 7.26 by 1000.

(A) 0.00726 (B) 0.726

(C) 726 (D) 7260

(C) **14.** Write 5.37×10^4 in standard form.

(A) 5.37 (B) 537

(C) 53,700 (D) 5,370,000

(B) **15.** Find all the factors of 20.

(A) 1,2,4,5,10 (B) 1,2,4,5,10,20

(C) 2,4,5,10 (D) 2,4,5,10,20

(D) **16.** The *value* of the digit 7 in 0.070 is

(A) seven (B) seven tenths

(C) hundredths (D) seven hundredths

(D) **17.** Add: $\frac{2}{5} + \frac{4}{3}$

(A) $\frac{3}{4}$ (B) $\frac{6}{8}$ (C) $\frac{8}{15}$ (D) $1\frac{11}{15}$

(C) **18.** Multiply: $\frac{2}{5} \times \frac{4}{3}$

(A) $\frac{3}{4}$ (B) $\frac{6}{8}$ (C) $\frac{8}{15}$ (D) $\frac{26}{15}$

(A) **19.** Subtract: $1\frac{5}{6} - \frac{7}{8}$

(A) $\frac{23}{24}$ (B) $1\frac{1}{24}$ (C) $1\frac{23}{24}$ (D) $2\frac{17}{24}$

(B) **20.** Divide: $\frac{5}{6} \div \frac{7}{8}$

(A) $\frac{35}{48}$ (B) $\frac{20}{21}$ (C) $\frac{21}{20}$ (D) $1\frac{17}{24}$

(C) **21.** The center of the Comet's basketball team is $71\frac{1}{4}$ inches tall. The center of the Planet's team is $68\frac{3}{4}$ inches tall. How much taller is the Comet's center?

(A) $3\frac{1}{2}$ in. (B) 3 in.

(C) $2\frac{1}{2}$ in. (D) 2 in.

(B) **22.** Juan decided to wallpaper a room in his house. He estimated that the 4 walls would take the following amount of wallpaper: $4\frac{1}{4}$ rolls, $2\frac{3}{4}$ rolls, $4\frac{3}{4}$ rolls and $1\frac{3}{8}$ rolls. How many rolls does he need for the entire room?

(A) 14 rolls (B) $13\frac{1}{8}$ rolls

(C) 13 rolls (D) $11\frac{5}{4}$ rolls

(D) **23.** Maria drove for $3\frac{3}{4}$ hours and averaged 60 miles per hour. How many miles did she drive?

(A) 2250 miles (B) 16 miles

(C) 180 miles (D) 225 miles

(D) **24.** George is putting molding around his room. The total amount of wood is 48 feet. He plans to put a decoration every $\frac{3}{4}$ foot. How many decorations will he need?

(A) 36 decorations (B) $47\frac{1}{4}$ decorations

(C) $48\frac{3}{4}$ decorations (D) 64 decorations

Name ____________________ Class __________ Date ______________

CHAPTER 4 PRETEST

Fill in the correct circle to answer each question.

(D) **1.** Round 2.364 to the nearest *tenth.*

(A) 2 (B) 2.36 (C) 2.3 (D) 2.4

(A) **2.** Round 36.78 to the nearest *whole number.*

(A) 37 (B) 36 (C) 36.8 (D) 40

(C) **3.** Round 16.804 to the nearest *tenth.*

(A) 17 (B) 16.9 (C) 16.8 (D) 16

(B) **4.** Round 7.12 to the nearest *whole number.*

(A) 6 (B) 7 (C) 8 (D) 7.1

(D) **5.** $123 \times 100 =$ ■

(A) 1.23 (B) 12.3 (C) 1230 (D) 12,300

(B) **6.** $0.56 \times 100 =$ ■

(A) 5.6 (B) 56 (C) 560 (D) 5600

(C) **7.** $897 \div 1000 =$ ■

(A) 897,000 (B) 89,700
(C) 0.897 (D) 0.00897

(A) **8.** $73.2 \div 100 =$ ■

(A) 0.732 (B) 7.32
(C) 73.2 (D) 732

(C) **9.** Multiply: 12×5

(A) 48 (B) 50 (C) 60 (D) 72

(D) **10.** Multiply: 16×3

(A) 19 (B) 32 (C) 38 (D) 48

(A) **11.** $37 \times 12 =$ ■

(A) 444 (B) 111 (C) 49 (D) 25

(B) **12.** $285 \div 3 =$ ■

(A) 85 (B) 95 (C) 105 (D) 288

(D) **13.** Divide and write the remainder as a fraction in simplest form: $40 \div 12$

(A) 34 (B) 3 R 4 (C) $3\frac{4}{12}$ (D) $3\frac{1}{3}$

(C) **14.** Divide and write the remainder as a fraction in simplest form: $440 \div 60$

(A) $70\frac{1}{3}$ (B) 7 R 20 (C) $7\frac{1}{3}$ (D) $7\frac{20}{60}$

(A) **15.** $3\frac{1}{2} \div 5 =$ ■

(A) $\frac{7}{10}$ (B) $1\frac{3}{7}$ (C) $8\frac{1}{2}$ (D) $17\frac{1}{2}$

(C) **16.** $9 \times \frac{3}{4} =$ ■

(A) 12 (B) $7\frac{3}{4}$ (C) $6\frac{3}{4}$ (D) $6\frac{1}{4}$

(C) **17.** Add: $13 + 8 + 9$

(A) 20 (B) 29 (C) 30 (D) 40

(C) **18.** Subtract: $127 - 89$

(A) 48 (B) 42 (C) 38 (D) 32

(D) **19.** Add: $\begin{array}{r} 5280 \\ +5280 \\ \hline \end{array}$

(A) 1056 (B) 10,460
(C) 10,550 (D) 10,560

(B) **20.** Subtract: $\begin{array}{r} 60 \\ -32 \\ \hline \end{array}$

(A) 22 (B) 28 (C) 38 (D) 92

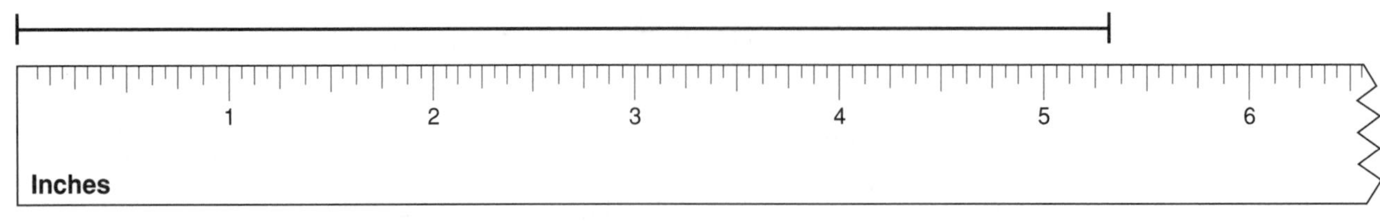

Figure 1

Use Figure 1 to answer questions 21-22.

Ⓑ **21.** To the nearest *quarter-inch*, the line segment is ■ inches long.

Ⓐ 5 Ⓑ $5\frac{1}{4}$ Ⓒ $5\frac{1}{2}$ Ⓓ $5\frac{3}{4}$

Ⓐ **22.** To the nearest *inch*, the line segment is ■ inches long.

Ⓐ 5 Ⓑ $5\frac{1}{4}$ Ⓒ $5\frac{1}{2}$ Ⓓ 6

Ⓑ **23.** 2 weeks = ■ days

Ⓐ 10 Ⓑ 14 Ⓒ 15 Ⓓ 21

Ⓒ **24.** 7 yd = ■ ft

Ⓐ $\frac{3}{7}$ Ⓑ $2\frac{1}{3}$ Ⓒ 21 Ⓓ 84

Ⓓ **25.** Subtract 7h 35min from 9h 25min.

Ⓐ 3 h Ⓑ 2h 10min
Ⓒ 1h 90min Ⓓ 1h 50min

Ⓒ **26.** Add 6lb 14oz and 5lb 11oz.

Ⓐ 11lb 25oz Ⓑ 12lb 11oz
Ⓒ 12lb 9oz Ⓓ 13lb 5oz

Ⓐ **27.** 12 kg = ■ g

Ⓐ 12,000 Ⓑ 1200 Ⓒ 0.12 D. 0.012

Ⓐ **28.** It is 4:15 P.M. What time will it be in 9 hours?

Ⓐ 1:15 A.M. Ⓑ 3:15 A.M.
Ⓒ 13:15 A.M. Ⓓ 1:15 P.M.

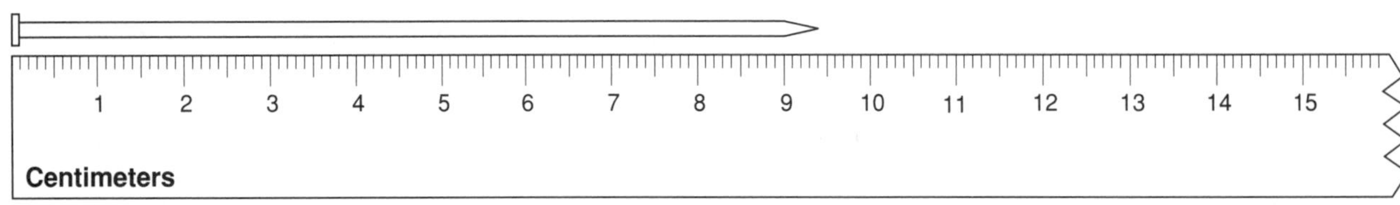

Figure 2

Use Figure 2 to answer question 29.

Ⓐ **29.** To the nearest cm this nail is ■ cm long.

Ⓐ 9 Ⓑ 9.4 Ⓒ 90 Ⓓ 94

Ⓐ **30.** 235 cm = ■ m

Ⓐ 2.35 Ⓑ 23.5 Ⓒ 2350 Ⓓ 23,500

Ⓑ **31.** 15,000 mL = ■ L

Ⓐ 1.5 Ⓑ 15 Ⓒ 150 Ⓓ 1500

Ⓒ **32.** 2 yd = ■ in

Ⓐ 2.3 Ⓑ 36 Ⓒ 72 Ⓓ 84

Ⓓ **33.** Kerry left her house at 7:50 A.M. She walked to school and arrived at 8:25 A.M. How long did her walk to school take?

Ⓐ 1h 35min Ⓑ 55 min Ⓒ 25 min Ⓓ 35 min

Name____________________ Class ________ Date __________

4.1 CUSTOMARY UNITS OF LENGTH

12 inches (in)	=	1 foot (ft)
36 in	=	1 yard (yd)
3 ft	=	1 yd
5280 ft	=	1 mile (mi)

Example 1: 8 yd = ▩ ft

1 yd = 3 ft • Determine the conversion factor: 3

$8 \times 3 = 24$ • Multiply since you are changing to smaller units.

8 yd = 24 ft

Example 2: Add 2 ft 7 in and 3 ft 9 in.

$$\begin{array}{r} 2\text{ ft}\ \ 7\text{ in} \\ +\ 3\text{ ft}\ \ 9\text{ in} \\ \hline 5\text{ ft}\ 16\text{ in} \end{array}$$

16 in is longer than one foot. Therefore, rename: 16 in = 1 ft 4 in

5 ft 16 in = 5 ft + 1 ft 4 in
= 6 ft 4 in

Example 3: Subtract 6 ft 8 in from 10 ft 3 in.

$$\begin{array}{r} \overset{9}{\cancel{10}}\text{ ft}\ \ \overset{15}{\cancel{3}}\text{ in} \\ -\ 6\text{ ft}\ \ 8\text{ in} \\ \hline 3\text{ ft}\ \ 7\text{ in} \end{array}$$

You can't subtract 8 in from 3 in. Therefore, rename:
10 ft 3 in. = 9 ft + 1 ft +3 in
= 9 ft + 12 in +3 in
= 9 ft + 15 in

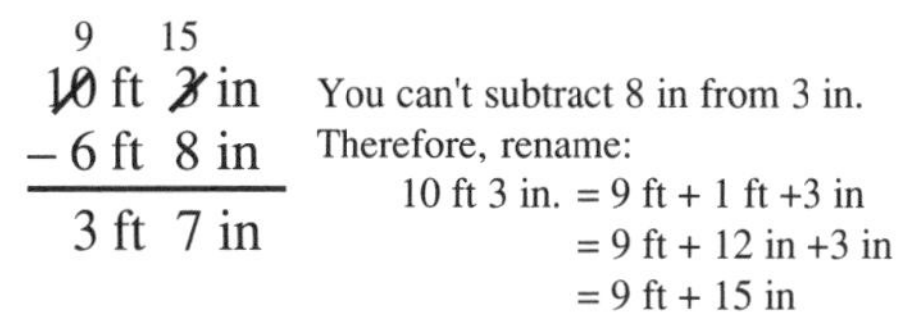

Example 4: Find the length of the segment to the nearest $\frac{1}{2}$, $\frac{1}{4}$ and $\frac{1}{8}$ inch.

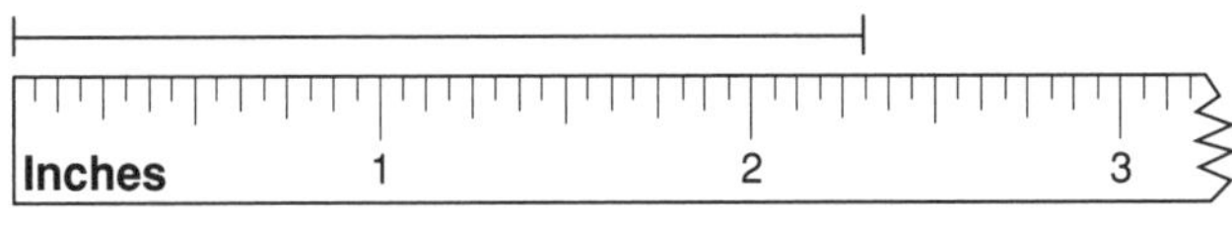

The line segment is: $2\frac{1}{2}$ inches long to the nearest *half-inch;* $2\frac{1}{4}$ inches long to the nearest *quarter-inch;* $2\frac{3}{8}$ inches long to the nearest *eighth-inch.*

Fill in the correct circle to answer each question.

Ⓓ **1.** 4 ft = ▩ in

Ⓐ 3 Ⓑ 12 Ⓒ 36 Ⓓ 48

Ⓒ **2.** 6 yd = ▩ ft

Ⓐ $\frac{1}{2}$ Ⓑ 2 Ⓒ 18 Ⓓ 72

Ⓒ **3.** Add 9 ft 8 in and 1 ft 9 in.

Ⓐ 7 ft 10 in Ⓑ 8 ft 2 in

Ⓒ 11 ft 5 in Ⓓ 11 ft 6 in

Ⓑ **4.** Subtract 3 yd 2 ft 9 in from 6 yd 2 ft 3 in.

Ⓐ 2 yd 9 ft 4 in Ⓑ 2 yd 2 ft 6 in

Ⓒ 9 yd 4 ft 12 in Ⓓ 10 yd 2 ft

Ⓒ **5.** 60 in = ▩ ft

Ⓐ 720 Ⓑ 6 Ⓒ 5 Ⓓ 4

Ⓑ **6.** 108 in = ▩ yd

Ⓐ 2 Ⓑ 3 Ⓒ 9 Ⓓ 36

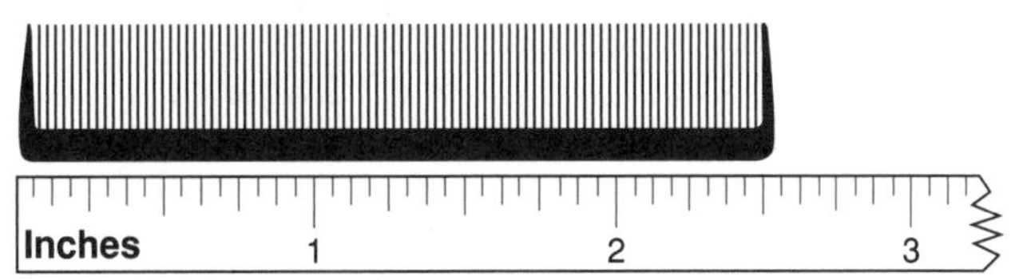

Ⓓ **7.** To the nearest *inch,* the comb is ▩ long.

Ⓐ 1″ Ⓑ 2″ Ⓒ $2\frac{1}{2}$″ Ⓓ 3″

Ⓐ **8.** To the nearest *half-inch,* the comb is ▩ long.

Ⓐ $2\frac{1}{2}$″ Ⓑ $2\frac{3}{4}$″ Ⓒ $2\frac{5}{8}$″ Ⓓ 3″

Ⓑ **9.** To the nearest *quarter-inch,* the comb is ▩ long.

Ⓐ $2\frac{1}{4}$″ Ⓑ $2\frac{1}{2}$″ Ⓒ $2\frac{3}{4}$″ Ⓓ 3″

Ⓐ **10.** To the nearest *eighth-inch,* the comb is ▩ long.

Ⓐ $2\frac{1}{2}$″ Ⓑ $2\frac{3}{8}$″ Ⓒ $2\frac{5}{8}$″ Ⓓ 3″

4.2 CUSTOMARY UNITS OF CAPACITY AND WEIGHT

CAPACITY
8 fluid ounces (fl oz) = 1 cup (c)
2 c = 1 pint (pt)
2 pt = 1 quart (qt)
4 qt = 1 gallon (gal)

WEIGHT
16 ounces (oz) = 1 pound (lb)
2000 lb = 1 ton (T)

Example 1: 3 qt = ■ pt

1 qt = 2 pt
$3 \times 2 = 6$
3 qt = 6 pt

- Conversion factor is 2.
- Multiply since you are changing to smaller units.

Example 2: 80 oz = ■ lb

16 oz = 1 lb
$80 \div 16 = 5$
80 oz = 5 lb

- Conversion factor is 16.
- Divide since you are changing to larger units.

Example 3:

3 gal 2 qt
+3 gal 3 qt
6 gal 5 qt = 6 gal + 1 gal 1 qt
= 7 gal 1qt

5 qt is more than 1 gal. Therefore, rename: 5 qt = 1 gal 1 qt

Example 4:

~~3~~ (2) lb ~~6~~ (22) oz
−1 lb 8 oz
1 lb 14 oz

You can't subtract 8 oz from 6 oz. Therefore, rename:
3 lb 6 oz = 2 lb + 1 lb + 6 oz
= 2 lb + 16 oz + 6 oz
= 2 lb + 22 oz

Fill in the circle to answer each question.

(C) **1.** 6000 lb = ■ T
Ⓐ 5 Ⓑ 4 Ⓒ 3 Ⓓ $\frac{1}{3}$

(C) **2.** 20 qt = ■ gal
Ⓐ 24 Ⓑ 4 Ⓒ 5 Ⓓ 80

(D) **3.** 2 lb = ■ oz
Ⓐ $\frac{1}{8}$ Ⓑ 8 Ⓒ 16 Ⓓ 32

(C) **4.** 8 gal = ■ qt
Ⓐ 2 Ⓑ 16 Ⓒ 32 Ⓓ 128

(B) **5.** 128 oz = ■ lb
Ⓐ 7 Ⓑ 8 Ⓒ 16 Ⓓ 2048

(D) **6.** 4 tons = ■ pounds
Ⓐ 500 Ⓑ 64 Ⓒ 4000 Ⓓ 8000

(B) **7.** Add 8 lb 12 oz and 3 lb 9 oz.
Ⓐ 13 lb 1 oz Ⓑ 12 lb 5 oz
Ⓒ 12 lb 1 oz Ⓓ 11 lb 21 oz

(A) **8.** Subtract 8 gal 3 qt from 12 gal 1 qt.
Ⓐ 3 gal 2 qt Ⓑ 4 gal 2 qt
Ⓒ 21 gal 4 qt Ⓓ 22 gal

(C) **9.** 2 pt = ■ c
Ⓐ 8 Ⓑ 6 Ⓒ 4 Ⓓ 1

(A) **10.** 3 c = ■ fl oz
Ⓐ 24 Ⓑ $2\frac{2}{3}$ Ⓒ $\frac{3}{8}$ Ⓓ 11

(C) **11.**
10 T 1200 lb
+ 3 T 800 lb

Ⓐ 7 T 400 lb Ⓑ 14 T 2000 lb
Ⓒ 14 T Ⓓ 13 T 2600 lb

(D) **12.**
3 qt
− 1 qt 1 pt

Ⓐ 2 qt 1 pt Ⓑ 2 qt
Ⓒ 1 qt Ⓓ 1 qt 1 pt

Name________________________________ Class __________ Date ______________

4.3 COMPUTING WITH TIME

60 seconds (sec)	= 1 minute (min)
60 min	= 1 hour (h)
24 h	= 1 day (d)
7 d	= 1 week (wk)

Example 1: 528 hours = ▩ days

24h = 1d • The conversion factor is 24.

528 ÷ 24 = 22 • Divide since you are changing to smaller units.

528 hours = 22 days

Example 2: A bus leaves Boston at 10:50 A.M. and arrives in New York at 3:40 P.M. How long was the trip?

10:50 A.M. to noon ⟶	1h 10 min
noon to 3:40 pm ⟶	3h 40 min
Total elapsed time:	4h 50 min

Example 3: Add 2 weeks 6 days, 1 week 4 days, and 3 weeks 5 days.

```
  2wk  6d
  1wk  4d
 +3wk  5d
 --------
  6wk 15d   = 6wk + 2wk 1d
            = 8wk 1d
```

• 15 days is longer than 1 week. Therefore, rename: 15d = 2wk 1d

Fill in the circle to answer each question.

Ⓓ **1.** From 3 P.M. to 7 A.M. is

Ⓐ 4h Ⓑ 8h Ⓒ 10h Ⓓ 16h

Ⓑ **2.** From 7 A.M. to 3 P.M. is

Ⓐ 4h Ⓑ 8h Ⓒ 10h Ⓓ 16h

Ⓒ **3.** 4 days = ▩ hours

Ⓐ 28 Ⓑ 48 Ⓒ 96 Ⓓ 240

Ⓐ **4.** 4 weeks = ▩ days

Ⓐ 28 Ⓑ 48 Ⓒ 96 Ⓓ 240

Ⓓ **5.** Add 10h 50min and 6h 20min.

Ⓐ 5h 10min Ⓑ 16h 10min

Ⓒ 16h 70min Ⓓ 17h 10min

Ⓐ **6.** Subtract 6h 40min from 10h 30min.

Ⓐ 3h 50min Ⓑ 4 h10min

Ⓒ 16h 70min Ⓓ 17h 10min

Ⓑ **7.** A plane left Boston at 10:10 A.M. and arrived in Miami at 3:35 P.M. How long was the flight?

Ⓐ 3h 25min Ⓑ 5h 25min

Ⓒ 6h 25min Ⓓ 7h 25min

Ⓐ **8.** A plane left Dallas at 9:55 A.M. and arrived in Chicago at 12:10 P.M. How long was the flight?

Ⓐ 2h 15min Ⓑ 2h 55min

Ⓒ 3h 55min Ⓓ 14h 15min

Ⓓ **9.** 20 min = ▩ sec

Ⓐ 300 Ⓑ 3000 Ⓒ 120 Ⓓ 1200

Ⓓ **10.** 168 h = ▩ d

Ⓐ 8 Ⓑ 6 Ⓒ 5 Ⓓ 7

Ⓑ **11.** $2\frac{1}{2}$ hours = ▩ min

Ⓐ 120 Ⓑ 150 Ⓒ 90 Ⓓ 250

Ⓐ **12.** 6 weeks = ▩ days

Ⓐ 42 Ⓑ 72 Ⓒ 144 Ⓓ 360

Ⓐ **13.**

```
   3wk 6d 15h
 + 1wk 5d 10h
```

Ⓐ 5wk 5d 1h Ⓑ 5wk 3d 5h

Ⓒ 5wk 3d 1h Ⓓ 5wk 1h

Ⓒ **14.** A plane leaves San Diego at 9:35 A.M. Eastern Standard Time (EST) and arrives in Boston at 3:15 P.M. EST. How long was the flight?

Ⓐ 6h 40min Ⓑ 5h 20min

Ⓒ 5h 40min Ⓓ 6h 20min

D 15. It is 6:30 P.M. on Tuesday. What time will it be in 3d 7h 45min?

Ⓐ 1:15 A.M. Friday

Ⓑ 2:15 A.M. Friday

Ⓒ 1:15 A.M. Saturday

Ⓓ 2:15 A.M. Saturday

C 16. It is 11:45 P.M. on Monday. What time will it be in 26h 30min?

Ⓐ 2:15 A.M. Tuesday

Ⓑ 2:15 P.M. Tuesday

Ⓒ 2:15 A.M. Wednesday

Ⓓ 8:15 A.M. Wednesday

C 17. Add 3wk 4d and 2wk 6d.

Ⓐ 5wk 3d Ⓑ 5wk 10d

Ⓒ 6wk 3d Ⓓ 6wk 10d

A 18. Add 4wk 2d, 3wk 5d, 1wk 6d and 4d.

Ⓐ 10wk 3d Ⓑ 10wk

Ⓒ 9wk 3d Ⓓ 8wk 3d

B 19. Subtract 3wk 2d from 5wk 1d.

Ⓐ 1wk 1d Ⓑ 1wk 6d

Ⓒ 2wk 1d Ⓓ 2wk 6d

B 20. It is 9:10 A.M. What time will it be in 9 hours?

Ⓐ 5:10 P.M. Ⓑ 6:10 P.M.

Ⓒ 7:10 P.M. Ⓓ 8:10 P.M.

D 21. The time is 6:15 P.M. What time was it 5 hours ago?

Ⓐ 11:15 A.M. Ⓑ 11:15 P.M.

Ⓒ 1:15 A.M. Ⓓ 1:15 P.M.

A 22. The time is 9:00 A.M. What time was it $\frac{3}{4}$ hour ago?

Ⓐ 8:15 A.M. Ⓑ 8:30 A.M.

Ⓒ 9:30 A.M. Ⓓ 9:45 A.M.

B 23. 3600 sec = ■ min

Ⓐ 1 Ⓑ 60 Ⓒ 600 Ⓓ 6

C 24. 16 weeks = ■ d

Ⓐ $2\frac{3}{16}$ Ⓑ 23 Ⓒ 112 Ⓓ 160

A 25.

```
  6h 35min
+ 4h 45min
```

Ⓐ 11h 20min Ⓑ 11h 10min

Ⓒ 10h 7.0min Ⓓ 10h 20min

C 26.

```
  2h 20min
−    35min
```

Ⓐ 2h 55min Ⓑ 2h 45min

Ⓒ 1h 45min Ⓓ 1h 25min

A 27. 18 d = ■

Ⓐ 2wk 4d Ⓑ 2wk 3d

Ⓒ 3wk 4d Ⓓ 3wk

C 28. 96 h = ■ d

Ⓐ 6 Ⓑ 5 Ⓒ 4 Ⓓ 3

B 29.

```
  5wk 4d
+     6d
```

Ⓐ 6wk Ⓑ 6wk 3d

Ⓒ 7wk 3d Ⓓ 7wk 4d

D 30.

```
  4d 5h
− 1d 8h
```

Ⓐ 5d 13h Ⓑ 3d 21h

Ⓒ 2d 22h Ⓓ 2d 21h

C 31. From 6:30 P.M. to 9:00 A.M. is

Ⓐ 2h 30min. Ⓑ 14h.

Ⓒ 14h 30min. Ⓓ 16h 30min.

D 32. It is 7:15 P.M. What time will it be in 50 minutes?

Ⓐ 6:05 A.M. Ⓑ 6:05 P.M.

Ⓒ 8:05 A.M. Ⓓ 8:05 P.M.

Name ______________________ Class __________ Date ______________

4.4 METRIC UNITS OF LENGTH

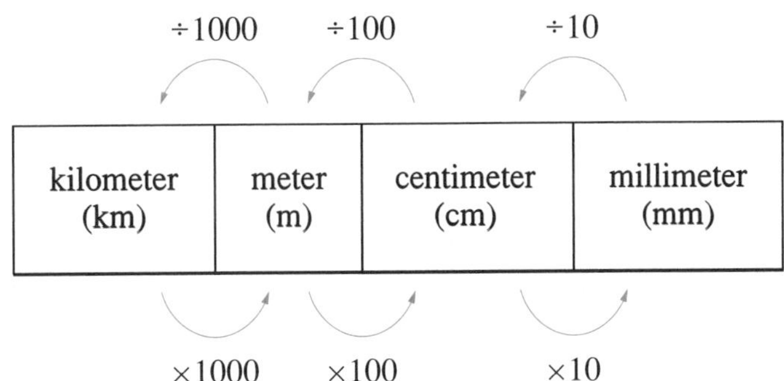

REMEMBER: To change from a smaller unit to a larger unit, DIVIDE.

To change from a larger unit to a smaller unit, MULTIPLY.

Example 1: 15 cm = ■ mm

15 x 10 = 150
15 cm = 150 mm

Example 2: 45 cm = ■ m

45 ÷ 100 = 0.45
45 cm = 0.45 m

Example 3: Measure the segment to the nearest *centimeter* and *millimeter*.

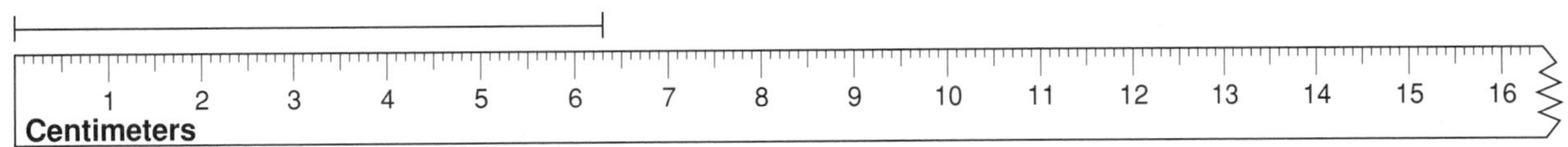

The line segment is 6 cm to the nearest cm, and 63 mm to the nearest mm.

Fill in the correct circle to answer each question.

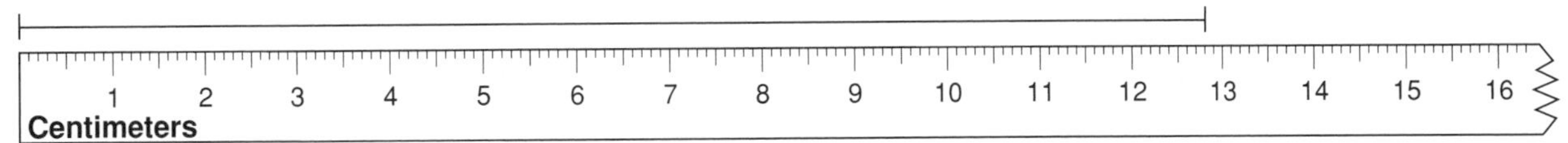

Ⓑ **1.** To the nearest *centimeter*, the line segment above is ■ cm long.
Ⓐ 12 Ⓑ 13 Ⓒ 128 Ⓓ 130

Ⓒ **2.** To the nearest *millimeter*, the line segment above is ■ mm long.
Ⓐ 12.8 Ⓑ 13 Ⓒ 128 Ⓓ 130

Ⓒ **3.** 5 km = ■ m
Ⓐ $\frac{1}{200}$ Ⓑ 500 Ⓒ 5000 Ⓓ 5,000,000

Ⓓ **4.** 6500 m = ■ km
Ⓐ 6,500,000 Ⓑ 650 Ⓒ 65 Ⓓ 6.5

Ⓑ **5.** 27 cm = ■ mm
Ⓐ 2.7 Ⓑ 270 Ⓒ 2700 Ⓓ 27,000

Ⓐ **6.** 12 m = ■ cm
Ⓐ 1200 Ⓑ 120 Ⓒ 1.2 Ⓓ 0.12

Ⓐ **7.** 127 cm = ■ m
Ⓐ 1.27 Ⓑ 12.7 Ⓒ 1270 Ⓓ 12,700

Ⓒ **8.** 96 mm = ■ cm
Ⓐ 9600 Ⓑ 960 Ⓒ 9.6 Ⓓ 0.96

Ⓒ **9.** 70 cm = ■ mm
Ⓐ 7 Ⓑ 70 Ⓒ 700 Ⓓ 7000

Ⓑ **10.** 900 cm = ■ m
Ⓐ 0.9 Ⓑ 9 Ⓒ 90 Ⓓ 900

4.5 METRIC UNITS OF CAPACITY AND MASS

CAPACITY

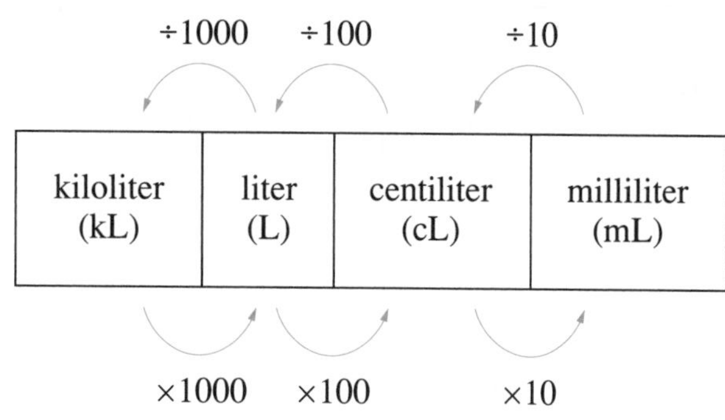

MASS

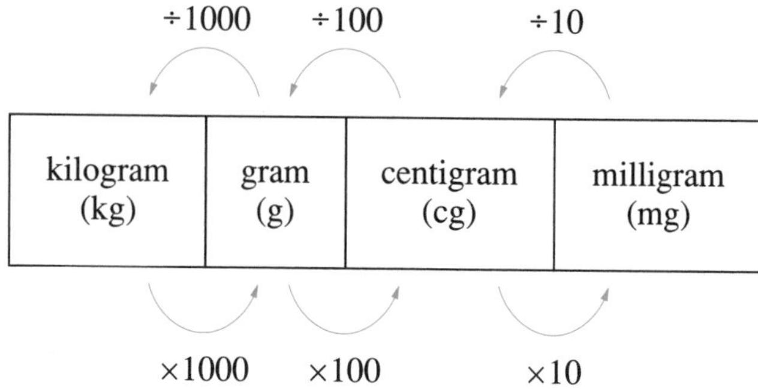

Example 1: 750 mL = ■ L

$750 \div 1000 = 0.75$

750 mL = 0.75 L

Example 2: 4 kg = ■ g

$4 \times 1000 = 4000$

4 kg = 4000 g

Fill in the correct circle to answer each question.

Ⓒ **1.** 9500 ml = ■ L
Ⓐ 950 Ⓑ 95 Ⓒ 9.5 Ⓓ 0.95

Ⓑ **2.** 5000g = ■ kg
Ⓐ 0.5 Ⓑ 5 Ⓒ 50 Ⓓ 500

Ⓐ **3.** 2 kg = ■ g
Ⓐ 2000 Ⓑ 200 Ⓒ 0.2 Ⓓ 0.002

Ⓓ **4.** 7 L = ■ mL
Ⓐ 0.007 Ⓑ 0.7 Ⓒ 700 Ⓓ 7000

Ⓓ **5.** 57 g = ■ kg
Ⓐ 57,000 Ⓑ 5700
Ⓒ 0.57 Ⓓ 0.057

Ⓑ **6.** 127 mL = ■ L
Ⓐ 0.0127 Ⓑ 0.127
Ⓒ 12,700 Ⓓ 127,000

Ⓓ **7.** 83 L = ■ ml
Ⓐ 0.083 Ⓑ 83 Ⓒ 830 Ⓓ 83,000

Ⓓ **8.** 114 g = ■ kg
Ⓐ 1114 Ⓑ 1.14 Ⓒ 11.4 Ⓓ 0.114

Ⓐ **9.** 14 kg = ■ g
Ⓐ 14,000 Ⓑ 1400
Ⓒ 0.14 Ⓓ 0.014

Ⓒ **10.** 2500 mL = ■ L
Ⓐ 250,000 Ⓑ 250
Ⓒ 2.5 Ⓓ 0.25

Ⓑ **11.** 2.5 L = ■ mL
Ⓐ 25,000 Ⓑ 2500 Ⓒ 250 Ⓓ 0.25

Ⓐ **12.** 4.5 g = ■ kg
Ⓐ 0.0045 Ⓑ 0.045 Ⓒ 4500 Ⓓ 45,000

Ⓓ **13.** 15 L = ■ mL
Ⓐ 1.5 Ⓑ 150 Ⓒ 1500 Ⓓ 15,000

Ⓓ **14.** 4900 mL = ■ L
Ⓐ 4900 Ⓑ 490 Ⓒ 49 Ⓓ 4.9

Ⓐ **15.** 7500 g = ■ kg
Ⓐ 7.5 Ⓑ 75 Ⓒ 750 Ⓓ 75,000

Ⓑ **16.** 6.2 kg = ■ g
Ⓐ 62,000 Ⓑ 6200 Ⓒ 620 Ⓓ 0.062

Name ______________________ Class __________ Date __________

CHAPTER 4 TEST

Fill in the correct circle to answer each question.

Ⓐ **1.** 8 kg = ▇ g

Ⓐ 8000 Ⓑ 800 Ⓒ 0.08 Ⓓ 0.008

Ⓒ **2.** 705 mm = ▇ cm

Ⓐ 70,500 Ⓑ 7050 Ⓒ 70.5 Ⓓ 7.05

Ⓓ **3.** 2 qt = ▇ fl oz

Ⓐ 16 Ⓑ 32 Ⓒ 48 Ⓓ 64

Ⓑ **4.** A plane leaves Houston at 9:25 P.M. and arrives in Minneapolis at 2:40 A.M. How long was the flight?

Ⓐ 6 h 45 min Ⓑ 5 h 15 min

Ⓒ 4 h 15 min Ⓓ 4 h 15 min

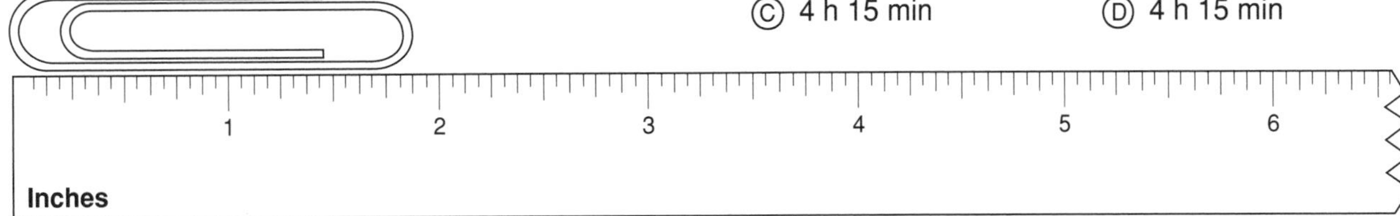

Ⓒ **5.** To the nearest $\frac{1}{2}$ inch, the paper clip is ▇ long.

Ⓐ $1\frac{1}{2}$ in Ⓑ $1\frac{3}{4}$ in Ⓒ 2 in Ⓓ $2\frac{1}{2}$ in

Ⓒ **6.** To the nearest $\frac{1}{8}$ inch, the paper clip is ▇ long.

Ⓐ $1\frac{5}{8}$ in Ⓑ $1\frac{3}{4}$ in Ⓒ $1\frac{7}{8}$ in Ⓓ 2 in

Ⓐ **7.** 3 tons = ▇ lb

Ⓐ 6000 Ⓑ 3000 Ⓒ 600 Ⓓ 300

Ⓒ **8.** Add 12 h 42 min and 7 h 38 min.

Ⓐ 19 h 20 min Ⓑ 19 h 70 min

Ⓒ 20 h 20 min Ⓓ 20 h 80 min

Ⓐ **9.** 9 yd = ▇ ft

Ⓐ 27 Ⓑ 21 Ⓒ $\frac{1}{3}$ Ⓓ 3

Ⓓ **10.** 12 g = ▇ kg

Ⓐ 12,000 Ⓑ 1200 Ⓒ 0.12 Ⓓ 0.012

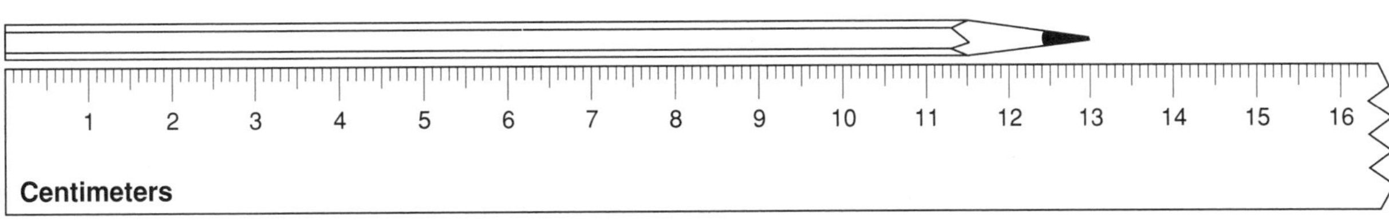

Ⓒ **11.** This pencil measures ▇ cm to the nearest cm.

Ⓐ 14 Ⓑ 140 Ⓒ 13 Ⓓ 130

Ⓓ **12.** This pencil measures ▇ mm to the nearest mm.

Ⓐ 14 Ⓑ 140 Ⓒ 13 Ⓓ 130

Ⓐ **13.** It is 7:45 P.M. on Thursday. What time and day will it be in 2 days 7 h 45 min?

Ⓐ 3:30 A.M. Sunday

Ⓑ 3:30 A.M. Saturday

Ⓒ 2:30 A.M. Sunday

Ⓓ 2:30 A.M. Saturday

Ⓒ **14.** Subtract 7 gal 2 qt from 11 gal 1 qt.

Ⓐ 18 gal 3qt Ⓑ 3 gal 9qt

Ⓒ 3 gal 3qt Ⓓ 3 gal 1qt

Ⓒ **15.** 5 lb = ■ oz

Ⓐ 40 Ⓑ 60 Ⓒ 80 Ⓓ 100

Ⓑ **16.** 32 qt = ■ gal

Ⓐ 4 Ⓑ 8 Ⓒ 16 Ⓓ 128

Ⓑ **17.** Add 11 ft 6 in and 5 ft 8 in.

Ⓐ 17 ft 4 in Ⓑ 17 ft 2 in
Ⓒ 16 ft 4 in Ⓓ 16 ft 2 in

Ⓒ **18.** Add 1wk 4d, 3wk 2d, and 4wk 5d.

Ⓐ 8 weeks 11 days Ⓑ 7 weeks 11 days
Ⓒ 9 weeks 4 days Ⓓ 9 weeks 3 days

Ⓒ **19.** 42 cm = ■ mm

Ⓐ 0.42 Ⓑ 4.2 Ⓒ 420 Ⓓ 4200

Ⓓ **20.** 3.2 L = ■ mL

Ⓐ 0.0032 Ⓑ 0.032 Ⓒ 320 Ⓓ 3200

Ⓑ **21.** 24 qt = ■ gal

Ⓐ 2 Ⓑ 6 Ⓒ 12 Ⓓ 96

Ⓐ **22.** 84 in = ■ ft

Ⓐ 7 Ⓑ 14 Ⓒ 28 Ⓓ 1008

Ⓓ **23.** Add 5 ft 9 in and 3 ft 5 in.

Ⓐ 2 ft 4 in Ⓑ 8 ft 2 in
Ⓒ 9 ft 4 in Ⓓ 9 ft 2 in

Ⓐ **24.** Subtract 3 lb 9 oz from 8 lb 12 oz.

Ⓐ 5 lb 3 oz Ⓑ 11 lb 5 oz
Ⓒ 12 lb 5 oz Ⓓ 4 lb 13 oz

Ⓒ **25.** A plane leaves Los Angeles at 10:50 A.M. and arrives in Seattle at 2:25 P.M. How long was the flight?

Ⓐ 8 h 25 min Ⓑ 4 h 25 min
Ⓒ 3 h 35 min Ⓓ 3 h 25 min

Ⓐ **26.** A 235 cm long board is cut into five equal pieces. How long is each piece?

Ⓐ 47 cm Ⓑ 47 mm Ⓒ 470 cm Ⓓ 4.7 cm

Ⓑ **27.** A piece of red and green cloth that was 7 yd long was cut into 3 equal pieces. How long was each piece?

Ⓐ 7 yd Ⓑ 7 ft
Ⓒ 3 yd Ⓓ 3 ft

Ⓒ **28.** Zheng Yi drove 247 km on Friday, 457 km on Saturday and 396 km on Sunday. How far did he drive?

Ⓐ 1000 km Ⓑ 1090 km
Ⓒ 1100 km Ⓓ 1200 km

Ⓐ **29.** 6 T = ■ lb

Ⓐ 12,000 Ⓑ 24,000 Ⓒ 6000 Ⓓ 18,000

Ⓓ **30.** 5 days = ■ hours

Ⓐ 60 Ⓑ 48 Ⓒ 90 Ⓓ 120

Ⓓ **31.** 8 mi = ■ ft

Ⓐ 24 Ⓑ 96 Ⓒ 8000 Ⓓ 42,240

Ⓐ **32.** Add 6 gal 2 qt and 5 gal 3 qt.

Ⓐ 12 gal 1 qt Ⓑ 11 gal 5 qt
Ⓒ 13 gal 1 qt Ⓓ 1 gal 1 qt

Ⓒ **33.** The marching band started practice at 7:35 A.M. Band practice ended at 10:15 A.M. How long did band practice last?

Ⓐ 3h 20min Ⓑ 2h 45min Ⓒ 2h 40min Ⓓ 2h 35min

Name ______________________ Class __________ Date __________

CHAPTER 5: RATIO, PROPORTION, PERCENT

TEST–TAKING STRATEGY: *Pull Out Information*

Pulling information out of a word problem may help you solve the problem.

- Find the key words.
- Pull out the given facts.
- Identify which facts will help solve the problem.
- Remember that not all facts will always be needed.

Example 1: Mary turned 21 years old in 1989. In what year was she born?

The key words are "in what year" and "was she born."
The given facts are "21 years old" and "1989."
You need both of these facts to solve the problem.
So, the solution is 1989 – 21 = 1968.

Example 2: One room is 20 feet long and 14 feet wide. The room next to it is 18 feet long and 9 feet wide. What is the total width of the two rooms?

The key words are "total width."
The given facts are "20 feet long," "14 feet wide," "18 feet long," and "9 feet wide."
So, the solution is 14 ft + 9 ft = 23 ft.

You only needed the width of each room to solve Example 2. Sometimes you may not have enough information to solve the problem.

Example 3: Jose spent $4.95 on a paperback, and $3.25 for a notebook. How much change did he receive?

To find out how much change Jose got, you need to know how much money he gave to the cashier. You do not have enough information to solve this problem.

Fill in the correct circle to answer each question.

(B) **1.** Jill has a test on Monday at 9:00 A.M. How much time should she spend on each question, if she has 20 minutes to answer 50 questions?

- (A) 20 minutes
- (B) 24 seconds
- (C) 40 seconds
- (D) Not enough information

(D) **2.** Joel is cutting a board into 5 pieces of equal length? How long should each piece be?

- (A) 2 feet
- (B) 5 pieces
- (C) Equal length and how long
- (D) Not enough information

(A) **3.** During a 3–day period Bernie walked 15 miles, 12 miles and 17 miles. How many miles did he walk altogether?

- (A) 44 miles
- (B) 54 miles
- (C) 29 miles
- (D) 47 miles

(D) **4.** A 30–item test is to last 20 minutes. Each question has 4 parts. How much time should you spend on each question?

- (A) 40 minutes
- (B) 10 seconds
- (C) 16 seconds
- (D) 40 seconds

Answer the following 20 questions in 30 minutes. Estimate the answer before you work the exercise. Pull out the given facts. You may find it helpful circle the key words.

Ⓒ **5.** How much time should you spend on each question?

Ⓐ 3 minutes Ⓑ 66 seconds
Ⓒ 90 seconds Ⓓ 40 seconds

Ⓒ **6.** 76 ten–thousandths is ▩ .

Ⓐ 0.7600 Ⓑ 0.076
Ⓒ 0.0076 Ⓓ 0.00076

Ⓑ **7.** Compare: 487.654 ▩ 4876.54

Ⓐ > Ⓑ < Ⓒ =

Ⓒ **8.** Round 247.469 to the nearest *hundredth.*

Ⓐ 200 Ⓑ 247 Ⓒ 247.47 Ⓓ 247.5

Ⓓ **9.** What is the sum of 87.326 and 127.54?

Ⓐ 100.80 Ⓑ 200.80 Ⓒ 214.86 Ⓓ 214.866

Ⓒ **10.** $7\frac{3}{8} - 3\frac{3}{4} =$ ▩

Ⓐ $27\frac{21}{32}$ Ⓑ $11\frac{1}{8}$ Ⓒ $3\frac{5}{8}$ Ⓓ $1\frac{29}{30}$

Ⓒ **11.** $\frac{7}{6} \times \frac{6}{5} =$ ▩

Ⓐ $\frac{13}{11}$ Ⓑ $\frac{35}{36}$ Ⓒ $1\frac{2}{5}$ Ⓓ $2\frac{11}{30}$

Ⓐ **12.** $(27 + 13) \div 0.4 =$ ▩

Ⓐ 100 Ⓑ 10 Ⓒ 1 Ⓓ 0.1

Ⓓ **13.** Divide 55.548 by 0.18.

Ⓐ 0.3086 Ⓑ 3.086
Ⓒ 30.86 Ⓓ 308.6

Ⓐ **14.** Write 5.37×10^3 in standard form.

Ⓐ 5370 Ⓑ 0.0537
Ⓒ 0.00537 Ⓓ 0.000537

Ⓒ **15.** $(72.5 - 16.3) \times 4.1 =$ ▩

Ⓐ 23,042 Ⓑ 2304.2
Ⓒ 230.42 Ⓓ 23.042

Ⓒ **16.** 9 yd = ▩ ft

Ⓐ $\frac{1}{3}$ Ⓑ 3 Ⓒ 27 Ⓓ 108

Ⓓ **17.** 35 days = ▩ weeks

Ⓐ 245 Ⓑ 7
Ⓒ 6 Ⓓ 5

Ⓒ **18.** It is 8:25 A.M. What time will it be in 9 h 45 min?

Ⓐ 5:10 P.M. Ⓑ 5:70 P.M.
Ⓒ 6:10 P.M. Ⓓ 7:10 P.M.

Ⓐ **19.** 276 cm = ▩ m

Ⓐ 2.76 Ⓑ 27.6 Ⓒ 2760 Ⓓ 27,600

Ⓑ **20.** 57 mL = ▩ L

Ⓐ 0.0057 Ⓑ 0.057 Ⓒ 0.57 Ⓓ 57,000

Ⓑ **21.** Suzi parked cars in a parking garage. She was paid $5.15 an hour. She worked from 6:30 P.M. to 11:45 P.M. How much money did she earn?

Ⓐ $20.32 Ⓑ $27.04
Ⓒ $16.73 Ⓓ $13.83

Ⓒ **22.** John decided to put some trim across the four windows in his room. Each window is the same size. How much can he allow for each window if he has 8 yds 2 ft 8 in of trim?

Ⓐ 207.25 in Ⓑ 20.725 in
Ⓒ 6 ft 8 in Ⓓ 6.685 in

Ⓓ **23.** Maria drove for 2.4 hours and averaged 60 miles per hour. How many miles did she drive?

Ⓐ 240 miles Ⓑ 24 miles
Ⓒ 1440 miles Ⓓ 144 miles

Ⓐ **24.** An airplane can carry 25,541.6 liters of fuel. Each liter weighs 0.6 kilograms. What is the weight of the fuel when the tanks are full?

Ⓐ 15324.96 kg Ⓑ 1532.496 kg
Ⓒ 153.2496 kg Ⓓ 15.32496 kg

Name ______________________ Class __________ Date __________

CHAPTER 5 PRETEST

Fill in the correct circle to answer each question.

(D) **1.** What is $\frac{18}{24}$ in simplest form?

Ⓐ $\frac{1}{2}$ Ⓑ $\frac{2}{3}$ Ⓒ $\frac{6}{8}$ Ⓓ $\frac{3}{4}$

(D) **2.** What is $\frac{72}{108}$ in simplest form?

Ⓐ $\frac{36}{54}$ Ⓑ $\frac{24}{36}$ Ⓒ $\frac{8}{12}$ Ⓓ $\frac{2}{3}$

(C) **3.** Which fraction is not in simplest form?

Ⓐ $\frac{13}{41}$ Ⓑ $\frac{2}{7}$ Ⓒ $\frac{17}{51}$ Ⓓ $\frac{9}{37}$

(B) **4.** Which fractions are equivalent?

Ⓐ $\frac{4}{12}, \frac{2}{7}$ Ⓑ $\frac{39}{13}, \frac{3}{1}$ Ⓒ $\frac{48}{12}, \frac{5}{1}$ Ⓓ $\frac{8}{56}, \frac{1}{8}$

(C) **5.** Complete: $\frac{■}{8} = 3$

Ⓐ 3 Ⓑ 21 Ⓒ 24 Ⓓ 32

(C) **6.** Complete: $\frac{72}{■} = 8$

Ⓐ 1 Ⓑ 8 Ⓒ 9 Ⓓ 72

(A) **7.** Complete: $\frac{■}{3} = \frac{8}{24}$

Ⓐ 1 Ⓑ 2 Ⓒ 3 Ⓓ 4

(A) **8.** Complete: $8 \times ■ = 168$

Ⓐ 21 Ⓑ 20 Ⓒ 8 Ⓓ 1

(B) **9.** $8\overline{)40} = ■$

Ⓐ 6 Ⓑ 5 Ⓒ 4 Ⓓ 3

(B) **10.** Complete: $■ \div 18 = 9$

Ⓐ 172 Ⓑ 162 Ⓒ 18 Ⓓ 1

Write as a fraction with a denominator of 100 for questions 11-14.

(C) **11.** $\frac{3}{4} = \frac{■}{100}$

Ⓐ 50 Ⓑ 65 Ⓒ 75 Ⓓ 750

(B) **12.** $\frac{8}{10} = \frac{■}{100}$

Ⓐ 800 Ⓑ 80 Ⓒ 8 Ⓓ 40

(C) **13.** $0.25 = \frac{■}{100}$

Ⓐ 250 Ⓑ 4 Ⓒ 25 Ⓓ 0.25

(C) **14.** $0.06 = \frac{■}{100}$

Ⓐ 0.06 Ⓑ 0.6 Ⓒ 6 Ⓓ 60

(A) **15.** $\frac{■}{3} = \frac{12}{18}$

Ⓐ 2 Ⓑ 3 Ⓒ 4 Ⓓ 6

(C) **16.** $\frac{7}{8} = \frac{■}{96}$

Ⓐ 70 Ⓑ 77 Ⓒ 84 Ⓓ 88

(D) **17.** $1.25 \times 0.8 = ■$

Ⓐ 1000 Ⓑ 100 Ⓒ 10 Ⓓ 1

(B) **18.** Multiply: 200×3.78

Ⓐ 7560 Ⓑ 756 Ⓒ 75.6 Ⓓ 7.56

(D) **19.** $2 \div 0.001 = ■$

Ⓐ 0.002 Ⓑ 10 Ⓒ 200 Ⓓ 2000

(A) **20.** Divide: $6284 \div 0.04$

Ⓐ 157,100 Ⓑ 15,710 Ⓒ 1571 Ⓓ 0.01571

(A) **21.** Write the ratio 2 to 3 in fraction form.

Ⓐ $\frac{2}{3}$ Ⓑ 3 to 2 Ⓒ $2\frac{1}{3}$ Ⓓ $\frac{3}{2}$

(B) **22.** The ratio 10:14 is proportional to ■.

Ⓐ 14:10 Ⓑ 15:21 Ⓒ 7:5 Ⓓ 28:20

Ⓒ **23.** Write 0.037% as a decimal.

Ⓐ 37.00 Ⓑ 3.7

Ⓒ 0.00037 Ⓓ 0.037

Ⓒ **24.** What is 25% of 240?

Ⓐ 6000 Ⓑ 400

Ⓒ 60 Ⓓ 6

Ⓐ **25.** Write 7.0 as a percent.

Ⓐ 700% Ⓑ 70% Ⓒ 7.0% Ⓓ 0.07%

Ⓑ **26.** If overtime pays time and a half, what is the ratio of regular pay to overtime pay?

Ⓐ 3 to 2. Ⓑ 2 to 3. Ⓒ 1.5 to 1. Ⓓ 1 to 2.

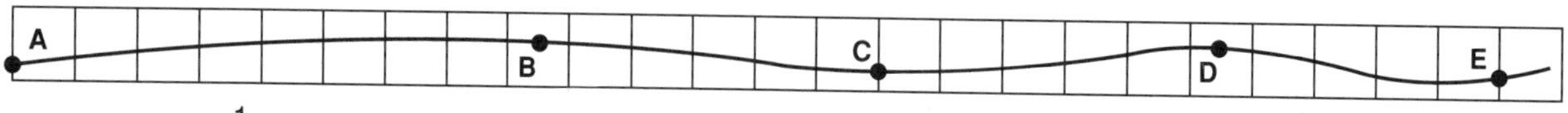

A B C D E

Scale: ⊢—⊣ = $\frac{1}{2}$ mile

Ⓒ **27.** The actual distance from A to B is ■ miles.

Ⓐ $8\frac{1}{2}$ Ⓑ 9

Ⓒ $4\frac{1}{4}$ Ⓓ 34

Ⓑ **28.** If 40 miles on the road is 2 inches on the map, what is the scale?

Ⓐ 1 inch per 10 miles Ⓑ 1 inch per 20 miles

Ⓒ 1 inch per 80 miles Ⓓ 1 inch per 40 miles

Ⓑ **29.** Write $\frac{5}{8}$ as a decimal.

Ⓐ 1.6 Ⓑ 0.625 Ⓒ 0.650 Ⓓ 0675

Ⓑ **30.** Which fraction is the same as 125%?

Ⓐ $\frac{4}{5}$ Ⓑ $\frac{5}{4}$ Ⓒ $\frac{1}{5}$ Ⓓ $\frac{1}{4}$

Ⓑ **31.** $\frac{3}{4} = \frac{■}{12}$

Ⓐ 8 Ⓑ 9 Ⓒ 10 Ⓓ 11

Ⓐ **32.** If the ratio of boys to girls in the school is 3 to 2, the ratio of boys to students is ■.

Ⓐ 3 to 5 Ⓑ 5 to 3 Ⓒ 1 to 3 Ⓓ 1 to 2

Ⓐ **33.** 101% of 2.4 is ■.

Ⓐ 2.424 Ⓑ 0.2424

Ⓒ 242.4 Ⓓ 24.24

Ⓒ **34.** 0.011% of 2.4 is ■.

Ⓐ 26.4 Ⓑ 2.64

Ⓒ 0.000264 Ⓓ 0.0264

Ⓓ **35.** 25% of the birds at a bird feeder are red-wing black birds. If there are 9 red-wing black birds, how many birds are there in all?

Ⓐ 12 Ⓑ 2 Ⓒ 3 Ⓓ 36

Ⓐ **36.** Write 0.01 as a percent.

Ⓐ 1% Ⓑ 0.01% Ⓒ 0.001% Ⓓ 0.0001%

Ⓐ **37.** 32 is 80% of what number?

Ⓐ 40 Ⓑ 25.6 Ⓒ 0.4 Ⓓ 2.5

Ⓓ **38.** Change 1.50 to a fraction.

Ⓐ $\frac{1}{3}$ Ⓑ $\frac{3}{1}$ Ⓒ $\frac{15}{3}$ Ⓓ $\frac{3}{2}$

Ⓓ **39.** A class of 25 students has 3 absent. What percent of students are present?

Ⓐ 12% Ⓑ 22% Ⓒ 8.8% Ⓓ 88%

Ⓐ **40.** In a school with 125 students, what percent is five students of the 125 students?

Ⓐ 4% Ⓑ 25% Ⓒ $\frac{5}{125}$% Ⓓ 5%

Name ____________________ Class ________ Date ____________

5.1 RATIO AND PROPORTION

A **ratio** is a comparison of two numbers by division. To write ratios, use the word *to,* a colon, or a fraction bar.

Example 1: John read 3 books in 4 days. Write the ratio of books to days in 3 different ways.

- With the word *to*: 3 to 4
- With a colon: 3:4
- As a fraction: $\frac{3}{4}$

A **proportion** is a statement that two ratios are equal.

Example 2: Is $\frac{2}{5} = \frac{6}{15}$ a proportion?

Find the cross products.

$\frac{2}{5} \times \frac{6}{15}$

$2 \times 15 = 30 \quad 5 \times 6 = 30$

$30 = 30$

So, $\frac{2}{5} = \frac{6}{15}$

The statement is a **proportion.**

Example 3: Is $\frac{4}{7} = \frac{3}{5}$ a proportion?

Find the cross products.

$\frac{4}{7} \times \frac{3}{5}$

$4 \times 5 = 20 \quad 7 \times 3 = 21$

$20 \neq 21$

So, $\frac{4}{7} \neq \frac{3}{5}$

The statement is a **not a proportion**.

Example 4: Solve the proportion: $\frac{■}{5} = \frac{4}{10}$

$\frac{■}{5} \times \frac{4}{10}$ Find the cross products.

$■ \times 10 = 5 \times 4$ Set the cross products equal.

$■ \times 10 = 20$ Simplify.

$■ \times 10 \div 10 = 20 \div 10$ Divide both sides by 10.

$■ = 2$

There are 5 boys and 6 girls in Grant School.

Ⓓ **1.** What is the ratio of girls to boys?

Ⓐ $\frac{5}{11}$ Ⓑ $\frac{6}{11}$ Ⓒ $\frac{5}{6}$ Ⓓ $\frac{6}{5}$

Ⓐ **2.** What is the ratio of boys to children in Grant School?

Ⓐ $\frac{5}{11}$ Ⓑ $\frac{6}{11}$ Ⓒ $\frac{5}{6}$ Ⓓ $\frac{6}{5}$

Ⓒ **3.** What is the ratio of girls to children in Grant School?

Ⓐ 5:6 Ⓑ 6:5 Ⓒ 6:11 Ⓓ 5:11

Ⓐ **4.** What is the ratio of boys to girls?

Ⓐ 5:6 Ⓑ 5:11 Ⓒ 6:5 Ⓓ 6:11

Ⓒ **5.** Which two ratios form a proportion?

Ⓐ $\frac{1}{3}$ and $\frac{2}{4}$ Ⓑ $\frac{1}{3}$ and $\frac{2}{5}$

Ⓒ $\frac{1}{3}$ and $\frac{2}{6}$ Ⓓ $\frac{1}{3}$ and $\frac{2}{7}$

Ⓑ **6.** Which two ratios form a proportion?

Ⓐ 2 to 3, 6 to 7 Ⓑ 2 to 3, 6 to 9

Ⓒ 2 to 3, 6 to 8 Ⓓ 2 to 3, 6 to 10

A bouquet of flowers had 3 red carnations, 6 white roses, 4 white daisies, and 2 yellow carnations.

(D) **7.** What is the ratio of roses to flowers?

(A) 1:3 (B) 15:6 (C) 6:9 (D) 6:15

(B) **8.** What is the ratio of carnations to daisies?

(A) $\frac{3}{4}$ (B) $\frac{5}{4}$ (C) $\frac{4}{5}$ (D) $\frac{5}{15}$

(B) **9.** What is the ratio of carnations to roses?

(A) 3:6 (B) 5:6 (C) 6:5 (D) 2:6

(B) **10.** What is the ratio of colored flowers to white flowers?

(A) $\frac{10}{5}$ (B) 5 to 10 (C) 9:6 (D) $\frac{3}{10}$

(A) **11.** Which ratio is equivalent to $\frac{2}{3}$?

(A) $\frac{4}{6}$ (B) $\frac{3}{2}$ (C) $\frac{9}{6}$ (D) $\frac{6}{4}$

(B) **12.** Which ratio is *not* equivalent to $\frac{4}{9}$?

(A) $\frac{8}{18}$ (B) $\frac{9}{20}$ (C) $\frac{12}{27}$ (D) $\frac{36}{81}$

(D) **13.** Ed ran 8 laps in 15 minutes. The ratio of laps to minutes is ■ .

(A) 15:8 (B) 15 to 8 (C) 8 to $\frac{1}{15}$ (D) 8:15

(C) **14.** The directions for mixing a can of concentrated orange juice recommend adding 3 cans of water to the can of juice. If there is 8 ounces of juice, how many ounces of water should be added?

(A) $\frac{8}{3}$ (B) 21 (C) 24 (D) 32

(A) **15.** Find ■ : $\frac{4}{20} = \frac{■}{5}$

(A) 1 (B) 2 (C) 3 (D) 4

(D) **16.** Find ■ : $\frac{9}{21} = \frac{3}{■}$

(A) 4 (B) 5 (C) 6 (D) 7

(A) **17.** Which two ratios form a proportion?

(A) 2 to 3 and 4 to 6 (B) 2 to 3 and 3 to 2
(C) 2 to 3 and 10 to 13 (D) 2 to 3 and 12 to 13

(B) **18.** Which two ratios do *not* form a proportion?

(A) 4 to 10 and 6 to 15 (B) 11 to 12 and 21 to 24
(C) 4 to 8 and 5 to 10 (D) 11 to 12 and 33 to 36

Use Table 5.1 to answer questions 19-21.

Table 5.1

Entrants in Grant School Pet Show	
Students	Pets
Bob	1 cat
Debbi	2 dogs
Diana	1 dog
Juanita	3 cats

(D) **19.** What is the ratio of cats to dogs?

(A) $\frac{2}{4}$ (B) $\frac{4}{2}$ (C) $\frac{3}{4}$ (D) $\frac{4}{3}$

(A) **20.** What is the ratio of boys to cats?

(A) 1:4 (B) 4:1 (C) 3:4 (D) 4:3

(C) **21.** What is the ratio of dogs to cats?

(A) 2 to 4 (B) 4 to 2 (C) 3 to 4 (D) 4 to 3

(D) **22.** Find ■ : $\frac{3}{■} = \frac{9}{21}$

(A) 4 (B) 5 (C) 6 (D) 7

(A) **23.** Find ■ : $\frac{■}{21} = \frac{3}{9}$

(A) 7 (B) 9 (C) 27 (D) 63

(A) **24.** Find ■ : $\frac{■}{4} = \frac{5}{10}$

(A) 2 (B) 4 (C) 6 (D) 8

(C) **25.** Find ■ : $\frac{1}{4} = \frac{3}{12} = \frac{9}{■}$

(A) 12 (B) 48 (C) 36 (D) 108

Name ______________________ Class __________ Date __________

5.2 SCALE DRAWINGS

A **scale drawing** is a drawing of an object with dimensions proportional to those of the actual object. To find lengths from scale drawings, set up and solve proportions.

Example 1: Here is a scale drawing of a rock band's concert stage:

Scale: $\frac{1}{4}$ in = 5 ft

($\frac{1}{4}$ in represents 5 ft)

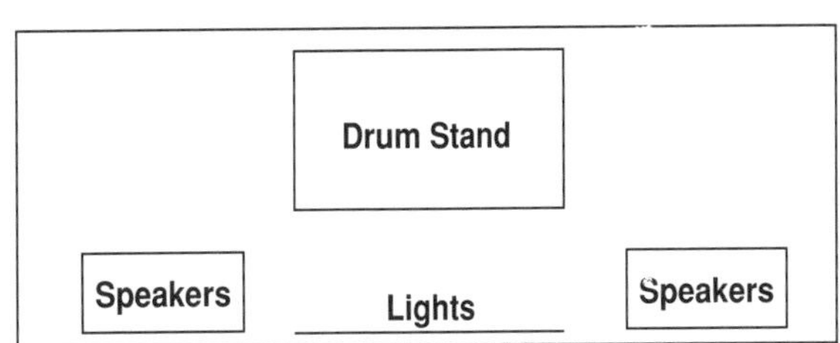

A. The scale length of the drum stand is 1 in. What is the actual length of the drum stand?

B. The actual length of the stage is 60 ft. What is the scale length of the stage?

A		B
$\frac{\frac{1}{4}}{5} = \frac{1}{\square}$	$\frac{\text{drawing(in)}}{\text{actual(ft)}} = \frac{\text{object(drawing)}}{\text{object(actual)}}$	$\frac{\frac{1}{4}}{5} = \frac{\square}{60}$
$\frac{1}{4} \times \square = 5 \times 1$	Set the cross products equal.	$\frac{1}{4} \times 60 = 5 \times \square$
$\frac{1}{4} \times \square = 5$	Simplify.	$15 = 5 \times \square$
$\frac{1}{4} \times \square \div \frac{1}{4} = 5 \div \frac{1}{4}$	Divide.	$15 \div 5 = 5 \times \square \div 5$
$\square = 20$		$3 = \square$

The actual length of the drum stand is 20 ft.

The scale length of the stage is 3 in.

Fill in the correct circle to answer each question.

Given a scale of $\frac{1}{2}$ in = 4 ft, find the actual length for each scale length given.

Ⓐ **1.** $2\frac{3}{4}$ in

Ⓐ 22 ft Ⓑ $5\frac{1}{2}$ ft Ⓒ 11 ft Ⓓ 19 ft

Ⓒ **2.** 5 in

Ⓐ 10 ft Ⓑ 20 in Ⓒ 40 ft Ⓓ 40 yd

Ⓓ **3.** $8\frac{1}{4}$ in

Ⓐ $16\frac{1}{2}$ ft Ⓑ 33 in Ⓒ 33 ft Ⓓ 66 ft

Ⓒ **4.** $2\frac{1}{3}$ in

Ⓐ $4\frac{1}{3}$ ft Ⓑ $9\frac{1}{3}$ ft Ⓒ $18\frac{2}{3}$ ft Ⓓ 56 ft

Given a scale of $\frac{1}{4}$ in = 6 ft, find the scale length for each actual length given.

Ⓐ **5.** 12 ft

Ⓐ $\frac{1}{2}$ in Ⓑ 3 in Ⓒ $\frac{1}{2}$ yd Ⓓ 24 in

Ⓑ **6.** 9 ft

Ⓐ $\frac{1}{8}$ in Ⓑ $\frac{3}{8}$ in Ⓒ $2\frac{1}{2}$ in Ⓓ 14 in

Ⓑ **7.** 33 ft

Ⓐ $1\frac{1}{8}$ in Ⓑ $1\frac{3}{8}$ in Ⓒ $49\frac{1}{2}$ in Ⓓ $1\frac{1}{8}$ yd

Ⓐ **8.** 36 ft

Ⓐ $1\frac{1}{2}$ in Ⓑ 3 in Ⓒ 9 in Ⓓ 54 in

Name________________________ Class ________ Date __________

5.3 PERCENTS AND DECIMALS

Percent (%) means *per hundred.* Percents and decimals are closely related.

To change a decimal to a percent, multiply the decimal by 100 and write a percent sign after it.

Example 1: Convert 0.25 to a percent.

$0.25 = 0.25 \times 100\%$

$= 25\%$

To change a percent to a decimal, divide the percent by 100 and omit the percent sign.

Example 2: Convert 35% to a decimal.

$35\% = 35. \div 100$

$= 0.35$

Fill in the correct circle to answer each question.

Ⓐ **1.** Convert 0.15 to a percent.
Ⓐ 15% Ⓑ 1.5% Ⓒ 0.15% Ⓓ 0.0015%

Ⓒ **2.** Convert 45% to a decimal.
Ⓐ 45 Ⓑ 4500 Ⓒ 0.45 Ⓓ 0.045

Ⓓ **3.** Write 23.45% in decimal form.
Ⓐ 2345 Ⓑ 23.45 Ⓒ 2.345 Ⓓ 0.2345

Ⓓ **4.** 0.9 = ■
Ⓐ 0.009% Ⓑ 0.9% Ⓒ 9% Ⓓ 90%

Ⓑ **5.** Convert 0.015 to a percent.
Ⓐ 15% Ⓑ 1.5% Ⓒ 0.15% Ⓓ 0.00015%

Ⓒ **6.** Write 0.445 in percent form.
Ⓐ 0.00445% Ⓑ 4.45% Ⓒ 44.5% Ⓓ 445%

Ⓑ **7.** Write 0.625 as a percent.
Ⓐ 625% Ⓑ 62.5% Ⓒ 6.25% Ⓓ 0.00625%

Ⓒ **8.** 0.1111 = ■
Ⓐ 0.001111% Ⓑ 1.111% Ⓒ 11.11% Ⓓ 111.1%

Ⓑ **9.** Write 25% in decimal form.
Ⓐ 2.5 Ⓑ 0.25 Ⓒ 0.025 Ⓓ 2.500

Ⓓ **10.** Convert 1.5% to a decimal.
Ⓐ 150 Ⓑ 1.5 Ⓒ 0.15 Ⓓ 0.015

Ⓒ **11.** Write 12.5% as a decimal.
Ⓐ 12.5 Ⓑ 1250 Ⓒ 0.125 Ⓓ 125

Ⓐ **12.** Write 35% in decimal form.
Ⓐ 0.35 Ⓑ 0.035 Ⓒ 0.0035 Ⓓ 3500

Use Figure 5.3 to answer questions 13-14.

Figure 5.3

Ⓓ **13.** What percentage of the cars are red?
Ⓐ $\frac{1}{5}\%$ Ⓑ 0.25% Ⓒ 5% Ⓓ 25%

Ⓒ **14.** What percentage of the cars are *not* red?
Ⓐ $\frac{3}{4}\%$ Ⓑ 15% Ⓒ 75% Ⓓ 90%

Name ________________ Class ________ Date ________

5.4 FRACTIONS AND DECIMALS

To write a fraction as a decimal, divide the numerator by the denominator.

Example 1: Write $\frac{5}{8}$ as a decimal.

$$\begin{array}{r} 0.625 \\ 8\overline{)5.000} \\ \underline{48} \\ 20 \\ \underline{16} \\ 40 \\ \underline{40} \end{array}$$

$\frac{5}{8} = 0.625$

Example 2: Write $2\frac{1}{4}$ as a decimal.

$2\frac{1}{4} = \frac{9}{4}$

$$\begin{array}{r} 2.25 \\ 4\overline{)9.00} \\ \underline{8} \\ 1\,0 \\ \underline{8} \\ 20 \\ \underline{20} \end{array}$$

$\frac{9}{4} = 2.25$

To change a decimal to a fraction, first use a denominator that is a power of 10. Then reduce the fraction to lowest terms.

Example 3: Write 0.35 as a fraction.

0.35 = 35 **hundredths** = $\frac{35}{100} = \frac{7}{20}$.

Example 4: Write 2.85 as a mixed number.

2.85 = 2 and 85 **hundredths** = $2\frac{85}{100} = 2\frac{17}{20}$

Fill in the correct circle to answer each question.

Ⓒ **1.** Write $\frac{1}{4}$ as a decimal.

Ⓐ 25 Ⓑ 2.5 Ⓒ 0.25 Ⓓ 0.025

Ⓒ **2.** Write $\frac{3}{5}$ as a decimal.

Ⓐ 0.3 Ⓑ 0.06 Ⓒ 0.6 Ⓓ 1.6

Ⓑ **3.** Write 0.75 as a fraction or mixed number.

Ⓐ $\frac{3}{40}$ Ⓑ $\frac{3}{4}$ Ⓒ $\frac{4}{3}$ Ⓓ $7\frac{1}{2}$

Ⓒ **4.** Write 0.48 as a fraction or mixed number.

Ⓐ $4\frac{8}{10}$ Ⓑ $\frac{25}{12}$ Ⓒ $\frac{12}{25}$ Ⓓ $\frac{5}{12}$

Ⓑ **5.** Write $3\frac{1}{4}$ as a decimal.

Ⓐ 31.4 Ⓑ 3.25 Ⓒ 3.14 Ⓓ 0.31

Ⓓ **6.** Write $5\frac{7}{8}$ as a decimal.

Ⓐ 0.875 Ⓑ 0.5875 Ⓒ 5.78 Ⓓ 5.875

Ⓒ **7.** Write 2.65 as a fraction or mixed number.

Ⓐ $\frac{53}{200}$ Ⓑ $\frac{53}{20}$ Ⓒ $2\frac{13}{20}$ Ⓓ $5\frac{3}{20}$

Ⓐ **8.** Write 8.2 as a fraction or mixed number.

Ⓐ $8\frac{1}{5}$ Ⓑ $8\frac{2}{5}$ Ⓒ $\frac{82}{5}$ Ⓓ $\frac{82}{100}$

Ⓒ **9.** Every morning Ms. Herlihy jogs $4\frac{2}{5}$ kilometers. Write that distance as a decimal.

Ⓐ 0.44 Ⓑ 4.25 Ⓒ 4.4 Ⓓ 0.23

Ⓒ **10.** Fred's recipe calls for 0.25 pounds of cheese. He buys a piece of cheese marked $\frac{2}{5}$ lb. He bought

Ⓐ too little. Ⓑ the right amount.

Ⓒ too much.

Ⓐ **11.** Write $\frac{3}{16}$ as a decimal.

Ⓐ 0.1875 Ⓑ 0.01875

Ⓒ 5.3 Ⓓ 1.875

Ⓓ **12.** Write 7.6 as a fraction or mixed number.

Ⓐ $\frac{73}{5}$ Ⓑ $\frac{76}{100}$ Ⓒ $7\frac{3}{50}$ Ⓓ $7\frac{3}{5}$

Name________________________________ Class __________ Date ____________

5.5 PERCENTS AND FRACTIONS

To change a percent to a fraction, write the percent over 100, drop the percent sign, and reduce.

Example 1: Write 50% as a fraction.

$$50\% = \frac{50}{100} = \frac{1}{2}$$

Example 2: Write 20.5% as a fraction.

$$20.5\% = \frac{20.5}{100} = \frac{20.5 \times 10}{100 \times 10} = \frac{205}{1000} = \frac{41}{200}$$

To change a fraction to a percent, first convert the fraction to a decimal.
Then convert the decimal to a percent.

Example 3: Write $\frac{1}{5}$ as a percent.

$$\frac{1}{5} = 0.2 \longrightarrow 5\overline{)1.0}\ \ (0.2;\ 10;\ 0)$$

$$= 0.2 \times 100\%$$

$$= 20\%$$

Example 4: Write $2\frac{3}{5}$ as a percent.

$$2\frac{3}{5} = \frac{13}{5} = 2.6 \longrightarrow 5\overline{)13.00}\ \ (2.6;\ 10;\ 30;\ 30;\ 0)$$

$$= 2.6 \times 100\%$$

$$= 260\%$$

Fill in the correct circle to answer each question.

Ⓑ **1.** Write $\frac{1}{4}$ as a percent.

Ⓐ 2.5% Ⓑ 25% Ⓒ $\frac{25}{100}$ Ⓓ 25

Ⓒ **2.** Write 15% as a fraction.

Ⓐ $\frac{1}{15}$ Ⓑ $\frac{3}{10}$ Ⓒ $\frac{3}{20}$ Ⓓ $\frac{2}{30}$

Ⓐ **3.** Write $\frac{1}{8}$ as a percent.

Ⓐ 12.5% Ⓑ 0.8% Ⓒ 0.125% Ⓓ 12%

Ⓐ **4.** Write $\frac{7}{8}$ as a percent.

Ⓐ 87.5% Ⓑ 78% Ⓒ 0.875% Ⓓ 87%

Ⓓ **5.** 40% = ■

Ⓐ $\frac{3}{4}$ Ⓑ $\frac{4}{5}$ Ⓒ $\frac{3}{5}$ Ⓓ $\frac{2}{5}$

Ⓒ **6.** $\frac{3}{4}$ = ■

Ⓐ 133% Ⓑ $133\frac{1}{3}$% Ⓒ 75% Ⓓ $\frac{3}{4}$%

Ⓑ **7.** Write 35% as a fraction.

Ⓐ $\frac{7}{10}$ Ⓑ $\frac{7}{20}$ Ⓒ $\frac{5}{7}$ Ⓓ $\frac{7}{5}$

Ⓒ **8.** Write 7% as a fraction.

Ⓐ $\frac{7}{10}$ Ⓑ $\frac{7}{20}$ Ⓒ $\frac{7}{100}$ Ⓓ $\frac{7}{50}$

Ⓓ **9.** $\frac{5}{8}$ = ■

Ⓐ 6.25% Ⓑ 0.625% Ⓒ 65% Ⓓ 62.5%

Ⓒ **10.** Write 6.25% as a fraction.

Ⓐ $\frac{5}{8}$ Ⓑ $\frac{1}{12}$ Ⓒ $\frac{1}{16}$ Ⓓ $\frac{1}{15}$

Ⓓ **11.** About one person out of five is left-handed. Write this as a percent.

Ⓐ $\frac{1}{5}$% Ⓑ 5% Ⓒ 10% Ⓓ 20%

Ⓓ **12.** About 30% of the earth's surface is land. The rest is water. Write a fraction showing the portion of earth's surface covered by water.

Ⓐ $\frac{7}{100}$ Ⓑ $\frac{3}{10}$ Ⓒ $\frac{70}{1000}$ Ⓓ $\frac{7}{10}$

Ⓓ **13.** Write $3\frac{1}{2}$ as a percent.

Ⓐ 0.035% Ⓑ 3.5% Ⓒ 35% Ⓓ 350%

Ⓐ **14.** Write $5\frac{4}{5}$ as a percent.

Ⓐ 580% Ⓑ 58% Ⓒ 5.8% Ⓓ 0.058%

Name ____________________ Class ________ Date ____________

5.6 PERCENTS LESS THAN 1 AND GREATER THAN 100

Example 1: Write 2.75 as a percent.

$2.75 = 2.75 \times 100\%$

$= 275\%$

Example 2: Write $\frac{1}{200}$ as a percent.

$\frac{1}{200} = 0.005 \longrightarrow 200\overline{)1.000}$ = 0.005

$= 0.005 \times 100\%$

$= 0.5\%$

Example 3: Write $\frac{1}{5}$ % as a fraction and as a decimal.

$\frac{1}{5}\% = \frac{1}{5} \div 100$

$= \frac{1}{5} \times \frac{1}{100}$

$= \frac{1}{500}$

$\frac{1}{5}\% = \frac{1}{500} \longrightarrow 500\overline{)1.000}$ = 0.002

$= 0.002$

REMEMBER: To *drop* a % sign, move the decimal 2 places to the *left*.
To *add* a % sign, move the decimal 2 places to the *right*.

Fill in the correct circle to answer each question.

Ⓒ **1.** Write 2 as a percent.

Ⓐ 2% Ⓑ 20% Ⓒ 200% Ⓓ 0.2%

Ⓒ **2.** Write 220% as a decimal.

Ⓐ 22,000 Ⓑ 220 Ⓒ 2.20 Ⓓ 0.22

Ⓓ **3.** Write 100 as a percent.

Ⓐ 1% Ⓑ 100% Ⓒ 1000% Ⓓ 10,000%

Ⓒ **4.** Write 100% as a decimal.

Ⓐ 10,000 Ⓑ 100 Ⓒ 1 Ⓓ 0.01

Ⓐ **5.** Write $2\frac{1}{2}$ as a percent.

Ⓐ 250% Ⓑ 2.5% Ⓒ 0.25% Ⓓ 0.025%

Ⓓ **6.** 2.5% = ▇

Ⓐ 250 Ⓑ 25 Ⓒ 2.5 Ⓓ 0.025

Ⓒ **7.** Write the decimal 0.003 as a percent.

Ⓐ 30% Ⓑ 3% Ⓒ 0.3% Ⓓ 0.03%

Ⓒ **8.** $\frac{1}{2}$ % = ▇

Ⓐ 0.5 Ⓑ 50 Ⓒ 0.005 Ⓓ 0.0005

Ⓓ **9.** 0.0001 = ▇

Ⓐ 0.000001% Ⓑ 0.00001%

Ⓒ 0.001% Ⓓ 0.01%

Ⓒ **10.** Write $\frac{7}{50}$ as a percent.

Ⓐ 0.014% Ⓑ 1.4% Ⓒ 14% Ⓓ 140%

Ⓐ **11.** Write the decimal 0.66 as a percent.

Ⓐ 66% Ⓑ 0.66% Ⓒ 6.6% Ⓓ 0.0066%

Ⓐ **12.** $\frac{1}{4}$ % = ▇

Ⓐ 0.0025 Ⓑ 0.25 Ⓒ 0.04 Ⓓ 0.004

Ⓒ **13.** Write 40 as a percent.

Ⓐ 40% Ⓑ 0.40% Ⓒ 4000% Ⓓ 40,000%

Ⓐ **14.** 0.04% = ▇

Ⓐ 0.0004 Ⓑ 0.004 Ⓒ 0.04 Ⓓ 4.0

Ⓓ **15.** 1.5 = ▇

Ⓐ 0.015% Ⓑ 1.5% Ⓒ 15% Ⓓ 150%

Ⓓ **16.** 0.15% = ▇

Ⓐ 15 Ⓑ 1.5 Ⓒ 0.15 Ⓓ 0.0015

Name ______________________________ Class __________ Date ______________

5.7 FINDING THE PERCENT OF A NUMBER

To find the percent of a number, first convert the percent to a decimal or fraction. Then multiply.

Example 1: 15% of 250 is ▪.

$$15\% = 0.15$$
$$15\% \text{ of } 250 = 0.15 \times 250$$
$$= 37.5$$

15% of 250 is 37.5

Example 2: Find $12\frac{1}{2}\%$ of 72.

$$12\tfrac{1}{2}\% = 12\tfrac{1}{2} \div 100 = \frac{25}{2} \div 100 = \frac{25}{2} \times \frac{1}{100} = \frac{25}{200} = \frac{1}{8}$$

$$12\tfrac{1}{2}\% \text{ of } 72 = \frac{1}{8} \times 72 = 9$$

$12\frac{1}{2}\%$ of 72 is 9.

REMEMBER: When working with percents, *of* means × and *is* means = .

Fill in the correct circle to answer each question.

Ⓒ **1.** Find 25% of \$1100.

Ⓐ \$27,500 Ⓑ \$2750 Ⓒ \$275 Ⓓ \$27.50

Ⓓ **2.** What is 250% of 11?

Ⓐ 27,500 Ⓑ 2750 Ⓒ 275 Ⓓ 27.5

Ⓓ **3.** Find 0.25% of \$11,000.

Ⓐ \$275,000 Ⓑ \$2750 Ⓒ \$275 Ⓓ \$27.50

Ⓒ **4.** Find $2\frac{1}{2}\%$ of 110.

Ⓐ 275 Ⓑ 27.5 Ⓒ 2.75 Ⓓ 0.0275

Ⓒ **5.** 65% of 40 is ▪.

Ⓐ 2600 Ⓑ 260 Ⓒ 26 Ⓓ 2.6

Ⓑ **6.** 22% of 22 is ▪.

Ⓐ 4.4 Ⓑ 4.84 Ⓒ 4.44 Ⓓ 44.4

Ⓐ **7.** 63% of 500 is ▪.

Ⓐ 315 Ⓑ 305 Ⓒ 301.5 Ⓓ 30.5

Ⓐ **8.** 500% of 63 is ▪.

Ⓐ 315 Ⓑ 305 Ⓒ 301.5 Ⓓ 3.05

Ⓒ **9.** 25% of 52 is ▪.

Ⓐ 2.08 Ⓑ 20.8 Ⓒ 13 Ⓓ 1300

Ⓐ **10.** 100% of 297 is ▪.

Ⓐ 297 Ⓑ 29.7 Ⓒ 2.97 Ⓓ 29,700

Ⓓ **11.** Willie and Ollie had lunch at the City Lights Diner. The bill was \$15. They left a 15% tip for the waiter. What was the total amount they paid for lunch?

Ⓐ \$2.25 Ⓑ \$15.15 Ⓒ \$16.25 Ⓓ \$17.25

Ⓑ **12.** Jeri buys a swim suit marked "40% off." The original cost was \$30. How much did the swimsuit cost?

Ⓐ \$12 Ⓑ \$18 Ⓒ \$28.80 Ⓓ \$42

Ⓒ **13.** Twenty-five percent of the students in a geometry class have curly hair. There are 28 students in the class. How many students have curly hair?

Ⓐ 3 Ⓑ 6 Ⓒ 7 Ⓓ 21

14. Ⓓ If Mark made 50% of a recipe that is supposed to make 60 cookies, how many cookies did he make?

Ⓐ 300 Ⓑ 120 Ⓒ 45 Ⓓ 30

Name ______________________ Class ________ Date ____________

5.8 FINDING WHAT PERCENT ONE NUMBER IS OF ANOTHER

To find what percent one number is of another, use the proportion: $\frac{\text{Part}}{\text{Whole}} = \frac{\%}{100}$

Example 1: 12 is what percent of 75? *Example 2:* What percent is 875 of 175?

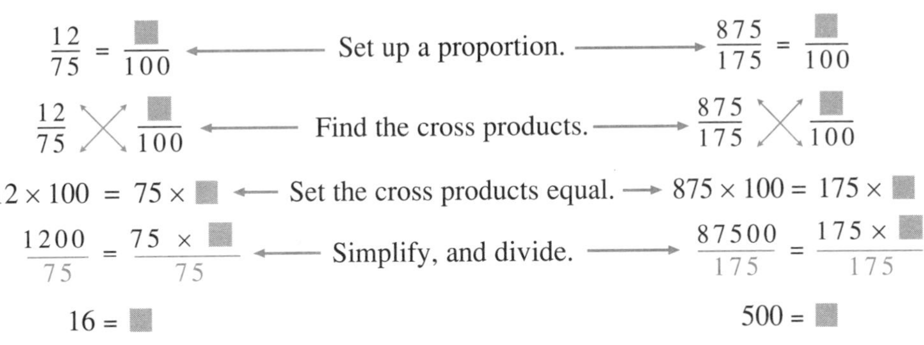

12 is 16% of 75. 875 is 500% of 175.

Fill in the correct circle to answer each question.

Ⓐ **1.** 17 is what percent of 85?

Ⓐ 20% Ⓑ 10% Ⓒ $7\frac{1}{2}$% Ⓓ 500%

Ⓓ **2.** 16 is what percent of 320?

Ⓐ 2000% Ⓑ 10 Ⓒ 7.5% Ⓓ 5%

Ⓒ **3.** 200 is what percent of 20?

Ⓐ 10% Ⓑ 100% Ⓒ 1000% Ⓓ 10,000

Ⓐ **4.** 1001 is what percent of 91?

Ⓐ 1100% Ⓑ $9\frac{1}{11}$% Ⓒ 11% Ⓓ 91%

Ⓐ **5.** 250 boys and 30 girls go to Ace High School. What percent of the students are boys?

Ⓐ about 89% Ⓑ about 58%
Ⓒ about 71% Ⓓ about 140%

Ⓒ **6.** What percent of the total number of states does each of the 50 states represent?

Ⓐ 5% Ⓑ 3% Ⓒ 2% Ⓓ 1%

Ⓒ **7.** 36 students are on a school bus. The school has 360 students in all. What percent of the school's students are on the bus?

Ⓐ 1% Ⓑ 5% Ⓒ 10% Ⓓ 20%

Ⓓ **8.** 270 of the 810 taxis in Potholeville are in the shop for repairs. What percent of the taxis are on the road?

Ⓐ 25% Ⓑ 30% Ⓒ $33\frac{1}{3}$% Ⓓ $66\frac{2}{3}$%

Ⓑ **9.** Clark's take home pay is $180 a week. He saves $36 of each paycheck. What percent of his earnings does he save?

Ⓐ 144% Ⓑ 20% Ⓒ 5% Ⓓ 0.2%

Ⓓ **10.** Of the 8 girls on the homecoming court, 3 are also cheerleaders. What percent of the girls on the homecoming court are also cheerleaders?

Ⓐ 0.375% Ⓑ 2.66% Ⓒ 5% Ⓓ 37.5%

Ⓓ **11.** 72 is what percent of 96?

Ⓐ 0.75% Ⓑ $7\frac{1}{2}$% Ⓒ 7.5% Ⓓ 75%

Ⓐ **12.** What percent is 180 of 120?

Ⓐ 150% Ⓑ 66% Ⓒ 0.66% Ⓓ 1.5%

Name _______________ Class _______ Date _______

5.9 FINDING A NUMBER WHEN A PERCENT OF IT IS KNOWN

REMEMBER: $\frac{\text{Part}}{\text{Whole}} = \frac{\%}{100}$

Example 1: 25% of what number is 30?

Example 2: 66 is 75% of what number?

Example 1	Step	Example 2
$\frac{30}{■} = \frac{25}{100}$	Set up a proportion.	$\frac{66}{■} = \frac{75}{100}$
$\frac{30}{■} \times \frac{25}{100}$	Find the cross products.	$\frac{66}{■} \times \frac{75}{100}$
$30 \times 100 = ■ \times 25$	Set the cross products equal.	$66 \times 100 = ■ \times 75$
$\frac{3000}{25} = \frac{■ \times 25}{25}$	Simplify and divide.	$\frac{6600}{75} = \frac{■ \times 75}{75}$
$120 = ■$		$88 = ■$
25% of 120 is 30.		66 is 75% of 88.

Fill in the correct circle to answer each question.

Ⓑ **1.** 13% of a number is 91. The number is ■.
Ⓐ 1300 Ⓑ 700 Ⓒ 910 Ⓓ 7

Ⓒ **2.** 25% of a number is 25. The number is ■.
Ⓐ 1 Ⓑ 4 Ⓒ 100 Ⓓ 400

Ⓐ **3.** 20 is 5% of ■.
Ⓐ 400 Ⓑ 0.40 Ⓒ 4 Ⓓ 4000

Ⓑ **4.** 35 is 7% of ■.
Ⓐ 5000 Ⓑ 500 Ⓒ 50 Ⓓ 5

Ⓒ **5.** 2.5 is 1% of ■.
Ⓐ 150 Ⓑ 200 Ⓒ 250 Ⓓ 300

Ⓓ **6.** 297 is 99% of ■.
Ⓐ 150 Ⓑ 200 Ⓒ 250 Ⓓ 300

Ⓑ **7.** 14.28 is 7% of ■.
Ⓐ 142.8 Ⓑ 204 Ⓒ 14.28 Ⓓ 205

Ⓓ **8.** 33 is 11% of ■.
Ⓐ 3300 Ⓑ 330 Ⓒ 3000 Ⓓ 300

Ⓑ **9.** 28.56 is 14% of ■.
Ⓐ 200 Ⓑ 204 Ⓒ 208 Ⓓ 408

Ⓓ **10.** 100 is 25% of ■.
Ⓐ 25 Ⓑ 40 Ⓒ 250 Ⓓ 400

Ⓒ **11.** Jules lifts weights as a hobby. He works out with a barbell weighing 32 pounds. That is 20% of his body weight. How much does Jules weigh?
Ⓐ 38.4 lb Ⓑ 130 lb Ⓒ 160 lb Ⓓ 640 lb

12. Ⓓ Mr. Lemke is a real estate agent. He earns a 6% commission on every house he sells. Today he sold a house and earned $7800. How much did the house sell for?
Ⓐ $1950 Ⓑ $46,800
Ⓒ $124,800 Ⓓ $130,000

Ⓐ **13.** Melissa received a 16% raise. This raised her salary $0.96 an hour. What was her former hourly rate?
Ⓐ $6.00 Ⓑ $5.00 Ⓒ $5.36 Ⓓ $6.67

Ⓑ **14.** Three friends shared an onion pizza. Brian ate 2 pieces, which was 25% of the pizza. How many pieces were left?
Ⓐ 8 Ⓑ 6 Ⓒ 4 Ⓓ 2

Name ______________________ Class ________ Date ____________

5.10 PROBLEM SOLVING

Problems that involve finding the *percent of increase* or the *percent of decrease* require more than one step and more than one operation to solve.

Example 1: Bonnie Pryor is the assistant manager at Super Burger. Her salary has been raised from $250 a week to $275 a week. What is the percent of increase in Bonnie's salary?

- Find the amount of the increase. — $275 – $250 = $25
- Write as a fraction: amount of the increase divided by the original amount. — $\frac{25}{250}$ (25 ← amount of increase; 250 ← original amount)
- Write the fraction as a percent. — $\frac{25}{250} = 0.10$, or 10%

Bonnie's salary increased by 10%.

Example 2: Last week Super Shakes were on sale at Super Burger and 875 Super Shakes were sold. This week only 350 Super Shakes were sold. What is the percent of decrease in the number of Super Shakes sold?

- Find the amount of decrease. — 875 – 350 = 525
- Write as a fraction: amount of the decrease divided by the original amount. — $\frac{525}{875}$ (525 ← amount of decrease; 875 ← original amount)
- Write the fraction as a percent. — $\frac{525}{875} = 0.60$, or 60%

The number of milkshakes sold decreased by 60%.

REMEMBER: Use the original amount as the denominator when finding *percent of increase* or *percent of decrease*.

Solve.

Ⓑ **1.** Patty Chung is a secretary. Her salary was raised from $300 to $345 a week. What was the percent of increase in Patty's salary?

Ⓐ 13% Ⓑ 15% Ⓒ 45% Ⓓ 87%

Ⓒ **2.** Ken Brooks works at an auto shop. He cut the number of hours he works each week from 40 to 28. What is the percent of decrease in the number of hours Ken works?

Ⓐ 12% Ⓑ 28% Ⓒ 30% Ⓓ 43%

Ⓑ **3.** Coffeemakers are on sale. They were $60. Now they sell for $45. By what percent did the price decrease?

Ⓐ 15% Ⓑ 25% Ⓒ 33% Ⓓ 45%

Ⓑ **4.** The rent on Karen Rizzo's apartment was increased from $400 to $460 a month. What was the percent of increase in Karen's rent?

Ⓐ 13% Ⓑ 15% Ⓒ 20% Ⓓ 60%

Ⓒ **5.** The latest issue of the Rosemont High School Record sold 490 copies. The previous issue sold only 350 copies. By what percent did the number of copies sold increase?

Ⓐ 140% Ⓑ 71% Ⓒ 40% Ⓓ 29%

Ⓓ **6.** A sound system is on sale at Susan's Stereo Shop for $770. The original price was $1100. By what percent was the price decreased?

Ⓐ 330% Ⓑ 70% Ⓒ 43% Ⓓ 30%

Ⓓ **7.** During summer vacation, Maria Cortez increased the number of hours she worked at the florist from 25 to 40 hours each week. By what percent did Maria increase her working hours?

Ⓐ 15% Ⓑ 25% Ⓒ 37.5% Ⓓ 60%

Ⓒ **8.** Paul Kumata owns a drugstore. One sunny day, he sold 92 bottles of sunscreen. The next day was cloudy and he sold only 23 bottles. What was the percent of decrease in the number of bottles sold?

Ⓐ 25% Ⓑ 300% Ⓒ 75% Ⓓ 30%

Ⓑ **9.** Last year, 200 students belonged to the Pep Club. This year, 300 students belong to the club. By what percent did the number of club members increase?

Ⓐ 33% Ⓑ 50% Ⓒ 66% Ⓓ 150%

Ⓐ **10.** Last month, 600 flights at City Airport arrived on time. This month, 462 flights arrived on time. By what percent did the number of on-time flights decrease?

Ⓐ 23% Ⓑ 30% Ⓒ 138% Ⓓ 230%

Ⓓ **11.** When Paul Jacobs began delivering newspapers, he had 60 customers. Now he has 150 customers. What is the percent of increase in the number of Paul's customers?

Ⓐ 15% Ⓑ 60% Ⓒ 90% Ⓓ 150%

Ⓒ **12.** Last year, the rock band Wild Things played 60 concerts. This year, they will play 42 concerts. What is the percentage decrease in the number of concerts the band will play this year?

Ⓐ 3% Ⓑ 18% Ⓒ 30% Ⓓ 43%

Ⓓ **13.** The Movie Palace raised the price of a ticket from $5 to $7. What is the percent of increase in the price of a ticket?

Ⓐ 2% Ⓑ 20% Ⓒ 28.5% Ⓓ 40%

Ⓑ **14.** Last year Debbie Shapiro was 5 ft tall. Now she is 5 ft 3 in tall. To the nearest whole percent, what is the percent of increase in Debbie's height?

Ⓐ 6% Ⓑ 5% Ⓒ 50% Ⓓ 60%

Ⓒ **15.** In last year's basketball season, Wilma Edwards scored 250 points. This season, she scored 235 points. By what percent did the number of points scored by Wilma decrease?

Ⓐ 0.06% Ⓑ 0.6% Ⓒ 6% Ⓓ 60%

Ⓑ **16.** During December, the Electric Shock Shop sold 120 televisions. In January, the shop sold 18 televisions. By what percent did television sales decrease?

Ⓐ 102% Ⓑ 85% Ⓒ 567% Ⓓ 0.85%

Ⓐ **17.** Last year, Harper's Department Store received 720 letters of complaint. This year, they received 468 complaint letters. By what percent did the number of complaint letters decrease?

Ⓐ 35% Ⓑ 54% Ⓒ 65% Ⓓ 252%

Ⓑ **18.** From 1975 to 1985, the population of Grove City increased from 3500 people to 15,540 people. By what percent did the city's population increase?

Ⓐ 3.44% Ⓑ 344% Ⓒ 77% Ⓓ 23%

Ⓑ **19.** The library at Coyote High School had 3684 books last year. This year, the library has 4605 books. By what percent did the number of books increase?

Ⓐ 20% Ⓑ 25% Ⓒ 80% Ⓓ 921%

Ⓐ **20.** Last summer, 48,920 people saw The Planets' perform in Center City. This year, 41,582 people attended the Planets' concert in Center City. By what percent did attendance at the concert decrease?

Ⓐ 15% Ⓑ 18% Ⓒ 85% Ⓓ 7338%

Ⓒ **21.** Slinky Jeans usually sell for $35. This week, they are on sale for $22.75. By what percent did the price decrease?

Ⓐ 65% Ⓑ 54% Ⓒ 35% Ⓓ 12.25%

Ⓑ **22.** Last year's yearbook at Foxdale High School has 640 pages. This year's yearbook has 800 pages. By what percent did the number of pages increase?

Ⓐ 20% Ⓑ 25% Ⓒ 80% Ⓓ 160%

Name ____________________ Class ________ Date ____________

CHAPTER 5 TEST

Fill in the correct circle to answer each question.

(D) **1.** 10% is equivalent to the fraction ▇ .

Ⓐ 10 Ⓑ $\frac{1}{2}$ Ⓒ $\frac{1}{5}$ Ⓓ $\frac{1}{10}$

(A) **2.** Write 2.87 as a percent.

Ⓐ 287% Ⓑ 28.7% Ⓒ 2.87% Ⓓ 0.0287

Use Figure 1 to answer questions 3 and 4.

Figure 1

A B C D E

(D) **3.** The ratio of AB to CD is ▇ .

Ⓐ 1:1 Ⓑ 1:2 Ⓒ 2:1 Ⓓ 2:3

(C) **4.** The ratio of CE to AC is ▇ .

Ⓐ 4:5 Ⓑ 5:4 Ⓒ 5:3 Ⓓ 3:5

(C) **5.** John makes $48 for 6 hours work. What does he earn in 9 hours?

Ⓐ $56 Ⓑ $54 Ⓒ $72 Ⓓ $81

(C) **6.** The ratio of overtime pay to regular pay is 3:2. If Marie earns $48 for a regular 8 hour day, what does she earn for 2 hours of overtime?

Ⓐ $66 Ⓑ $60 Ⓒ $18 Ⓓ $12

(D) **7.** Which two ratios form a proportion?

Ⓐ 12 to 25, 6 to 11 Ⓑ 9 to 3, 1 to 3
Ⓒ 12 to 6, 3 to 1 Ⓓ 26 to 13, 18 to 9

(B) **8.** If the price of a $150,000 house rises to $300,000, what is the percent of increase?

Ⓐ 50% Ⓑ 100% Ⓒ 150% Ⓓ 200%

(A) **9.** $\frac{2}{7}$ ▇ 0.42

Ⓐ < Ⓑ > Ⓒ =

(C) **10.** What is 15% of 60?

Ⓐ 90 Ⓑ 15 Ⓒ 9 Ⓓ 6

(C) **11.** What percent of 75 is 15?

Ⓐ 5% Ⓑ 15% Ⓒ 20% Ⓓ 500%

(B) **12.** 8 is $12\frac{1}{2}$ % of ▇ .

Ⓐ 60 Ⓑ 64 Ⓒ 84 Ⓓ 100

(D) **13.** 5% is the same as the decimal ▇ .

Ⓐ 50 Ⓑ 5 Ⓒ 0.5 Ⓓ 0.05

(C) **14.** 1% of what number is 0.0123?

Ⓐ 123 Ⓑ 12.3 Ⓒ 1.23 Ⓓ 0.123

(B) **15.** 0.125 = ▇

Ⓐ 125% Ⓑ 12.5% Ⓒ 1.25% Ⓓ 0.125%

(D) **16.** What fraction is 0.125?

Ⓐ $\frac{1}{125}$ Ⓑ $\frac{1}{12}$ Ⓒ $\frac{1}{16}$ Ⓓ $\frac{1}{8}$

Use Figure 2 to answer questions 17 and 18.

Figure 2

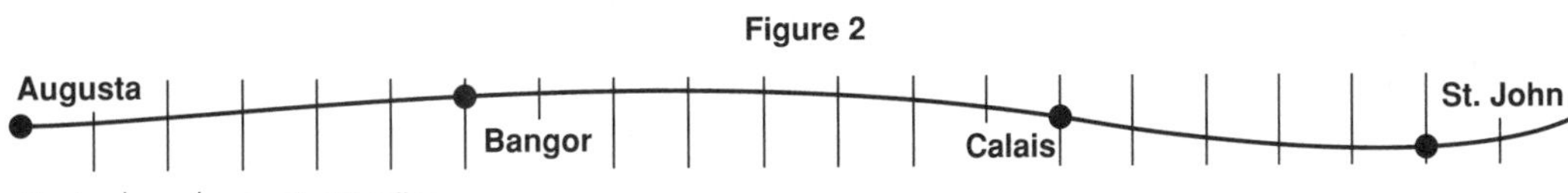

(C) **17.** How far is it from Bangor to Calais?

Ⓐ 91 miles Ⓑ 100 miles
Ⓒ 104 miles Ⓓ 117 miles

(C) **18.** How far is it from Augusta to St. John?

Ⓐ 260 miles Ⓑ 250 miles
Ⓒ 247 miles Ⓓ 243 miles

Ⓒ **19.** If 35 miles is 2 inches on a map, what is the scale?

Ⓐ 1 inch to 35 miles

Ⓑ 35 inches to 1 mile

Ⓒ 1 inch to $17\frac{1}{2}$ miles

Ⓓ $77\frac{1}{2}$ inches to 1 mile

Ⓑ **20.** A map has a scale of $\frac{1}{2}$ inch to the mile. Hudson is 9 inches from Orono on the map. What is the actual distance in miles?

Ⓐ $4\frac{1}{2}$ miles Ⓑ 18 miles

Ⓒ $9\frac{1}{2}$ miles Ⓓ 180 miles

Ⓒ **21.** What is the decimal for $45\frac{3}{4}$?

Ⓐ 0.4575 Ⓑ 4.575 Ⓒ 45.75 Ⓓ 4575%

Ⓓ **22.** What fraction is $66\frac{2}{3}$ %?

Ⓐ $\frac{1}{2}$ Ⓑ $\frac{1}{3}$ Ⓒ $\frac{3}{2}$ Ⓓ $\frac{2}{3}$

Ⓐ **23.** A store ordered 96 pairs of new aerobic shoes. 72 pairs were red. All the red pairs and 12 white pairs were sold on Saturday. What percent of the shoes sold on Saturday were red?

Ⓐ 85.7% Ⓑ 87.5% Ⓒ 12.5% Ⓓ 72%

Ⓐ **24.** Sixteen mice in a pet store were spotted. This was 8% of the mice in the store. How many mice were in the store?

Ⓐ 200 Ⓑ 128

Ⓒ 64 Ⓓ 24

Ⓒ **25.** The ratio $\frac{10}{14}$ is proportional to the ratio ■.

Ⓐ $\frac{7}{2}$ Ⓑ $\frac{7}{5}$ Ⓒ $\frac{5}{7}$ Ⓓ $\frac{2}{7}$

Ⓑ **26.** Write 0.037 as a percent.

Ⓐ 0.37% Ⓑ 3.7% Ⓒ 37% Ⓓ 370%

Ⓓ **27.** What is 80% of 102?

Ⓐ 8.16 Ⓑ 20.4 Ⓒ 81 Ⓓ 81.6

Ⓐ **28.** 101.5 is what percent of 29?

Ⓐ 350% Ⓑ 313% Ⓒ 35% Ⓓ 3.5%

Ⓐ **29.** 0.0872% = ■.

Ⓐ 0.000872 Ⓑ 0.0872

Ⓒ 8.72 Ⓓ 87.2

Ⓐ **30.** Write 125% as a fraction.

Ⓐ $\frac{5}{4}$ Ⓑ $\frac{3}{4}$ Ⓒ $\frac{4}{3}$ Ⓓ $\frac{125}{25}$

Use Table 3 to answer questions 31-34.

Table 3

Chocolate Chip Cookies
$2\frac{1}{2}$ cups flour
$1\frac{1}{4}$ cups brown sugar
1 cup butter or margarine
2 eggs – Note: 1 egg = $\frac{1}{4}$ cup
2 teaspoon vanilla
1 teaspoon baking soda
$1\frac{1}{2}$ cups semi-sweet chocolate pieces
1 cup chopped nuts
Makes 50 large cookies or 80 small cookies

Ⓐ **31.** What is the ratio of baking soda to vanilla?

Ⓐ 1:2 Ⓑ 2:1 Ⓒ 1:1 Ⓓ 2

Ⓑ **32.** What is the ratio of cups of flour to cups of brown sugar?

Ⓐ 1:2 Ⓑ 2:1 Ⓒ 2:2 Ⓓ 1:1

Ⓓ **33.** Steven baked small cookies. If he used 60% of the dough from the recipe, how many cookies could he make?

Ⓐ 80 Ⓑ 32 Ⓒ 42 Ⓓ 48

Ⓒ **34.** How many more cups of flour than brown sugar are used in the recipe?

Ⓐ $3\frac{3}{4}$ Ⓑ $1\frac{1}{2}$ Ⓒ $1\frac{1}{4}$ Ⓓ $\frac{3}{4}$

Name ____________________ Class ________ Date ____________

CHAPTERS 1-5 CUMULATIVE REVIEW

Fill in the correct circle to answer each question.

(D) **1.** $52.755 \div 1.5 =$ ■

Ⓐ 3.511 Ⓑ 3.517 Ⓒ 35.11 Ⓓ 35.17

(A) **2.** $5^3 =$ ■

Ⓐ 125 Ⓑ 85 Ⓒ 75 Ⓓ 15

(A) **3.** Which fraction is *greatest?*

Ⓐ $\frac{5}{3}$ Ⓑ $\frac{3}{8}$ Ⓒ $\frac{5}{8}$ Ⓓ $\frac{3}{5}$

(D) **4.** Which is the prime factorization of 54?

Ⓐ 1×54 Ⓑ 9×6

Ⓒ 2×27 Ⓓ $2 \times 3 \times 3 \times 3$

(C) **5.** The least common multiple of 6 and 15 is ■.

Ⓐ 3 Ⓑ 12 Ⓒ 30 Ⓓ 90

(A) **6.** Which fraction is *least?*

Ⓐ $\frac{2}{3}$ Ⓑ $\frac{5}{6}$ Ⓒ $\frac{12}{15}$ Ⓓ $\frac{7}{8}$

(A) **7.** $12 \div 3\frac{1}{3} =$ ■

Ⓐ $3\frac{3}{5}$ Ⓑ $5\frac{1}{7}$ Ⓒ $5\frac{3}{5}$ Ⓓ 40

(A) **8.** Subtract $3\frac{5}{6}$ from $8\frac{1}{4}$.

Ⓐ $4\frac{5}{12}$ Ⓑ $4\frac{5}{6}$ Ⓒ $5\frac{5}{12}$ Ⓓ $5\frac{5}{4}$

(D) **9.** Which of the following is an example of the Associative Property of Addition?

Ⓐ $(5 + 2) \times 3 = (5 \times 3) + (2 \times 2)$

Ⓑ $5 + 2 = 2 + 5$

Ⓒ $5 = 2 + 3$: $3 + 2 = 5$

Ⓓ $(5 + 2) + 3 = 5 + (2 + 3)$

(A) **10.** Kevin swims 1.5 hours every day. How many hours does he swim in 4 weeks?

Ⓐ 42 hours Ⓑ 10.5 hours

Ⓒ 6 hours Ⓓ 5.5 hours

(B) **11.** $7.39 \times 10^6 =$ ■

Ⓐ 73,900,000 Ⓑ 7,390,000

Ⓒ 739,000 Ⓓ 0.000739

(D) **12.** $\frac{7}{8}$ is equivalent to ■.

Ⓐ $\frac{8}{7}$ Ⓑ $\frac{24}{21}$ Ⓒ $\frac{27}{32}$ Ⓓ $\frac{35}{40}$

(A) **13.** Multiply: $\frac{2}{3} \times \frac{7}{8}$

Ⓐ $\frac{7}{12}$ Ⓑ $\frac{8}{12}$ Ⓒ $\frac{14}{3}$ Ⓓ $\frac{16}{21}$

(D) **14.** Find the sum: $\frac{13}{15} + \frac{2}{3} + \frac{1}{6}$

Ⓐ $2\frac{1}{30}$ Ⓑ $\frac{16}{24}$ Ⓒ $1\frac{51}{30}$ Ⓓ $1\frac{7}{10}$

(C) **15.** Subtract: $6\frac{3}{5} - 1\frac{1}{2}$

Ⓐ $7\frac{11}{10}$ Ⓑ $5\frac{2}{3}$ Ⓒ $5\frac{1}{10}$ Ⓓ $4\frac{3}{5}$

(B) **16.** The prime factorization of 40 is ■.

Ⓐ $3^2 \times 5$ Ⓑ $2^3 \times 5$

Ⓒ 2×5^2 Ⓓ $2^2 \times 10$

(C) **17.** Order from *least to greatest:*

$\frac{2}{3}, \frac{2}{11}, \frac{2}{5}, \frac{2}{7}$

Ⓐ $\frac{2}{5}, \frac{2}{3}, \frac{2}{11}, \frac{2}{7}$ Ⓑ $\frac{2}{3}, \frac{2}{5}, \frac{2}{7}, \frac{2}{11}$

Ⓒ $\frac{2}{11}, \frac{2}{7}, \frac{2}{5}, \frac{2}{3}$ Ⓓ $\frac{2}{7}, \frac{2}{11}, \frac{2}{5}, \frac{2}{3}$

(A) **18.** Add: $\frac{3}{4} + \frac{3}{16}$

Ⓐ $\frac{15}{16}$ Ⓑ $\frac{6}{8}$ Ⓒ $\frac{6}{4}$ Ⓓ $\frac{6}{20}$

(A) **19.** $270 \div 1000 =$ ■

Ⓐ 0.27 Ⓑ 27 Ⓒ 1 Ⓓ 0

(C) **20.** Compare: $\frac{3}{12}$ ■ $\frac{1}{4}$

Ⓐ > Ⓑ < Ⓒ =

(A) **21.** 62 kg = ■ g

Ⓐ 62,000 Ⓑ 6200
Ⓒ 0.62 Ⓓ 0.062

(A) **22.** Find the difference: 19 – 1.087

Ⓐ 17.913 Ⓑ 18.913
Ⓒ 18.023 Ⓓ 20.087

(D) **23.** $7\frac{1}{3} \div \frac{11}{12} \doteq$ ■

Ⓐ $\frac{1}{2}$ Ⓑ $\frac{1}{2}$ Ⓒ $6\frac{13}{18}$ Ⓓ 8

(C) **24.** $\frac{1}{3} + \frac{1}{2} + \frac{1}{4}$

Ⓐ $\frac{1}{24}$ Ⓑ $\frac{1}{3}$ Ⓒ $1\frac{1}{12}$ Ⓓ $1\frac{1}{6}$

(B) **25.** The distance between Newport and Middletown is 48 miles. On a map, the towns are 4 inches apart. How many miles does each inch on the map represent?

Ⓐ 192 mi Ⓑ 12 mi
Ⓒ 4 mi Ⓓ $\frac{1}{4}$ mi

26. (C) Championship Sneakers are on sale for $48. The original price was $60. By what percent was the price decreased?

Ⓐ 80% Ⓑ 25% Ⓒ 20% Ⓓ 12%

(C) **27.**

$$\begin{array}{r} 26.21 \\ \times\ 0.67 \\ \hline \end{array}$$

Ⓐ 1.75607 Ⓑ 16.6607
Ⓒ 17.5607 Ⓓ 1755.07

(A) **28.** 1500 g = ■ kg

Ⓐ 1.5 Ⓑ 15
Ⓒ 150 Ⓓ 150,000

(D) **29.**

$$\begin{array}{r} 4\text{ yd }1\text{ ft} \\ -\quad 2\text{ ft} \\ \hline \end{array}$$

Ⓐ 4 yd 1 ft Ⓑ 4 yd 2 ft
Ⓒ 3 yd 9 ft Ⓓ 3 yd 2 ft

(A) **30.** Order from *greatest to least*: $\frac{3}{5}, \frac{3}{10}, \frac{3}{7}, \frac{3}{17}$

Ⓐ $\frac{3}{5}, \frac{3}{7}, \frac{3}{10}, \frac{3}{17}$ Ⓑ $\frac{3}{17}, \frac{3}{10}, \frac{3}{7}, \frac{3}{5}$
Ⓒ $\frac{3}{7}, \frac{3}{17}, \frac{3}{10}, \frac{3}{5}$ Ⓓ $\frac{3}{17}, \frac{3}{10}, \frac{3}{7}, \frac{3}{5}$

(B) **31.** Round $279.51 to the nearest *dollar*.

Ⓐ $300.00 Ⓑ $280
Ⓒ $279 Ⓓ $200

(A) **32.** What is the *value* of the digit 7 in 6,079,835,111?

Ⓐ 70,000,000 Ⓑ 7,000,000
Ⓒ 700,000 Ⓓ 70,000

(D) **33.** Estimate the difference: 67,849 – 12,085

Ⓐ 80,000 Ⓑ 50,000
Ⓒ 70,000 Ⓓ 60,000

(B) **34.** Subtract: 5 yd – 2 ft 9 in

Ⓐ 7 ft 9 in Ⓑ 4 yd 3 in
Ⓒ 4 ft 3 in Ⓓ 2 ft 3 in

(D) **35.** The student lounge at Pineview High School has 24 tables that each seat 4 people and 18 tables that each seat 2 people. How many people can be seated in the lounge?

Ⓐ 36 Ⓑ 48 Ⓒ 96 Ⓓ 132

36. (C) Jessica spent $10 on decorations for a party. She spent $20.50 on food. There were 10 people at the party. How much did she spend per person on food and decorations?

Ⓐ $1.05 Ⓑ $2.05 Ⓒ $3.05 Ⓓ $30.05

Name ______________________ Class __________ Date __________

Use Table 1 to answer questions 37–40.

Table 1

Elizabeth Ziegfeld's Earnings	
Month	Amount
January	$2650
February	$4685
March	$3928
April	$2800
May	$5200

(C) **37.** Estimate Ms. Ziegfeld's least monthly earnings as a percentage of her greatest monthly earnings.

(A) 20% (B) 40% (C) 50% (D) 200%

(B) **38.** Ms. Ziegfeld wants to earn enough in June to make $24,000 for all six months. She needs to earn about as much in June as she did in:

(A) Jan. (B) Feb. (C) March (D) April

(D) **39.** Rank the incomes from *least* to *greatest.*

(A) $5200, $4685, $3928, $2800, $2650

(B) $2800, $2650, $3928, $4685, $5200

(C) $4685, $5200, $3928, $2800, $2650

(D) $2650, $2800, $3928, $4685, $5200

(B) **40.** The greatest monthly difference in earnings occurred between

(A) Jan.–Feb. (B) Feb.–March

(C) March–April (D) April–May

(A) **41.** 12 qt = ■ gal

(A) 3 (B) 4 (C) 6 (D) 8

(C) **42.** 4 h = ■ min

(A) 40 (B) 64 (C) 240 (D) 400

(B) **43.** Find n: $\frac{8}{14} = \frac{n}{35}$

(A) 14 (B) 20 (C) 21 (D) 29

(D) **44.** Multiply: 46×6000

(A) 276 (B) 2760

(C) 27,600 (D) 276,000

(A) **45.** Estimate the quotient: $470 \div 77$

(A) 6 (B) 7 (C) 60 (D) 70

(A) **46.** What is 15% of 3600?

(A) 540 (B) 3585

(C) 5400 (D) 54,000

(D) **47.** 73 m = ■ mm

(A) 0.073 (B) 0.73

(C) 7300 (D) 73,000

(D) **48.** Divide: $0.02\overline{)8.32}$

(A) 0.416 (B) 4.16 (C) 41.6 (D) 416

(B) **49.** 285 is what percent of 475?

(A) 190% (B) 60% (C) 1.66% (D) 0.6%

(B) **50.** Estimate: 43×329

(A) 1200 (B) 12,000

(C) 7 000 (D) 20,000

(A) **51.**

  6 gal 3 qt
\+ 2 gal 2 qt

(A) 9 gal 1 qt (B) 9 gal 5 qt

(C) 8 gal 1 qt (C) 4 gal 1 qt

(D) **52.** Find n: $\frac{30}{18} = \frac{n}{30}$

(A) 18 (B) 30 (C) 42 (D) 50

(C) **53.** Barbara works 20 hours a week at the Ice Cream Factory. During summer vacation, she plans to work 28 hours a week. By what percent will Barbara increase the number of hours she works?

(A) 8% (B) 28.5% (C) 40% (D) 71%

54. (B) At the World of Records, Sean bought 3 cassette tapes at $7.99 each and 2 packages of batteries at $2.99 each. How much change did he receive from $40.00?

(A) $0.05 (B) $10.05

(C) $15.05 (D) $29.02

(D) **55.** Which of the following is *not* a proportion?

(A) $\frac{24}{1} = \frac{96}{4}$ (B) $\frac{1}{2} = \frac{4}{8}$

(C) $\frac{9}{4} = \frac{18}{8}$ (D) $\frac{16}{2} = \frac{80}{5}$

(A) **56.** Subtract:

$$\begin{array}{r} 9 \text{ min} \\ -\ 2 \text{ min } 32 \text{ sec} \\ \hline \end{array}$$

(A) 6 min 28 sec (B) 7 min 28 sec

(C) 7 min 32 sec (D) 11 min 32 sec

(D) **57.** 25% of what number is 69?

(A) 0.0036 (B) 2.76

(C) 17.25 (D) 276

(D) **58.** What is the *value* of the digit 3 in 457.863?

(A) 3000 (B) 3 (C) 0.03 (D) 0.003

(B) **59.** What percent of 400 is 84?

(A) 4.76% (B) 21% (C) 79% (D) 316%

(D) **60.** Round 4.385 to the nearest *tenth*.

(A) 4.39 (B) 4.3 (C) 4.39 (D) 4.4

(A) **61.** Donna needs 280 paper cups for a party. Cups come in packages of 20. She has 8 packages. How many more packages should she buy?

(A) 6 (B) 10 (C) 14 (D) 120

62. Compare: 9501 ■ 9510

(B)

(A) > (B) < (C) =

(C) **63.** What is the *place value* of 7 in 43,705?

(A) ones (B) tens

(C) hundreds (D) thousands

(B) **64.** From 8 A.M. to 4:30 P.M. is ■ hours.

(A) $16\frac{1}{2}$ (B) $8\frac{1}{2}$ (C) 8 (D) $4\frac{1}{2}$

(B) **65.** 7 yd = ■ ft

(A) 24 (B) 21 (C) 14 (D) 2.5

(D) **66.** $63 \times 109 =$ ■

(A) 172 (B) 981

(C) 6767 (D) 6867

(C) **67.** 2.89 + 43.682 = ■

(A) 72.582 (B) 61.582

(C) 46.572 (D) 45.472

(B) **68.** 38 cm = ■ mm

(A) 3.8 (B) 380

(C) 3800 (D) 38,000

(C) **69.** Estimate: 2.9×4.48

(A) 6 (B) 8

(C) 12 (D) 120

(A) **70.** 4 – 2.29 = ■

(A) 1.71 (B) 2.71 (C) 2.81 (D) 6.29

(B) **71.** Sam bought two compact disks on sale. Each disk cost $11.99. He gave the clerk $25. What was his change?

(A) $0.02 (B) $1.02 (C) $1.12 (D) $13.02

72. Compare: 4.32 ■ 4.320

(C)

(A) > (B) < (C) =

(B) **73.** Add: 356 + 5102 + 74

(A) 16,062 (B) 5532

(C) 5432 (D) 5422

(A) **74.** The time is 11:00 P.M. What time was it 45 minutes ago?

(A) 10:15 P.M. (B) 10:30 P.M.

(C) 11:30 P.M. (D) 11:45 P.M.

(C) **75.** 3007 – 128 = ■

(A) 3135 (B) 2989 (C) 2879 (D) 1879

Name ______________________ Class ________ Date ____________

CHAPTER 6: PROBABILITY AND STATISTICS

TEST-TAKING STRATEGY: *Compare Numbers*

Key words such as *least, greatest, ascending, descending,* and *between* are signals to you. They mean that two or more numbers are to be compared.

Example 1: Arrange in *ascending* order: $0.5, \frac{3}{4}, \frac{2}{3}$

- *Ascending* means from *smallest to largest.*
- Write each number as a decimal: $0.5 = 0.5,\ \frac{3}{4} = 0.75,\ \frac{2}{3} = 0.66$
- Compare the decimals: $0.5 < 0.66 < 0.75$
- Replace the original numbers: $0.5 < \frac{2}{3} < \frac{3}{4}$

The answer is $0.5, \frac{2}{3}, \frac{3}{4}$.

Example 2: Which number is between $\frac{8}{25}$ and $\frac{2}{5}$.

Ⓐ 0.30 Ⓑ 0.41 Ⓒ 0.038 Ⓓ 0.38

- First convert the fractions to decimals: $\frac{8}{25} = 0.32$ $\frac{2}{5} = 0.40$
- Then find the answer choice between 0.32 and 0.40:

  $0.30 < 0.32$, so choice Ⓐ is *not* correct.

  $0.41 > 0.40$, so choice Ⓑ is *not* correct.

  $0.038 < 0.32$, so choice Ⓒ is *not* correct.

  $0.32 < 0.38 < 0.40$, so choice Ⓓ is the correct answer.

  $\frac{8}{25} < 0.38 < \frac{2}{5}$

Fill in the correct circle to answer each question.

Ⓐ **1.** Which number is the *greatest*?
$\frac{7}{8}, 0.625, \frac{1}{8}, 0.25$

Ⓐ $\frac{7}{8}$ Ⓑ 0.625
Ⓒ $\frac{1}{8}$ Ⓓ 0.25

Ⓐ **2.** Arrange the numbers in *ascending* order:
$\frac{1}{3}, 0.125, \frac{1}{16}, 0.20$

Ⓐ $\frac{1}{16}, 0.125, 0.20, \frac{1}{3}$ Ⓑ $0.125, \frac{1}{3}, 0.20, \frac{1}{16}$
Ⓒ $0.20, \frac{1}{3}, 0.125, \frac{1}{16}$ Ⓓ $\frac{1}{3}, 0.20, 0.125, \frac{1}{16}$

Ⓒ **3.** Which decimal is between 0.35 and 0.379?

Ⓐ 0.0365 Ⓑ 0.34 Ⓒ 0.36 Ⓓ 0.38

Ⓒ **4.** ■ is between 1.23 and $1\frac{1}{4}$.

Ⓐ 1.5 Ⓑ $1\frac{2}{5}$ Ⓒ $1\frac{6}{25}$ Ⓓ 1.26

Ⓓ **5.** Arrange in *descending* order: 169.69; 168.68; 170.70; 162.62.

Ⓐ 162.61; 168.68; 169.69; 170.70

Ⓑ 168.68; 169.69; 162.62; 170.70

Ⓒ 169.69; 162.62; 168.68; 170.70

Ⓓ 170.70; 169.69; 168.68; 162.62

Ⓓ **6.** Order 2.175; 2.75; 2.1057; and 2.7 from *least to greatest.*

Ⓐ 2.75; 2.7; 2.175; 2.1057

Ⓑ 2.7; 2.75; 2.175; 2.1057

Ⓒ 2.175; 2.1057; 2.7; 2.75

Ⓓ 2.1057; 2.175; 2.7; 2.75

Ⓑ **7.** Which fraction is between $\frac{2}{5}$ and $\frac{2}{3}$?

Ⓐ $\frac{1}{3}$ Ⓑ $\frac{3}{5}$ Ⓒ $\frac{7}{10}$ Ⓓ $\frac{11}{15}$

Ⓒ **8.** Which fraction is between 0.009 and 0.09?

Ⓐ $\frac{1}{3}$ Ⓑ $\frac{9}{10}$ Ⓒ $\frac{8}{100}$ Ⓓ $\frac{1000}{1000}$

Ⓑ **9.** Stanley runs 3 times a week. On Monday, he ran 2.35 miles. On Wednesday, he ran 2.5 miles. On Friday, Stanley wants to run more than he ran on Monday but less than he ran on Wednesday. How many miles should Stanley run?

Ⓐ 2.2 miles Ⓑ 2.4 miles

Ⓒ 3 miles Ⓓ 3.25 miles

10. Tuesday was a good day for the stock market. Ⓓ Which stock showed the greatest gain?

ConDuct $+\frac{1}{2}$	DayGon $+\frac{3}{8}$
SunBlt $+\frac{1}{4}$	TicTac $+\frac{7}{8}$

Ⓐ SunBlt Ⓑ DayGon

Ⓒ ConDuct Ⓓ TicTac

Ⓐ **11.** Compare: $\frac{2}{3}$ ■ $\frac{3}{4}$

Ⓐ < Ⓑ = Ⓒ >

Ⓓ **12.** $\frac{7}{8}$ is *greater* than ■.

Ⓐ $\frac{9}{10}$ Ⓑ $\frac{8}{9}$ Ⓒ $\frac{8}{7}$ Ⓓ $\frac{6}{7}$

Ⓓ **13.** Which group of decimals is in *ascending* order?

Ⓐ 702.5; 7.205; 72.5; 702.5

Ⓑ 72.5; 702.5; 0.725; 7.205

Ⓒ 7.205; 0.725; 72.5; 702.5

Ⓓ 0.725; 7.205; 72.5; 702.5

14. Which number has the *least* value? Ⓐ

Ⓐ 1.064 Ⓑ $1\frac{2}{5}$

Ⓒ 1.604 Ⓓ $1\frac{13}{50}$

Ⓑ **15.** Which group of fractions is in *descending* order?

Ⓐ $\frac{97}{100}, \frac{49}{50}, \frac{24}{25}, \frac{2}{5}$ Ⓑ $\frac{96}{100}, \frac{43}{50}, \frac{21}{25}, \frac{4}{5}$

Ⓒ $\frac{98}{100}, \frac{47}{50}, \frac{19}{25}, \frac{4}{5}$ Ⓓ $\frac{99}{100}, \frac{39}{50}, \frac{23}{25}, \frac{3}{5}$

16. Which number has the *greatest* value? Ⓓ

Ⓐ $\frac{2}{9}$ Ⓑ 0.5 Ⓒ $\frac{2}{3}$ Ⓓ $\frac{5}{6}$

Ⓐ **17.** Arrange in *ascending* order: 0.52; $\frac{1}{2}$; $\frac{3}{5}$; 0.25

Ⓐ 0.25; $\frac{1}{2}$; 0.52; $\frac{3}{5}$ Ⓑ $\frac{1}{2}$; 0.25; 0.52; $\frac{3}{5}$

Ⓒ 0.52; $\frac{1}{2}$; $\frac{3}{5}$; 0.25 Ⓓ $\frac{3}{5}$; 0.52 ; $\frac{1}{2}$; 0.25

Ⓓ **18.** Order $\frac{6}{7}, \frac{1}{3}, \frac{1}{6}$ and $\frac{5}{21}$ from *greatest to least.*

Ⓐ $\frac{1}{6}, \frac{5}{21}, \frac{1}{3}, \frac{6}{7}$ Ⓑ $\frac{1}{3}, \frac{1}{6}, \frac{6}{7}, \frac{5}{21}$

Ⓒ $\frac{6}{7}, \frac{5}{21}, \frac{1}{6}, \frac{1}{3}$ Ⓓ $\frac{6}{7}, \frac{1}{3}, \frac{5}{21}, \frac{1}{6}$

Name ____________________ Class __________ Date __________

CHAPTER 6 PRETEST

Fill in the correct circle to answer each question.

(B) **1.** What fraction of the squares is red?

Ⓐ $\frac{2}{2}$ Ⓑ $\frac{3}{4}$ Ⓒ $\frac{1}{2}$ Ⓓ $\frac{1}{4}$

(C) **2.** $\frac{1}{5}$ is represented by:

Ⓐ ○ ● ○ / ○ ● ○

Ⓑ ● ● ● / ○ ○

Ⓒ ○ ● ○ / ○ ○

Ⓓ ○ ● ○ / ○

(D) **3.** Order 0.3, 1.12, 0.36, 2.12, and 21.12 from *least to greatest.*

Ⓐ 0.36, 0.3, 1.12, 21.12, 2.12

Ⓑ 0.3, 0.36, 1.12, 21.12, 2.12

Ⓒ 0.36, 0.3, 1.12, 2.12, 21.12

Ⓓ 0.3, 0.36, 1.12, 2.12, 21.12

(A) **4.** Compare: 19.978 ■ 19.798

Ⓐ > Ⓑ < Ⓒ =

(C) **5.** Compare: 1.30 ■ 1.3

Ⓐ > Ⓑ < Ⓒ =

(C) **6.** What is 15% of 40?

Ⓐ 600 Ⓑ 8 Ⓒ 6 Ⓓ 2.40

(B) **7.** 19 is 50% of ■ .

Ⓐ 9.5 Ⓑ 38 Ⓒ 105 Ⓓ 950

(B) **8.** $1000 \times 7 =$ ■

Ⓐ 70,000 Ⓑ 7000 Ⓒ 1007 Ⓓ 700

(A) **9.** $5500 \div 100 =$ ■

Ⓐ 55 Ⓑ 550 Ⓒ 5600 Ⓓ 55,000

(D) **10.** $3142 \div 5 =$ ■

Ⓐ 6284 Ⓑ 636.4 Ⓒ 628.5 Ⓓ 628.4

(A) **11.** $16.23 + 31.3 + 41.07 + 10.12 =$ ■

Ⓐ 98.72 Ⓑ 98.75 Ⓒ 98.92 Ⓓ 99.35

(D) **12.** How much time passes from 6:30 P.M. to 8:00 P.M.?

Ⓐ 1 hour 50 minutes

Ⓑ 2 hours 30 minutes

Ⓒ 1 hour 70 minutes

Ⓓ 1 hour 30 minutes

(C) **13.** 3 hours 15 minutes
\+ 2 hours 35 minutes

Ⓐ 6 hours 50 minutes

Ⓑ 6 hours

Ⓒ 5 hours 50 minutes

Ⓓ 5 hours 40 minutes

(C) **14.** Round $105.59 to the nearest *dollar.*

Ⓐ $105.60 Ⓑ $105.00

Ⓒ $106.00 Ⓓ $110.00

(B) **15.** Round 14,272 to the nearest *thousand.*

Ⓐ 10,000 Ⓑ 14,000

Ⓒ 14,300 Ⓓ 15,000

(B) **16.** Which number appears more than once: 32, 35, 42, 35, 22?

Ⓐ 42 Ⓑ 35 Ⓒ 32 Ⓓ 22

(A) **17.** Add 208, 419, 352, 663, and 511.

Ⓐ 2153 Ⓑ 2143 Ⓒ 2142 Ⓓ 2053

Ⓒ **18.** What is the probability of the spinner landing on 18?

Ⓐ $\frac{3}{4}$ Ⓑ $\frac{1}{3}$

Ⓒ $\frac{1}{4}$ Ⓓ $\frac{2}{9}$

Ⓐ **19.** A bag contains 5 blue marbles and 8 red marbles. What is the probability of choosing a blue marble from the bag?

Ⓐ $\frac{5}{13}$ Ⓑ $\frac{1}{2}$ Ⓒ $\frac{8}{13}$ Ⓓ $\frac{5}{8}$

Use Figure 1 to answer questions 20-22.

Ⓒ **20.** In which year were 1250 copies of the cookbook sold?

Ⓐ 1984 Ⓑ 1985 Ⓒ 1986 Ⓓ 1988

Ⓒ **21.** How many more copies of the cookbook were sold in 1985 than in 1987?

Ⓐ 3000 Ⓑ 150 Ⓒ 1500 Ⓓ 500

Ⓐ **22.** In which year were the least number of copies sold?

Ⓐ 1984 Ⓑ 1988 Ⓒ 1986 Ⓓ 1987

Figure 1

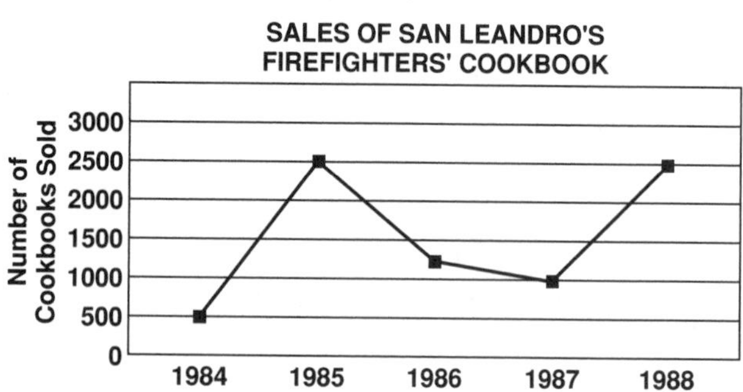

Use Figure 2 to answer questions 23-24.

Ⓓ **23.** Which material(s) showed a decrease in tons recycled from 1984 to 1986?

Ⓐ aluminum cans and newspapers

Ⓑ newspapers only

Ⓒ aluminum cans only

Ⓓ glass only

Ⓐ **24.** By how many tons did the recycling of newspapers increase from 1984 to 1986?

Ⓐ 2 Ⓑ 3 Ⓒ 4 Ⓓ 1

Figure 2

SAN LEANDRA RECYCLING PROGRAM

Tons Recycled: 0, 2, 4, 6, 8, 10, 12

Aluminum Cans | Newspapers | Glass

1984 | 1986

Use Figure 3 to answer question 25.

Ⓐ **25.** Of all materials recycled in 1988, newspapers accounted for ▇ .

Ⓐ 45% Ⓑ 30% Ⓒ 20% Ⓓ 5%

Figure 3

SAN LEANDRA RECYCLING PROGRAM 1988

Newspapers 45%

Glass 20%

Aluminum Cans 30%

Other 5%

Name ______________________ Class ________ Date ____________

6.1 PROBABILITY

$$\text{Probability} = \frac{\text{Number of Favorable Outcomes}}{\text{Number of Possible Outcomes}}$$

Example 1: Jorge tosses a number cube whose faces are labeled 1, 2, 3, 4, 5, and 6. What is the probability that he will roll a 4?

- Find the number of possible outcomes: Since the cube has 6 faces, there are 6 possible outcomes.
- Find the number of favorable outcomes: 1

The probability that Jorge will roll a 4 is $\frac{1}{6}$.

Example 2: There are 6 blue marbles, 2 red marbles, and 4 yellow marbles in a bag. What is the probability of drawing a blue marble or a yellow marble?

- Find the number of possible outcomes: There are 12 marbles in all.
- Find the number of favorable outcomes: There are 6 blue marbles and 4 yellow marbles. Therefore, there are 10 favorable outcomes.

The probability of drawing a blue or yellow marble is $\frac{10}{12}$, or $\frac{5}{6}$.

Fill in the correct circle to answer each question.

Ⓓ **1.** Abe rolls a cube labelled with the numbers 1, 2, 3, 4, 5, and 6. What is the probability he will roll a 3?

Ⓐ 6 Ⓑ $\frac{1}{2}$ Ⓒ $\frac{1}{3}$ Ⓓ $\frac{1}{6}$

Ⓑ **2.** A number cube is labelled with the numbers 6, 14, 19, 21, 25, and 33. What is the probability of rolling an odd number?

Ⓐ $\frac{1}{3}$ Ⓑ $\frac{2}{3}$ Ⓒ $\frac{1}{2}$ Ⓓ 3

A shoebox contains 20 marbles. Five are yellow, six are black, and nine are brown. You reach into the shoebox without looking, and choose a marble.

Ⓑ **3.** What is the probability of drawing a yellow marble?

Ⓐ $\frac{1}{5}$ Ⓑ $\frac{1}{4}$ Ⓒ $\frac{3}{10}$ Ⓓ $\frac{9}{20}$

Ⓒ **4.** What is the probability of drawing a marble that is black or yellow?

Ⓐ $\frac{1}{20}$ Ⓑ $\frac{1}{2}$ Ⓒ $\frac{11}{20}$ Ⓓ $\frac{7}{10}$

Use Figure 6.1A to answer questions 5-7.

Figure 6.1 A

Ⓐ **5.** What is the probability that the spinner will land on 16?

Ⓐ $\frac{1}{8}$ Ⓑ $\frac{1}{6}$ Ⓒ $\frac{1}{2}$ Ⓓ 2

Ⓑ **6.** What is the probability that the spinner will land on an even number?

Ⓐ 5 Ⓑ $\frac{5}{8}$ Ⓒ $\frac{1}{2}$ Ⓓ $\frac{3}{8}$

Ⓒ **7.** What is the probability that the spinner will land on a number less than 9?

Ⓐ 5 Ⓑ $\frac{4}{8}$ Ⓒ $\frac{5}{8}$ Ⓓ $\frac{6}{8}$

Use figure 6.1B to answer questions 8-9.

Figure 6.1 B

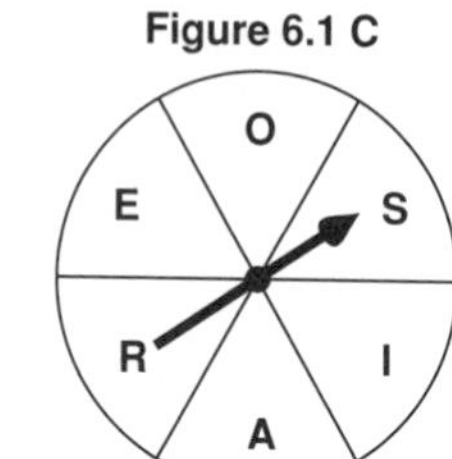

Figure 6.1 C

(C) **8.** What is the probability that the spinner will land on an even number?

(A) 4 (B) $\frac{5}{8}$ (C) $\frac{1}{2}$ (D) $\frac{3}{8}$

(D) **9.** What is the probability the spinner will land on 67?

(A) $\frac{8}{1}$ (B) 1 (C) $\frac{1}{4}$ (D) $\frac{1}{8}$

(D) **10.** If you scramble the letters in the word "MATHEMATICS," what is the probability that the first letter will be "A"?

(A) $\frac{11}{2}$ (B) 2 (C) $\frac{1}{11}$ (D) $\frac{2}{11}$

(B) **11.** If you scramble the letters in the word "MATHEMATICS," what is the probability that the first letter will be "E"?

(A) 5 (B) $\frac{1}{11}$ (C) $\frac{1}{5}$ (D) $\frac{2}{11}$

Use Figure 6.1C to answer questions 12-13.

(C) **12.** What is the probability of landing on a vowel?

(A) $\frac{3}{2}$ (B) $\frac{5}{6}$ (C) $\frac{2}{3}$ (D) $\frac{1}{2}$

(D) **13.** What is the probability of landing on a consonant?

(A) $\frac{3}{1}$ (B) 2 (C) $\frac{2}{3}$ (D) $\frac{1}{3}$

(B) **14.** Belinda buys a package of beads. The label says there are 24 white beads, 20 rose beads, 32 aqua beads, and 14 amber beads. Belinda closes her eyes and chooses a bead. What is the probability that she will choose an amber bead?

(A) $\frac{2}{15}$ (B) $\frac{7}{45}$ (C) $\frac{7}{40}$ (D) $\frac{14}{100}$

(D) **15.** Suzanne and Howard want to play a board game called *Drive Your Way Across America*. The colors of the tokens are red, green, black, yellow, and white. Suzanne closes her eyes and chooses a token first. What is the probability she will choose a token that is red, yellow, or blue?

(A) $\frac{5}{2}$ (B) $\frac{3}{5}$ (C) $\frac{1}{2}$ (D) $\frac{2}{5}$

Use Figure 6.1D to answer questions 16 and 17.

Figure 6.1 D

(D) **16.** What is the probability the spinner will land on ×?

(A) $\frac{4}{3}$ (B) $\frac{3}{4}$ (C) $\frac{1}{2}$ (D) $\frac{1}{4}$

(A) **17.** What is the probability the spinner will land on =?

(A) 0 (B) 1 (C) 4 (D) $\frac{1}{4}$

(C) **18.** Avis tosses a number cube labeled with 10, 20, 30, 40, 50, and 60. What is the probability she will throw a 50?

(A) $\frac{25}{3}$ (B) $\frac{6}{1}$ (C) $\frac{1}{6}$ (D) $\frac{3}{25}$

(B) **19.** If you scramble the letters in the word "MISSISSIPPI," what is the probability that the first letter will be an "S" or a "P"?

(A) $\frac{3}{5}$ (B) $\frac{6}{11}$ (C) $\frac{1}{2}$ (D) $\frac{5}{11}$

(B) **20.** There are 8 polka-dot sweaters, 8 striped sweaters, and 8 reindeer-patterned sweaters in a drawer. If you close your eyes and grab a sweater, what is the probability that it will be striped?

(A) 8 (B) $\frac{1}{3}$ (C) $\frac{1}{2}$ (D) 1

(D) **21.** Paul has 6 brown socks, 4 black socks, and 8 blue socks. If he closes his eyes and grabs a sock, what is the possibility that it will be black?

(A) $\frac{9}{2}$ (B) 4 (C) $\frac{1}{3}$ (D) $\frac{2}{9}$

Name ____________________ Class ________ Date ____________

Use Table 1 to answer questions 37–40.

Table 1

Elizabeth Ziegfeld's Earnings	
Month	Amount
January	$2650
February	$4685
March	$3928
April	$2800
May	$5200

Ⓒ **37.** Estimate Ms. Ziegfeld's least monthly earnings as a percentage of her greatest monthly earnings.

Ⓐ 20% Ⓑ 40% Ⓒ 50% Ⓓ 200%

Ⓑ **38.** Ms. Ziegfeld wants to earn enough in June to make $24,000 for all six months. She needs to earn about as much in June as she did in:

Ⓐ Jan. Ⓑ Feb. Ⓒ March Ⓓ April

Ⓓ **39.** Rank the incomes from *least* to *greatest*.

Ⓐ $5200, $4685, $3928, $2800, $2650

Ⓑ $2800, $2650, $3928, $4685, $5200

Ⓒ $4685, $5200, $3928, $2800, $2650

Ⓓ $2650, $2800, $3928, $4685, $5200

Ⓑ **40.** The greatest monthly difference in earnings occurred between

Ⓐ Jan.–Feb. Ⓑ Feb.–March

Ⓒ March–April Ⓓ April–May

Ⓐ **41.** 12 qt = ■ gal

Ⓐ 3 Ⓑ 4 Ⓒ 6 Ⓓ 8

Ⓒ **42.** 4 h = ■ min

Ⓐ 40 Ⓑ 64 Ⓒ 240 Ⓓ 400

Ⓑ **43.** Find n: $\frac{8}{14} = \frac{n}{35}$

Ⓐ 14 Ⓑ 20 Ⓒ 21 Ⓓ 29

Ⓓ **44.** Multiply: 46×6000

Ⓐ 276 Ⓑ 2760

Ⓒ 27,600 Ⓓ 276,000

Ⓐ **45.** Estimate the quotient: $470 \div 77$

Ⓐ 6 Ⓑ 7 Ⓒ 60 Ⓓ 70

Ⓐ **46.** What is 15% of 3600?

Ⓐ 540 Ⓑ 3585

Ⓒ 5400 Ⓓ 54,000

Ⓓ **47.** 73 m = ■ mm

Ⓐ 0.073 Ⓑ 0.73

Ⓒ 7300 Ⓓ 73,000

Ⓓ **48.** Divide: $0.02\overline{)8.32}$

Ⓐ 0.416 Ⓑ 4.16 Ⓒ 41.6 Ⓓ 416

Ⓑ **49.** 285 is what percent of 475?

Ⓐ 190% Ⓑ 60% Ⓒ 1.66% Ⓓ 0.6%

Ⓑ **50.** Estimate: 43×329

Ⓐ 1200 Ⓑ 12,000

Ⓒ 7 000 Ⓓ 20,000

Ⓐ **51.**

```
  6 gal 3 qt
+ 2 gal 2 qt
```

Ⓐ 9 gal 1 qt Ⓑ 9 gal 5 qt

Ⓒ 8 gal 1 qt Ⓒ 4 gal 1 qt

Ⓓ **52.** Find n: $\frac{30}{18} = \frac{n}{30}$

Ⓐ 18 Ⓑ 30 Ⓒ 42 Ⓓ 50

Ⓒ **53.** Barbara works 20 hours a week at the Ice Cream Factory. During summer vacation, she plans to work 28 hours a week. By what percent will Barbara increase the number of hours she works?

Ⓐ 8% Ⓑ 28.5% Ⓒ 40% Ⓓ 71%

54. Ⓑ At the World of Records, Sean bought 3 cassette tapes at $7.99 each and 2 packages of batteries at $2.99 each. How much change did he receive from $40.00?

Ⓐ $0.05 Ⓑ $10.05

Ⓒ $15.05 Ⓓ $29.02

Ⓓ **55.** Which of the following is *not* a proportion?

Ⓐ $\frac{24}{1} = \frac{96}{4}$ Ⓑ $\frac{1}{2} = \frac{4}{8}$

Ⓒ $\frac{9}{4} = \frac{18}{8}$ Ⓓ $\frac{16}{2} = \frac{80}{5}$

Ⓐ **56.** Subtract: 9 min − 2 min 32 sec

Ⓐ 6 min 28 sec Ⓑ 7 min 28 sec

Ⓒ 7 min 32 sec Ⓓ 11 min 32 sec

Ⓓ **57.** 25% of what number is 69?

Ⓐ 0.0036 Ⓑ 2.76

Ⓒ 17.25 Ⓓ 276

Ⓓ **58.** What is the *value* of the digit 3 in 457.863?

Ⓐ 3000 Ⓑ 3 Ⓒ 0.03 Ⓓ 0.003

Ⓑ **59.** What percent of 400 is 84?

Ⓐ 4.76% Ⓑ 21% Ⓒ 79% Ⓓ 316%

Ⓓ **60.** Round 4.385 to the nearest *tenth.*

Ⓐ 4.39 Ⓑ 4.3 Ⓒ 4.39 Ⓓ 4.4

Ⓐ **61.** Donna needs 280 paper cups for a party. Cups come in packages of 20. She has 8 packages. How many more packages should she buy?

Ⓐ 6 Ⓑ 10 Ⓒ 14 Ⓓ 120

62. Compare: 9501 ■ 9510

Ⓑ

Ⓐ > Ⓑ < Ⓒ =

Ⓒ **63.** What is the *place value* of 7 in 43,705?

Ⓐ ones Ⓑ tens

Ⓒ hundreds Ⓓ thousands

Ⓑ **64.** From 8 A.M. to 4:30 P.M. is ■ hours.

Ⓐ $16\frac{1}{2}$ Ⓑ $8\frac{1}{2}$ Ⓒ 8 Ⓓ $4\frac{1}{2}$

Ⓑ **65.** 7 yd = ■ ft

Ⓐ 24 Ⓑ 21 Ⓒ 14 Ⓓ 2.5

Ⓓ **66.** 63 × 109 = ■

Ⓐ 172 Ⓑ 981

Ⓒ 6767 Ⓓ 6867

Ⓒ **67.** 2.89 + 43.682 = ■

Ⓐ 72.582 Ⓑ 61.582

Ⓒ 46.572 Ⓓ 45.472

Ⓑ **68.** 38 cm = ■ mm

Ⓐ 3.8 Ⓑ 380

Ⓒ 3800 Ⓓ 38,000

Ⓒ **69.** Estimate: 2.9 × 4.48

Ⓐ 6 Ⓑ 8

Ⓒ 12 Ⓓ 120

Ⓐ **70.** 4 − 2.29 = ■

Ⓐ 1.71 Ⓑ 2.71 Ⓒ 2.81 Ⓓ 6.29

Ⓑ **71.** Sam bought two compact disks on sale. Each disk cost $11.99. He gave the clerk $25. What was his change?

Ⓐ $0.02 Ⓑ $1.02 Ⓒ $1.12 Ⓓ $13.02

72. Compare: 4.32 ■ 4.320

Ⓒ

Ⓐ > Ⓑ < Ⓒ =

Ⓑ **73.** Add: 356 + 5102 + 74

Ⓐ 16,062 Ⓑ 5532

Ⓒ 5432 Ⓓ 5422

Ⓐ **74.** The time is 11:00 P.M. What time was it 45 minutes ago?

Ⓐ 10:15 P.M. Ⓑ 10:30 P.M.

Ⓒ 11:30 P.M. Ⓓ 11:45 P.M.

Ⓒ **75.** 3007 − 128 = ■

Ⓐ 3135 Ⓑ 2989 Ⓒ 2879 Ⓓ 1879

Name ______________________________ Class __________ Date ______________

CHAPTER 6: PROBABILITY AND STATISTICS

TEST-TAKING STRATEGY: *Compare Numbers*

Key words such as *least, greatest, ascending, descending,* and *between* are signals to you. They mean that two or more numbers are to be compared.

Example 1: Arrange in *ascending* order: $0.5, \frac{3}{4}, \frac{2}{3}$

- *Ascending* means from *smallest to largest.*
- Write each number as a decimal: $0.5 = 0.5,\ \frac{3}{4} = 0.75,\ \frac{2}{3} = 0.66$
- Compare the decimals: $0.5 < 0.66 < 0.75$
- Replace the original numbers: $0.5 < \frac{2}{3} < \frac{3}{4}$

The answer is $0.5, \frac{2}{3}, \frac{3}{4}$.

Example 2: Which number is between $\frac{8}{25}$ and $\frac{2}{5}$.

Ⓐ 0.30 Ⓑ 0.41 Ⓒ 0.038 Ⓓ 0.38

- First convert the fractions to decimals: $\frac{8}{25} = 0.32 \quad \frac{2}{5} = 0.40$
- Then find the answer choice between 0.32 and 0.40:

  $0.30 < 0.32$, so choice Ⓐ is *not* correct.

  $0.41 > 0.40$, so choice Ⓑ is *not* correct.

  $0.038 < 0.32$, so choice Ⓒ is *not* correct.

  $0.32 < 0.38 < 0.40$, so choice Ⓓ is the correct answer.

  $\frac{8}{25} < 0.38 < \frac{2}{5}$

Fill in the correct circle to answer each question.

Ⓐ **1.** Which number is the *greatest*?
$\frac{7}{8}, 0.625, \frac{1}{8}, 0.25$

Ⓐ $\frac{7}{8}$ Ⓑ 0.625

Ⓒ $\frac{1}{8}$ Ⓓ 0.25

Ⓐ **2.** Arrange the numbers in *ascending* order:
$\frac{1}{3}, 0.125, \frac{1}{16}, 0.20$

Ⓐ $\frac{1}{16}, 0.125, 0.20, \frac{1}{3}$ Ⓑ $0.125, \frac{1}{3}, 0.20, \frac{1}{16}$

Ⓒ $0.20, \frac{1}{3}, 0.125, \frac{1}{16}$ Ⓓ $\frac{1}{3}, 0.20, 0.125, \frac{1}{16}$

Ⓒ **3.** Which decimal is between 0.35 and 0.379?

Ⓐ 0.0365 Ⓑ 0.34 Ⓒ 0.36 Ⓓ 0.38

Ⓒ **4.** ■ is between 1.23 and $1\frac{1}{4}$.

Ⓐ 1.5 Ⓑ $1\frac{2}{5}$ Ⓒ $1\frac{6}{25}$ Ⓓ 1.26

(D) **5.** Arrange in *descending* order: 169.69; 168.68; 170.70; 162.62.

Ⓐ 162.61; 168.68; 169.69; 170.70

Ⓑ 168.68; 169.69; 162.62; 170.70

Ⓒ 169.69; 162.62; 168.68; 170.70

Ⓓ 170.70; 169.69; 168.68; 162.62

(D) **6.** Order 2.175; 2.75; 2.1057; and 2.7 from *least to greatest.*

Ⓐ 2.75; 2.7; 2.175; 2.1057

Ⓑ 2.7; 2.75; 2.175; 2.1057

Ⓒ 2.175; 2.1057; 2.7; 2.75

Ⓓ 2.1057; 2.175; 2.7; 2.75

(B) **7.** Which fraction is between $\frac{2}{5}$ and $\frac{2}{3}$?

Ⓐ $\frac{1}{3}$ Ⓑ $\frac{3}{5}$ Ⓒ $\frac{7}{10}$ Ⓓ $\frac{11}{15}$

(C) **8.** Which fraction is between 0.009 and 0.09?

Ⓐ $\frac{1}{3}$ Ⓑ $\frac{9}{10}$ Ⓒ $\frac{8}{100}$ Ⓓ $\frac{1000}{1000}$

(B) **9.** Stanley runs 3 times a week. On Monday, he ran 2.35 miles. On Wednesday, he ran 2.5 miles. On Friday, Stanley wants to run more than he ran on Monday but less than he ran on Wednesday. How many miles should Stanley run?

Ⓐ 2.2 miles Ⓑ 2.4 miles

Ⓒ 3 miles Ⓓ 3.25 miles

10. Tuesday was a good day for the stock market. (D) Which stock showed the greatest gain?

ConDuct $+\frac{1}{2}$	DayGon $+\frac{3}{8}$
SunBlt $+\frac{1}{4}$	TicTac $+\frac{7}{8}$

Ⓐ SunBlt Ⓑ DayGon

Ⓒ ConDuct Ⓓ TicTac

(A) **11.** Compare: $\frac{2}{3}$ ■ $\frac{3}{4}$

Ⓐ $<$ Ⓑ $=$ Ⓒ $>$

(D) **12.** $\frac{7}{8}$ is *greater* than ■.

Ⓐ $\frac{9}{10}$ Ⓑ $\frac{8}{9}$ Ⓒ $\frac{8}{7}$ Ⓓ $\frac{6}{7}$

(D) **13.** Which group of decimals is in *ascending* order?

Ⓐ 702.5; 7.205; 72.5; 702.5

Ⓑ 72.5; 702.5; 0.725; 7.205

Ⓒ 7.205; 0.725; 72.5; 702.5

Ⓓ 0.725; 7.205; 72.5; 702.5

14. Which number has the *least* value?
(A)

Ⓐ 1.064 Ⓑ $1\frac{2}{5}$

Ⓒ 1.604 Ⓓ $1\frac{13}{50}$

(B) **15.** Which group of fractions is in *descending* order?

Ⓐ $\frac{97}{100}, \frac{49}{50}, \frac{24}{25}, \frac{2}{5}$ Ⓑ $\frac{96}{100}, \frac{43}{50}, \frac{21}{25}, \frac{4}{5}$

Ⓒ $\frac{98}{100}, \frac{47}{50}, \frac{19}{25}, \frac{4}{5}$ Ⓓ $\frac{99}{100}, \frac{39}{50}, \frac{23}{25}, \frac{3}{5}$

16. Which number has the *greatest* value?
(D)

Ⓐ $\frac{2}{9}$ Ⓑ 0.5 Ⓒ $\frac{2}{3}$ Ⓓ $\frac{5}{6}$

(A) **17.** Arrange in *ascending* order: 0.52; $\frac{1}{2}$; $\frac{3}{5}$; 0.25

Ⓐ 0.25; $\frac{1}{2}$; 0.52; $\frac{3}{5}$ Ⓑ $\frac{1}{2}$; 0.25; 0.52; $\frac{3}{5}$

Ⓒ 0.52; $\frac{1}{2}$; $\frac{3}{5}$; 0.25 Ⓓ $\frac{3}{5}$; 0.52 ; $\frac{1}{2}$; 0.25

(D) **18.** Order $\frac{6}{7}, \frac{1}{3}, \frac{1}{6}$ and $\frac{5}{21}$ from *greatest to least.*

Ⓐ $\frac{1}{6}, \frac{5}{21}, \frac{1}{3}, \frac{6}{7}$ Ⓑ $\frac{1}{3}, \frac{1}{6}, \frac{6}{7}, \frac{5}{21}$

Ⓒ $\frac{6}{7}, \frac{5}{21}, \frac{1}{6}, \frac{1}{3}$ Ⓓ $\frac{6}{7}, \frac{1}{3}, \frac{5}{21}, \frac{1}{6}$

Name ______________________ Class __________ Date __________

CHAPTER 6 PRETEST

Fill in the correct circle to answer each question.

Ⓑ **1.** What fraction of the squares is red?

Ⓐ $\frac{2}{2}$ Ⓑ $\frac{3}{4}$ Ⓒ $\frac{1}{2}$ Ⓓ $\frac{1}{4}$

Ⓒ **2.** $\frac{1}{5}$ is represented by:

Ⓐ ○ ● ○
○ ● ○

Ⓑ ● ● ●
○ ○

Ⓒ ○ ● ○
○ ○

Ⓓ ○ ● ○
○

Ⓓ **3.** Order 0.3, 1.12, 0.36, 2.12, and 21.12 from *least to greatest*.

Ⓐ 0.36, 0.3, 1.12, 21.12, 2.12

Ⓑ 0.3, 0.36, 1.12, 21.12, 2.12

Ⓒ 0.36, 0.3, 1.12, 2.12, 21.12

Ⓓ 0.3, 0.36, 1.12, 2.12, 21.12

Ⓐ **4.** Compare: 19.978 ■ 19.798

Ⓐ > Ⓑ < Ⓒ =

Ⓒ **5.** Compare: 1.30 ■ 1.3

Ⓐ > Ⓑ < Ⓒ =

Ⓒ **6.** What is 15% of 40?

Ⓐ 600 Ⓑ 8 Ⓒ 6 Ⓓ 2.40

Ⓑ **7.** 19 is 50% of ■.

Ⓐ 9.5 Ⓑ 38 Ⓒ 105 Ⓓ 950

Ⓑ **8.** $1000 \times 7 =$ ■

Ⓐ 70,000 Ⓑ 7000 Ⓒ 1007 Ⓓ 700

Ⓐ **9.** $5500 \div 100 =$ ■

Ⓐ 55 Ⓑ 550 Ⓒ 5600 Ⓓ 55,000

Ⓓ **10.** $3142 \div 5 =$ ■

Ⓐ 6284 Ⓑ 636.4 Ⓒ 628.5 Ⓓ 628.4

Ⓐ **11.** $16.23 + 31.3 + 41.07 + 10.12 =$ ■

Ⓐ 98.72 Ⓑ 98.75 Ⓒ 98.92 Ⓓ 99.35

Ⓓ **12.** How much time passes from 6:30 P.M. to 8:00 P.M.?

Ⓐ 1 hour 50 minutes

Ⓑ 2 hours 30 minutes

Ⓒ 1 hour 70 minutes

Ⓓ 1 hour 30 minutes

Ⓒ **13.** 3 hours 15 minutes
+ 2 hours 35 minutes

Ⓐ 6 hours 50 minutes

Ⓑ 6 hours

Ⓒ 5 hours 50 minutes

Ⓓ 5 hours 40 minutes

Ⓒ **14.** Round $105.59 to the nearest *dollar*.

Ⓐ $105.60 Ⓑ $105.00

Ⓒ $106.00 Ⓓ $110.00

Ⓑ **15.** Round 14,272 to the nearest *thousand*.

Ⓐ 10,000 Ⓑ 14,000

Ⓒ 14,300 Ⓓ 15,000

Ⓑ **16.** Which number appears more than once: 32, 35, 42, 35, 22?

Ⓐ 42 Ⓑ 35 Ⓒ 32 Ⓓ 22

Ⓐ **17.** Add 208, 419, 352, 663, and 511.

Ⓐ 2153 Ⓑ 2143 Ⓒ 2142 Ⓓ 2053

Ⓒ **18.** What is the probability of the spinner landing on 18?

Ⓐ $\frac{3}{4}$ Ⓑ $\frac{1}{3}$

Ⓒ $\frac{1}{4}$ Ⓓ $\frac{2}{9}$

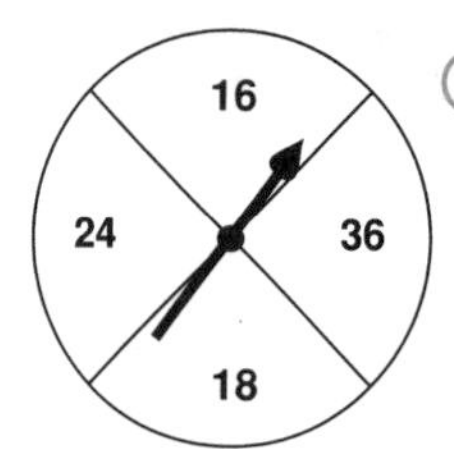

Ⓐ **19.** A bag contains 5 blue marbles and 8 red marbles. What is the probability of choosing a blue marble from the bag?

Ⓐ $\frac{5}{13}$ Ⓑ $\frac{1}{2}$ Ⓒ $\frac{8}{13}$ Ⓓ $\frac{5}{8}$

Use Figure 1 to answer questions 20-22.

Figure 1

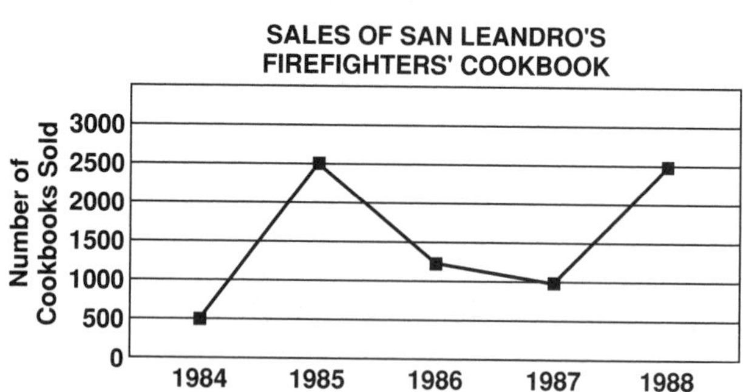

Ⓒ **20.** In which year were 1250 copies of the cookbook sold?

Ⓐ 1984 Ⓑ 1985 Ⓒ 1986 Ⓓ 1988

Ⓒ **21.** How many more copies of the cookbook were sold in 1985 than in 1987?

Ⓐ 3000 Ⓑ 150 Ⓒ 1500 Ⓓ 500

Ⓐ **22.** In which year were the least number of copies sold?

Ⓐ 1984 Ⓑ 1988 Ⓒ 1986 Ⓓ 1987

Use Figure 2 to answer questions 23-24.

Figure 2

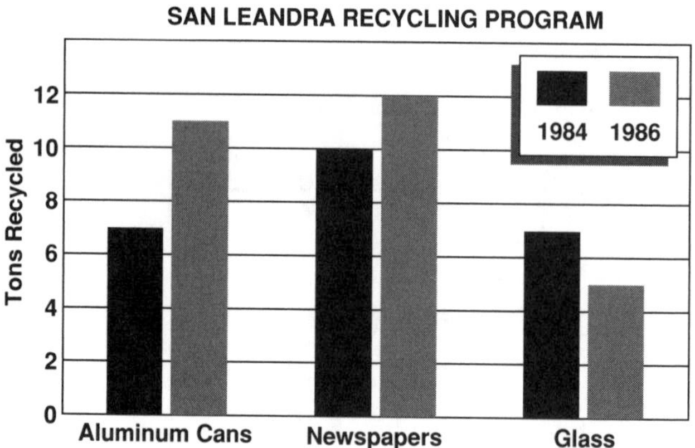

Ⓓ **23.** Which material(s) showed a decrease in tons recycled from 1984 to 1986?

Ⓐ aluminum cans and newspapers

Ⓑ newspapers only

Ⓒ aluminum cans only

Ⓓ glass only

Ⓐ **24.** By how many tons did the recycling of newspapers increase from 1984 to 1986?

Ⓐ 2 Ⓑ 3 Ⓒ 4 Ⓓ 1

Use Figure 3 to answer question 25.

Figure 3

SAN LEANDRA RECYCLING PROGRAM 1988

Newspapers 45%

Glass 20%

Aluminum Cans 30%

Other 5%

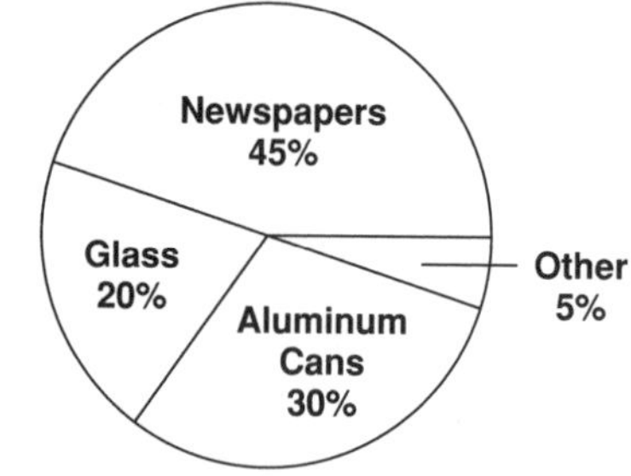

Ⓐ **25.** Of all materials recycled in 1988, newspapers accounted for ■.

Ⓐ 45% Ⓑ 30% Ⓒ 20% Ⓓ 5%

Name ____________________ Class ________ Date ____________

6.1 PROBABILITY

$$\text{Probability} = \frac{\text{Number of Favorable Outcomes}}{\text{Number of Possible Outcomes}}$$

Example 1: Jorge tosses a number cube whose faces are labeled 1, 2, 3, 4, 5, and 6. What is the probability that he will roll a 4?

- Find the number of possible outcomes: Since the cube has 6 faces, there are 6 possible outcomes.
- Find the number of favorable outcomes: 1

The probability that Jorge will roll a 4 is $\frac{1}{6}$.

Example 2: There are 6 blue marbles, 2 red marbles, and 4 yellow marbles in a bag. What is the probability of drawing a blue marble or a yellow marble?

- Find the number of possible outcomes: There are 12 marbles in all.
- Find the number of favorable outcomes: There are 6 blue marbles and 4 yellow marbles. Therefore, there are 10 favorable outcomes.

The probability of drawing a blue or yellow marble is $\frac{10}{12}$, or $\frac{5}{6}$.

Fill in the correct circle to answer each question.

Ⓓ **1.** Abe rolls a cube labelled with the numbers 1, 2, 3, 4, 5, and 6. What is the probability he will roll a 3?

Ⓐ 6 Ⓑ $\frac{1}{2}$ Ⓒ $\frac{1}{3}$ Ⓓ $\frac{1}{6}$

Ⓑ **2.** A number cube is labelled with the numbers 6, 14, 19, 21, 25, and 33. What is the probability of rolling an odd number?

Ⓐ $\frac{1}{3}$ Ⓑ $\frac{2}{3}$ Ⓒ $\frac{1}{2}$ Ⓓ 3

A shoebox contains 20 marbles. Five are yellow, six are black, and nine are brown. You reach into the shoebox without looking, and choose a marble.

Ⓑ **3.** What is the probability of drawing a yellow marble?

Ⓐ $\frac{1}{5}$ Ⓑ $\frac{1}{4}$ Ⓒ $\frac{3}{10}$ Ⓓ $\frac{9}{20}$

Ⓒ **4.** What is the probability of drawing a marble that is black or yellow?

Ⓐ $\frac{1}{20}$ Ⓑ $\frac{1}{2}$ Ⓒ $\frac{11}{20}$ Ⓓ $\frac{7}{10}$

Use Figure 6.1A to answer questions 5-7.

Figure 6.1 A

Ⓐ **5.** What is the probability that the spinner will land on 16?

Ⓐ $\frac{1}{8}$ Ⓑ $\frac{1}{6}$ Ⓒ $\frac{1}{2}$ Ⓓ 2

Ⓑ **6.** What is the probability that the spinner will land on an even number?

Ⓐ 5 Ⓑ $\frac{5}{8}$ Ⓒ $\frac{1}{2}$ Ⓓ $\frac{3}{8}$

Ⓒ **7.** What is the probability that the spinner will land on a number less than 9?

Ⓐ 5 Ⓑ $\frac{4}{8}$ Ⓒ $\frac{5}{8}$ Ⓓ $\frac{6}{8}$

Use figure 6.1B to answer questions 8-9.

Figure 6.1 B

Figure 6.1 C

(C) **8.** What is the probability that the spinner will land on an even number?

(A) 4 (B) $\frac{5}{8}$ (C) $\frac{1}{2}$ (D) $\frac{3}{8}$

(D) **9.** What is the probability the spinner will land on 67?

(A) $\frac{8}{1}$ (B) 1 (C) $\frac{1}{4}$ (D) $\frac{1}{8}$

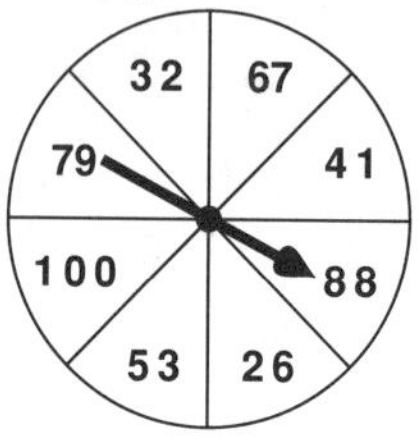

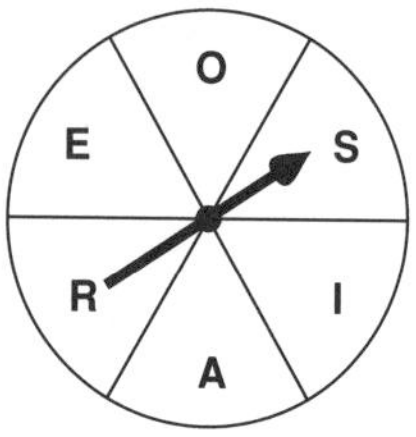

(D) **10.** If you scramble the letters in the word "MATHEMATICS," what is the probability that the first letter will be "A"?

(A) $\frac{11}{2}$ (B) 2 (C) $\frac{1}{11}$ (D) $\frac{2}{11}$

(B) **11.** If you scramble the letters in the word "MATHEMATICS," what is the probability that the first letter will be "E"?

(A) 5 (B) $\frac{1}{11}$ (C) $\frac{1}{5}$ (D) $\frac{2}{11}$

Use Figure 6.1C to answer questions 12-13.

(C) **12.** What is the probability of landing on a vowel?

(A) $\frac{3}{2}$ (B) $\frac{5}{6}$ (C) $\frac{2}{3}$ (D) $\frac{1}{2}$

(D) **13.** What is the probability of landing on a consonant?

(A) $\frac{3}{1}$ (B) 2 (C) $\frac{2}{3}$ (D) $\frac{1}{3}$

(B) **14.** Belinda buys a package of beads. The label says there are 24 white beads, 20 rose beads, 32 aqua beads, and 14 amber beads. Belinda closes her eyes and chooses a bead. What is the probability that she will choose an amber bead?

(A) $\frac{2}{15}$ (B) $\frac{7}{45}$ (C) $\frac{7}{40}$ (D) $\frac{14}{100}$

(D) **15.** Suzanne and Howard want to play a board game called *Drive Your Way Across America*. The colors of the tokens are red, green, black, yellow, and white. Suzanne closes her eyes and chooses a token first. What is the probability she will choose a token that is red, yellow, or blue?

(A) $\frac{5}{2}$ (B) $\frac{3}{5}$ (C) $\frac{1}{2}$ (D) $\frac{2}{5}$

Use Figure 6.1D to answer questions 16 and 17.

Figure 6.1 D

(D) **16.** What is the probability the spinner will land on ×?

(A) $\frac{4}{3}$ (B) $\frac{3}{4}$ (C) $\frac{1}{2}$ (D) $\frac{1}{4}$

(A) **17.** What is the probability the spinner will land on =?

(A) 0 (B) 1 (C) 4 (D) $\frac{1}{4}$

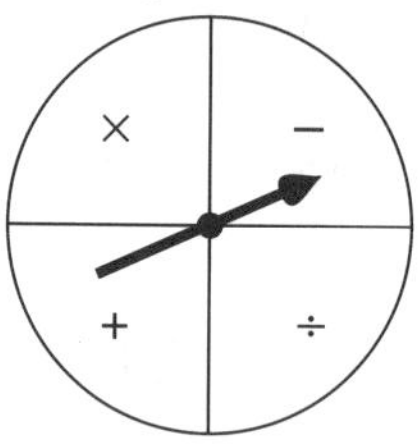

(C) **18.** Avis tosses a number cube labeled with 10, 20, 30, 40, 50, and 60. What is the probability she will throw a 50?

(A) $\frac{25}{3}$ (B) $\frac{6}{1}$ (C) $\frac{1}{6}$ (D) $\frac{3}{25}$

(B) **19.** If you scramble the letters in the word "MISSISSIPPI," what is the probability that the first letter will be an "S" or a "P"?

(A) $\frac{3}{5}$ (B) $\frac{6}{11}$ (C) $\frac{1}{2}$ (D) $\frac{5}{11}$

(B) **20.** There are 8 polka-dot sweaters, 8 striped sweaters, and 8 reindeer-patterned sweaters in a drawer. If you close your eyes and grab a sweater, what is the probability that it will be striped?

(A) 8 (B) $\frac{1}{3}$ (C) $\frac{1}{2}$ (D) 1

(D) **21.** Paul has 6 brown socks, 4 black socks, and 8 blue socks. If he closes his eyes and grabs a sock, what is the possibility that it will be black?

(A) $\frac{9}{2}$ (B) 4 (C) $\frac{1}{3}$ (D) $\frac{2}{9}$

Name ________________ Class ________ Date ____________

6.2 MEAN

The **mean** is the average of a set of numbers.

Example 1: Find the mean of the set of numbers: 12, 20, 13, 42, 23, 34

- Add the numbers: $12 + 20 + 13 + 42 + 23 + 34 = 144$
- Divide the sum by the number of terms: $144 \div 6 = 24$

The mean is 24.

Example 2:

Amount Spent on Groceries – Feb.	
Week	Amount
Feb. 1-5	$ 56.59
Feb. 6-12	81.02
Feb. 13-19	75.16
Feb. 20-28	103.05

What was the average amount spent on groceries each week in February?

- Add the amounts:

  $56.59 + $81.02 + $75.16 + $103.05 = $315.82
- Divide by the number of weeks:

  $315.82 ÷ 4 = $78.955
- Round to the nearest cent:

  $78.955 ≈ $78.96

The average amount spent on groceries each week was $78.96.

Fill in the correct circle to answer each question.

Ⓒ **1.** Find the mean: 1, 3, 5, 7, 9, and 11

Ⓐ 36 Ⓑ 6.33 Ⓒ 6 Ⓓ 5.67

Ⓑ **2.** Find the mean: 100, 98, 78, and 80

Ⓐ 89.5 Ⓑ 89 Ⓒ 88.5 Ⓓ 71.2

Ⓑ **3.** Find the mean: 3.6, 8.9, 6.1, 4.5, and 2.4

Ⓐ 4.25 Ⓑ 5.1 Ⓒ 5.14 Ⓓ 5.32

Ⓑ **4.** What is the average of $1.19, $0.89, and $2.99?

Ⓐ $1.70 Ⓑ $1.69 Ⓒ $1.66 Ⓓ $0.89

Ⓓ **5.** The average monthly temperatures in Atlanta, Georgia, were: 42°, 45°, 53°, 62°, 69°, 76°, 79°, 78°, 73°, 62°, 52°, and 45°. What was the mean temperature for the year? Round your answer to the nearest *whole number*.

Ⓐ 45° Ⓑ 58° Ⓒ 62° Ⓓ 61°

Ⓐ **6.** Debbie Parma is training for a marathon. In five days, she ran 12 mi, 12.5 mi, 16 mi, 14.5 mi, and 15 mi. What was the mean number of miles she ran during the five days?

Ⓐ 14 mi Ⓑ 14.5 mi Ⓒ 65 mi Ⓓ 70 mi

Use Figure 6.2 to answer questions 7-8.

Figure 6.2

Prices of Flower Bouquets	
Flower	Price
Tulips	$4.99
Daisies	$1.95
Irises	$2.50
Freesias	$3.99

Ⓓ **7.** What is the average price for a bouquet of flowers? Round to the nearest *cent*.

Ⓐ $2.69 Ⓑ $3.35 Ⓒ $3.34 Ⓓ $3.36

Ⓓ **8.** A man buys 2 daisy bouquets and 3 iris bouquets. What is the average price of his bouquets?

Ⓐ $3.36 Ⓑ $2.22 Ⓒ $2.23 Ⓓ $2.28

Name ______________________________ Class __________ Date ______________

6.3 TABLES

A **table** organizes data and makes information easy to read.

Train Schedule - San Francisco, CA to Madera, CA					
Destination	Miles	Departs	Destination	Miles	Departs
San Francisco	–	6:45 A.M.	Antioch-Pittsburg	54	8:35 A.M.
Oakland	7	7:30 A.M.	Stockton	85	9:15 A.M.
Berkeley	11	7:35 A.M.	Riverbank	111	9:45 A.M.
Richmond	17	7:42 A.M.	Merced	150	10:25 A.M.
Martinez	36	8:12 A.M.	Madera	187	10:56 A.M.

Example 1: What time does the train leave Richmond, CA?

- Locate Richmond in the *Destination* column and read across to the *Departs* column.

The train leaves Richmond at 7:42 A.M.

Example 2: What is the approximate travel time between Martinez and Riverbank?

- Locate the cities and read across to the *Departs* column.

Martinez – 8:12 A.M. Riverbank – 9:45 A.M.

- Subtract.

$$\begin{array}{r} 9{:}45 \\ -\underline{8{:}12} \\ 1{:}33 \end{array} \qquad \begin{array}{r} 9\text{ h } 45\text{ min} \\ -\underline{8\text{ h } 12\text{ min}} \\ 1\text{ h } 33\text{ min} \end{array}$$

It takes about 1 hour and 33 minutes to travel from Martinez to Riverbank.

Fill in the correct circle to answer each question. Use the table above to answer questions 1-8.

Ⓑ **1.** What time does the train leave Berkeley?

Ⓐ 7:30 A.M. Ⓑ 7:35 A.M.
Ⓒ 7:42 A.M. Ⓓ 7:42 P.M.

Ⓐ **2.** The train leaves Antioch-Pittsburg at ■ .

Ⓐ 8:35 A.M. Ⓑ 9:15 A.M.
Ⓒ 6:45 A.M. Ⓓ 8:35 P.M.

Ⓒ **3.** San Francisco is ■ miles from Merced?

Ⓐ 187 miles Ⓑ 157 miles
Ⓒ 150 miles Ⓓ 143 miles

Ⓓ **4.** Martinez is ■ miles from Stockton.

Ⓐ 85 miles Ⓑ 59 miles
Ⓒ 51 miles Ⓓ 49 miles

Ⓒ **5.** About how long does the trip from San Francisco to Madera take?

Ⓐ 17h 41min Ⓑ 10h 56min
Ⓒ 4h 11min Ⓓ 3h 26min

Ⓑ **6.** The trip from Berkeley to Merced takes about ■ .

Ⓐ 2h 30min Ⓑ 2h 50min
Ⓒ 3h 5min Ⓓ 18 h

Ⓐ **7.** About how long does the trip from Richmond to Martinez take?

Ⓐ 30 min Ⓑ 54 min
Ⓒ 70 min Ⓓ 1h 30min

Ⓑ **8.** Rick Costa boarded the train in Oakland and got off in Riverbank. About how long was his trip?

Ⓐ 1h 45min Ⓑ 2h 15min
Ⓒ 2h 45min Ⓓ 3 h

Name ____________________ Class ________ Date ____________

6.4 RANGE, MEDIAN, MODE

The **range** is the difference between the greatest number and the least number in a set.

The **median** is the middle number in an ordered set of numbers.

The **mode** is the number that appears most often in a set of numbers.

Example 1: Given the set of numbers: 97, 79, 97, 69, 76

A. Find the *range*:
- Order the numbers from least to greatest: 69, 76, 79, 97, 97
- Subtract the least number from the greatest number: 97 – 69 = 28

The range is 28.

B. Find the *median*:
- Order the numbers from least to greatest: 69, 76, 79, 97, 97
- Find the middle number: 69, 76, (79), 97, 97

The median is 79.

C. Find the *mode*:
- Find the number that occurs most often: 69, 76, 79, (97, 97)

The mode is 97.

Example 2: Find the *median*: 28, 21, 38, 32, 23, 38
- Order the numbers from least to greatest: 21, 23, 28, 32, 38, 38
- Find the middle number: 21, 23, (28, 32), 38, 38
- If there are two middle numbers, the average of those numbers is the median. $(28 + 32) \div 2 = 30$

The median is 30.

Fill in the correct circle to answer each question.

(C) **1.** Find the range: $129,300; $154,500; $174,250; $147,900; $152,750

Ⓐ $19,750 Ⓑ $20,250 Ⓒ $44,950 Ⓓ $152,750

(A) **2.** The range of 2.892, 4.136, 6.48, 9.786, and 4.136 is ■ .

Ⓐ 6.894 Ⓑ 4.136 Ⓒ 3.738 Ⓓ 3.306

(B) **3.** What is the median temperature of 90°, 69°, 72°, 104°, 88°, 96° ?

Ⓐ 90° Ⓑ 89° Ⓒ 88° Ⓓ 72°

(D) **4.** Paperback books sell for $6.95, $3.95, $7.95, $4.95, and $5.95. What is the median price?

Ⓐ $7.95 Ⓑ $4.95 Ⓒ $5.45 Ⓓ $5.95

Use Figure 6.4A to answer questions 5-6.

(B) **5.** Find the range.

Ⓐ 5¢ Ⓑ 5.5¢ Ⓒ 10¢ Ⓓ 13¢

(C) **6.** Find the mode.

Ⓐ 8¢ Ⓑ 10¢ Ⓒ 13¢ Ⓓ 13.5¢

Figure 6.4A

Gas Tax by State (¢/gal)

State	Tax
Alabama	13¢
Arkansas	13.5¢
Nevada	13¢
Texas	10¢
Wyoming	8¢

Use this set of numbers for questions 7-10: 16, 19, 23, 21, 17, 16

Ⓓ **7.** Find the range.

Ⓐ 23 Ⓑ 16 Ⓒ 11 Ⓓ 7

Ⓑ **8.** Find the median.

Ⓐ 17 Ⓑ 18 Ⓒ 22 Ⓓ 16

Ⓒ **9.** Find the mode.

Ⓐ 19 Ⓑ 18 Ⓒ 16 Ⓓ 10

Ⓐ **10.** Find the mean. Round to the nearest *whole number.*

Ⓐ 19 Ⓑ 18 Ⓒ 16 Ⓓ 21

Use Figure 6.4B to answer questions 11-13.

Ⓒ **11.** Find the median exam score.

Ⓐ 72 Ⓑ 75 Ⓒ 88 Ⓓ 92

Ⓓ **12.** Find the range.

Ⓐ 92 Ⓑ 83 Ⓒ 75 Ⓓ 20

Ⓐ **13.** Find the mode.

Ⓐ 92 Ⓑ 88 Ⓒ 75 Ⓓ 72

Figure 6.4B

Final Exam Scores	
Mathematics	92
History	75
French	88
Literature	92
Biology	72

Use Figure 6.4C to answer questions 14-16.

Ⓑ **14.** Find the range of average life spans.

Ⓐ 12 Ⓑ 10 Ⓒ 8 Ⓓ 7

Ⓐ **15.** Find the mode.

Ⓐ 12 Ⓑ 8 Ⓒ 7 Ⓓ 2

Ⓒ **16.** Find the median.

Ⓐ 2 Ⓑ 7 Ⓒ 8 Ⓓ 12

Figure 6.4C

Animal	Average Life Span
Cat	12 years
Goat	8 years
Dog	12 years
Goldfish	7 years
Hamster	2 years

Use Figure 6.4D to answer questions 17-19.

Ⓑ **17.** Find the median speed.

Ⓐ 43 Ⓑ 40 Ⓒ 32 Ⓓ 56

Ⓒ **18.** Find the mode.

Ⓐ 30 Ⓑ 32 Ⓒ 40 Ⓓ 43

Ⓓ **19.** Find the range.

Ⓐ 73 Ⓑ 40 Ⓒ 30 Ⓓ 13

Figure 6.4D

Animal	Speed (mph)
Coyote	43
Hyena	40
Zebra	40
Giraffe	32
Deer	30
Greyhound	40

Name ______________________ Class __________ Date __________

6.5 BAR GRAPHS

A **bar graph** displays data in columns, or bars.

Example 1: **Bar Graph**

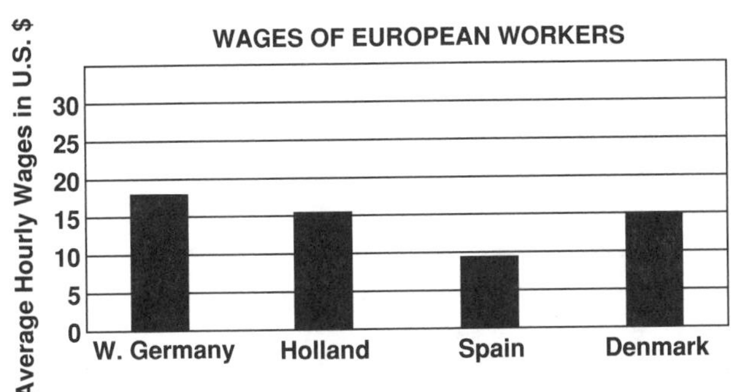

In which two countries do the workers earn about the same amount of money?

- Determine which two bars are about the same height: Holland and Denmark

The workers in Holland and Denmark earn about $15 per hour in U.S.dollars.

Example 2: **Double-Bar Graph**

ANNUAL COST OF ENERGY USE OF NEW APPLIANCES

Dollars: 0, 20, 40, 60, 80, 100, 120

1981 1986

Refrigerator Dishwasher Air-Conditioner

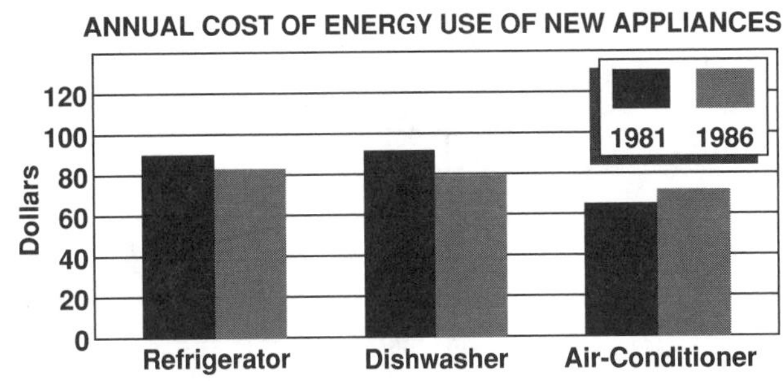

Which appliance(s) showed a decrease in the cost of energy use from 1981 to 1986?

- Find the double bars where the 1986 bar is shorter than the 1981 bar.

Refrigerators and dishwashers showed a decrease in the cost of energy use.

Fill in the correct circle to answer each question. Use the graphs above.

Ⓒ **1.** About how much do the workers in Spain earn per hour?

Ⓐ $2 Ⓑ $5 Ⓒ $10 Ⓓ $30

Ⓒ **2.** About how much do the workers in West Germany earn per hour?

Ⓐ $3.50 Ⓑ $15 Ⓒ $18 Ⓓ $20

Ⓐ **3.** Which country has the highest hourly wage?

Ⓐ West Germany Ⓑ Holland
Ⓒ Spain Ⓓ Denmark

Ⓒ **4.** Which appliance showed an increase in the cost of energy use?

Ⓐ refrigerator Ⓑ dishwasher
Ⓒ air-conditioner Ⓓ none of the above

Ⓑ **5.** The ■ showed the greatest change in the cost of energy use.

Ⓐ air-conditioner Ⓑ dishwasher
Ⓒ refrigerator Ⓓ none of the above

Ⓓ **6.** Which country has the lowest hourly wage?

Ⓐ West Germany Ⓑ Holland
Ⓒ Denmark Ⓓ Spain

Ⓑ **7.** Estimate the annual cost of using a refrigerator in 1981.

Ⓐ $80 Ⓑ $90 Ⓒ $99 Ⓓ $100

Ⓓ **8.** Estimate the difference in the annual cost of using a dishwasher in 1986 from that of 1981.

Ⓐ $90 Ⓑ $80 Ⓒ $20 Ⓓ $10

Ⓒ **9.** Estimate the difference in the hourly wage between Denmark and Spain.

Ⓐ $15 Ⓑ $10 Ⓒ $5 Ⓓ $3

Ⓒ **10.** About how much did it cost to use an air conditioner in 1986?

Ⓐ $50 Ⓑ $60 Ⓒ $70 Ⓓ $80

Name ______________________ Class __________ Date __________

6.6 LINE GRAPHS

A **line graph** displays changes in data over a period of time.

Example 1:

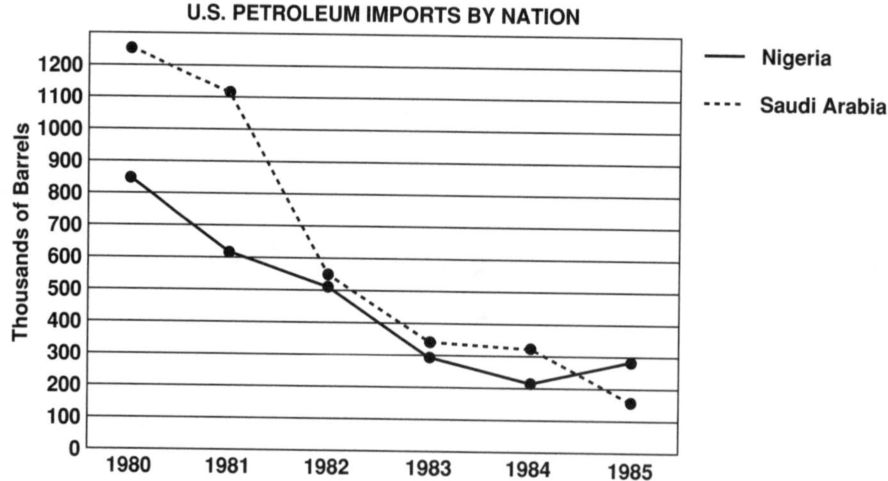

From which country did the U.S. import the greater amount of petroleum in 1982?

- Find the year 1982. Compare the plotted points to find the higher one.
- Look at the key to determine which country is represented by a broken line: Saudi Arabia

In 1982 the U.S. imported the greater amount of petroleum from Saudi Arabia, approximately 550 thousand barrels.

Fill in the correct circle to answer each question. Use the line graph above.

Ⓑ **1.** About how many thousands of barrels of petroleum did the U.S. import from Saudi Arabia in 1983?

Ⓐ 200 Ⓑ 350 Ⓒ 450 Ⓓ 550

Ⓑ **2.** About how many thousands of barrels of petroleum did the U.S. import from Nigeria in 1981?

Ⓐ 500 Ⓑ 600 Ⓒ 850 Ⓓ 1100

Ⓒ **3.** About how many thousands of barrels of petroleum did the U.S. import from both Nigeria and Saudi Arabia in all in 1980?

Ⓐ 2000 Ⓑ 2050 Ⓒ 2100 Ⓓ 2700

Ⓓ **4.** About how many more thousands of barrels of petroleum did the U.S. import from Saudi Arabia in 1980 than it did from Nigeria?

Ⓐ 2100 Ⓑ 1250 Ⓒ 450 Ⓓ 400

Ⓐ **5.** In which year was the U.S. import from Nigeria greatest?

Ⓐ 1980 Ⓑ 1981 Ⓒ 1984 Ⓓ 1985

Ⓒ **6.** In which year was the U.S. import from Saudi Arabia greatest?

Ⓐ 1985 Ⓑ 1984 Ⓒ 1980 Ⓓ 1982

Ⓓ **7.** In which year did the U.S. import more petroleum from Nigeria than from Saudi Arabia?

Ⓐ 1982 Ⓑ 1981 Ⓒ 1983 Ⓓ 1985

Ⓓ **8.** In which year were U.S. imports from Saudi Arabia lowest ?

Ⓐ 1983 Ⓑ 1980 Ⓒ 1984 Ⓓ 1985

Ⓒ **9.** Estimate how many more thousands of barrels the U.S. imported from Saudi Arabia than from Nigeria in 1981.

Ⓐ 50 Ⓑ 400 Ⓒ 500 Ⓓ 600

Ⓑ **10.** Estimate how many more thousands of barrels the U.S. imported from Saudi Arabia than from Nigeria in 1982.

Ⓐ 500 Ⓑ 50 Ⓒ 50,000 Ⓓ 500,000

Name ____________________ Class ________ Date ____________

6.7 CIRCLE GRAPHS

A **circle graph** can represent data as a percent of the total. The percents of a circle graph always add up to 100%.

The circle graph at the right shows the sources of income for the *Big Bend Courier* in July. Income for the month totaled $9000.

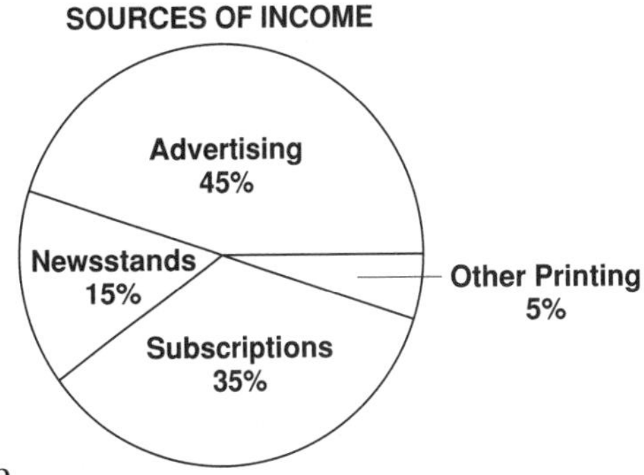

Example 1: What was the greatest source of income for the newspaper in July?

- Find the largest portion of the circle graph.

The greatest source of income was advertising, which represented 45% of the newspaper's earnings.

Example 2: What was the dollar amount of the advertising income?

- Write the percent in decimal form: $45\% = 0.45$
- Multiply by the total monthly income: $0.45 \times \$9000 = \$4050$

The dollar amount of advertising income was $4050.

Fill in the correct circle to answer each question. Use the circle graph above.

Ⓑ **1.** What is the sum of the percents of the circle graph?

Ⓐ 360% Ⓑ 100% Ⓒ 90% Ⓓ 45%

Ⓑ **2.** What percent of income came from Newsstands?

Ⓐ 5% Ⓑ 15% Ⓒ 35% Ⓓ 45%

Ⓐ **3.** What was the dollar amount of income from Other Printing?

Ⓐ $450 Ⓑ $3150
Ⓒ $45,000 Ⓓ $180,000

Ⓒ **4.** What was the dollar amount of income from Subscriptions?

Ⓐ $315,000 Ⓑ $135,000
Ⓒ $3150 Ⓓ $2250

Ⓓ **5.** How much more did the newspaper earn from Advertising than from Subscriptions?

Ⓐ 45% Ⓑ 35% Ⓒ 15% Ⓓ 10%

Ⓐ **6.** How much more did the newspaper earn from Advertising than from Subscriptions?

Ⓐ $900 Ⓑ $1260 Ⓒ $9000 Ⓓ $90,000

Ⓒ **7.** What percent of the newspaper's income came from Newsstands and Other Printing?

Ⓐ 50% Ⓑ 40% Ⓒ 20% Ⓓ 15%

Ⓑ **8.** How much did the newspaper earn from Newsstands and Other Printing?

Ⓐ $180 Ⓑ $1800 Ⓑ $3600 Ⓓ $180,000

Ⓒ **9.** What percent of income came from Advertising and Other Printing?

Ⓐ 5% Ⓑ 45% Ⓒ 50% Ⓓ 60%

Ⓑ **10.** What was the dollar amount of income from Newstands?

Ⓐ $135 Ⓑ $1350
Ⓑ $13,500 Ⓓ $135,000

Name ______________________ Class ________ Date ____________

6.8 PICTOGRAPHS

A **pictograph** uses symbols to represent data.

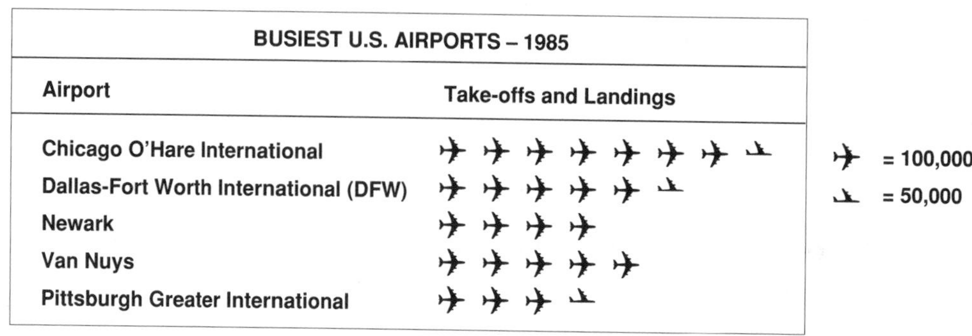

Example 1: About how many planes took off from and landed at the Van Nuys airport in 1985?

- Count the number of symbols beside Van Nuys: (5 planes)
- Multiply by 100,000: $5 \times 100{,}000 = 500{,}000$

There were about 500,000 take-offs and landings at the Van Nuys airport.

Fill in the correct circle to answer each question. Use the pictograph.

(D) **1.** Which airport was the busiest?

Ⓐ Pittsburgh Ⓑ Van Nuys
Ⓒ Newark Ⓓ Chicago O'Hare

(A) **2.** Which airport was the least busy?

Ⓐ Pittsburgh Ⓑ Newark
Ⓒ DFW Ⓓ Chicago O'Hare

(C) **3.** About how many planes took off from and landed at DFW?

Ⓐ 750,000 Ⓑ 650,000
Ⓒ 550,000 Ⓓ 550

(B) **4.** About how many planes took off from and landed at Newark?

Ⓐ 200,000 Ⓑ 400,000
Ⓒ 450,000 Ⓓ 500,000

(A) **5.** There were a total of ▇ take-offs and landings at Van Nuys and Pittsburgh.

Ⓐ 850,000 Ⓑ 750,000
Ⓒ 500,000 Ⓓ 8.5

(C) **6.** What was the total number of take-offs and landings at Chicago O'Hare and Newark?

Ⓐ 750,000 Ⓑ 1,100,000
Ⓒ 1,150,000 Ⓓ 1,300,000

(B) **7.** About how many planes took off from and landed at all five airports?

Ⓐ 3,550,000 Ⓑ 2,550,000
Ⓒ 2,500,000 Ⓓ 2,450,000

(B) **8.** About how many more take-offs and landings occurred at DFW than at Pittsburgh?

Ⓐ 2 Ⓑ 200,000
Ⓒ 350,000 Ⓓ 900,000

(B) **9.** About how many more take-offs and landings occurred at Newark than at Pittsburgh?

Ⓐ 0 Ⓑ 50,000
Ⓒ 100,000 Ⓓ 150,000

(D) **10.** About how many fewer take-offs and landings occurred at Van Nuys than Chicago O' Hare?

Ⓐ 750,000 Ⓑ 500,000
Ⓒ 300,000 Ⓓ 250,000

Name ____________________ Class ________ Date ____________

CHAPTER 6 TEST

Fill in the correct circle to answer each question.

Ⓑ **1.** A number cube has 10, 20, 30, 40, 50, and 60 on its faces. What is the probability a 40 or a 50 will be rolled?

Ⓐ $\frac{1}{6}$ Ⓑ $\frac{1}{3}$ Ⓒ $\frac{2}{5}$ Ⓓ $\frac{1}{2}$

2. What is the probability Ⓓ the spinner will land on a vowel?

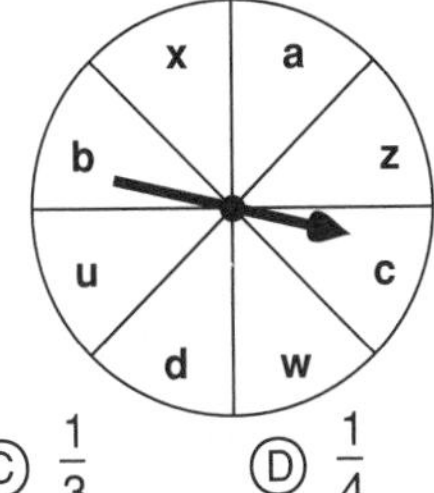

Ⓐ $\frac{3}{4}$ Ⓑ $\frac{2}{3}$ Ⓒ $\frac{1}{3}$ Ⓓ $\frac{1}{4}$

Use Figure 1 to answer questions 3-6.

Figure 1 **AVERAGE HOME PRICES BY STATE** = $10,000 = $5,000

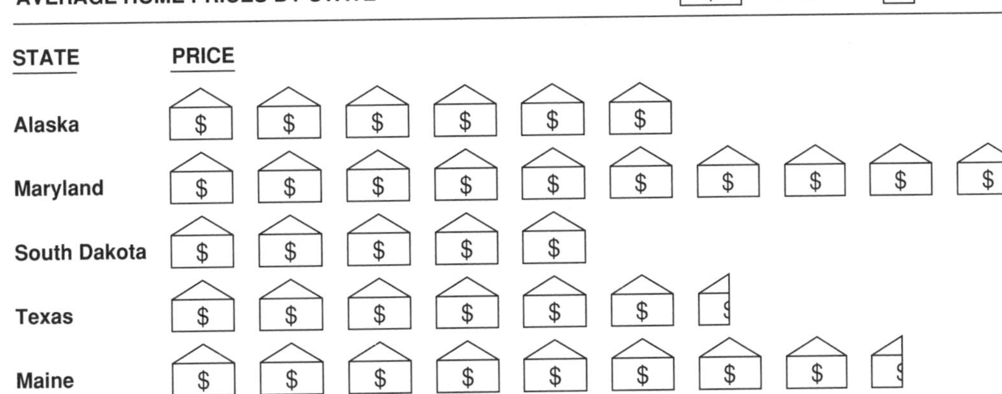

Ⓒ **3.** What is the average price of a home in Maryland?

Ⓐ $50,000 Ⓑ $90,000
Ⓒ $100,000 Ⓓ $110,000

Ⓓ **4.** What is the difference in price between a home in Maine and one in Alaska?

Ⓐ $1500 Ⓑ $2500
Ⓒ $15,000 Ⓓ $25,000

Ⓐ **5.** In which state does a home cost twice as much as a home in South Dakota?

Ⓐ Maryland Ⓑ Maine
Ⓒ Texas Ⓓ Alaska

Ⓒ **6.** Suppose you want to spend between $75,000 and $90,000 on a home. Which state has homes in your price range?

Ⓐ South Dakota Ⓑ Texas
Ⓒ Maine Ⓓ Maryland

Use Figure 2 to answer questions 7-8.

Ⓓ **7.** What percent of students wanted to visit New Orleans?

Ⓐ 30% Ⓑ 26%
Ⓒ 20% Ⓓ 14%

Ⓑ **8.** How many students wanted to visit New Orleans?

Ⓐ 140 Ⓑ 56
Ⓒ 28 Ⓓ 14

Figure 2

Dobie High Senior Class Trip Choices
Total - 400 Students

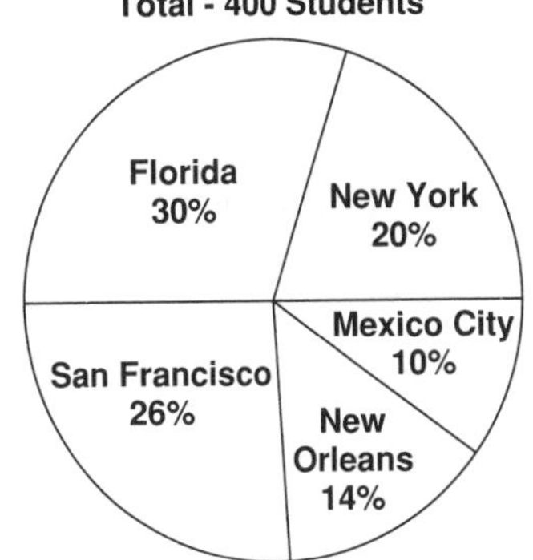

Florida 30%
New York 20%
Mexico City 10%
New Orleans 14%
San Francisco 26%

Use Figure 3 to answer questions 9-10.

Figure 3

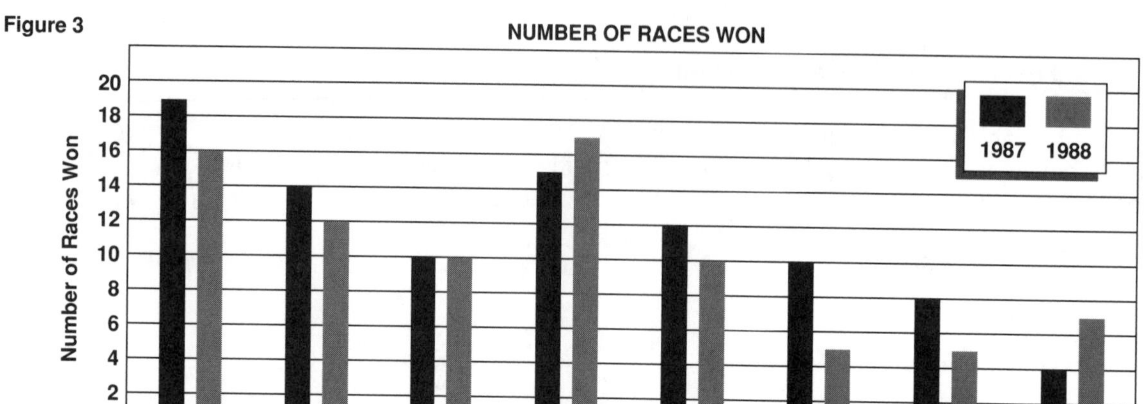

(A) **9.** How many more races did Abilene Alice win in 1988 than in 1987?

(A) 3 (B) 4
(C) 5 (D) 11

(C) **10.** Which horse won the same number of races in 1987 and 1988?

(A) Hibiscus Moon (B) Wind Song
(C) Charlie's Angel (D) Abilene Alice

Use Figure 4 to answer questions 11-12.

Figure 4

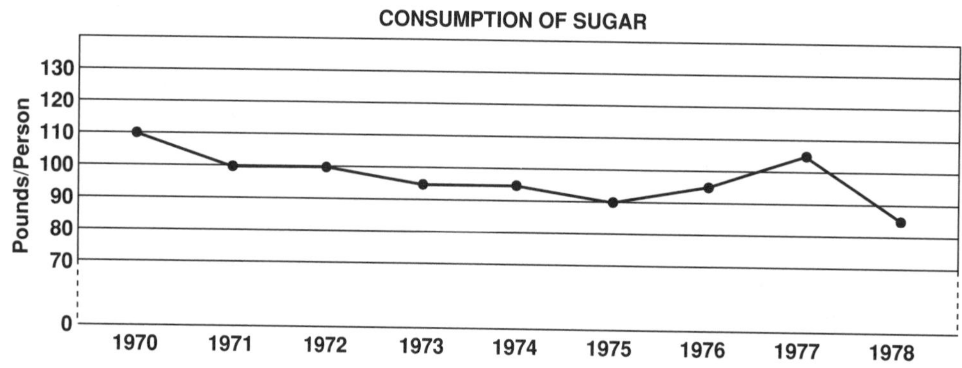

(C) **11.** About how much sugar per person was consumed in 1974?

(A) 103 pounds (B) 100 pounds
(C) 97 pounds (D) 195 pounds

(A) **12.** In which year was the average sugar consumption about 85 pounds?

(A) 1978 (B) 1976
(C) 1973 (D) 1970

Use this set of numbers to answer questions 13-16: 28, 31, 19, 28, 21, 24.

(B) **13.** Find the mean. Round to the nearest *tenth*.

(A) 30.2 (B) 25.2 (C) 25 (D) 9

(B) **14.** Find the median.

(A) 28 (B) 26 (C) 24 (D) 19

(A) **15.** Find the mode.

(A) 28 (B) 24 (C) 21 (D) 19

(C) **16.** Find the range.

(A) 24 (B) 21 (C) 12 (D) 9

Name ______________________ Class ________ Date ____________

CHAPTER 7: GEOMETRY

TEST-TAKING STRATEGY: *Think on Paper*

When taking a standardized exam, you are often given scrap paper. If this is not the case, you will probably be allowed to write in the test booklet. You should always take advantage of this opportunity. Jotting down the information given in a problem is a way of thinking on paper. It helps you to organize your thoughts and work quickly.

Example 1: Bill Creel bought 2 shirts for \$12.99 each and a pair of socks for \$3.49. How much change should he receive from a \$50 bill?

- Write \$12.99 twice since Bill bought 2 shirts. Remember to align the decimal points when adding a list of numbers.

$$\begin{array}{r} \$12.99 \\ 12.99 \\ +\ \ 3.49 \\ \hline \$29.47 \end{array}$$

- To find the amount of change, subtract. Since you are subtracting dollars and cents, write \$50 as \$50.00.

$$\begin{array}{r} \$50.00 \\ -29.47 \\ \hline \$20.53 \end{array}$$

Bill should receive \$20.53 in change.

Example 2: Jill Roberts had \$302.49 in her checking account. She made a deposit of \$83.45 and then wrote a check for \$152.75. What is the new balance in her checking account?

- Making a deposit will increase your balance. Therefore, add the amount of the deposit.

$$\begin{array}{r} \$302.49 \\ +\ \ 83.45 \\ \hline \$385.94 \end{array}$$

- Writing a check will decrease your balance. Therefore, subtract the amount of the check.

$$\begin{array}{r} \$385.94 \\ -152.75 \\ \hline \$233.19 \end{array}$$

Jill's new balance is \$233.19.

Example 3: On a blueprint, 3 inches represents 1 foot. How many feet does 24 inches represent?

- The first sentence translates to: 3 inches per 1 foot, or $\frac{3}{1}$.
- The second sentence translates to: 24 inches per ■ feet, or $\frac{24}{■}$.
- Blueprints are drawn to scale, so the ratios must form a proportion.

$$\frac{3 \text{ inches}}{1 \text{ foot}} = \frac{24 \text{ inches}}{■ \text{ feet}}$$

$$\frac{3}{1} = \frac{24}{■}$$

$$3 \times ■ = 1 \times 24$$

$$3 \times ■ = 24$$

$$■ = 8$$

24 inches represents 8 feet.

Solve.

(D) **1.** Jan had bowling scores of 189 on Monday, 153 on Tuesday, and 169 on Wednesday. After Thursday's game, her average score for four days was 172. What was her bowling score on Thursday?

(A) 170.33 (B) 170.75
(C) 172 (D) 177

(B) **2.** Lyle bought a baseball glove for \$26.95, a bat for \$12.99, and two baseballs for \$2.99 each. If the sales tax on these items is 6%, how much will the sales tax be?

(A) \$2.57 (B) \$2.76
(C) \$27.55 (D) \$48.67

(C) **3.** The regular price of an exercise bike is \$220. It is on sale this week for 40% off. What is the sale price?

(A) \$220.40 (B) \$180
(C) \$132 (D) \$88

(A) **4.** Emily spent 9 hours bicycling Monday through Thursday. On Monday, Wednesday, and Thursday, she spent two and a half hours riding each day. How long did she bicycle on Tuesday?

(A) 1.5 hours (B) 2.5 hours
(C) 7.5 hours (D) 9 hours

(D) **5.** The scale for a map is $\frac{1}{2}$ inch = 10 miles. How many miles apart are two cities that are $3\frac{1}{2}$ inches apart on the map?

(A) 0.175 mi (B) 17.5 mi
(C) 35 mi (D) 70 mi

(D) **6.** A marble is selected at random from a bag that contains 5 red marbles and 3 white marbles. What is the probability that a white marble will be selected?

(A) $\frac{5}{3}$ (B) $\frac{3}{5}$ (C) $\frac{1}{3}$ (D) $\frac{3}{8}$

(A) **7.** Earl uses 3 tablespoons of iced tea mix to make 24 ounces of iced tea. How many tablespoons of mix must he use to make 64 ounces of iced tea?

(A) 8 (B) 16 (C) 24 (D) 512

8. In the Science Club there are 18 girls and 6 boys.
(B) The ratio of boys to girls is ▒.

(A) $\frac{3}{1}$ (B) $\frac{1}{3}$ (C) $\frac{4}{1}$ (D) $\frac{1}{4}$

(D) **9.** Holly correctly answered 40 questions on a math test which has a total of 50 questions. What was her score on the test?

(A) 10% (B) 20% (C) 40% (D) 80%

(B) **10.** If 6 ears of corn cost \$0.78, how much will 2 ears cost?

(A) \$0.13 (B) \$0.26 (C) \$1.56 (D) \$2.34

(C) **11.** Shirts cost \$15.00, pants cost \$25.00, and jackets cost \$50.00. Kevin has \$175 to buy 1 jacket, 2 pairs of pants and some shirts. What is the greatest number of shirts he can buy?

(A) 3 (B) 4 (C) 5 (D) 6

(B) **12.** Joanne wants to buy a stereo. A store offers her two payment plans. She can pay \$1580 in cash, or she can make a \$600 down payment and 48 monthly payments of \$22 each. How much money will Joanne save if she pays cash?

(A) \$24 (B) \$76 (C) \$92 (D) \$100

(A) **13.** The first class period begins at 8:20 A.M. The fifth class period begins 4 hours and 10 minutes later. What time does fifth period begin?

(A) 12:30 P.M. (B) 12:20 P.M.
(C) 12:30 A.M. (D) 12:20 A.M.

(C) **14.** A clock radio that usually sells for \$89.95 is on sale at 20% discount. What is the sale price of the clock radio?

(A) \$17.99 (B) \$69.95
(C) \$71.96 (D) \$107.94

Name ______________________ Class __________ Date __________

CHAPTER 7 PRETEST

Add.

Ⓒ **1.** $12 + 68 = \blacksquare$

Ⓐ 56 Ⓑ 70 Ⓒ 80 Ⓓ 90

Ⓓ **2.** $108 + 23 = \blacksquare$

Ⓐ 85 Ⓑ 121 Ⓒ 125 Ⓓ 131

Ⓒ **3.** $95 + 87 = \blacksquare$

Ⓐ 172 Ⓑ 173 Ⓒ 182 Ⓓ 183

Ⓒ **4.** $114 + 98 = \blacksquare$

Ⓐ 102 Ⓑ 202 Ⓒ 212 Ⓓ 222

Subtract.

Ⓒ **5.** $90 - 41 = \blacksquare$

Ⓐ 59 Ⓑ 51 Ⓒ 49 Ⓓ 39

Ⓑ **6.** $180 - 16 = \blacksquare$

Ⓐ 154 Ⓑ 164 Ⓒ 174 Ⓓ 184

Ⓓ **7.** $180 - 112 = \blacksquare$

Ⓐ 178 Ⓑ 168 Ⓒ 78 Ⓓ 68

Ⓑ **8.** $90 - 12 = \blacksquare$

Ⓐ 68 Ⓑ 78 Ⓒ 88 Ⓓ 102

Multiply.

Ⓓ **9.** $4 \times 12 = \blacksquare$

Ⓐ 36 Ⓑ 38 Ⓒ 42 Ⓓ 48

Ⓒ **10.** $16 \times 8 = \blacksquare$

Ⓐ 118 Ⓑ 124 Ⓒ 128 Ⓓ 144

Ⓒ **11.** $6 \times 9 = \blacksquare$

Ⓐ 45 Ⓑ 48 Ⓒ 54 Ⓓ 63

Ⓒ **12.** $3 \times 21 = \blacksquare$

Ⓐ 53 Ⓑ 61 Ⓒ 63 Ⓓ 71

Find the product.

Ⓓ **13.** $4^2 = \blacksquare$

Ⓐ 2 Ⓑ 8 Ⓒ 12 Ⓓ 16

Ⓓ **14.** $16^2 = \blacksquare$

Ⓐ 4 Ⓑ 8 Ⓒ 32 Ⓓ 256

Ⓑ **15.** $12^2 = \blacksquare$

Ⓐ 244 Ⓑ 144 Ⓒ 24 Ⓓ 6

Ⓑ **16.** $15^2 = \blacksquare$

Ⓐ 255 Ⓑ 225 Ⓒ 30 Ⓓ $7\frac{1}{2}$

Solve for *n*.

Ⓒ **17.** $\frac{3}{4} = \frac{n}{12}$

Ⓐ 6 Ⓑ 8 Ⓒ 9 Ⓓ 12

Ⓐ **18.** $\frac{2}{20} = \frac{n}{10}$

Ⓐ 1 Ⓑ 2 Ⓒ 10 Ⓓ 20

Ⓓ **19.** $\frac{4}{7} = \frac{12}{n}$

Ⓐ 7 Ⓑ 14 Ⓒ 15 Ⓓ 21

Ⓒ **20.** $\frac{n}{15} = \frac{3}{5}$

Ⓐ 25 Ⓑ 12 Ⓒ 9 Ⓓ 6

Find the missing number that makes the sentence true.

(D) **21.** $3 \times 25 = 5 \times$ ▇

(A) 375 (B) 80 (C) 60 (D) 15

(B) **22.** $48 +$ ▇ $= 122$

(A) 170 (B) 74 (C) 76 (D) 84

(D) **23.** ▇ $+ 4 = 192$

(A) 178 (B) 184 (C) 196 (D) 188

(B) **24.** $40° <$ ▇ $< 90°$

(A) 0° (B) 45° (C) 95° (D) 180°

Choose the best answer.

(A) **25.** What kind of angle is shown?

(A) acute
(B) right
(C) obtuse
(D) straight

(A) **26.** Which pair of lines appears to be perpendicular?

(A) $\overleftrightarrow{FG}$ and $\overleftrightarrow{GH}$
(B) $\overleftrightarrow{EF}$ and $\overleftrightarrow{EH}$
(C) $\overleftrightarrow{EH}$ and $\overleftrightarrow{FG}$
(D) $\overleftrightarrow{EF}$ and $\overleftrightarrow{GH}$

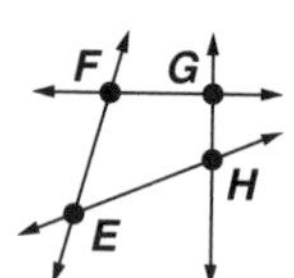

(A) **27.** $\sqrt{64} =$

(A) 8 (B) 32 (C) 128 (D) 4096

(C) **28.** A triangle has two angles with measures of 16° and 64°. What is the measure of the third angle?

(A) 10° (B) 20° (C) 100° (D) 280°

(C) **29.** Name the polygon.

(A) quadrilateral
(B) pentagon
(C) hexagon
(D) nonagon

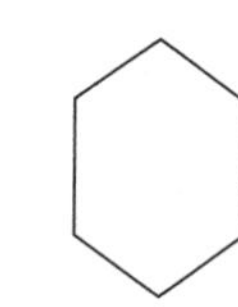

(A) **30.** Find the missing length.

(A) 15
(B) 20
(C) 25
(D) 32

(B) **31.** Name the quadrilateral.

(A) trapezoid
(B) parallelogram
(C) rectangle
(D) nonagon

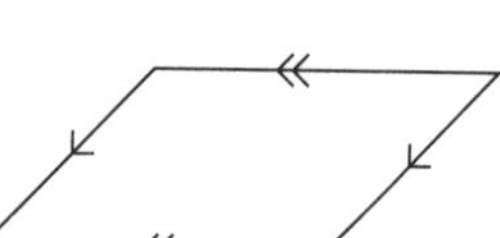

(D) **32.** What part of the circle is $\overline{AC}$?

(A) radius
(B) diameter
(C) arc
(D) chord

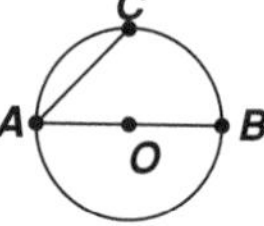

(B) **33.** The trapezoids are similar. Find the length of $\overline{CD}$.

(A) 4
(B) 6
(C) 8
(D) 13

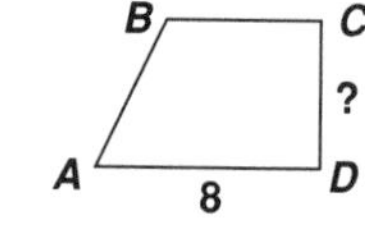

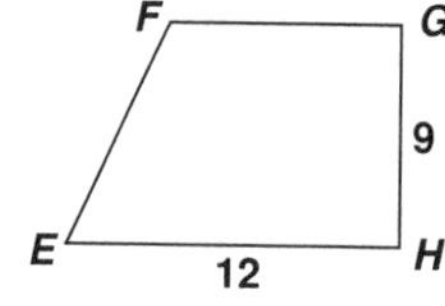

Name ______________________ Class __________ Date __________

7.1 CLASSIFYING ANGLES

An angle can be classified by its measure.

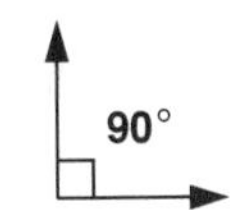

A **right angle** measures 90°.

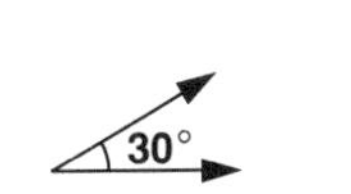

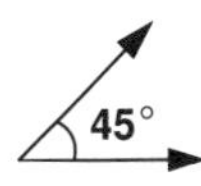

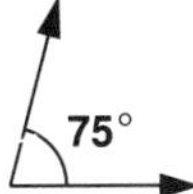

An **acute angle** measures more than 0° but less than 90°.

An **obtuse angle** measures more than 90° but less than 180°.

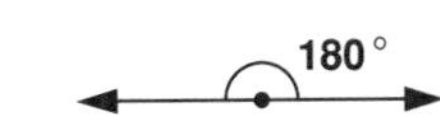

A **straight angle** measures 180°.

Example 1: Classify the angle as **acute, right, obtuse,** or **straight.**

Figure 7.1A

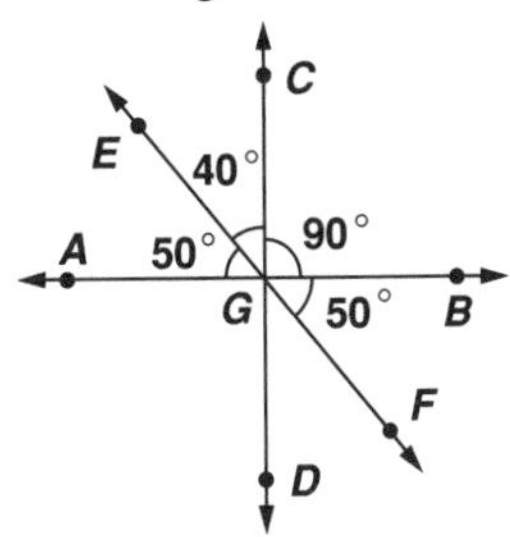

A. $\angle AGB$

- The degree measure of $\angle AGB$ is written m$\angle AGB$.
- m$\angle AGB = 50 + 40 + 90 = 180$

$\angle AGB$ is a straight angle.

B. $\angle BGF$

- m$\angle BGF = 50$.

$\angle BGF$ is an acute angle.

Two angles are **complementary** when the sum of their measures is 90.
For example, the measure of the complement of a 60° angle is 30 because 60 + 30 = 90.

Angles are **supplementary** when the sum of their measures is 180.
For example, the measure of the supplement of a 130° angle is 50 because 130 + 50 = 180.

Example 2: Use the diagram above. Are the angles complementary or supplementary?

A. $\angle AGE$ and $\angle EGB$

- m∠AGE + m∠EGB = 50 + 130
  = 180

$\angle AGE$ and $\angle EGB$ are supplementary angles.

B. $\angle AGE$ and $\angle EGC$

- m∠AGE + m∠EGC = 50 + 40
  = 90

$\angle AGE$ and $\angle EGC$ are complementary angles.

Vertical angles are two opposite and equal angles formed by the intersection of two lines.

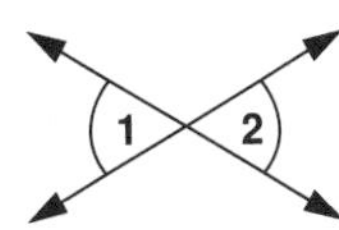

$\angle 1$ and $\angle 2$ are vertical angles.

Use Figure 7.1A to answer questions 1-7.

Ⓒ **1.** $\angle AGF$ is

Ⓐ acute Ⓑ right
Ⓒ obtuse Ⓓ straight

Ⓐ **2.** $\angle EGC$ is

Ⓐ acute Ⓑ right
Ⓒ obtuse Ⓓ straight

(B) **3.** Which pair of angles is complementary?

(A) ∠*AGE* and ∠*BGF* (B) ∠*AGE* and ∠*EGC*
(C) ∠*EGC* and ∠*CGF* (D) ∠*CGB* and ∠*AGB*

(B) **4.** ∠*AGD* is

(A) acute (B) right
(C) obtuse (D) straight

(C) **5.** Which pair of angles is vertical?

(A) ∠*AGE* and ∠*EGC* (B) ∠*AGE* and ∠*DGF*
(C) ∠*EGC* and ∠*DGF* (D) ∠*EGC* and ∠*CGF*

(D) **6.** Which pair of angles is supplementary?

(A) ∠*AGD* and ∠*AGB* (B) ∠*AGE* and ∠*BGF*
(C) ∠*DGF* and ∠*FGB* (D) ∠*EGC* and ∠*CGF*

(D) **7.** ∠*AGD* and ■ are vertical angles.

(A) ∠*BGD* (B) ∠*AGC*
(C) ∠*CGF* (D) ∠*CGB*

(A) **8.** An angle measures 35°. The angle is

(A) acute (B) right
(C) obtuse (D) straight

(B) **9.** What kind of angle is shown?

(A) acute
(B) right
(C) obtuse
(D) straight

90°

(C) **10.** What kind of angle is shown?

(A) acute
(B) right
(C) obtuse
(D) straight

(B) **11.** m∠1 = 72. Its complement has measure of

(A) 8 (B) 18
(C) 28 (D) 108

(A) **12.** m∠1 = 65 and m∠2 = 115. The angles are

(A) supplementary (B) acute
(C) obtuse (D) straight

(B) **13.** If m∠1 = 45, then the measure of its supplement is

(A) 45 (B) 135
(C) 180 (D) 225

(D) **14.** Which pair of angles is supplementary?

(A) 12°, 2° (B) 90°, 180°
(C) 45°, 45° (D) 175°, 5°

Figure 7.1B

Use Figure 7.1B to answer questions 15-17.

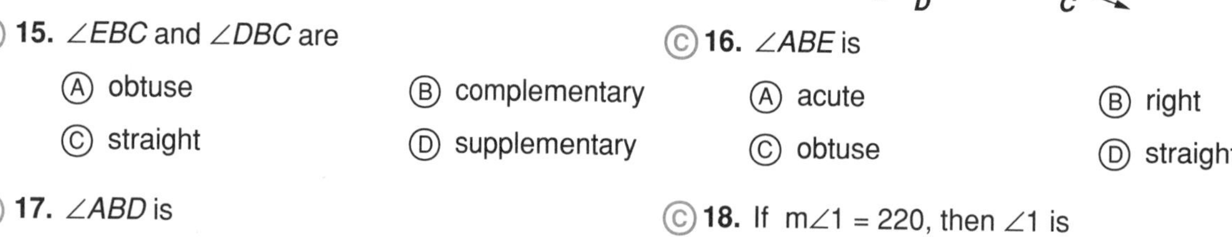

(D) **15.** ∠*EBC* and ∠*DBC* are

(A) obtuse (B) complementary
(C) straight (D) supplementary

(C) **16.** ∠*ABE* is

(A) acute (B) right
(C) obtuse (D) straight

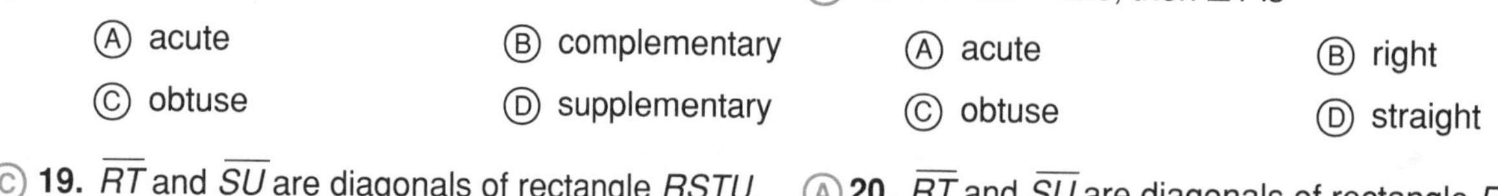

(A) **17.** ∠*ABD* is

(A) acute (B) complementary
(C) obtuse (D) supplementary

(C) **18.** If m∠1 = 220, then ∠1 is

(A) acute (B) right
(C) obtuse (D) straight

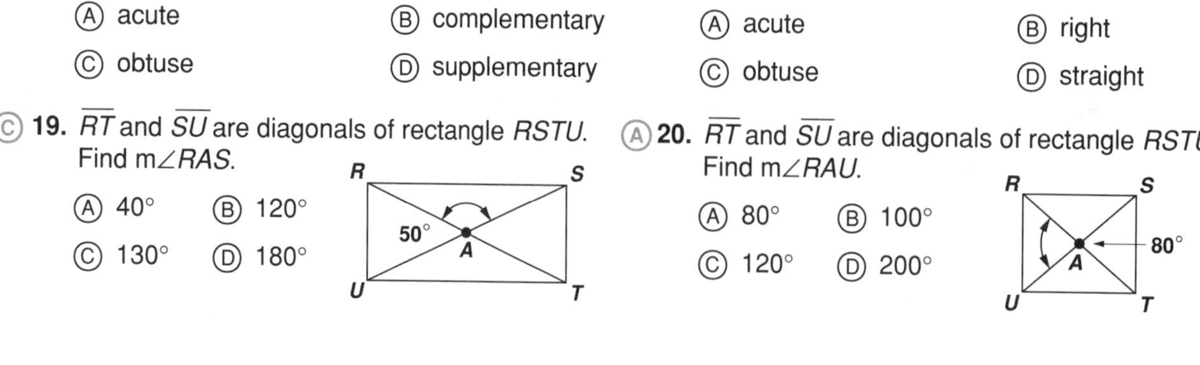

(C) **19.** $\overline{RT}$ and $\overline{SU}$ are diagonals of rectangle *RSTU*. Find m∠*RAS*.

(A) 40° (B) 120°
(C) 130° (D) 180°

(A) **20.** $\overline{RT}$ and $\overline{SU}$ are diagonals of rectangle *RSTU*. Find m∠*RAU*.

(A) 80° (B) 100°
(C) 120° (D) 200°

Name________________ Class ________ Date ________

7.2 CLASSIFYING LINES

Intersecting lines are lines that meet at a point.

Parallel lines are lines in the same plane that do not intersect.

Perpendicular lines are lines that intersect to form right angles.

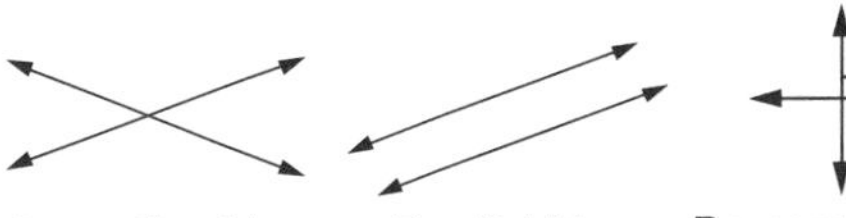

Example 1: Classify $\overleftrightarrow{AB}$ and $\overleftrightarrow{DE}$.

- $\overleftrightarrow{AB}$ and $\overleftrightarrow{DE}$ never intersect.

  Therefore, $\overleftrightarrow{AB}$ and $\overleftrightarrow{DE}$ are parallel lines.

Example 2: $\overleftrightarrow{AC}$ is perpendicular to what line?

- $\overleftrightarrow{AC}$ intersects $\overleftrightarrow{BE}$ at a right angle.

  Therefore, $\overleftrightarrow{AC}$ is perpendicular to $\overleftrightarrow{BE}$.

Figure 7.2A

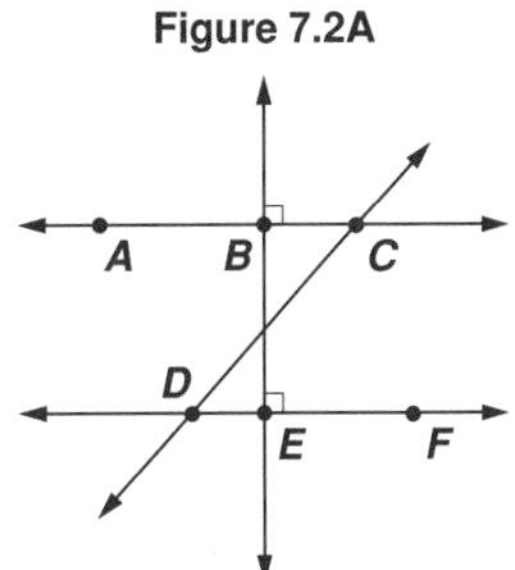

Use Figure 7.2B to answer questions 1-7.

Figure 7.2B

Ⓒ **1.** Which pair of lines is parallel?

Ⓐ $\overleftrightarrow{AB}$ and $\overleftrightarrow{CD}$ Ⓑ $\overleftrightarrow{CD}$ and $\overleftrightarrow{BD}$
Ⓒ $\overleftrightarrow{AC}$ and $\overleftrightarrow{BD}$ Ⓓ $\overleftrightarrow{EF}$ and $\overleftrightarrow{AB}$

Ⓒ **2.** Which pair of lines is perpendicular?

Ⓐ $\overleftrightarrow{AB}$ and $\overleftrightarrow{AC}$ Ⓑ $\overleftrightarrow{CD}$ and $\overleftrightarrow{AB}$
Ⓒ $\overleftrightarrow{CD}$ and $\overleftrightarrow{BD}$ Ⓓ $\overleftrightarrow{AC}$ and $\overleftrightarrow{BD}$

Ⓑ **3.** $\overleftrightarrow{AB}$ intersects $\overleftrightarrow{BD}$ at point

Ⓐ A Ⓑ B
Ⓒ C Ⓓ D

Ⓑ **4.** $\overleftrightarrow{AB}$ and $\overleftrightarrow{BD}$ appear to be

Ⓐ parallel Ⓑ intersecting
Ⓒ the same line Ⓓ perpendicular

Ⓐ **5.** $\overleftrightarrow{BD}$ and $\overleftrightarrow{AC}$ appear to be

Ⓐ parallel Ⓑ intersecting
Ⓒ the same line Ⓓ perpendicular

Ⓐ **6.** Which two lines intersect at point C?

Ⓐ $\overleftrightarrow{AC}$ and $\overleftrightarrow{DC}$ Ⓑ $\overleftrightarrow{CD}$ and $\overleftrightarrow{AB}$
Ⓒ $\overleftrightarrow{DC}$ and $\overleftrightarrow{DB}$ Ⓓ $\overleftrightarrow{CA}$ and $\overleftrightarrow{BA}$

Ⓒ **7.** $\overleftrightarrow{BD}$ is perpendicular to

Ⓐ $\overleftrightarrow{AB}$ Ⓑ $\overleftrightarrow{AC}$
Ⓒ $\overleftrightarrow{CD}$ Ⓓ $\overleftrightarrow{DB}$

Ⓓ **8.** Which pair of lines is perpendicular?

Ⓐ 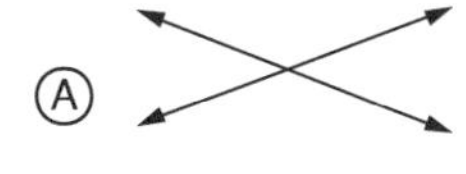 Ⓑ

Ⓒ 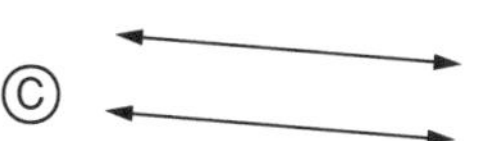 Ⓓ 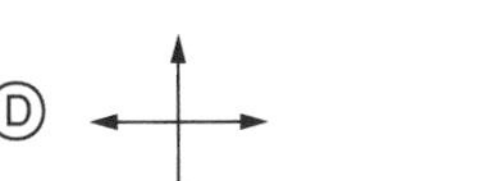

Ⓒ **9.** Which pair of lines is parallel?

Ⓐ Ⓑ

Ⓒ  Ⓓ

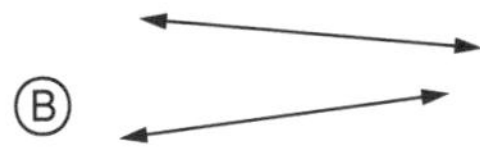

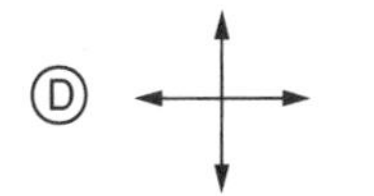

Ⓓ **10.** Perpendicular lines can never

Ⓐ form right angles Ⓑ have one point in common
Ⓒ intersect Ⓓ be parallel

Ⓒ **11.** Parallel lines

Ⓐ intersect at right angles Ⓑ always intersect
Ⓒ never intersect Ⓓ sometimes intersect

Name ______________________ Class __________ Date __________

7.3 CLASSIFYING POLYGONS

A **polygon** is a closed figure made up of 3 or more line segments. Polygons are classified by the number of sides or angles.

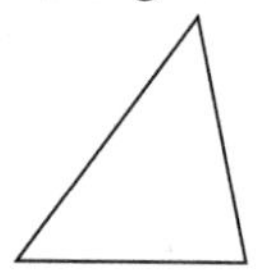

Triangle
3 sides
3 angles

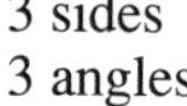

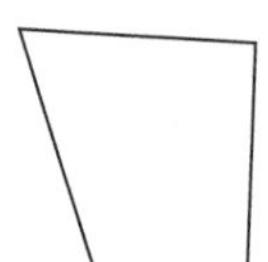

Quadrilateral
4 sides
4 angles

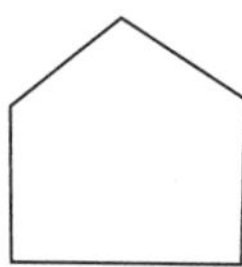

Pentagon
5 sides
5 angles

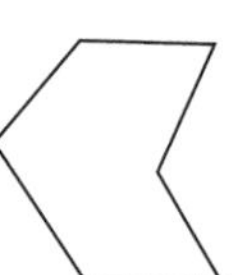

Hexagon
6 sides
6 angles

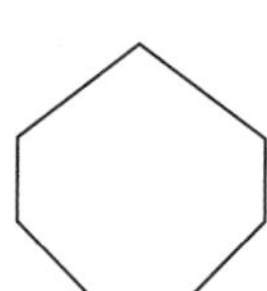

Heptagon
7 sides
7 angles

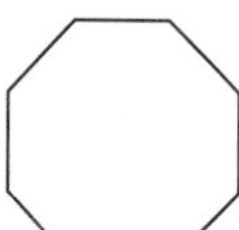

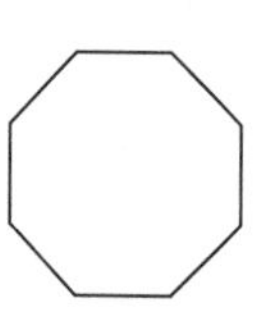

Octagon
8 sides
8 angles

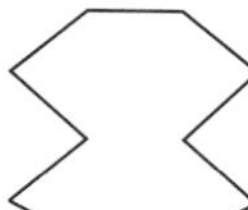

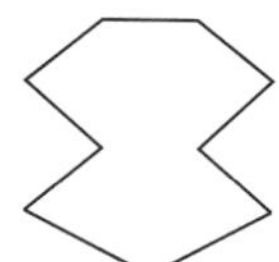

Nonagon
9 sides
9 angles

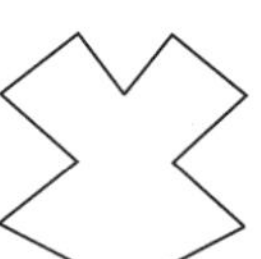

Decagon
10 sides
10 angles

Find the answer.

Ⓒ **1.** Name the polygon.

Ⓐ pentagon
Ⓑ quadrilateral
Ⓒ hexagon
Ⓓ octagon

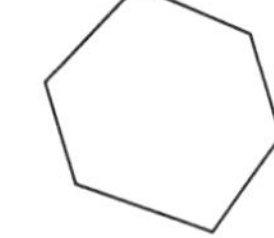

Ⓓ **2.** Name the polygon.

Ⓐ octagon
Ⓑ hexagon
Ⓒ pentagon
Ⓓ quadrilateral

Ⓓ **3.** An octagon has

Ⓐ 4 sides Ⓑ 5 sides
Ⓒ 6 sides Ⓓ 8 sides

Ⓑ **4.** A hexagon has

Ⓐ 8 angles Ⓑ 6 angles
Ⓒ 5 angles Ⓓ 4 angles

Ⓒ **5.** How many angles does the polygon have?

Ⓐ 3
Ⓑ 4
Ⓒ 5
Ⓓ 6

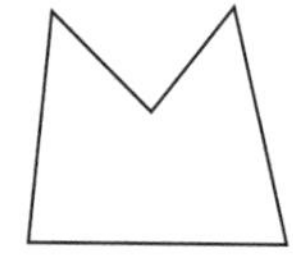

Ⓑ **6.** What kind of polygon is figure *ABCDEF?*

Ⓐ octagon
Ⓑ hexagon
Ⓒ pentagon
Ⓓ quadrilateral

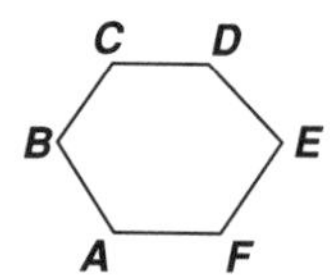

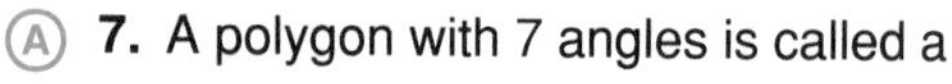

Ⓐ **7.** A polygon with 7 angles is called a

Ⓐ heptagon Ⓑ quadrilateral
Ⓒ octagon Ⓓ hexagon

Ⓐ **8.** A polygon with 9 sides is called a

Ⓐ nonagon Ⓑ heptagon
Ⓒ pentagon Ⓓ hexagon

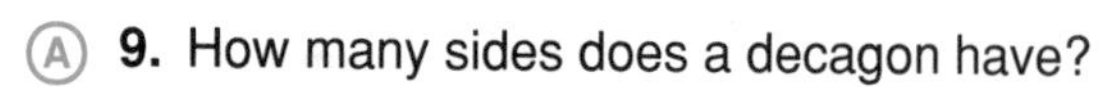

Ⓐ **9.** How many sides does a decagon have?

Ⓐ 10 Ⓑ 9 Ⓒ 8 Ⓓ 7

Ⓓ **10.** How many angles does a quadrilateral have?

Ⓐ 9 Ⓑ 6 Ⓒ 5 Ⓓ 4

Name ______________________ Class __________ Date ______________

7.4 CONGRUENT AND SIMILAR FIGURES

Congruent figures have the same size and shape. The symbol ≅ means "is congruent to."

The triangles in Example 1 are congruent.
Therefore, the corresponding sides have the same length: $AB = DE$, $BC = EF$, and $AC = DF$.

And, the corresponding angles have the same measure: $m\angle A = m\angle D$, $m\angle B = m\angle E$, and $m\angle C = m\angle F$.

Example 1: ΔABC is congruent to ΔDEF. Which line segment is congruent to $\overline{AB}$?

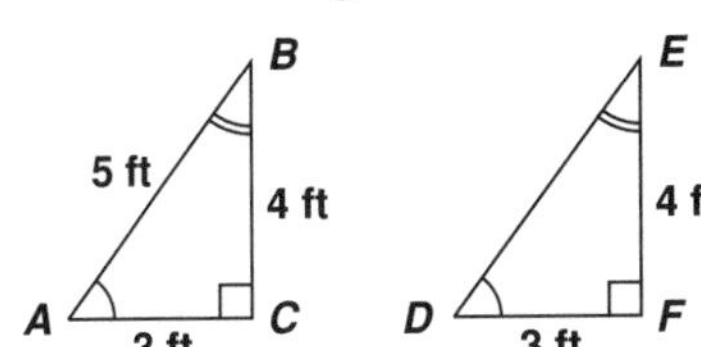

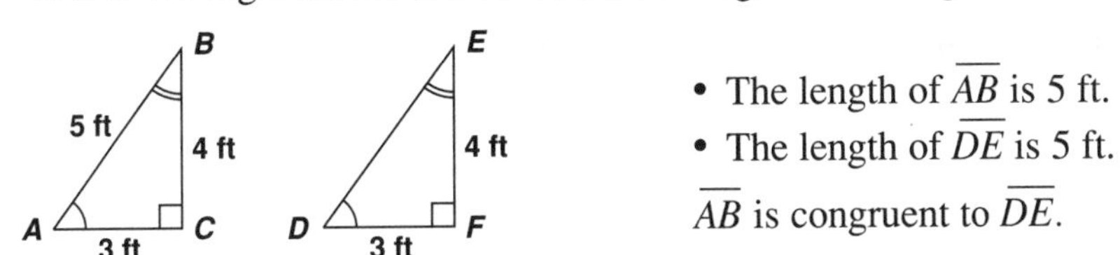

- The length of $\overline{AB}$ is 5 ft.
- The length of $\overline{DE}$ is 5 ft.

$\overline{AB}$ is congruent to $\overline{DE}$.

Similar figures have the same shape, but not necessarily the same size. In similar figures, corresponding angles are congruent, and corresponding sides are in proportion.

The quadrilaterals in Example 2 are similar.
Therefore, the corresponding angles are congruent: $\angle A \cong \angle Q$, $\angle B \cong \angle R$, $\angle C \cong \angle S$, $\angle D \cong \angle T$.
And, the corresponding sides are in proportion: $\frac{BC}{RS} = \frac{36}{18} = \frac{2}{1}$, $\frac{CD}{ST} = \frac{32}{16} = \frac{2}{1}$, $\frac{DA}{TQ} = \frac{50}{25} = \frac{2}{1}$, $\frac{AB}{QR} = \frac{24}{n}$

Example 2: Quadrilaterals $ABCD$ and $QRST$ are similar. Find the length of $\overline{QR}$.

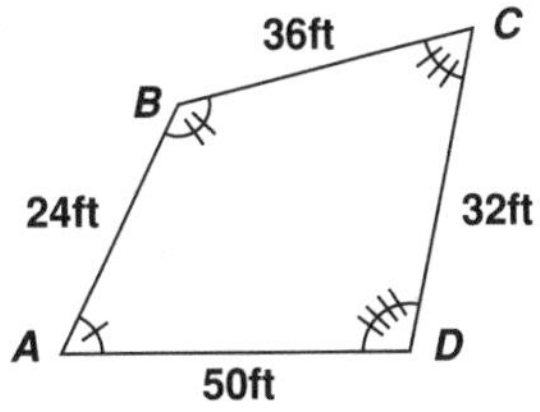

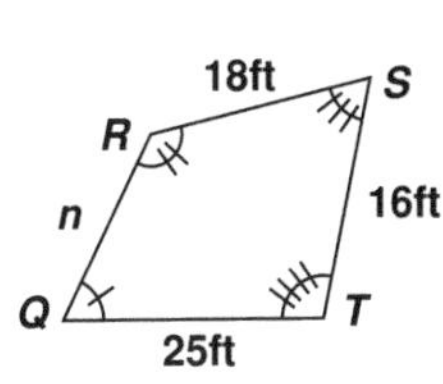

- Write a proportion.

$$\begin{matrix} AB \longrightarrow \\ QR \longrightarrow \end{matrix} \frac{24}{n} = \frac{36}{18} \begin{matrix} \longleftarrow BC \\ \longleftarrow RS \end{matrix}$$

- Solve the proportion.

$$24 \times 18 = n \times 36$$
$$432 = n \times 36$$
$$432 \div 36 = n \times 36 \div 36$$
$$12 = n$$

The length of $\overline{QR}$ is 12.

Find the answer.

Ⓐ **1.** Which pentagons are congruent?

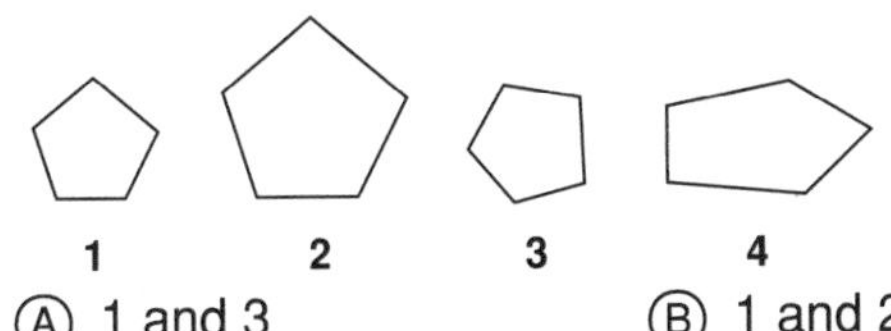

Ⓐ 1 and 3 Ⓑ 1 and 2
Ⓒ 2 and 3 Ⓓ 3 and 4

Ⓒ **2.** The trapezoids are congruent. Angle G is congruent to

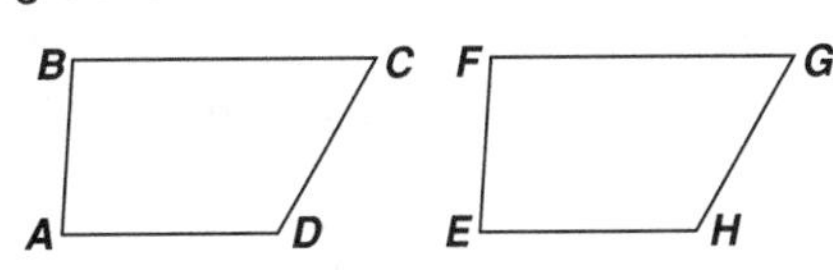

Ⓐ angle A Ⓑ angle B
Ⓒ angle C Ⓓ angle D

(D) **3.** Figure *RSTUV* is congruent to figure *ABCDE*. $\overline{ST}$ is congruent to

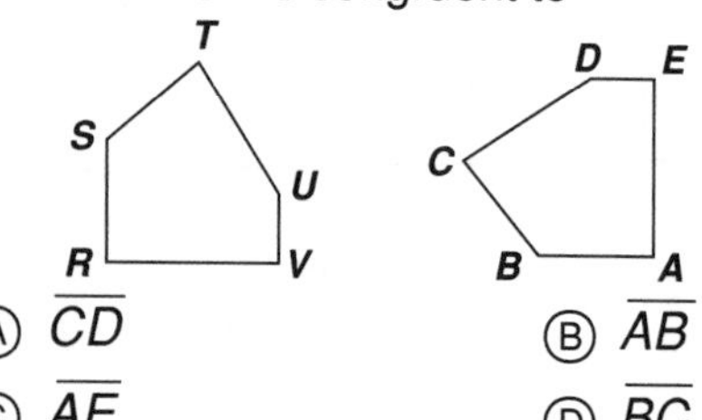

(A) $\overline{CD}$ (B) $\overline{AB}$

(C) $\overline{AE}$ (D) $\overline{BC}$

(A) **4.** Triangle *ABC* is congruent to triangle *EFD*. $\overline{AB}$ is congruent to

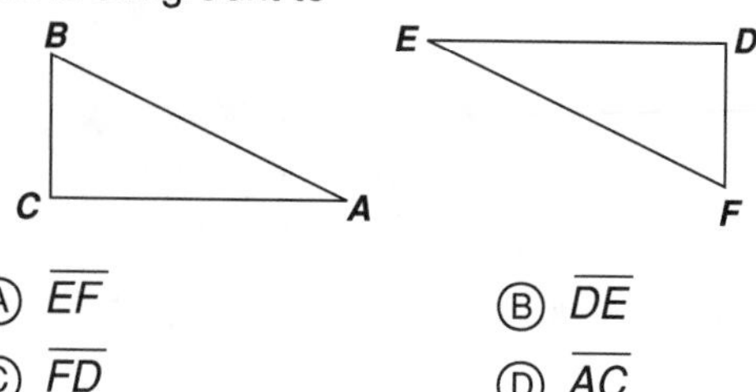

(A) $\overline{EF}$ (B) $\overline{DE}$

(C) $\overline{FD}$ (D) $\overline{AC}$

(D) **5.** Which two figures appear to be similar?

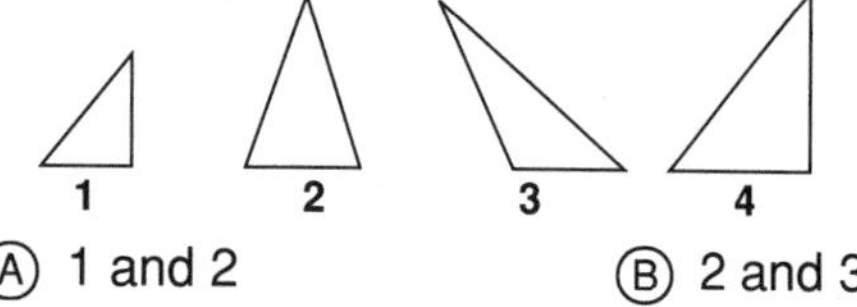

(A) 1 and 2 (B) 2 and 3

(C) 3 and 4 (D) 1 and 4

(A) **6.** Triangle *BCA* is similar to triangle *ECD*. Angle *E* is congruent to

(A) ∠*ABC*

(B) ∠*CAB*

(C) ∠*BCA*

(D) ∠*CDE*

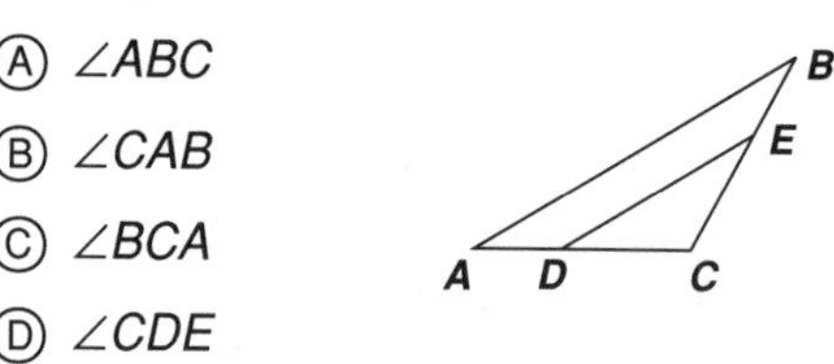

(D) **7.** The figures are similar. Find *GJ*.

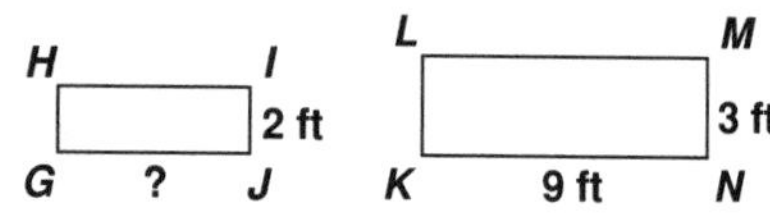

(A) 2 ft (B) 3 ft (C) 4 ft (D) 6 ft

(B) **8.** ΔABC is similar to ΔXYZ. Find the length of $\overline{XY}$.

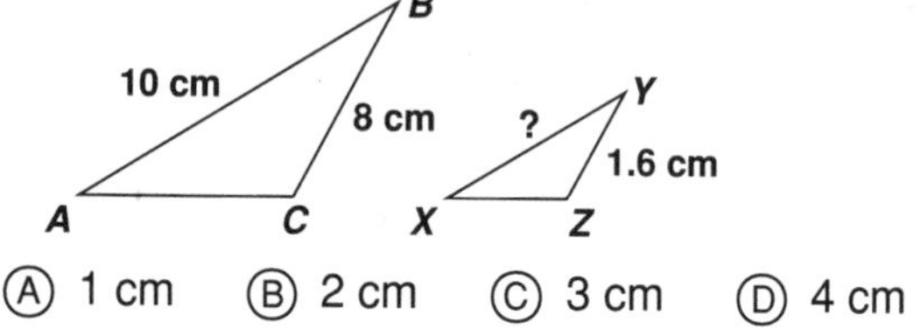

(A) 1 cm (B) 2 cm (C) 3 cm (D) 4 cm

(D) **9.** Figure *ABCD* is similar to figure *QRST*. $\overline{AB}$ corresponds to

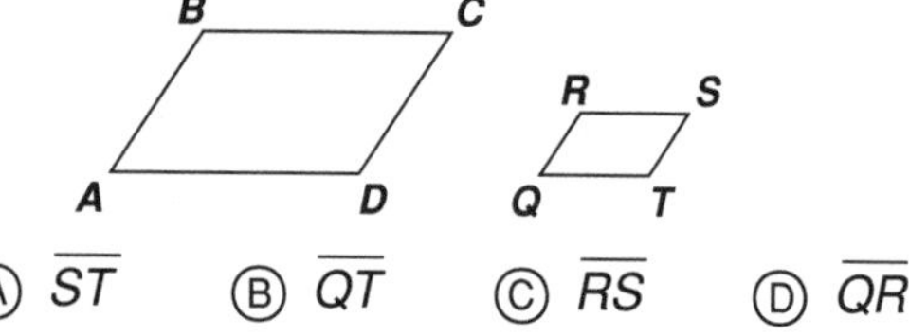

(A) $\overline{ST}$ (B) $\overline{QT}$ (C) $\overline{RS}$ (D) $\overline{QR}$

(A) **10.** The hexagons are congruent. $\overline{AF}$ is congruent to

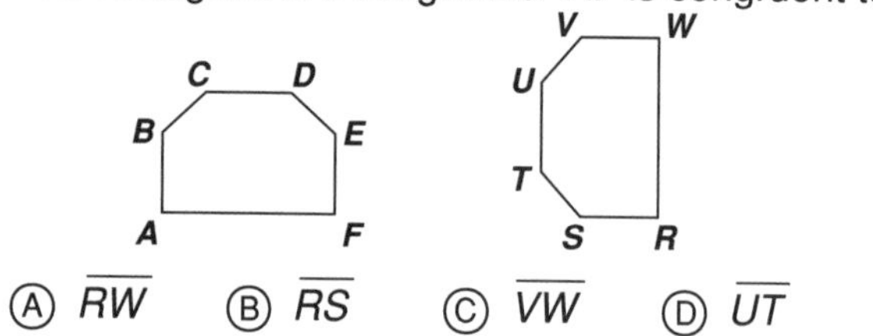

(A) $\overline{RW}$ (B) $\overline{RS}$ (C) $\overline{VW}$ (D) $\overline{UT}$

(B) **11.** The figures are similar. Find the length of $\overline{QR}$.

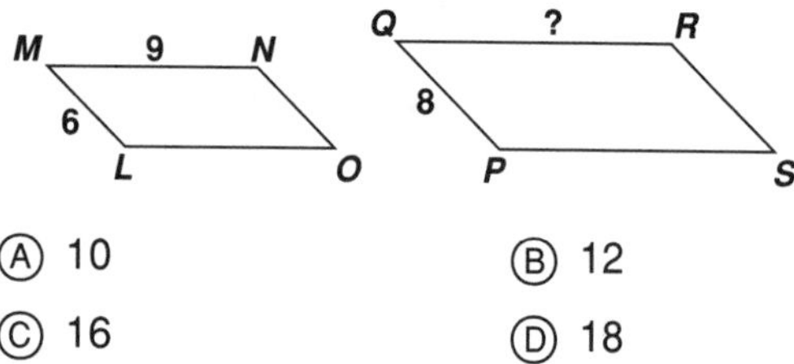

(A) 10 (B) 12

(C) 16 (D) 18

(C) **12.** Figure *ABCD* is congruent to figure *PQRS*. Angle *R* is congruent to

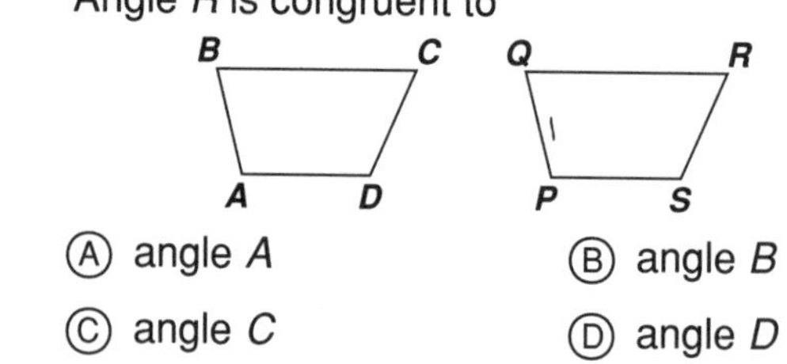

(A) angle *A* (B) angle *B*

(C) angle *C* (D) angle *D*

(D) **15.** Figure *ABCD* is similar to figure *EFGD*. Which line segment in *EFGD* corresponds to $\overline{DC}$ in *ABCD?*

(A) $\overline{AD}$ (B) $\overline{AB}$

(C) $\overline{DE}$ (D) $\overline{DG}$

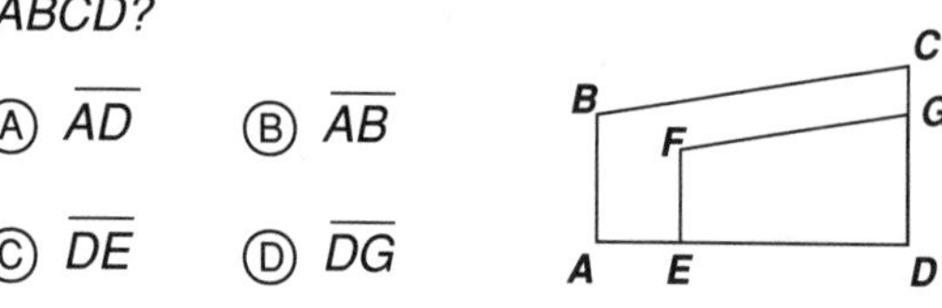

(A) **16.** In triangle *ABC* below, which is the ratio *AC:BC?*

(A) $\frac{18}{11}$ (B) $\frac{18}{20}$

(C) $\frac{20}{18}$ (D) $\frac{11}{18}$

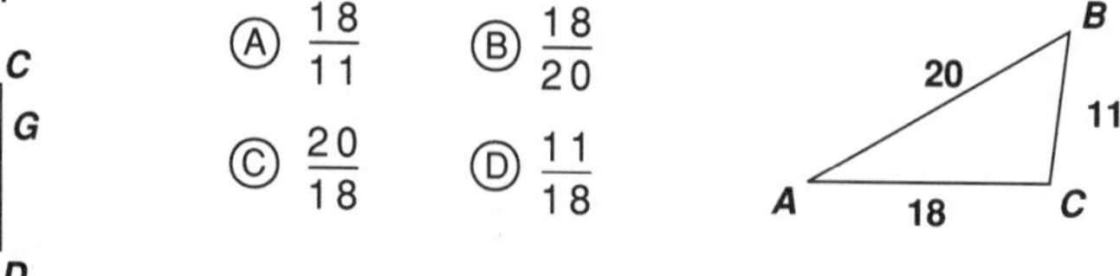

Name ______________________ Class __________ Date ______________

7.5 CLASSIFYING QUADRILATERALS

Quadrilaterals are four–sided polygons. Quadrilaterals can be classified by their sides and angles. The symbols below are used to show congruent and parallel sides.

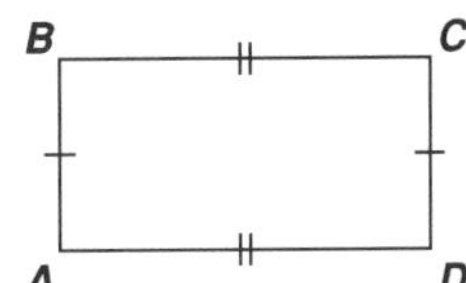

$\overline{AB}$ is congruent to $\overline{CD}$.
$\overline{BC}$ is congruent to $\overline{AD}$.

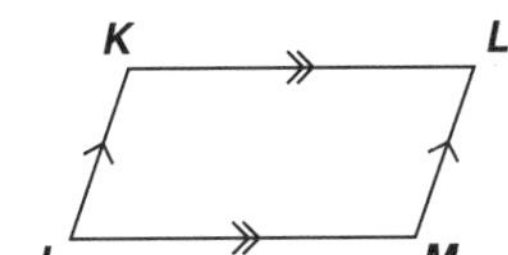

$\overline{JK}$ is parallel to $\overline{LM}$.
$\overline{KL}$ is parallel to $\overline{JM}$.

Name	Figure	Characteristics
Trapezoid	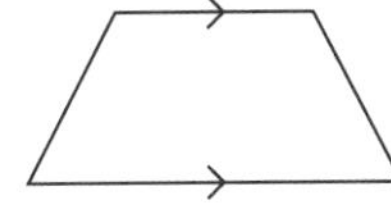	• Exactly one pair of sides are parallel.
 **Parallelogram**	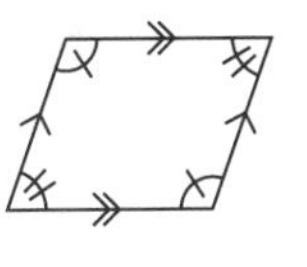	• Opposite sides are parallel and congruent. • Opposite angles are congruent.
 **Rectangle**	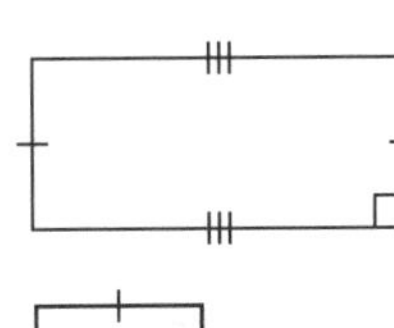	• All 4 angles are right angles. 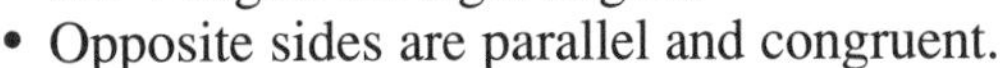 • Opposite sides are parallel and congruent.
Square	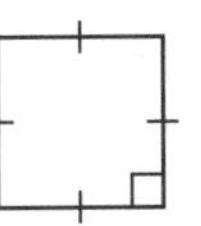	• All 4 angles are right angles. • All 4 sides are parallel and congruent.

Find the answer.

(B) **1.** Name the quadrilateral.

Ⓐ trapezoid
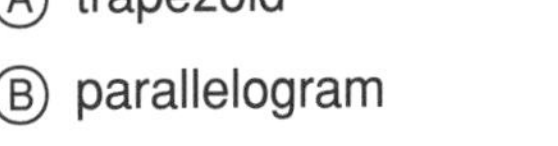
Ⓑ parallelogram
Ⓒ rectangle
Ⓓ square

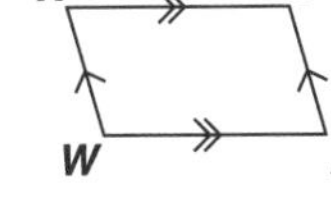

(A) **2.** Name the quadrilateral.

Ⓐ trapezoid
Ⓑ parallelogram

Ⓒ rectangle
Ⓓ square

(C) **3.** ∠*A* and ∠*C* are opposite angles of a parallelogram. If m ∠*A* = 50 , find m ∠*C*.

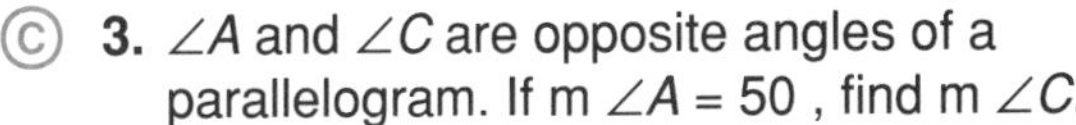
Ⓐ 260 Ⓑ 130 Ⓒ 50 Ⓓ 40

(D) **4.** Find the sum of the measures of all the angles of a rectangle.

Ⓐ 90° Ⓑ 180° Ⓒ 270° Ⓓ 360°

(C) **5.** Quadrilateral *ABCD* has opposite sides parallel and congruent. m∠*A* = 90°. The figure is a

Ⓐ trapezoid Ⓑ square
Ⓒ rectangle Ⓓ none of these

(A) **6.** Quadrilateral *JKLM* has exactly one pair of parallel sides. The figure is a

Ⓐ trapezoid Ⓑ parallelogram
Ⓒ rectangle Ⓓ none of these

(B) **7.** The opposite angles in a parallelogram are

Ⓐ parallel Ⓑ congruent
Ⓒ right Ⓓ acute

(A) **8.** A rectangle with 4 congruent sides is a

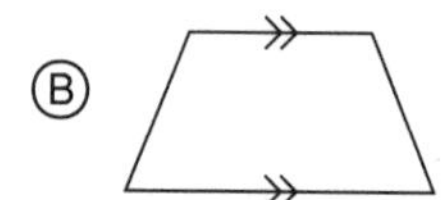

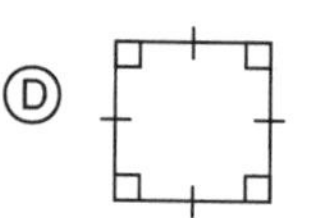

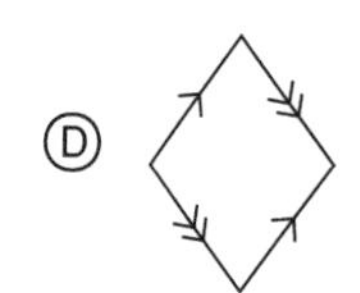

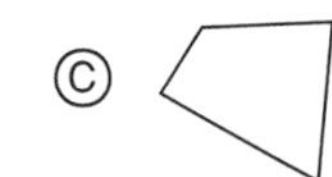

Ⓐ square Ⓑ heptagon
Ⓒ trapezoid Ⓓ none of these

(D) **9.** Choose the parallelogram.

(A) 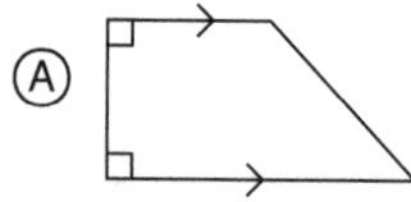

(C) 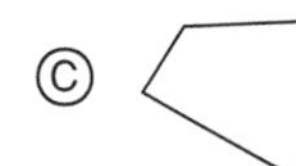

(B)

(D)

(A) **10.** Choose the trapezoid.

(A) 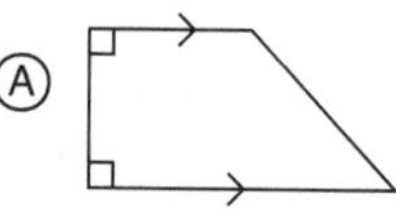

(C) 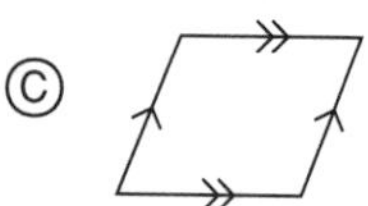

(B)

(D)

(D) **11.** Opposite sides are congruent in a

Ⓐ parallelogram
Ⓑ rectangle
Ⓒ square
Ⓓ all of the above

(B) **12.** Opposite angles are congruent in a

Ⓐ trapezoid
Ⓑ rectangle
Ⓒ quadrilateral
Ⓓ none of the above

(B) **13.** In parallelogram *ABCD*, $\overline{AB}$ is congruent to

Ⓐ $\overline{AD}$
Ⓑ $\overline{CD}$
Ⓒ $\overline{BC}$
Ⓓ $\overline{AC}$

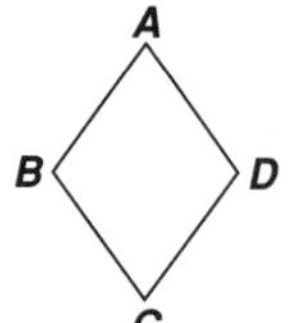

(D) **14.** In rectangle *XYZW*, $\angle X$ is congruent to

Ⓐ $\angle Y$
Ⓑ $\angle Z$
Ⓒ $\angle W$
Ⓓ all of the above

X Y W Z

(C) **15.** Which statement is true?

Ⓐ Every square is a trapezoid.
Ⓑ Some trapezoids are parallelograms.
Ⓒ Every square is a rectangle.
Ⓓ Every rectangle is a square.

(D) **16.** Which statement is false?

Ⓐ Some parallelograms are rectangles.
Ⓑ Every square is a parallelogram.
Ⓒ No trapezoid is a square.
Ⓓ Every parallelogram is a square.

Use Figure 7.5A to answer questions 17-19. *XYZW* is a rectangle, as shown.

Figure 7.5A

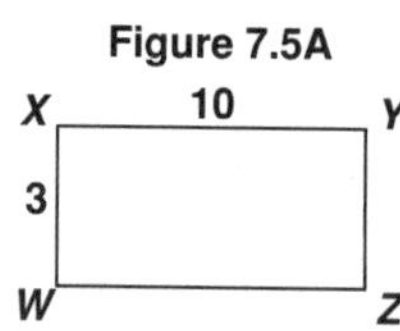

(A) **17.** $\overline{WZ}$ has length

Ⓐ 10 Ⓑ 3 Ⓒ 13 Ⓓ 7

(B) **18.** $\overline{YZ}$ has length

Ⓐ 10 Ⓑ 3 Ⓒ 13 Ⓓ 7

(B) **19.** $m\angle X$ =

Ⓐ 180 Ⓑ 90
Ⓒ 13 Ⓓ not enough information

Use Figure 7.5B to answer questions 20-22. *ABCD* is a parallelogram, as shown.

Figure 7.5B

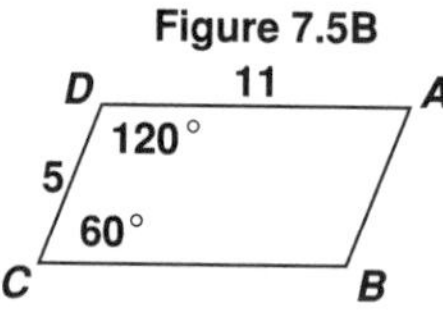

(C) **20.** $m\angle A$ =

Ⓐ 120 Ⓑ 90 Ⓒ 60 Ⓓ 30

(A) **21.** $m\angle B$ =

Ⓐ 120 Ⓑ 90 Ⓒ 60 Ⓓ 30

(D) **22.** $\overline{BC}$ has length

Ⓐ 16 Ⓑ 6 Ⓒ 5 Ⓓ 11

Name____________________ Class ________ Date ____________

7.6 CIRCLES

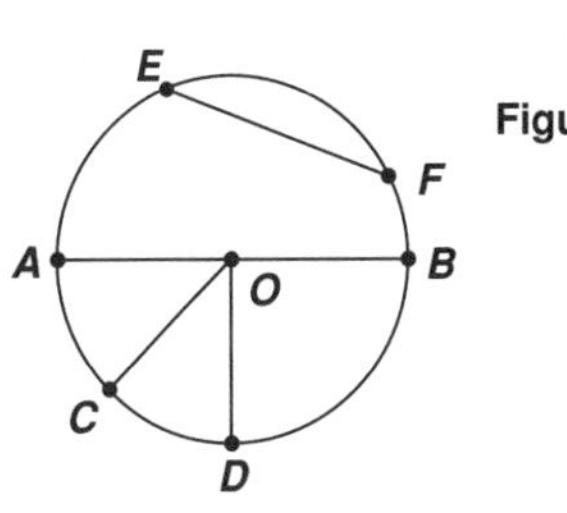

Figure 7.6A

A **circle** is the set of all points in a plane that are the same distance from a fixed point, called its center. In Figure 7.6A, O is the center of the circle.

An **arc** is any unbroken portion of a circle. The portion of the circle between points A and D, with point C on it, is an arc. Arc AD is written $\overset{\frown}{AD}$.

A **chord** is a line segment with endpoints on a circle. $\overline{EF}$ is a chord in Figure 7.6A.

A **diameter** is a chord that passes through the center of a circle. $\overline{AB}$ is a diameter in Figure 7.6A.

A **radius** is a line segment whose endpoints are the center of the circle and a point on the circle. $\overline{OC}$ is a radius in Figure 7.6A. Can you name 3 other radii in Figure 7.6A?

A **central angle** is an angle whose vertex is at the center of a circle. $\angle AOC$ is a central angle in Figure 7.6A.

Example 1: In Figure 7.6B, R is the center of the circle. Identify the following parts of the circle.

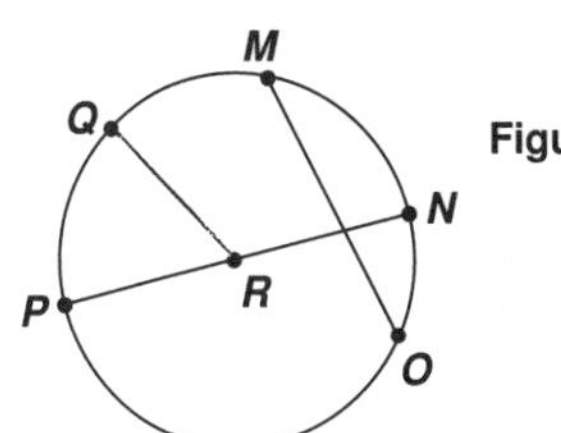

Figure 7.6B

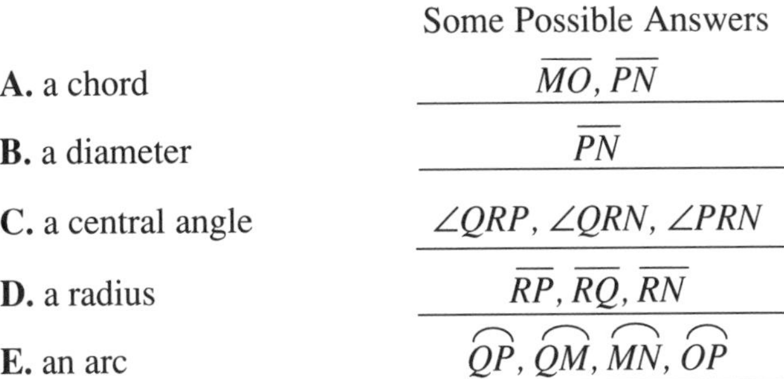

	Some Possible Answers
A. a chord	$\overline{MO}, \overline{PN}$
B. a diameter	$\overline{PN}$
C. a central angle	$\angle QRP, \angle QRN, \angle PRN$
D. a radius	$\overline{RP}, \overline{RQ}, \overline{RN}$
E. an arc	$\overset{\frown}{QP}, \overset{\frown}{QM}, \overset{\frown}{MN}, \overset{\frown}{OP}$

A circle can be measured in degrees, using angles formed at its center. Notice in the circle below that two diameters form four 90° angles at its center. For this reason, we say that a circle contains 360° (90° × 4).

Example 2: How many degrees are in a semi circle, or half circle?

- In Figure 7.6C, the diameter $\overline{YZ}$ divides the circle in half.
- $\angle YOZ$ is a straight angle with a measure of 180°.

There are 180° in a half circle.

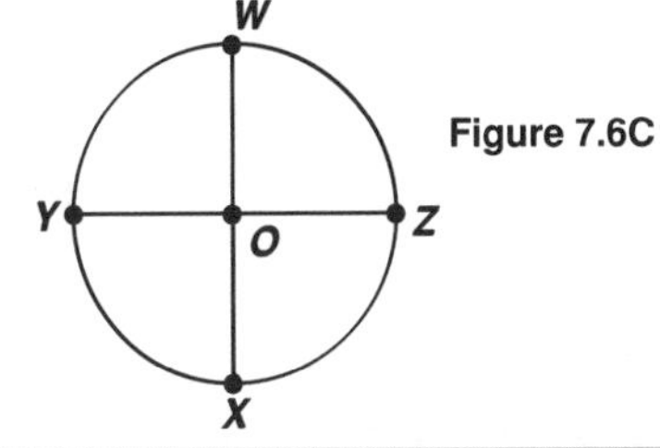

Figure 7.6C

Use Figure 7.6D to answer questions 1-6.

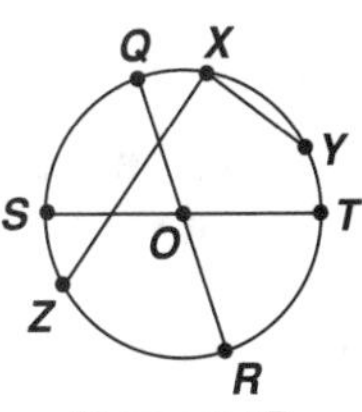

Figure 7.6D

(C) **1.** What part of the circle is $\overline{OS}$?

(A) chord (B) diameter
(C) radius (D) center

(A) **2.** $\overline{XZ}$ is a

(A) chord (B) diameter
(C) radius (D) arc

(D) **3.** What part of the circle is $\overset{\frown}{ZR}$?

(A) chord (B) diameter
(C) radius (D) arc

(A) **4.** Name a diameter of the circle.

(A) $\overline{QR}$ (B) $\overline{SQ}$ (C) $\overline{XY}$ (D) $\overline{OT}$

(D) **5.** What point is the same distance from Q as it is from S?

(A) Z (B) X (C) R (D) O

(C) **6.** If QR = 4m, then OR =

(A) 8m (B) 4m (C) 2m (D) 1m

Use Figure 7.6E to answer questions 7-11.

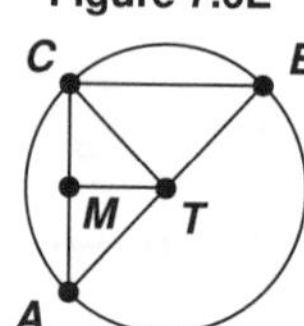

Figure 7.6E

Ⓓ **7.** $\overline{CB}$ is a

Ⓐ diameter Ⓑ radius
Ⓒ arc Ⓓ chord

Ⓒ **8.** Which of the following is a central angle?

Ⓐ $\angle BCT$ Ⓑ $\angle BCA$
Ⓒ $\angle ATC$ Ⓓ $\angle CAT$

Ⓐ **9.** Name a diameter of the circle.

Ⓐ $\overline{AB}$ Ⓑ $\overline{TC}$ Ⓒ $\overline{CTA}$ Ⓓ $\overline{CTB}$

Ⓑ **10.** If $TA = 10''$, then $TC =$

Ⓐ 5″ Ⓑ 10″ Ⓒ 20″ Ⓓ 40″

Ⓒ **11.** If $AB = 8$ ft, then $CT =$

Ⓐ 1 ft Ⓑ 2 ft Ⓒ 4 ft Ⓓ 8 ft

Ⓓ **12.** Which statement is false?

Ⓐ $TA = TB$ Ⓑ $TM < TC$
Ⓒ $\overline{AC}$ is a chord Ⓓ $TM = TB$

Ⓒ **13.** Which statement is true?

Ⓐ $TC < TA$ Ⓑ TB is a diameter
Ⓒ $TA = TB = TC$ Ⓓ $TM = TA$

Ⓑ **14.** m $\angle ATB$

Ⓐ < 180 Ⓑ = 180
Ⓒ > 180 Ⓓ not enough information

Ⓓ **15.** $\overline{TC}$ is a

Ⓐ chord Ⓑ diameter
Ⓒ arc Ⓓ radius

Ⓒ **16.** $\overset{\frown}{CB}$ is

Ⓐ a chord Ⓑ a diameter
Ⓒ an arc Ⓓ a radius

Ⓒ **17.** $\overset{\frown}{AC}$ is

Ⓐ a chord Ⓑ a diameter
Ⓒ an arc Ⓓ a radius

Choose the correct answer.

Ⓐ **18.** Which of the following contains exactly one point on a circle?

Ⓐ a radius Ⓑ a diameter
Ⓒ a chord Ⓓ an arc

Ⓓ **19.** On a circle, which of the following is *not* a line segment?

Ⓐ a radius Ⓑ a diameter
Ⓒ a chord Ⓓ an arc

Use Figure 7.6F to answer questions 20-22. M is the center of the circle, and $\overline{AB}$ is a diameter.

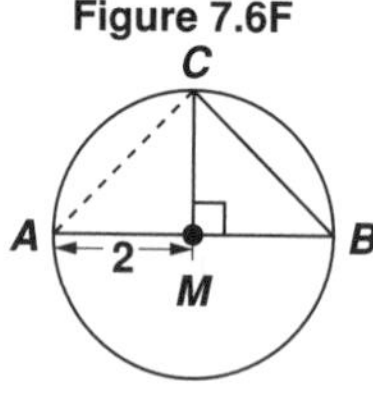

Figure 7.6F

Ⓑ **20.** $MC =$

Ⓐ 1 Ⓑ 2
Ⓒ 4 Ⓓ not enough information

Ⓐ **21.** m$\angle AMC$ =

Ⓐ 90 Ⓑ 180
Ⓒ 360 Ⓓ not enough information

Ⓑ **22.** m$\angle AMB$ =

Ⓐ 90 Ⓑ 180
Ⓒ 360 Ⓓ not enough information

7.7 TRIANGLES

A **triangle** is a polygon with 3 sides. Triangles can be classified by the number of congruent sides or angles.

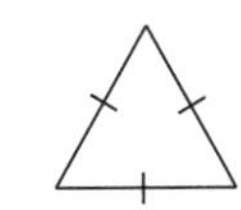

Equilateral
3 congruent sides

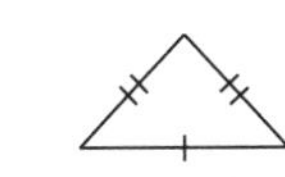

Isosceles
2 congruent sides

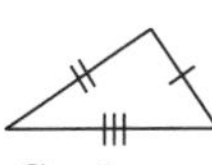

Scalene
No congruent sides

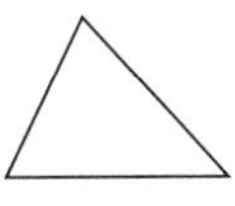

Acute
3 acute angles

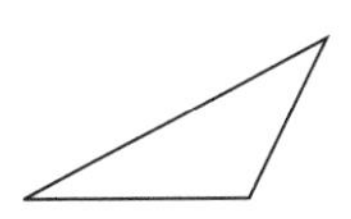

Obtuse
1 obtuse angle

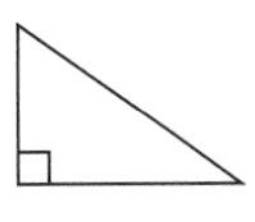

Right
1 right angle

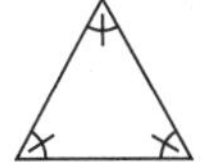

Equiangular
3 congruent angles

REMEMBER: In every triangle, the sum of the measures of the 3 angles is 180°.

Example 1: Find the measure of $\angle K$.

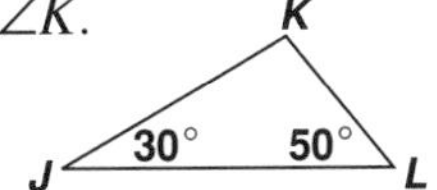

- The sum of the measures of the 3 angles is 180°.

$$30 + 50 + m\angle K = 180$$
$$80 + m\angle K = 180$$
$$80 + m\angle K - 80 = 180 - 80$$
$$m\angle K = 100$$

The measure of $\angle K$ is 100.

Example 2: Classify the triangle.

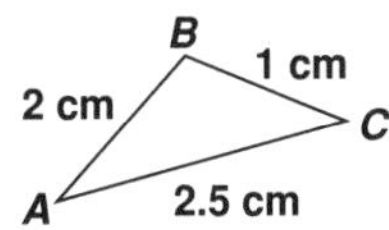

- ΔABC has no congruent sides. ΔABC is a scalene triangle.

Example 3: Find $m\angle D$.

- ΔDEF is an isosceles triangle. In an isosceles triangle, the angles opposite the ≅ sides are equal in measure. Therefore, $m\angle D = m\angle F$.

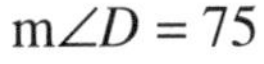

$$m\angle D = 75$$

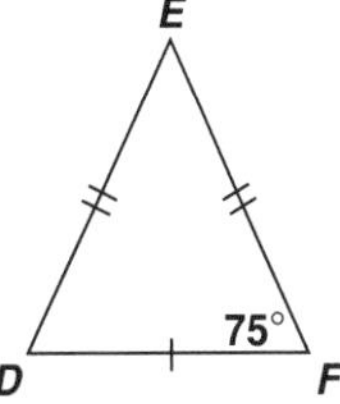

Find the answer.

(A) **1.** Classify the triangle.

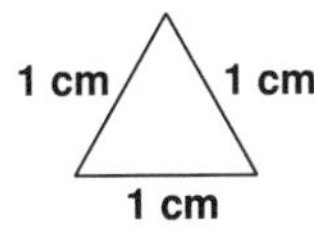

(A) equilateral (B) right
(C) scalene (D) obtuse

(A) **2.** Classify the triangle.

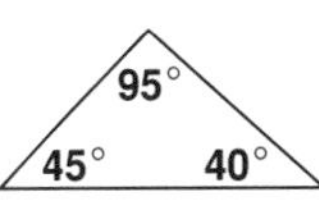

(A) acute (B) equiangular
(C) obtuse (D) isosceles

(B) **3.** Classify the triangle.

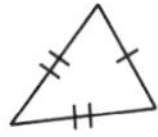

(A) equilateral (B) isosceles
(C) scalene (D) obtuse

(D) **4.** Classify the triangle.

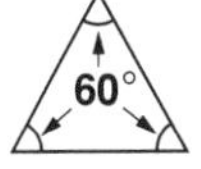

(A) obtuse (B) right
(C) scalene (D) equiangular

Ⓒ **5.** The measures of two angles of a triangle are 45 and 50. What is the measure of the third angle?

Ⓐ 45 Ⓑ 75 Ⓒ 85 Ⓓ 95

Ⓒ **6.** A triangle has 3 congruent angles. What is the measure of one of its angles?

Ⓐ 30 Ⓑ 40 Ⓒ 60 Ⓓ none of these

Ⓑ **7.** An isosceles triangle has

Ⓐ no congruent sides Ⓑ 2 congruent sides

Ⓒ 3 congruent sides Ⓓ 3 congruent angles

Ⓐ **8.** A scalene triangle has

Ⓐ no congruent sides Ⓑ 2 congruent sides

Ⓒ 3 congruent sides Ⓓ 3 congruent angles

Ⓐ **9.** Find m∠*X*.

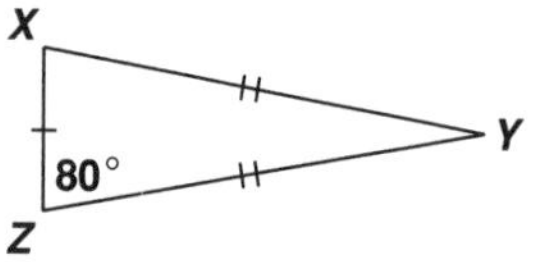

X Y Z 80°

Ⓐ 80 Ⓑ 100

Ⓒ 20 Ⓓ 50

Ⓓ **10.** Classify the triangle.

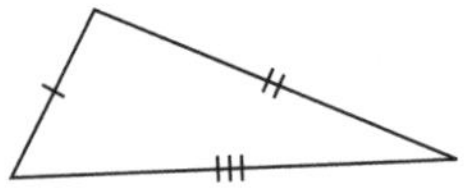

Ⓐ acute Ⓑ equilateral

Ⓒ isosceles Ⓓ scalene

Ⓐ **11.** Find m∠ F.

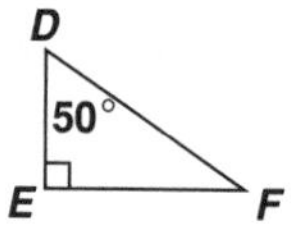

D 50° E F

Ⓐ 40 Ⓑ 90

Ⓒ 110 Ⓓ 180

Ⓓ **12.** Classify the triangle.

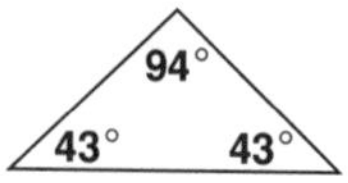

94° 43° 43°

Ⓐ right Ⓑ equilateral

Ⓒ scalene Ⓓ isosceles

Ⓒ **13.** What is the measure of ∠*Y*?

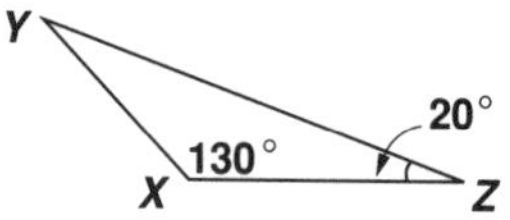

Y 20° 130° X Z

Ⓐ 20 Ⓑ 40 Ⓒ 30 Ⓓ 130

Ⓒ **14.** Find the missing measurement.

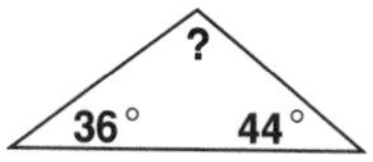

? 36° 44°

Ⓐ 280° Ⓑ 90° Ⓒ 100° Ⓓ 180°

Ⓑ **15.** A triangle has angles with measures of 45°, 90°, and 45°. It is

Ⓐ scalene Ⓑ right

Ⓒ equilateral Ⓓ obtuse

Ⓒ **16.** Two angles of a triangle measure 42 and 78. What is the measure of the third angle?

Ⓐ 300 Ⓑ 160

Ⓒ 60 Ⓓ 45

Ⓐ **17.** Classify the triangle.

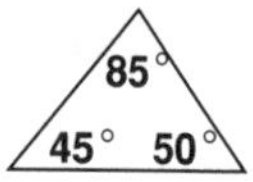

85° 45° 50°

Ⓐ acute Ⓑ obtuse

Ⓒ right Ⓓ isosceles

Ⓓ **18.** Classify the triangle.

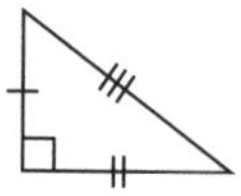

Ⓐ acute Ⓑ obtuse

Ⓒ isosceles Ⓓ right

Ⓓ **19.** Find m∠*A*.

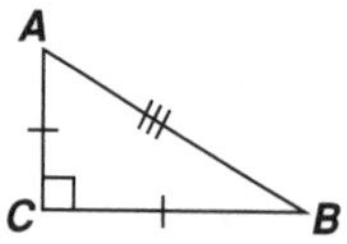

A C B

Ⓐ 30 Ⓑ 60 Ⓒ 90 Ⓓ 45

Ⓒ **20.** What is the measure of ∠*C*?.

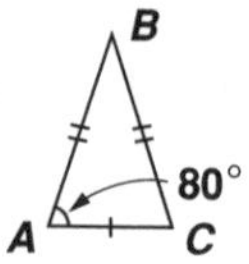

B 80° A C

Ⓐ 20° Ⓑ 60° Ⓒ 80° Ⓓ 100°

Name ________________ Class ________ Date ________

7.8 SQUARE ROOT

The **square root** of a given number is the number which, when multiplied by itself, gives the original number. For example, the square root of 9 is 3 because $3 \times 3 = 9$. The square root of 9 is written $\sqrt{9}$.

The letter n can be used to represent any number. A given number n multiplied by itself is written as $n \times n$ or n^2. The square root of n is written $\sqrt{n}$.

Example 1: Find the square root of 16.

- What number when multiplied by itself equals 16? Try some numbers.
  $2 \times 2 = 4$; $3 \times 3 = 9$; $4 \times 4 = 16$

  The square root of 16 is 4. $\sqrt{16} = 4$

Example 2: Estimate the square root of 60.

- Use squares that you already know.
  $7^2 = 49$ $8^2 = 64$

$$49 < 60 < 64$$
$$\sqrt{49} < \sqrt{60} < \sqrt{64}$$
$$7 < \sqrt{60} < 8$$

The square root of 60 is between 7 and 8.

When the square root is not a whole number, you can use a table to estimate it.

n	n^2	$\sqrt{n}$	n	n^2	$\sqrt{n}$
1	1	1	19	361	4.359
2	4	1.414	20	400	4.472
3	9	1.732	21	441	4.583
4	16	2	22	484	4.690
5	25	2.236	23	529	4.796
6	36	2.449	24	576	4.899
7	49	2.646	25	625	5
8	64	2.828	26	676	5.099
9	81	3	27	729	5.196
10	100	3.162	28	784	5.292
11	121	3.317	36	1296	6
12	144	3.464	37	1369	6.083
13	169	3.606	38	1444	6.164
14	196	3.742	39	1521	6.245
15	225	3.873	40	1600	6.325
16	256	4	41	1681	6.403
17	289	4.123	42	1764	6.481
18	324	4.243	43	1849	6.557

Example 3: Find $\sqrt{13}$.

- Find the column labeled n.
- Move down the column to find 13.
- Move across the column labeled $\sqrt{n}$.

The square root of 13 is about 3.606. $\sqrt{13} \approx 3.606$

Find the answer. Use the table of square roots as needed.

Ⓓ **1.** $\sqrt{100}$ =
Ⓐ 50 Ⓑ 10,000 Ⓒ 1,000 Ⓓ 10

Ⓐ **2.** $\sqrt{25}$ =
Ⓐ 5 Ⓑ 25 Ⓒ 50 Ⓓ 625

Ⓑ **3.** $\sqrt{17}$ =
Ⓐ 4.243 Ⓑ 4.123 Ⓒ 6.481 Ⓓ 289

Ⓒ **4.** $\sqrt{73}$ is between
Ⓐ 6 and 7 Ⓑ 7 and 8 Ⓒ 8 and 9 Ⓓ 9 and 10

Ⓒ **5.** $\sqrt{270}$ is between
Ⓐ 13 and 14 Ⓑ 15 and 16
Ⓒ 16 and 17 Ⓓ 17 and 18

Ⓒ **6.** $\sqrt{43}$ =
Ⓐ 1,849 Ⓑ 324
Ⓒ 6.557 Ⓓ 4.359

Ⓒ **7.** Order the following numbers from *least to greatest:* 3, $\sqrt{11}$, 2, $\sqrt{7}$,
Ⓐ 2, 3, $\sqrt{7}$, $\sqrt{11}$ Ⓑ $\sqrt{11}$, 3, 2, $\sqrt{7}$
Ⓒ 2, $\sqrt{7}$, 3, $\sqrt{11}$ Ⓓ 2, $\sqrt{7}$, $\sqrt{11}$, 3

Ⓑ **8.** Order the following numbers from *greatest to least:* 5, $\sqrt{15}$, 25, $\sqrt{5}$
Ⓐ 25, $\sqrt{15}$, 5, $\sqrt{5}$ Ⓑ 25, 5, $\sqrt{15}$, $\sqrt{5}$
Ⓒ $\sqrt{15}$, 25, $\sqrt{5}$, 5 Ⓓ $\sqrt{5}$, $\sqrt{15}$, 5, 25

Name____________________ Class ________ Date __________

7.9 PYTHAGOREAN THEOREM

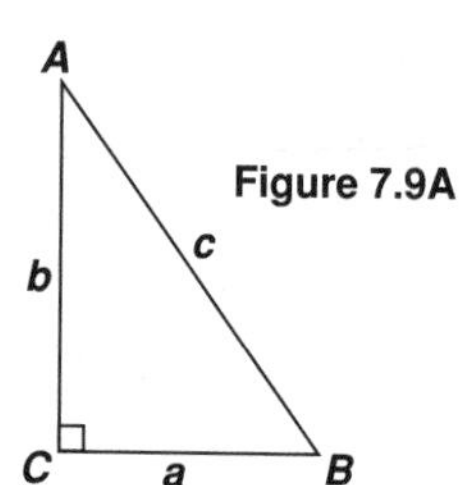

Figure 7.9A

Triangle *ABC* is a right triangle.

In a right triangle, the **hypotenuse** is the side opposite the right angle. In Figure 7.9A, $\overline{AB}$ is the hypotenuse. Its length is *c*.

The **legs** of a right triangle are the sides that form its right angle. In Figure 7.9A, $\overline{BC}$ and $\overline{AC}$ are legs. Their lengths are *a* and *b*, respectively.

There is a relationship between the hypotenuse and the legs of a right triangle. This relationship is true for all right triangles. It is called the **Pythagorean Theorem.**

PYTHAGOREAN THEOREM: For every right triangle, $a^2 + b^2 = c^2$

Example 1: Find the length of $\overline{AB}$.

- Use the Pythagorean Theorem.

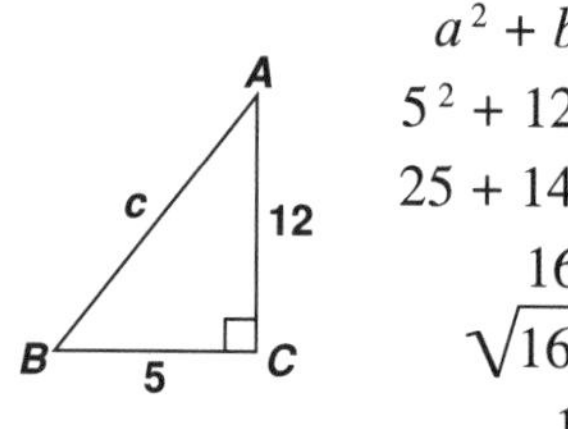

$$a^2 + b^2 = c^2$$
$$5^2 + 12^2 = c^2$$
$$25 + 144 = c^2$$
$$169 = c^2$$
$$\sqrt{169} = c$$
$$13 = c$$

The length of $\overline{AB}$ is 13.

Example 2: Find the length of $\overline{BC}$.

- Use the Pythagorean Theorem.

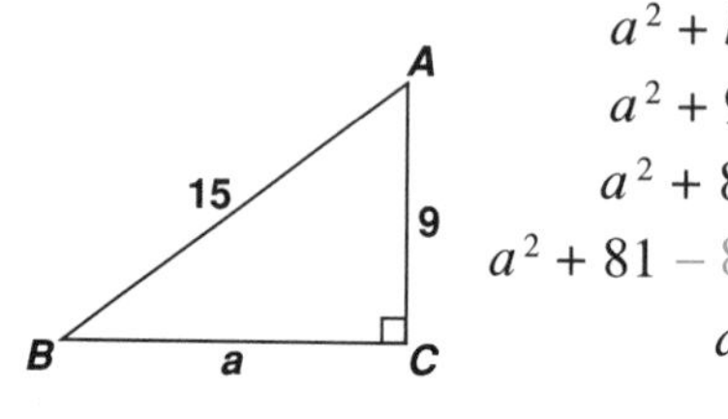

$$a^2 + b^2 = c^2$$
$$a^2 + 9^2 = 15^2$$
$$a^2 + 81 = 225$$
$$a^2 + 81 - 81 = 225 - 81$$
$$a^2 = 144$$
$$a = \sqrt{144}, \text{ or } 12$$

The length of $\overline{BC}$ is 12.

Find the answer.

Ⓑ **1.** Find *n*.

Ⓐ 10 ft Ⓑ 20 ft Ⓒ 21 ft Ⓓ 400 ft

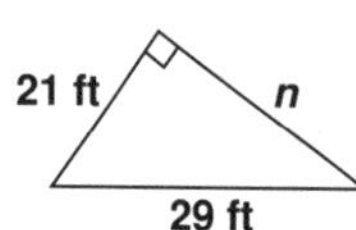

Ⓒ **2.** Find *n*.

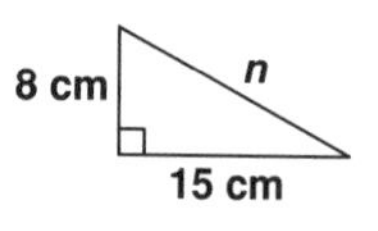

Ⓐ 15 cm Ⓑ 16 cm Ⓒ 17 cm Ⓓ 18 cm

8 cm, *n*, 15 cm

Ⓒ **3.** Find the missing length, *b*, for right ΔABC when $a = 9$ and $c = 41$.

Ⓐ 42 Ⓑ 41 Ⓒ 40 Ⓓ 39

Ⓓ **4.** Find the missing length, *c*, for right ΔABC when $a = 12$ and $b = 16$.

Ⓐ $\sqrt{34}$ Ⓑ $\sqrt{28}$ Ⓒ 10 Ⓓ 20

Ⓐ **5.** Which set of lengths does *not* give a right triangle?

Ⓐ 12, 14, 20 Ⓑ 15, 20, 25 Ⓒ 12, 16, 20 Ⓓ 10, 24, 26

Ⓓ **6.** Which set of lengths gives a right triangle?

Ⓐ 3, 5, 6 Ⓑ 15, 20, 21 Ⓒ 10, 11, 12 Ⓓ 16, 30, 34

Ⓒ **7.** Find *n*.

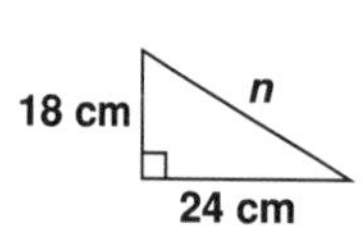

Ⓐ 20 cm Ⓑ 26 cm Ⓒ 30 cm Ⓓ 34 cm

18 cm, *n*, 24 cm

Ⓒ **8.** Find *n*.

Ⓐ 4 ft Ⓑ 5 ft Ⓒ 6 ft Ⓓ 7 ft

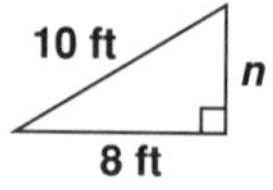

Ⓒ **9.** Which set of lengths gives a right triangle?

Ⓐ 2, 3, 4 Ⓑ 3, 2, 5 Ⓒ 3, 4, 5 Ⓓ 3, 4, 25

Ⓓ **10.** Which set of lengths gives a right triangle?

Ⓐ 7, 9, 13 Ⓑ 5, 6, 9 Ⓒ 10, 11, 12 Ⓓ 6, 8, 10

Name ______________________ Class __________ Date __________

CHAPTER 7 TEST

Fill in the correct circle to answer each question.

(D) **1.** Which pair of lines is parallel?

Ⓐ $\overleftrightarrow{AB}$ and $\overleftrightarrow{BE}$
Ⓑ $\overleftrightarrow{BE}$ and $\overleftrightarrow{DF}$
Ⓒ $\overleftrightarrow{CF}$ and $\overleftrightarrow{AD}$
Ⓓ $\overleftrightarrow{AC}$ and $\overleftrightarrow{DF}$

(C) **2.** Name the quadrilateral.

Ⓐ heptagon
Ⓑ parallelogram
Ⓒ trapezoid
Ⓓ hexagon

(C) **3.** What kind of angle is shown?

Ⓐ obtuse
Ⓑ acute
Ⓒ right
Ⓓ complementary

(C) **4.** Classify the triangle.

Ⓐ right
Ⓑ isosceles
Ⓒ obtuse
Ⓓ acute

(B) **5.** $\sqrt{626}$ is between ■ .

Ⓐ 24 and 25 Ⓑ 25 and 26
Ⓒ 311 and 313 Ⓓ 313 and 315

(D) **6.** Which two figures appear to be congruent?

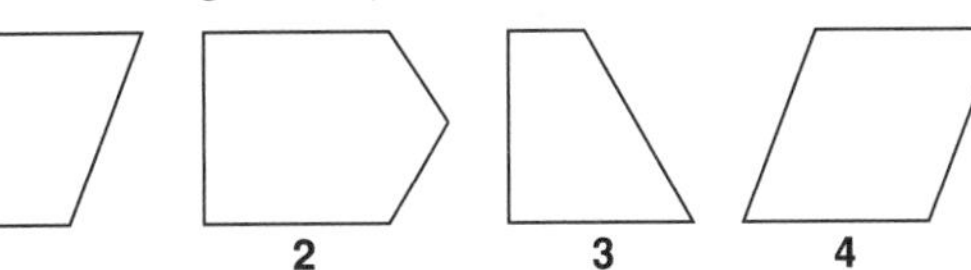

Ⓐ 1 and 3 Ⓑ 2 and 3 Ⓒ 2 and 4 Ⓓ 1 and 4

(C) **7.** In circle *O*, $\overline{CD}$ is a ■ .

Ⓐ diameter
Ⓑ radius
Ⓒ chord
Ⓓ arc

(C) **8.** Name the polygon.

Ⓐ trapezoid
Ⓑ hexagon
Ⓒ quadrilateral
Ⓓ pentagon

(C) **9.** Figure *QRST* is similar to figure *QEFG*. Find the length of $\overline{QE}$.

Ⓐ 10
Ⓑ 9
Ⓒ 8
Ⓓ 6

(B) **10.** Find the missing length.

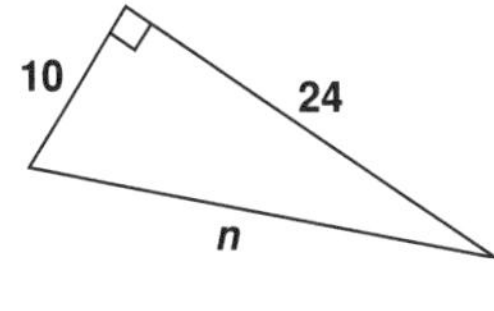

Ⓐ 34
Ⓑ 26
Ⓒ 24
Ⓓ 476

(D) **11.** Which two figures appear to be similar?

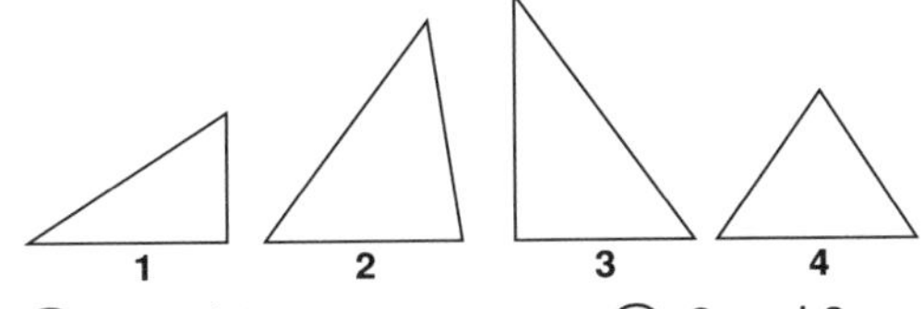

Ⓐ 1 and 2 Ⓑ 2 and 3
Ⓒ 3 and 4 Ⓓ 1 and 3

(A) **12.** In relation to line $\overleftrightarrow{EF}$, line $\overleftrightarrow{GH}$ is

Ⓐ perpendicular
Ⓑ vertical
Ⓒ parallel
Ⓓ complementary

(A) **13.** If m∠1 = 50, then the measure of its complement is

Ⓐ 40° Ⓑ 50° Ⓒ 130° Ⓓ 150°

(B) **14.** △*ABC* is similar to △*DEF*. Find the length of $\overline{BC}$.

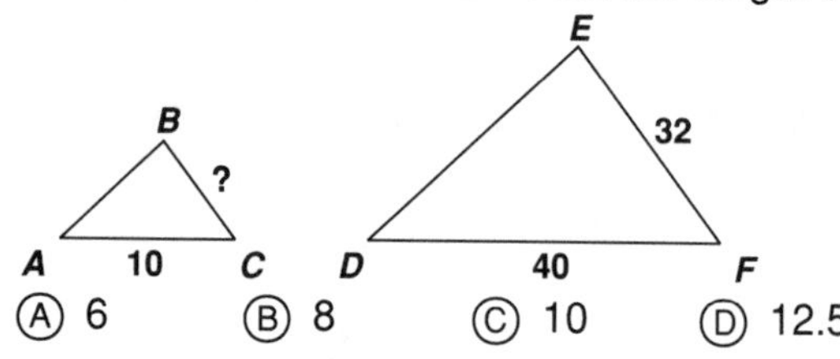

Ⓐ 6 Ⓑ 8 Ⓒ 10 Ⓓ 12.5

(C) **15.** Name the polygon.

Ⓐ decagon

Ⓑ nonagon

Ⓒ heptagon

Ⓓ hexagon

(B) **16.** Classify the triangle.

Ⓐ scalene

Ⓑ obtuse

Ⓒ right

Ⓓ acute

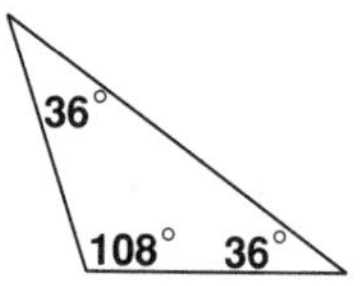

(D) **17.** $\sqrt{81}$ =

Ⓐ 6,561 Ⓑ 162 Ⓒ 40.5 Ⓓ 9

(D) **18.** An angle measures 180°. The angle is

Ⓐ acute Ⓑ right

Ⓒ obtuse Ⓓ straight

(A) **19.** Name a radius of the circle.

Ⓐ $\overline{OX}$

Ⓑ $\overline{XY}$

Ⓒ $\overline{YZ}$

Ⓓ $\overline{XZ}$

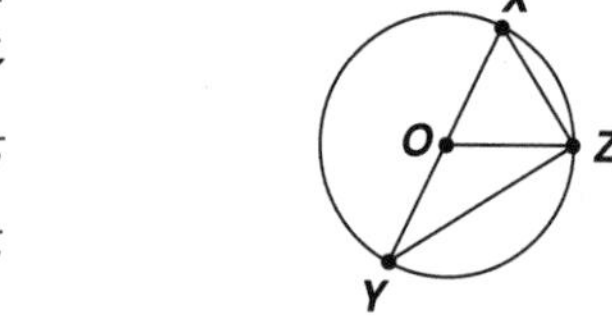

(B) **20.** Which line segment is perpendicular to $\overline{ST}$?

Ⓐ $\overline{RU}$

Ⓑ $\overline{VW}$

Ⓒ $\overline{RW}$

Ⓓ $\overline{RS}$

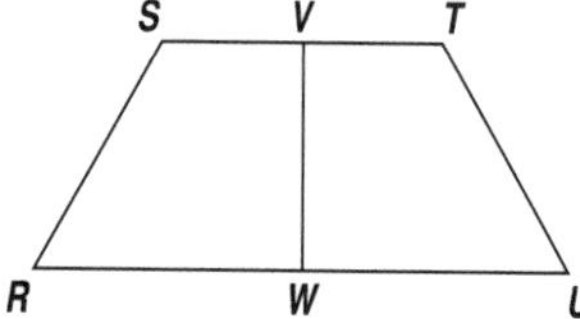

(B) **21.** A rectangle is a

Ⓐ pentagon Ⓑ quadrilateral

Ⓒ decagon Ⓓ heptagon

(C) **22.** The angle appears to have a measure of about ■.

Ⓐ 185° Ⓑ 170°

Ⓒ 110° Ⓓ 85°

(A) **23.** Which pair of lines is parallel?

Ⓐ $\overleftrightarrow{EH}$ and $\overleftrightarrow{FG}$

Ⓑ $\overleftrightarrow{HG}$ and $\overleftrightarrow{FG}$

Ⓒ $\overleftrightarrow{EF}$ and $\overleftrightarrow{FG}$

Ⓓ $\overleftrightarrow{EF}$ and $\overleftrightarrow{HG}$

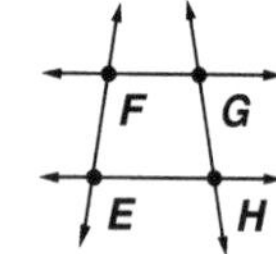

(C) **24.** Name the quadrilateral.

Ⓐ trapezoid

Ⓑ square

Ⓒ parallelogram

Ⓓ nonagon

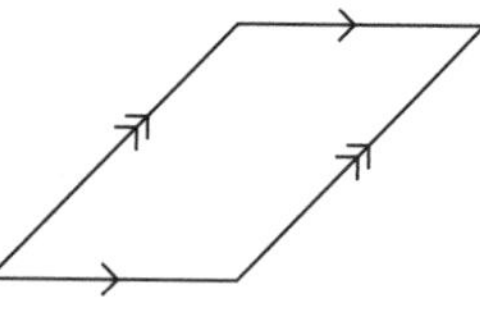

(B) **25.** $\overline{AC}$ and $\overline{BD}$ are diagonals of rectangle *ABCD*. What is the measure of the angle shown by the arrows ?

Ⓐ 70° Ⓑ 110°

Ⓒ 130° Ⓓ 230°

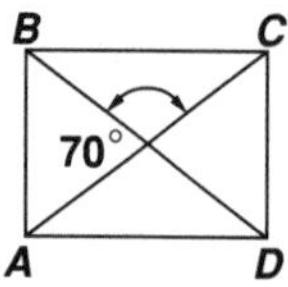

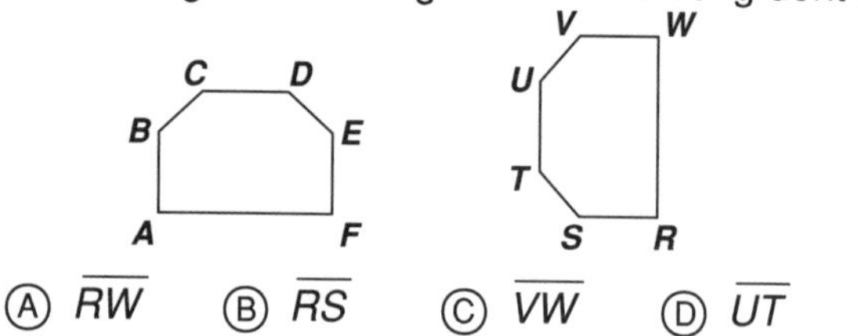

Name____________________ Class ________ Date __________

CHAPTERS 1-7 CUMULATIVE REVIEW

Fill in the correct circle to answer each question.

(A) **1.** Which expression shows the Addition Property of 0?

(A) $7 + 0 = 7$

(B) $7 + 0 = 0$

(C) $7 + 0 = 0 + 7$

(D) $(7 + 0) \times 8 = 7 \times (0 + 8)$

(B) **2.** There were 12 brownies in the pan. Jason ate 3 of them. What is the ratio of brownies eaten to the number of brownies left?

(A) 9:3 (B) 3:9 (C) 3:12 (D) 12:3

(A) **3.** Estimate: 82,000 divided by 21

(A) 4000 (B) 40,000

(C) 60,000 (D) 100,000

(B) **4.** Find the sum of 8.278, 13.19, 22.22 and 53.1.

(A) 86.678 (B) 96.788

(C) 97.778 (D) 123.50

(B) **5.** Scramble the letters in "commutative." What is the probability of choosing the letter " u?"

(A) $\frac{2}{11}$ (B) $\frac{1}{11}$ (C) $\frac{2}{9}$ (D) $\frac{9}{2}$

(D) **6.** Write 2,793,000 in scientific notation.

(A) 27.93×10^6 (B) 27.93×10^5

(C) 2.793×10^5 (D) 2.793×10^6

(A) **7.** 336 h = ■ d

(A) 14 (B) 12 (C) 28 (D) 8064

(D) **8.** Multiply: $2\frac{1}{4} \times 2\frac{1}{2}$

(A) $\frac{40}{8}$ (B) 7 (C) $\frac{13}{8}$ (D) $5\frac{5}{8}$

(A) **9.** What fraction equals 30%?

(A) $\frac{3}{10}$ (B) $\frac{30}{1}$ (C) $\frac{3}{7}$ (D) $\frac{1}{30}$

(D) **10.** Subtract $\frac{3}{4}$ from $2\frac{1}{2}$.

(A) $\frac{13}{4}$ (B) 2 (C) $1\frac{1}{2}$ (D) $1\frac{3}{4}$

Use Figure 1 to answer questions 11-12.

Figure 1

(A) **11.** Suppose you choose one of the squares without looking. What is the probability of choosing a white square?

(A) $\frac{8}{13}$ (B) $\frac{5}{13}$ (C) $\frac{5}{8}$ (D) $\frac{8}{5}$

(C) **12.** Suppose each square is 3 feet long on each side. Using this scale, what is the length of the shaded portion?

(A) 5 ft (B) 10 ft (C) 15 ft (D) 18 ft

(D) **13.** Which pair of angles is complementary?

(A) 180°, 90° (B) 65°, 65°

(C) 60°, 120° (D) 30°, 60°

(A) **14.** Round 258,750 to the nearest *ten thousand.*

(A) 260,000 (B) 250,000

(C) 258,750 (D) 259,000

(C) **15.**

$$\begin{array}{r} 70{,}030 \\ -\ 1279 \\ \hline \end{array}$$

(A) 71,309 (B) 69,751

(C) 68,751 (D) 68,741

(D) **16.** 12 out of every 15 workers at a restaurant are teenagers. What percent of the employees are not teenagers?

(A) 0.8 (B) 80 (C) 0.2 (D) 20

Figure 2

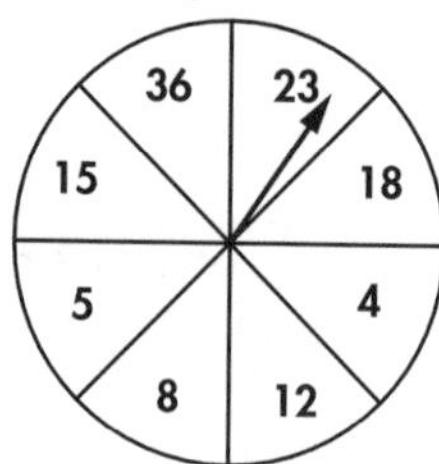

Refer to Figure 2 to answer questions 17–21.

(C) **17.** In a single spin, what is the probability of landing on a prime number?

Ⓐ $\frac{1}{8}$ Ⓑ $\frac{1}{6}$

Ⓒ $\frac{1}{4}$ Ⓓ $\frac{1}{2}$

(D) **18.** Which spin has the least probability of occurring?

Ⓐ An odd number Ⓑ An even number

Ⓒ A single-digit number Ⓓ A multiple of 5

(B) **19.** Give the probability of landing on an even number that is also a multiple of 3.

Ⓐ $\frac{1}{8}$ Ⓑ $\frac{3}{8}$

Ⓒ $\frac{1}{2}$ Ⓓ $\frac{3}{5}$

(B) **20.** Manny spins once. What is his percentage chance of landing on number 23?

Ⓐ 8% Ⓑ 12.5%

Ⓒ 20% Ⓓ 25%

(C) **21.** Manny spins 24 times. Which proportion gives his total chances (x) of landing on 23?

Ⓐ $\frac{1}{8} = \frac{x}{3}$ Ⓑ $\frac{8}{24} = \frac{x}{8}$

Ⓒ $\frac{x}{24} = \frac{1}{8}$ Ⓓ $\frac{3}{8} = \frac{x}{24}$

(D) **22.** Which pair of lines is perpendicular?

Ⓐ 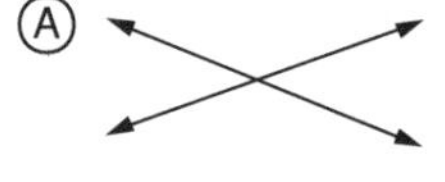 Ⓑ 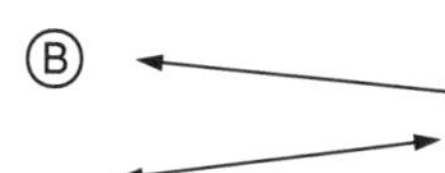

Ⓒ 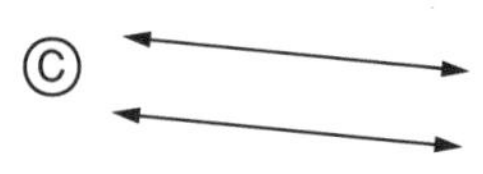 Ⓓ 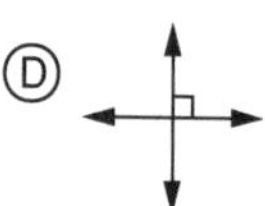

(A) **23.** Subtract 0.0279 from 8.

Ⓐ 7.9721 Ⓑ 7.9731

Ⓒ 7.9831 Ⓓ 8.9721

(D) **24.** A triangle has angles with measures of 30°, 30° and 120°. Name the triangle.

Ⓐ equilateral Ⓑ scalene

Ⓒ right Ⓓ isosceles

(B) **25.** $4.203 \times 9 =$ ■

Ⓐ 0.467 Ⓑ 37.827

Ⓒ 37.836 Ⓓ 38.027

Use Figure 3 to answer questions 26–28.

(A) **26.** Which two lines intersect at point E?

Ⓐ $\overleftrightarrow{FD}$ and $\overleftrightarrow{BE}$ Ⓑ $\overleftrightarrow{CD}$ and $\overleftrightarrow{ED}$

Ⓒ $\overleftrightarrow{AF}$ and $\overleftrightarrow{FE}$ Ⓓ $\overleftrightarrow{AC}$ and $\overleftrightarrow{FD}$

Figure 3

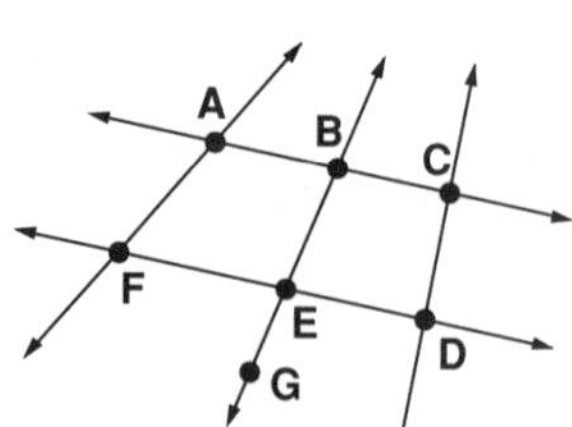

(C) **27.** $\angle FEG$ and $\angle BED$ are ■ angles.

Ⓐ straight Ⓑ supplementary

Ⓒ vertical Ⓓ complementary

(B) **28.** $ABEF$ defines a polygon, which can be classified as ■ .

Ⓐ rectangle Ⓑ quadrilateral

Ⓒ square Ⓓ parallelogram

Name ____________________ Class ________ Date ________

(D) **29.** Divide 1404 by 0.09.

Ⓐ 126.36 Ⓑ 146
Ⓒ 156 Ⓓ 15,600

(D) **30.** 4^3 = ■

Ⓐ 7 Ⓑ 12 Ⓒ 32 Ⓓ 64

(A) **31.** Order from *least to greatest:* $\frac{1}{2}, \frac{3}{5}, \frac{4}{7}, \frac{3}{8}$

Ⓐ $\frac{3}{8}, \frac{1}{2}, \frac{4}{7}, \frac{3}{5}$ Ⓑ $\frac{3}{8}, \frac{4}{7}, \frac{3}{5}, \frac{1}{2}$
Ⓒ $\frac{1}{2}, \frac{3}{8}, \frac{3}{5}, \frac{4}{7}$ Ⓓ $\frac{1}{2}, \frac{3}{8}, \frac{4}{7}, \frac{3}{5}$

(C) **32.** $3\frac{1}{5} + \frac{7}{20}$ = ■

Ⓐ $\frac{23}{20}$ Ⓑ $3\frac{8}{25}$ Ⓒ $3\frac{11}{20}$ Ⓓ $3\frac{7}{100}$

(A) **33.** What is the decimal for 3.5%?

Ⓐ 0.035 Ⓑ 0.35 Ⓒ 3.5 Ⓓ 350

(D) **34.** Randy ordered a small pizza and a glass of juice. The total bill was $6.53. Round this amount to the nearest *dollar.*

Ⓐ $6.53 Ⓑ $6.50 Ⓒ $6.00 Ⓓ $7.00

(C) **35.** Which is an example of the Associative Property?

Ⓐ $3 \times 2 = 5, 2 \times 3 = 5$
Ⓑ $(3 + 2) \times 5 = (3 \times 5) + (2 \times 5)$
Ⓒ $(3 \times 2) \times 5 = 3 \times (2 \times 5)$
Ⓓ $(3 \times 2) + 5 = (3 \times 5) + (2 \times 5)$

(A) **36.** What is the *place value* of 3 in 27.0043?

Ⓐ ten thousandths Ⓑ thousandths
Ⓒ hundredths Ⓓ ten thousands

Use Table 4 to answer questions 37–38.

Table 4

Road Mileage from Boston to Several Cities

City	Miles
Atlanta, GA	1037
Chicago, IL	963
New York, NY	206
Los Angeles, CA	2979
Detroit, MI	695

(B) **37.** How much farther is Atlanta than Chicago from Boston?

Ⓐ 73 miles Ⓑ 74 miles
Ⓒ 164 miles Ⓓ 174 miles

(C) **38.** The Swenson family is planning to drive from Los Angeles to Boston. They estimate that they will drive at average of 50 miles per hour. Estimate the number of hours the drive from Los Angeles to Boston will take.

Ⓐ 600 Ⓑ 400 Ⓒ 60 Ⓓ 40

(B) **39.** Write $2\frac{3}{8}$ as a decimal.

Ⓐ 2.38 Ⓑ 2.375 Ⓒ 0.375 Ⓓ 0.238

(D) **40.** 328×974 = ■

Ⓐ 23,124 Ⓑ 43,752
Ⓒ 319,464 Ⓓ 319,472

(A) **41.** $\sqrt{64}$ = ■

Ⓐ 8 Ⓑ 9 Ⓒ 16 Ⓓ 32

(A) **42.** $20,740 \div 12$ = ■

Ⓐ 1728 R4 Ⓑ 1729
Ⓒ 1730 Ⓓ 1828.5

(B) **43.** 6 is the greatest common factor of ▇ .

(A) 12 and 24 (B) 12 and 18

(C) 18 and 21 (D) 5 and 7

(B) **44.** $6.25 + 0.731 + 99.089 + 5 =$ ▇

(A) 117.649 (B) 111.07

(C) 111.061 (D) 105.445

Use Figure 5 to answer questions 45–48.

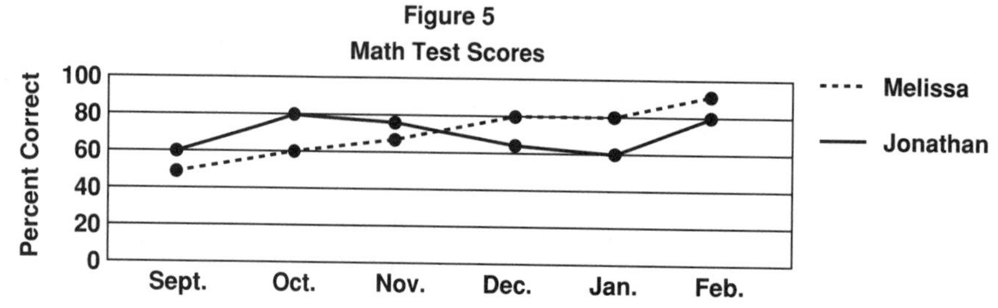

(B) **45.** What score did Jonathan receive on the November exam?

(A) 80 (B) 75 (C) 65 (D) 60

(D) **46.** In which month did Melissa receive her highest score?

(A) October (B) December

(C) January (D) February

(C) **47.** How much higher was Melissa's score than Jonathan's score on the math test in January?

(A) 5% (B) 10% (C) 20% (D) 40%

(A) **48.** What was the highest score that Melissa received on a math test?

(A) 90% (B) 80% (C) 75% (D) 50%

(B) **49.** 37 students wear sneakers. If there are 185 students, what percent wear sneakers?

(A) 5% (B) 20% (C) 29% (D) 37%

(C) **50.** $2.7\overline{)473.58}$

(A) 17.4 (B) 18.54 (C) 175.4 (D) 1754

(A) **51.** $\frac{3}{7} \div \frac{5}{8} =$ ▇

(A) $\frac{24}{35}$ (B) $\frac{3}{5}$ (C) $\frac{11}{2}$ (D) $\frac{15}{56}$

(D) **52.** $\frac{2}{5} + \frac{3}{4} - \frac{1}{2} =$ ▇

(A) $\frac{3}{5}$ (B) $\frac{4}{7}$ (C) $\frac{10}{15}$ (D) $\frac{13}{20}$

Use Figure 6 to answer questions 53–54.

Figure 6
Trophies in High School Sports

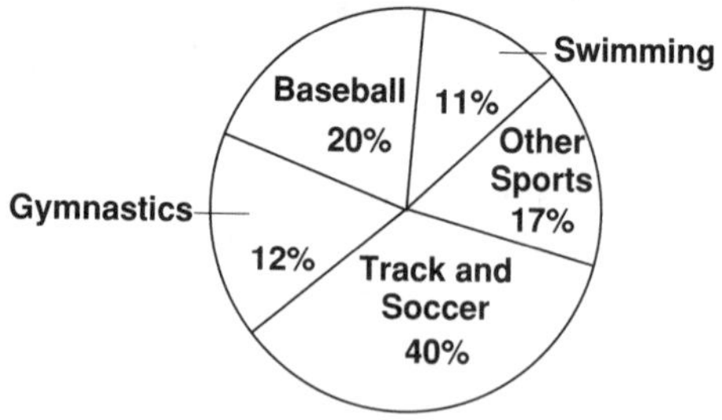

Baseball 20%
Swimming 11%
Other Sports 17%
Track and Soccer 40%
Gymnastics 12%

(C) **53.** What percent of trophies awarded were in baseball?

(A) 11% (B) 12% (C) 20% (D) 80%

(C) **54.** If 36 trophies were awarded in gymnastics, how many trophies were awarded in all sports?

(A) 41 (B) 264 (C) 300 (D) 432

(D) **55.** Estimate the product of 45,391 and 79.

(A) 45,080 (B) 600

(C) 400,000 (D) 4,000,000

(A) **56.** Divide $2\frac{2}{3}$ by 8.

(A) $\frac{1}{3}$ (B) 1 (C) $\frac{7}{23}$ (D) $\frac{64}{3}$

(A) **57.** Which fractions are reciprocals?

(A) $\frac{2}{7}, \frac{7}{2}$ (B) $\frac{12}{7}, \frac{17}{2}$ (C) $\frac{3}{2}, \frac{4}{3}$ (D) $\frac{1}{3}, \frac{7}{9}$

(D) **58.** Write 7.4 as a percent.

(A) 0.0074% (B) 0.074%

(C) 74% (D) 740%

Name ______________________ Class ________ Date ____________

CHAPTER 8: PERIMETER, AREA, VOLUME

TEST-TAKING STRATEGY: *Mark or Draw a Diagram*

Diagrams can be very helpful in solving problems. When a diagram is given, mark each known fact on the drawing to help you understand the problem.

Example 1: Here is part of a floor plan. The bedroom is 15 ft by 10 ft. The hall is 6 ft by 5 ft. What are the measurements of the bathroom?

- Write each measurement given in the problem on the diagram (shown in red).
- Find the missing measurements. The bathroom has the same width as the hall. Each is 5 ft wide.

  Notice that the combined length of the bathroom and the hall is equal to the length of the bedroom.

?	+	6 ft	=	15 ft
length of bathroom		length of hall		length of bedroom

  Subtract to find the missing measurement: $15 - 6 = 9$

The measurements of the bathroom are 5 ft by 9 ft.

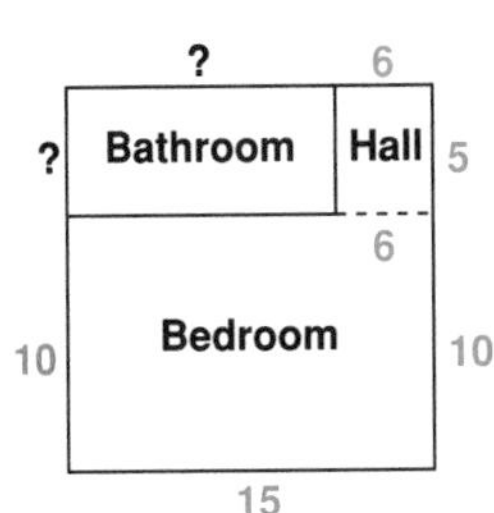

When a diagram is not given, draw your own.

Example 2: One side of an equilateral triangle is 7 inches long. Find its perimeter.

- Draw the diagram. In an equilateral triangle, all sides have the same length.
- Mark the diagram. Each side is 7 inches long.
- The perimeter is the distance around the triangle. To find the perimeter, add the lengths of the sides.

  $7 + 7 + 7 = 21$

The perimeter of the triangle is 21 inches.

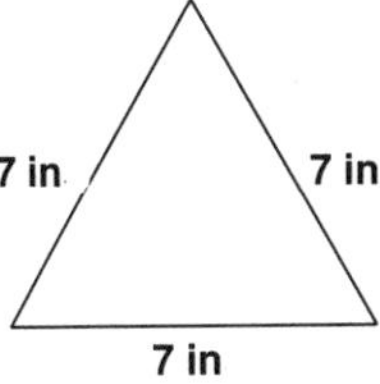

Find the answer by marking the given diagram.

Ⓐ **1.** Paula leaves the store and walks 2 blocks west. She then walks 3 blocks south and 1 block west. How many blocks is she from the library?

Ⓐ 1
Ⓑ 2
Ⓒ 3
Ⓓ 4

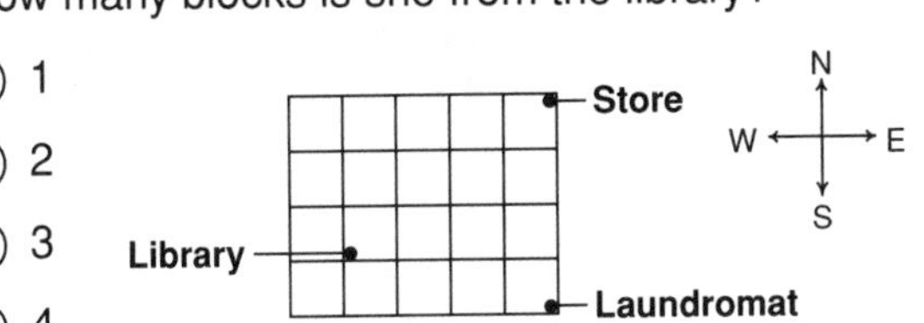

Ⓑ **2.** $\angle AEB$ is a straight line. If $\angle AEC$ measures 45°, what is the measure of $\angle CEB$?

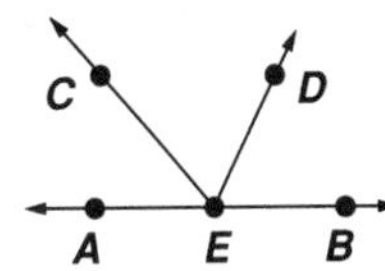

Ⓐ 45° Ⓑ 135° Ⓒ 180° Ⓓ 225°

(C) **3.** Ian has a pair of blue jeans and a pair of black slacks. He has a green, a blue, and a red shirt. How many different outfits are possible?

(A) 3 (B) 4 (C) 6 (D) 5

Pants	Shirts	Outfits
J	G	JG
	B	JB
	R	JR
S	G	SG
	B	SB
	R	SR

(C) **4.** Find the perimeter of the square below.

(A) 8 ft
(B) 16 ft
(C) 32 ft
(D) 64 sq ft

8 ft

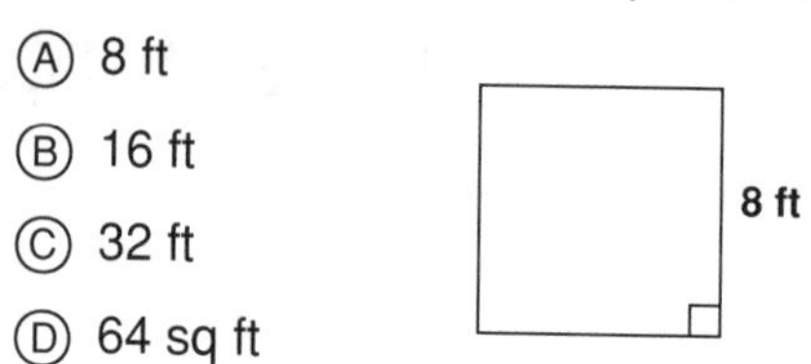

(C) **5.** The rooms on the first floor of a house are shown on the floor plan. The living room is 25 ft × 14 ft, the TV room is 10 ft × 10 ft, the dining room is 14 ft × 10 ft, and the kitchen is 10 ft × 25 ft. What are the measurements of the entire first floor?

(A) 25 ft × 14 ft
(B) 25 ft × 25 ft
(C) 35 ft × 24 ft
(D) 25 ft × 24 ft

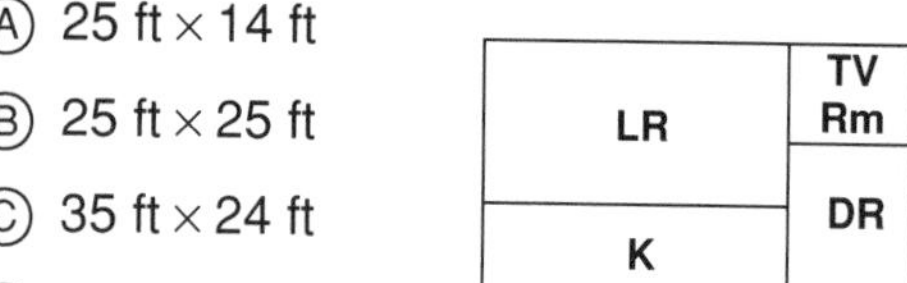

(A) **6.** How many 3 ft × 3 ft tiles can be laid on a floor of size 12 ft × 9 ft?

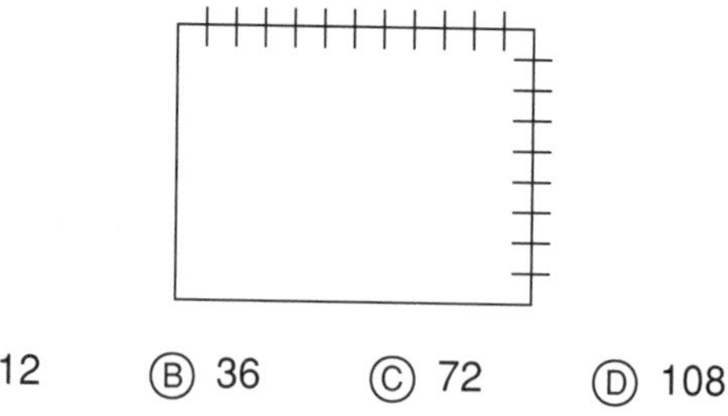

(A) 12 (B) 36 (C) 72 (D) 108

Find the answer by drawing a diagram.

(D) **7.** Jess leaves his house and rides his bicycle 10 mi north, 3 mi east, 10 mi south, and 5 mi west. How many miles is he from his house?

(A) 28 (B) 15 (C) 8 (D) 2

(D) **8.** What is the area of a rectangle if its length is 12 centimeters and its width is 8 centimeters?

(A) 20 sq cm (B) 40 cm
(C) 440 sq cm (D) 96 sq cm

(D) **9.** How much fencing is needed to enclose a rectangular playing field that is 120 yd long and $53\frac{1}{3}$ yd wide?

(A) 6400 yd (B) $226\frac{2}{3}$ yd
(C) $293\frac{1}{3}$ yd (D) $346\frac{2}{3}$ yd

(C) **10.** The first floor of a cabin is 16 ft by 24 ft. There are 3 rectangular rooms. The living room takes up one half of the cabin and is 16 ft × 12 ft. The kitchen is 12 ft × 12 ft. What size is the pantry?

(A) 4 ft × 8 ft (B) 3 ft × 12 ft
(C) 4 ft × 12 ft (D) 6 ft × 12 ft

(B) **11.** The cafeteria offers a turkey or egg sandwich on whole wheat, rye, or pumpernickel bread. How many choices of sandwich are there?

(A) 8 (B) 6 (C) 4 (D) 3

(B) **12.** In triangle *JKL*, angle *J* measures 40° and angle *K* measures 35°. What is the the measure of angle *L*?

(A) 285° (B) 105° (C) 75° (D) 15°

(B) **13.** Find the pattern of the diagram below. How many dots will appear in the next arrangement?

(A) 13 (B) 16 (C) 17 (D) 22

(C) **14.** The diagram below shows what a stack of cans looks like after making one row, two rows, and three rows. How many cans will be in the stack with five rows?

(A) 5
(B) 10
(C) 15
(D) 21

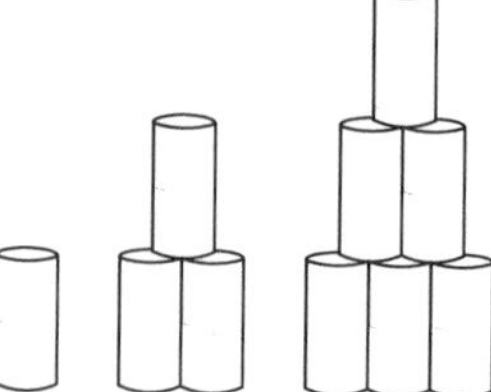

Name ____________________ Class __________ Date __________

CHAPTER 8 PRETEST

Fill in the correct circle to answer each question.

(D) **1.** $43 + 12 + 43 + 12 = \blacksquare$

(A) 55 (B) 98 (C) 100 (D) 110

(C) **2.** $28.3 + 1.01 + 1.1 + 2.3 = \blacksquare$

(A) 22.71 (B) 31.8 (C) 32.71 (D) 41.8

(D) **3.** $2\frac{3}{4} + 1\frac{1}{3} + 1\frac{1}{4} + 2\frac{2}{3} = \blacksquare$

(A) $6\frac{3}{4}$ (B) 7 (C) $7\frac{2}{3}$ (D) 8

(B) **4.** $322 + 104 + 322 + 104 = \blacksquare$

(A) 862 (B) 852 (C) 842 (D) 426

(C) **5.** $3 \times 50 = \blacksquare$

(A) 80 (B) 130 (C) 150 (D) 180

(C) **6.** $4 \times 3.14 = \blacksquare$

(A) 125.6 (B) 124.6 (C) 12.56 (D) 12.46

(A) **7.** $\frac{22}{7} \times \frac{1}{4} \times \frac{1}{4} = \blacksquare$

(A) $\frac{11}{56}$ (B) $\frac{11}{28}$ (C) $\frac{22}{56}$ (D) $\frac{22}{28}$

(C) **8.** $2 \times 3.14 \times 10 = \blacksquare$

(A) 0.628 (B) 6.28 (C) 62.8 (D) 628

(B) **9.** $7 \times 21.5 = \blacksquare$

(A) 160.5 (B) 150.5 (C) 147.5 (D) 140.5

(A) **10.** $15 \times 2\frac{1}{5} = \blacksquare$

(A) 33 (B) $30\frac{1}{5}$ (C) 37 (D) $37\frac{1}{2}$

(D) **11.** $9^2 = \blacksquare$

(A) 3 (B) $4\frac{1}{2}$ (C) 18 (D) 81

(B) **12.** $4^2 = \blacksquare$

(A) 8 (B) 16 (C) 42 (D) 32

(A) **13.** $400^2 = \blacksquare$

(A) 160,000 (B) 16,000
(C) 8,000 (D) 800

(A) **14.** $1.2^2 = \blacksquare$

(A) 1.44 (B) 2.4 (C) 2.64 (D) 3.6

(C) **15.** $0.7^2 = \blacksquare$

(A) 0.14 (B) 0.28 (C) 0.49 (D) 49

(D) **16.** $\left(\frac{3}{4}\right)^2 = \blacksquare$

(A) $\frac{3}{4}$ (B) $\frac{9}{4}$ (C) $\frac{6}{8}$ (D) $\frac{9}{16}$

Name each polygon.

(D) **17.**

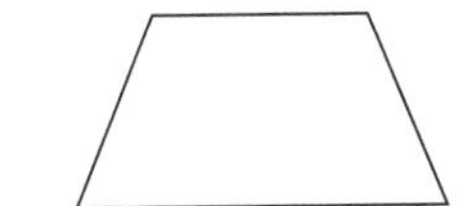

(A) square (B) rectangle
(C) parallelogram (D) trapezoid

(C) **18.**

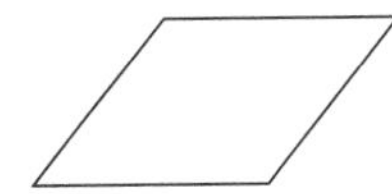

(A) pentagon (B) rectangle
(C) parallelogram (D) trapezoid

(A) **19.**

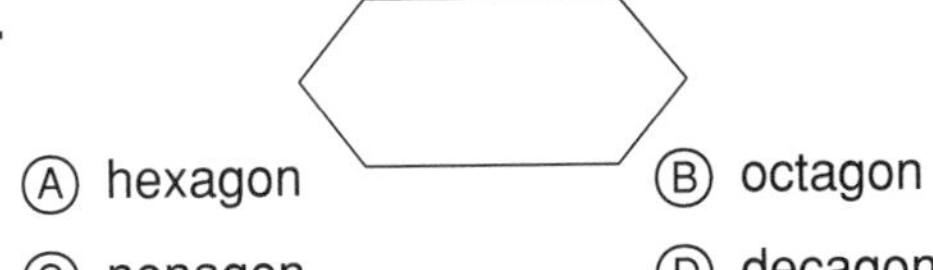

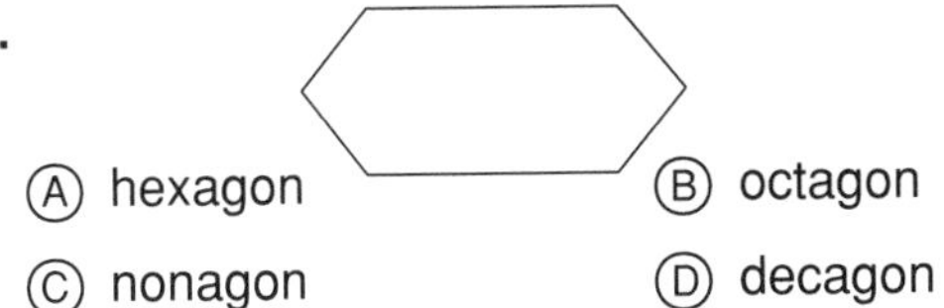

(A) hexagon (B) octagon
(C) nonagon (D) decagon

(C) **20.**

(A) square (B) trapezoid
(C) rectangle (D) rhombus

Use these formulas to help you answer the following questions.

Perimeter and Circumference		**Area**		**Volume**	
rectangle:	$P = 2l + 2w$	parallelogram:	$A = b \times h$	rectangular prism:	$V = l \times w \times h$
circumference:	$C = \pi \times d$, or $C = 2 \times \pi \times r$	rectangle:	$A = l \times w$	cube:	$V = s \times s \times s$
Surface area		square:	$A = s \times s$	cylinder:	$V = \pi \times r \times r \times h$
rectangular prism:	$A = 2(lw) + 2(wh) + 2(lh)$	triangle:	$A = \frac{1}{2} \times b \times h$		
cube:	$A = 6(s \times s)$	circle:	$A = \pi \times r \times r$	$\pi = 3.14$, or $\frac{22}{7}$	
cylinder:	$A = 2(\pi \times r \times r) + (2 \times \pi \times r \times h)$				

(C) **21.** Find the perimeter.

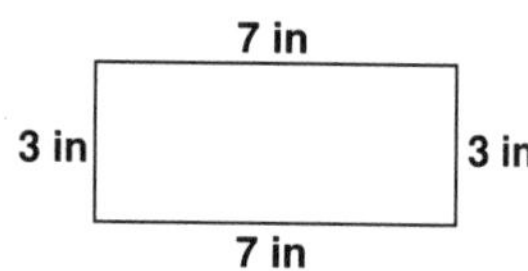

Ⓐ 10 in Ⓑ 17 in Ⓒ 20 in Ⓓ 21 in

(B) **22.** Find the area.

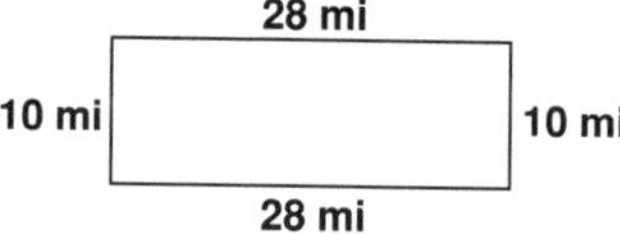

Ⓐ 280 mi Ⓑ 280 sq mi
Ⓒ 100 mi Ⓓ 38 sq mi

(A) **23.** Find the circumference.

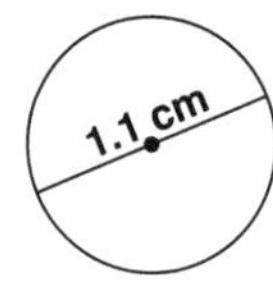

Ⓐ 3.454 cm Ⓑ 6.908 cm
Ⓒ 34.54 cm Ⓓ 69.08 cm

(B) **24.** Find the area.

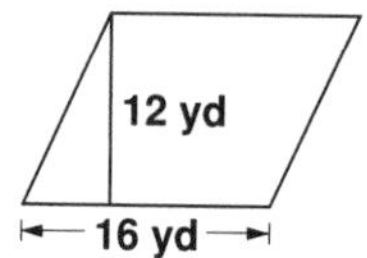

Ⓐ 256 sq yd Ⓑ 192 sq yd
Ⓒ 96 sq yd Ⓓ 28 sq yd

(C) **25.** Find the area.

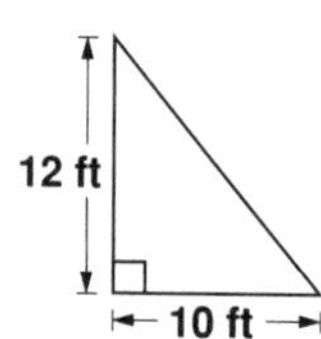

Ⓐ 244 sq ft Ⓑ 32 sq ft
Ⓒ 60 sq ft Ⓓ 120 sq ft

(B) **26.** Find the area.

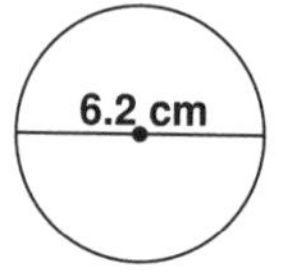

Ⓐ 19.468 sq cm Ⓑ 30.1754 sq cm
Ⓒ 9.734 sq cm Ⓓ 120.7016 sq cm

(A) **27.** Find the surface area.

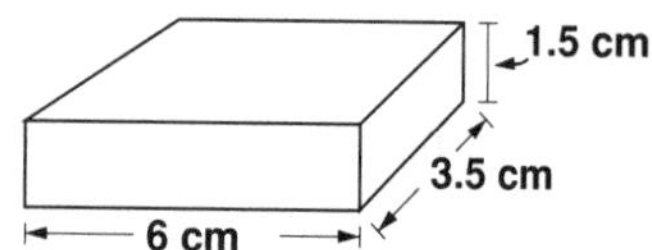

Ⓐ 70.5 sq cm Ⓑ 35.25 sq cm
Ⓒ 11 sq cm Ⓓ 31.5 sq cm

(D) **28.** Find the volume.

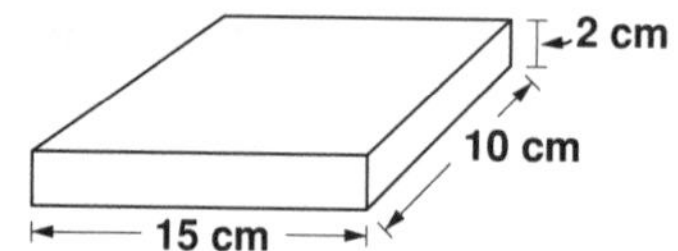

Ⓐ 270 cu cm Ⓑ 200 cu cm
Ⓒ 400 cu cm Ⓓ 300 cu cm

Name ______________________ Class __________ Date __________

8.1 PERIMETER

Perimeter is the distance around a polygon.
A **regular polygon** is a polygon in which all sides are equal in length and all angles are equal in measure. For example, a square is a regular polygon.

Example 1: What is the perimeter of the polygon?

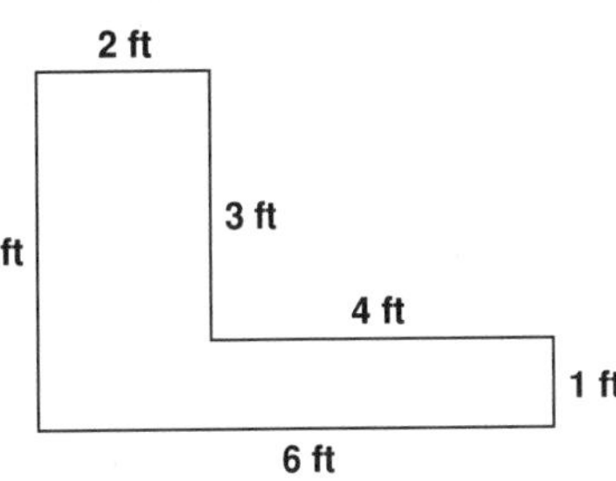

- To find the perimeter, add the lengths of the sides.

$P = 4 + 2 + 3 + 4 + 1 + 6$
$P = 20$

The perimeter is 20 feet, or 20 ft.

Example 2: Find the perimeter of this regular pentagon.

- All sides are of equal length.
  You can add the lengths or you can multiply the length of one side, *s*, by the number of sides.

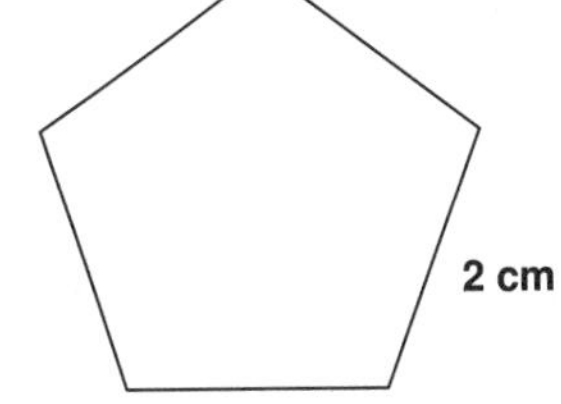

$P = 5$ (number of sides) $\times$ 2 cm (the length of one side)
$P = 10$ cm

The perimeter is 10 centimeters.

Example 3: Find the perimeter of the rectangle.

- To find the perimeter of a rectangle, you can use the formula $P = 2l + 2w$
  (P = perimeter, l = length, w = width)

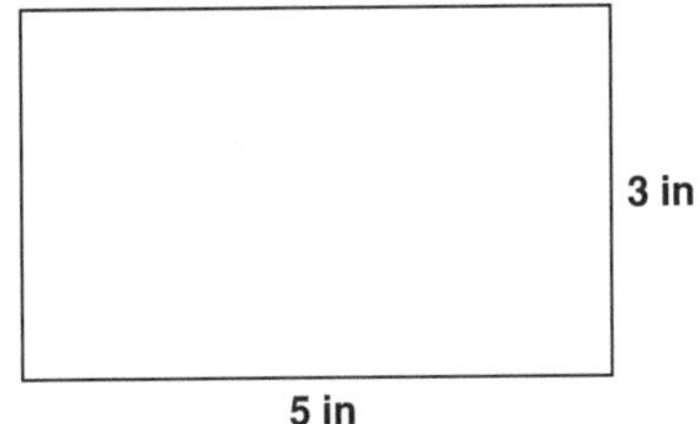

$P = 2l + 2w$
$P = (2 \times l) + (2 \times w)$
$P = (2 \times 5) + (2 \times 3)$
$P = 10 + 6$
$P = 16$

The perimeter is 16 inches.

Find the perimeter of each figure.

Ⓒ **1.**

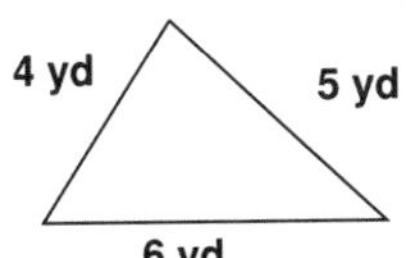

Ⓐ 1 yd Ⓑ 14 yd Ⓒ 15 yd Ⓓ 16 yd

Ⓓ **2.**

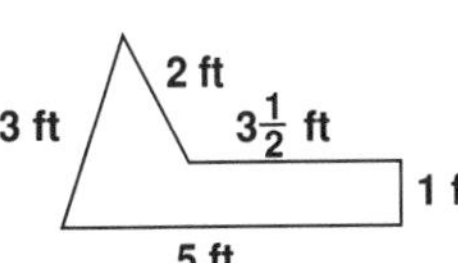

Ⓐ $9\frac{1}{2}$ ft Ⓑ $12\frac{1}{2}$ ft Ⓒ $13\frac{1}{2}$ ft Ⓓ $14\frac{1}{2}$ ft

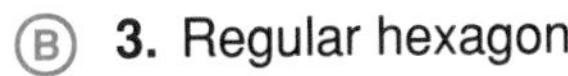
Ⓑ **3.** Regular hexagon

Ⓐ 30 mm
Ⓑ 36 mm
Ⓒ 42 mm
Ⓓ 48 mm

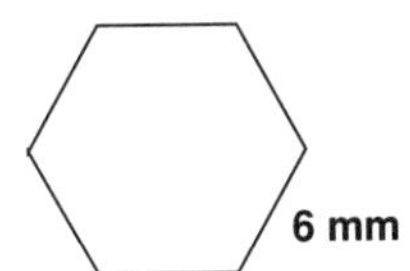

Ⓓ **4.** Regular quadrilateral

Ⓐ 17 in
Ⓑ 34 in
Ⓒ 51 in
Ⓓ 68 in

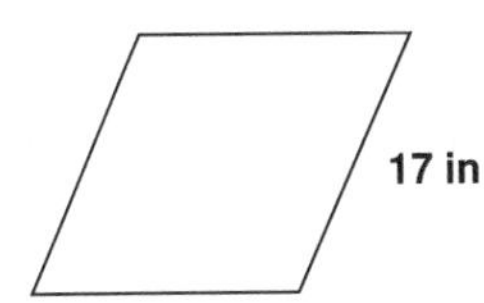

(A) **5.**

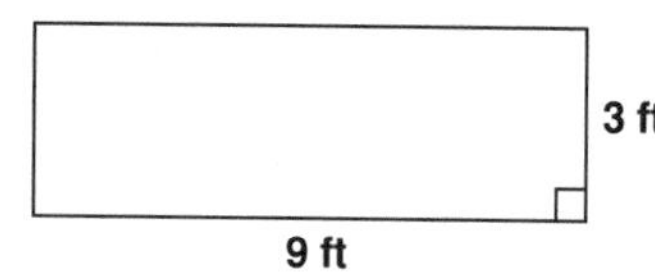

Ⓐ 24 ft Ⓑ 21 ft Ⓒ 18 ft Ⓓ 12 ft

(C) **6.** Square

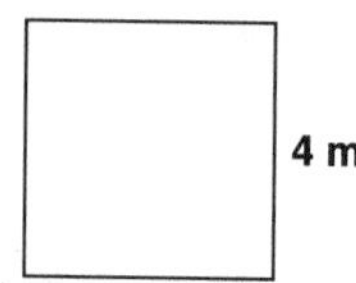

Ⓐ 8 m Ⓑ 12 m Ⓒ 16 m Ⓓ 20 m

(D) **7.** How much string would it take to mark off a rectangular garden 12 ft long and 10 ft wide?

Ⓐ 22 ft Ⓑ 24 ft Ⓒ 34 ft Ⓓ 44 ft

(C) **8.** Find the perimeter of a triangle with sides 1.4 cm, 2.6 cm, and 3 cm in length.

Ⓐ 5 cm Ⓑ 6 cm Ⓒ 7 cm Ⓓ 7.2 cm

(C) **9.** Equilateral triangle

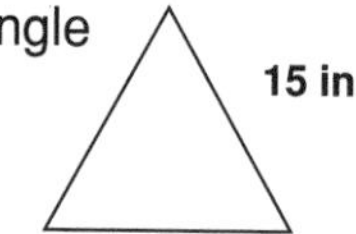

Ⓐ 15 in Ⓑ 30 in Ⓒ 45 in Ⓓ 60 in

(D) **10.**

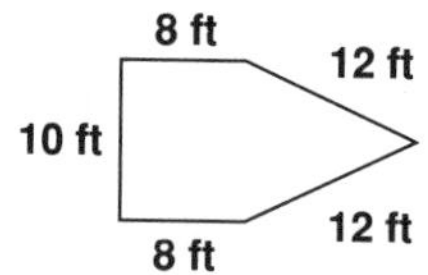

Ⓐ 20 ft Ⓑ 30 ft Ⓒ 42 ft Ⓓ 50 ft

(A) **11.** Rectangle: $l = 2$ m, $w = 1\frac{1}{2}$ m

Ⓐ 7 m Ⓑ $5\frac{1}{2}$ m Ⓒ 5 m Ⓓ $3\frac{1}{2}$ m

(D) **12.** Regular octagon: $s = 20.4$ mm

Ⓐ 81.6 mm Ⓑ 102 mm

Ⓒ 122.4 mm Ⓓ 163.2 mm

(B) **13.** How much fencing is needed to go around a square field if one side measures 8 yd?

Ⓐ 36 yd Ⓑ 32 yd Ⓒ 28 yd Ⓓ 24 yd

(C) **14.** How far is it around a lake whose path forms a pentagon with sides $\frac{1}{2}$ mi, $\frac{3}{4}$ mi, 1 mi, $1\frac{1}{4}$ mi, and 2 mi?

Ⓐ $4\frac{3}{4}$ mi Ⓑ $5\frac{3}{4}$ mi Ⓒ $5\frac{1}{2}$ mi Ⓓ 5 mi

(A) **15.**

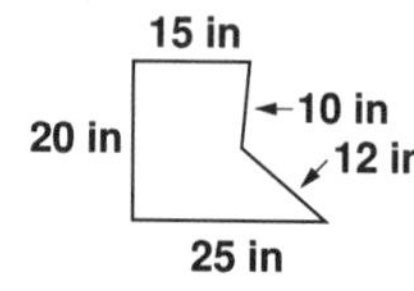

Ⓐ 82 in Ⓑ 72 in Ⓒ 70 in Ⓓ 57 in

(B) **16.**

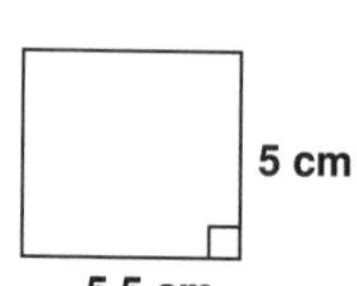

Ⓐ 20 cm Ⓑ 21 cm Ⓒ 22 cm Ⓓ 23 cm

(D) **17.** Square: $s = 201$ ft

Ⓐ 400 ft Ⓑ 402 ft Ⓒ 802 ft Ⓓ 804 ft

(C) **18.** Regular pentagon: $s = 12$ cm

Ⓐ 96 cm Ⓑ 72 cm Ⓒ 60 cm Ⓓ 48 cm

(C) **19.** Rectangle: $l = 9.2$ cm, $w = 5.6$ cm

Ⓐ 14.8 cm Ⓑ 24.8 cm

Ⓒ 29.6 cm Ⓓ 51.5 cm

(D) **20.** Triangle: $4\frac{1}{2}$ in, $3\frac{1}{4}$ in, $5\frac{5}{8}$ in

Ⓐ $12\frac{7}{14}$ in Ⓑ $12\frac{1}{2}$ in

Ⓒ $12\frac{11}{8}$ in Ⓓ $13\frac{3}{8}$ in

(B) **21.** Regular hexagon: $s = 4.7$ m

Ⓐ 37.6 m Ⓑ 28.2 m

Ⓒ 23.5 m Ⓓ 18.8 m

(C) **22.** Rectangle: $l = 7\frac{1}{2}$ ft, $w = 5\frac{1}{4}$ ft

Ⓐ $157\frac{1}{2}$ ft Ⓑ $39\frac{3}{8}$ ft

Ⓒ $25\frac{1}{2}$ ft Ⓓ $12\frac{3}{4}$ ft

Name ______________________ Class ________ Date ____________

8.2 CIRCUMFERENCE

Circumference is the distance around a circle.

There are two formulas for finding the circumference of a circle.

When the diameter is given, use $C = \pi \times d$, or $C = \pi d$

When the radius is given, use $C = 2 \times \pi \times r$, or $C = 2 \pi r$

In these formulas, C = Circumference, d = diameter, r = radius.

Use either 3.14 or $\frac{22}{7}$ for π.

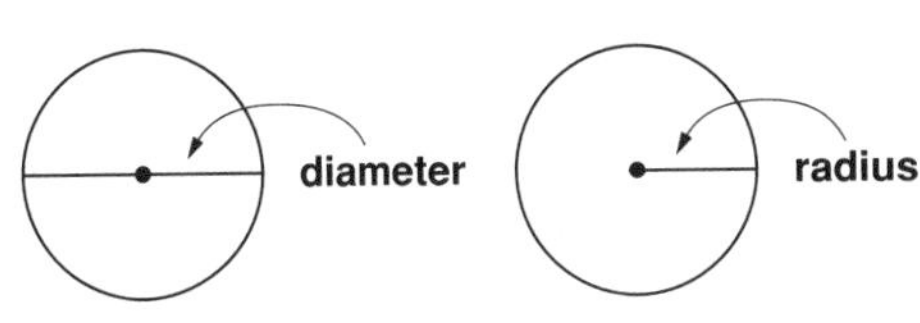

Example 1: Find the circumference.

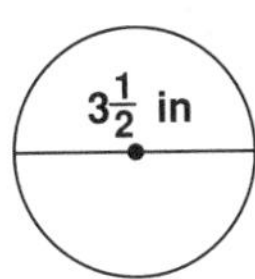

- The diameter is given. Use the formula $C = \pi \times d$
- The length of the diameter is a mixed number. Use $\frac{22}{7}$ for π.

$$C = \pi \times d$$
$$C = \frac{22}{7} \times 3\frac{1}{2}$$
$$C = \frac{22}{7} \times \frac{7}{2}$$
$$C = 11$$

The circumference is 11 inches.

Example 2: Find the circumference.

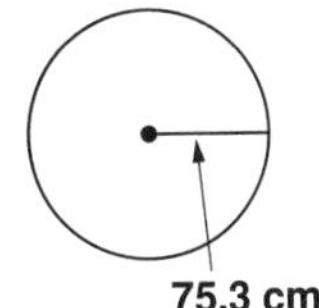

- The radius is given. Use $C = 2 \times \pi \times r$
- The length of the radius is a decimal. Use 3.14 for π.

$$C = 2 \times \pi \times r$$
$$C = 2 \times 3.14 \times 75.3$$
$$C = 2 \times 236.442$$
$$C = 472.884$$

The circumference is 472.884 centimeters.

Example 3: A circle has a circumference of 25.12 inches. What is its diameter?

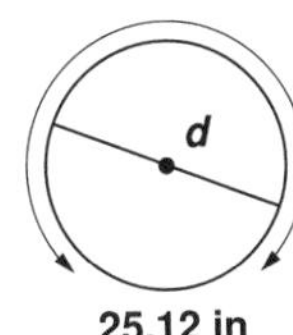

- The circumference is given. You need to find the diameter. Use $C = \pi \times d$.

$$C = \pi \times d$$
$$25.12 = 3.14 \times d$$
$$25.12 \div 3.14 = d$$
$$8 = d$$

The diameter of the circle is 8 inches.

Example 4: A circle has a circumference of 31.4 centimeters. What is its radius?

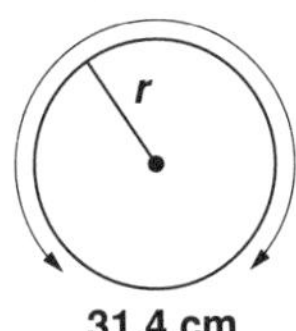

- The circumference is given. You need to find the radius. Use $C = 2 \times \pi \times r$.

$$C = 2 \times \pi \times r$$
$$31.4 = 2 \times 3.14 \times r$$
$$31.4 = 6.28 \times r$$
$$31.4 \div 6.28 = r$$
$$5 = r$$

The radius of the circle is 5 centimeters.

Find the circumference of each circle.

Ⓑ **1.**

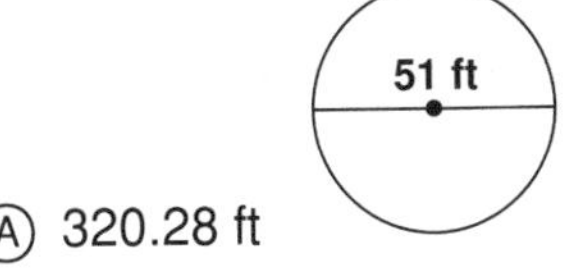

Ⓐ 320.28 ft Ⓑ 160.14 ft
Ⓒ 80.07 ft Ⓓ 40.035 ft

Ⓒ **2.**

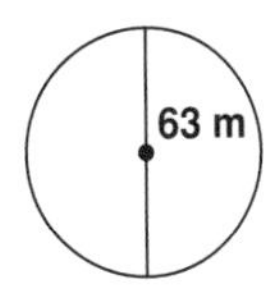

Ⓐ 99 m Ⓑ 176 m
Ⓒ 198 m Ⓓ 396 m

Ⓓ **3.**

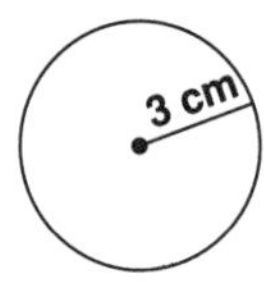

Ⓐ 9 cm Ⓑ 9.42 cm

Ⓒ 18.64 cm Ⓓ 18.84 cm

Ⓒ **4.**

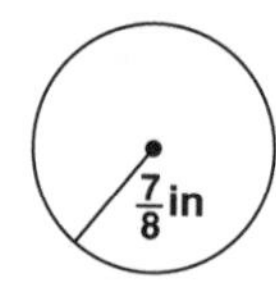

Ⓐ 44 in Ⓑ $38\frac{1}{2}$ in

Ⓒ $5\frac{1}{2}$ in Ⓓ $2\frac{3}{4}$ in

Find the answer.

Ⓒ **5.** Find the circumference of a circle with a radius of 11 in.

Ⓐ 34.54 in Ⓑ 36.54 in

Ⓒ 69.08 in Ⓓ 70.14 in

Ⓓ **6.** The diameter of a circle is 7 ft. What is its circumference?

Ⓐ $\frac{11}{7}$ ft Ⓑ $\frac{22}{7}$ ft Ⓒ 11 ft Ⓓ 22 ft

Ⓒ **7.** A circular flower garden has a radius of 7 ft. How much fencing is needed to enclose the garden?

Ⓐ $\frac{22}{7}$ ft Ⓑ 22 ft Ⓒ 44 ft Ⓓ 88 ft

Ⓒ **8.** A quarter has a diameter of 2.4 cm. What is its circumference?

Ⓐ 4.8 cm Ⓑ 5.54 cm

Ⓒ 7.536 cm Ⓓ 15.072 cm

Ⓑ **9.** A circle has a circumference of 37.68 cm. What is its diameter?

Ⓐ 118.3152 cm Ⓑ 12 cm

Ⓒ 6 cm Ⓓ 3.14 cm

Ⓓ **10.** The circumference of a circle is 43.96 in. What is its radius?

Ⓐ 276.0688 in Ⓑ 138.0344 in

Ⓒ 14 in Ⓓ 7 in

Ⓒ **11.** The diameter of a circle is 3 yd. What is its circumference?

Ⓐ 4.71 yd Ⓑ 6.14 yd

Ⓒ 9.42 yd Ⓓ 18.84 yd

Ⓑ **12.** Find the circumference of a circle with a radius of 10.5 cm.

Ⓐ 131.88 cm Ⓑ 65.94 cm

Ⓒ 32.97 cm Ⓓ 15.64 cm

Ⓒ **13.** The circumference of a circle is 9.42 yards. What is its diameter?

Ⓐ 29.5788 yd Ⓑ 3.14 yd

Ⓒ 3 yd Ⓓ 1.5 yd

Ⓐ **14.** A circle has a circumference of 65.94 centimeters. What is its radius?

Ⓐ 10.5 cm Ⓑ 21 cm

Ⓒ 207.0516 cm Ⓓ 414.1032 cm

Ⓒ **15.** The diameter of a bicycle wheel is 26 inches. How far forward will the bicycle move when the wheel makes one complete revolution?

Ⓐ 3.14 in Ⓑ 26 in

Ⓒ 81.64 in Ⓓ 163.28 in

Ⓒ **16.** A lake is shaped like a circle. The distance from one side of the lake to the center is about $1\frac{3}{4}$ mi. What is the distance around the lake?

Ⓐ $\frac{11}{7}$ mi Ⓑ $\frac{22}{7}$ mi Ⓒ 11 mi Ⓓ 22 mi

Ⓑ **17.** A circular swimming pool has a circumference of 62.8 feet. If you swim from one side of the pool to the other, how far do you swim?

Ⓐ 197.192 ft Ⓑ 20 ft

Ⓒ 10 ft Ⓓ 3.14 ft

Ⓐ **18.** A flag pole stands in the center of a circular flower garden. The garden has a circumference of 376.8 yards. How far is it from any point along the edge of the garden to the flag pole?

Ⓐ 60 yd Ⓑ 120 yd

Ⓒ 1183.152 yd Ⓓ 2336.304 yd

Name ______________________ Class __________ Date __________

8.3 AREA: PARALLELOGRAM, RECTANGLE, SQUARE

The **area** of a region is the number of square units needed to cover the region. The area of the rectangle at the right is 18 square units, (3 units × 6 units).

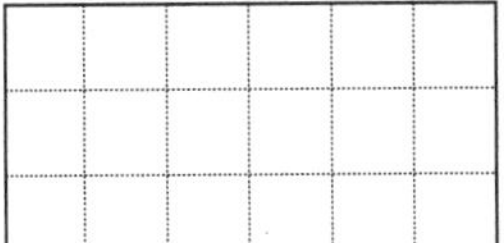

To find the area of a parallelogram, rectangle, or square, use the appropriate formula.

Example 1: Find the area of the parallelogram.

- Use the formula $A = b \times h$, or $A = bh$ (A = area, b = base, h = height)

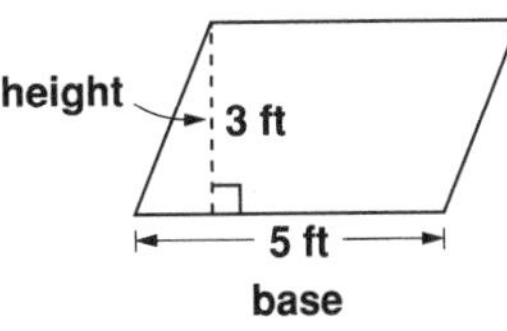

$A = b \times h$
$A = 5 \times 3$
$A = 15$

The area is 15 square feet, or 15 sq ft.

Example 2: Find the area of the rectangle.

- Use the formula, $A = l \times w$, or $A = lw$ (A = area, l = length, w = width)

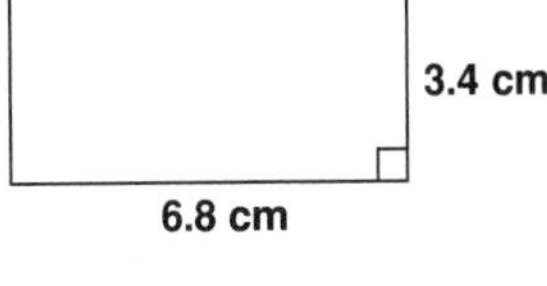

$A = l \times w$
$A = 6.8 \times 3.4$
$A = 23.12$

The area is 23.12 square centimeters, or 23.12 sq cm.

Example 3: Find the area of the square.

- Use the formula $A = s \times s$, or $A = s^2$. (A = area, s = the length of one side.)

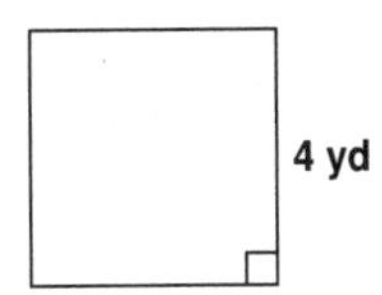

$A = s \times s$
$A = 4 \times 4$
$A = 16$

The area is 16 square yards, or 16 sq yd.

Find the area of each figure.

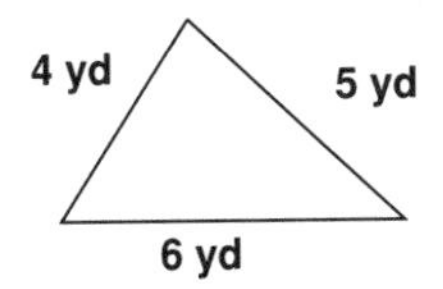

(C) **1.**

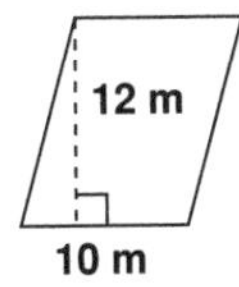

(A) 22 sq m (B) 120 m
(C) 120 sq m (D) 144 sq m

(B) **2.**

43 mm

(A) 25 sq mm (B) 215 sq mm
(C) 1849 mm (D) 1849 sq mm

(A) **3.**

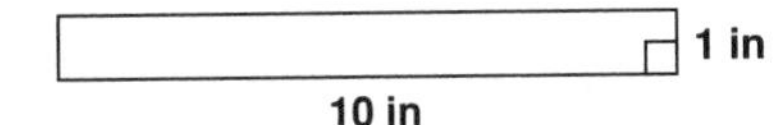

(A) 10 sq in (B) 11 in
(C) 100 sq in (D) 110 in

(D) **4.**

40 m
42 m

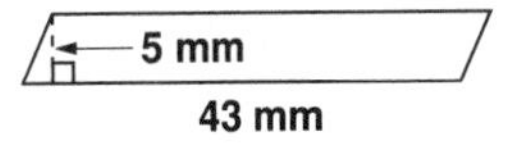

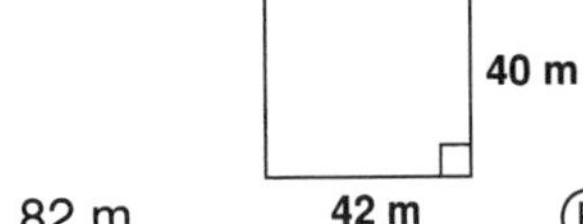

(A) 82 m (B) 164 sq m
(C) 1680 m (D) 1680 sq m

(C) **5.** Square

- (A) $4\frac{1}{16}$ sq yd
- (B) $4\frac{1}{4}$ sq yd
- (C) $5\frac{1}{16}$ sq yd
- (D) $5\frac{1}{4}$ sq yd

$2\frac{1}{4}$ **yd**

(D) **6.** Square

- (A) 24 mi
- (B) 24 sq mi
- (C) 144 mi
- (D) 144 sq mi

12 mi

(D) **7.** Rectangle

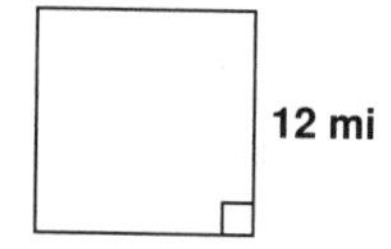

- (A) 20 ft
- (B) 20 sq ft
- (C) 64 ft
- (D) 64 sq ft

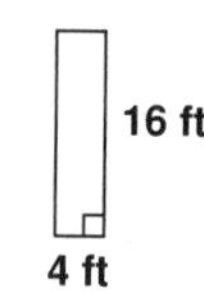

(B) **8.** Square

- (A) 14 in
- (B) 12.25 sq in
- (C) 9.25 sq in
- (D) 7 in

3.5 in

(A) **9.**

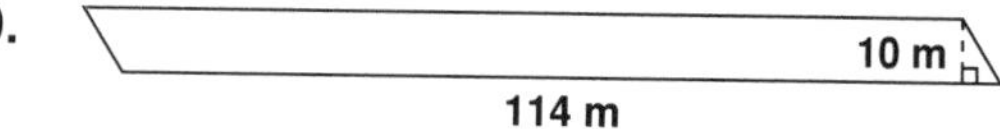

- (A) 1,140 sq m
- (B) 248 m
- (C) 124 sq m
- (D) 1,140 m

(D) **10.** Rectangle

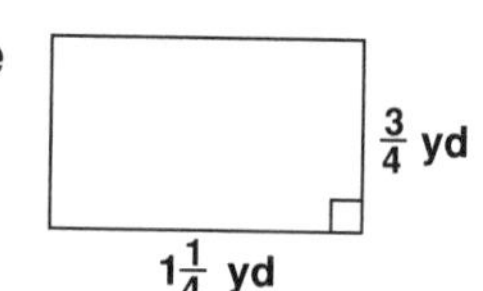

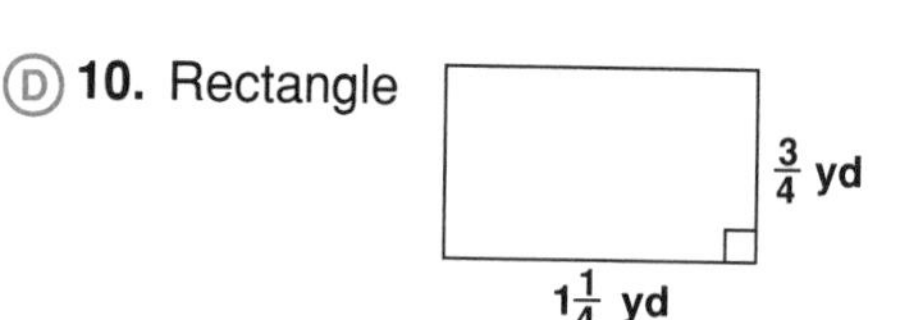

- (A) 4 sq yd
- (B) $3\frac{3}{4}$ sq yd
- (C) 2 sq yd
- (D) $\frac{15}{16}$ sq yd

(D) **11.** The length of one side of a square is 22 mm. What is the area of this square?

- (A) 44 sq mm
- (B) 88 sq mm
- (C) 848 sq mm
- (D) 484 sq mm

(A) **12.** A rectangle is 15 m long and $\frac{1}{2}$ m wide. What is the area of this rectangle?

- (A) $7\frac{1}{2}$ sq m
- (B) $15\frac{1}{2}$ sq m
- (C) 30 sq m
- (D) 31 sq m

(B) **13.** Find the area of this parallelogram.

- (A) 16 sq m
- (B) 6 sq m
- (C) 5.5 sq m
- (D) 2.25 sq m

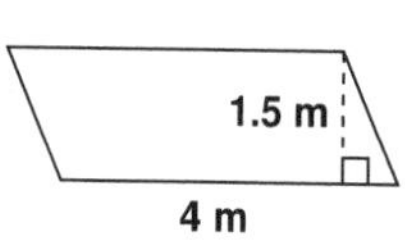

(C) **14.** What is the area of this rectangle?

- (A) 33 in
- (B) 256 sq in
- (C) 272 sq in
- (D) 289 sq in

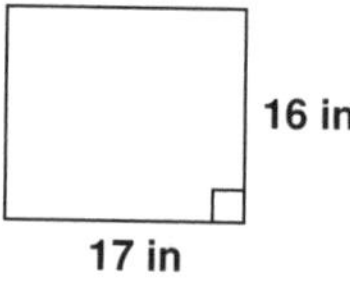

(C) **15.** What is the area of a square with a side that measures $\frac{2}{3}$ ft?

- (A) $\frac{4}{3}$ sq ft
- (B) $\frac{4}{6}$ sq ft
- (C) $\frac{4}{9}$ sq ft
- (D) $\frac{2}{9}$ sq ft

(B) **16.** The base of a parallelogram is $4\frac{1}{4}$ in. The height is 5 in. Find its area.

- (A) 25 sq in
- (B) $21\frac{1}{4}$ sq in
- (C) $20\frac{1}{4}$ sq in
- (D) $20\frac{1}{16}$ sq in

(C) **17.** How many square feet of tile are needed to cover a counter that measures $8\frac{1}{2}$ ft by 6 ft ?

- (A) $14\frac{1}{2}$
- (B) 29
- (C) 51
- (D) 102

(C) **18.** How many square meters of carpeting are needed to cover a floor that measures 4.5 m by 3.7 m?

- (A) 8.2 sq m
- (B) 16.4 sq m
- (C) 16.65 sq m
- (D) 1665 sq m

Name ______________________ Class ________ Date ____________

8.4 AREA OF A TRIANGLE

To find the area of a triangle, use the formula $A = \frac{1}{2}\, b \times h$, or $A = \frac{1}{2}\, bh$ (A = area, b = base, h = height).

Example 1: Find the area.

$A = \frac{1}{2} \times b \times h$

$A = \frac{1}{2} \times 12 \times 5$

$A = \frac{1}{2} \times 60$

$A = 30$

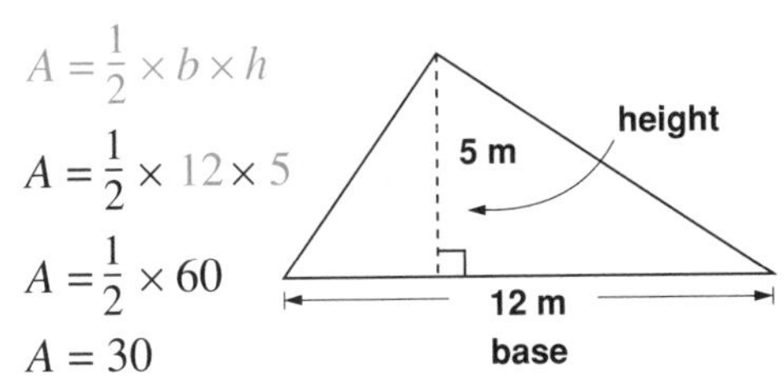

The area is 30 square meters, or 30 sq m.

Example 2: Find the area.

$A = \frac{1}{2} \times b \times h$

$A = \frac{1}{2} \times 10 \times 8$

$A = \frac{1}{2} \times 80$

$A = 40$

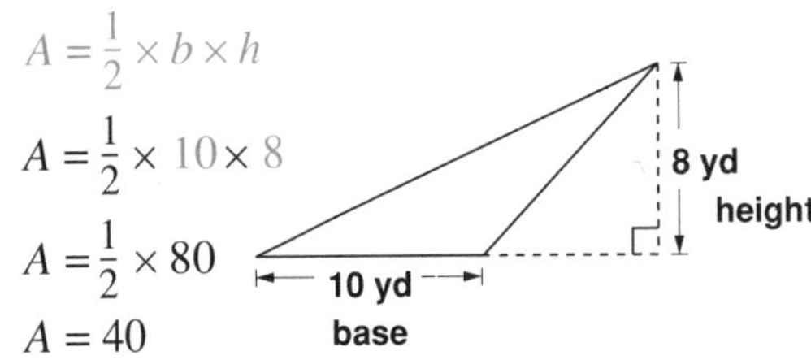

The area is 40 square yards, or 40 sq yd.

Find the area of each triangle.

(A) **1.**

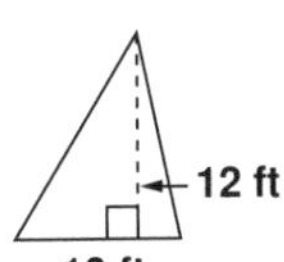

(A) 60 sq ft (B) 120 ft

(C) 120 sq ft (D) 144 sq ft

(C) **2.**

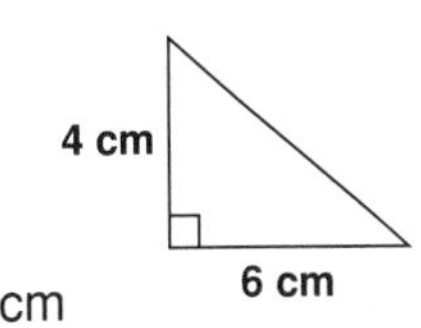

(A) 10 cm (B) 12 cm

(C) 12 sq cm (D) 24 sq cm

(B) **3.**

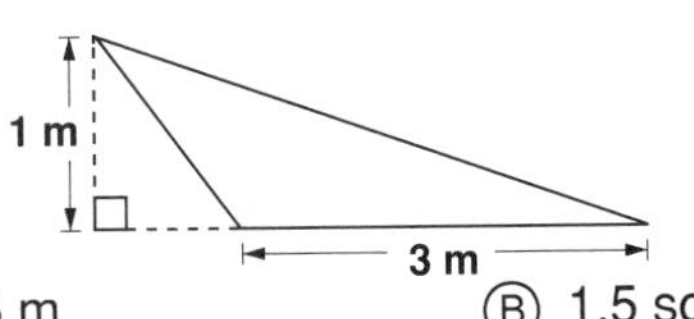

(A) 1.5 m (B) 1.5 sq m

(C) 3 m (D) 3 sq m

(D) **4.**

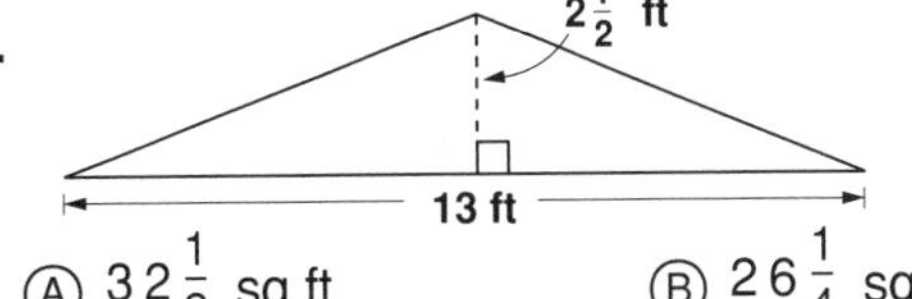

(A) $32\frac{1}{2}$ sq ft (B) $26\frac{1}{4}$ sq ft

(C) $26\frac{1}{2}$ sq ft (D) $16\frac{1}{4}$ sq ft

(C) **5.** A triangle has a base of 2 cm and a height of 4.5 cm. What is its area?

(A) 2.25 sq cm (B) 4.5 cm

(C) 4.5 sq cm (D) 9 sq cm

(B) **6.** Find the area of a triangle with a base of 6.2 mm and a height of 4.3 mm.

(A) 5.25 sq mm (B) 13.33 sq mm

(C) 26.66 sq mm (D) 1,333 sq mm

(D) **7.** How many square inches of material are in the pennant below?

(A) 130 sq in

(B) 120 sq in

(C) 65 sq in

(D) 60 sq in

13 in
12 in
10 in

(B) **8.** What is the area of the entire wall shown below?

(A) 68 sq ft

(B) 240 sq ft

(C) 288 sq ft

(D) 768 sq ft

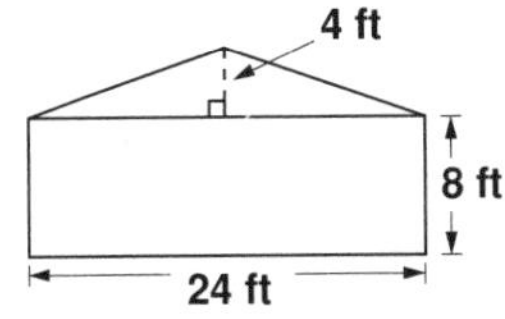

Name ____________________ Class ________ Date ____________

8.5 AREA OF A CIRCLE

To find the area of a circle, use the formula $A = \pi \times r^2$, or $A = \pi r^2$ (A = area, r = radius).

REMEMBER: Use either 3.14 or $\frac{22}{7}$ for π.

Example 1: Find the area.

$A = \pi \times r^2$
$A = 3.14 \times 2.5^2$
$A = 3.14 \times 2.5 \times 2.5$
$A = 3.14 \times 6.25$
$A = 19.625$

2.5 m

The area is 19.625 square meters, or 19.625 sq m.

Example 2: Find the area. The diameter is given.

- First find the radius.

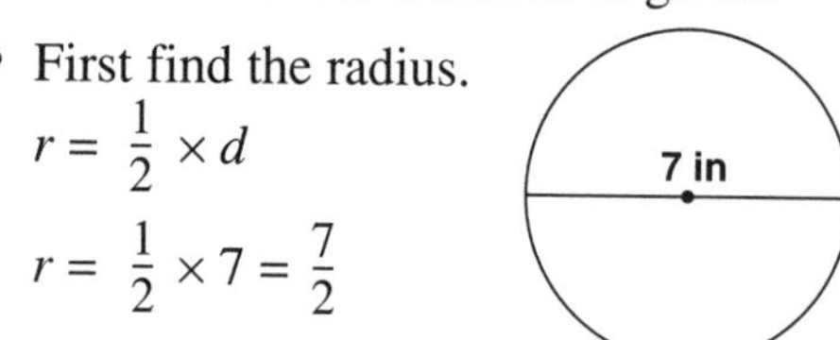

$r = \frac{1}{2} \times d$

$r = \frac{1}{2} \times 7 = \frac{7}{2}$

- Use $A = \pi \times r^2$

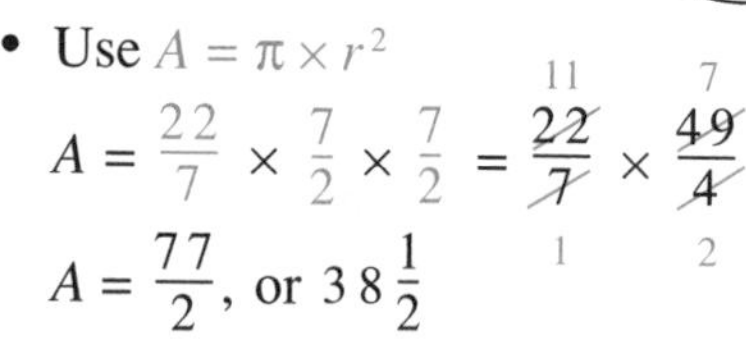

$A = \frac{22}{7} \times \frac{7}{2} \times \frac{7}{2} = \frac{\overset{11}{\cancel{22}}}{\underset{1}{\cancel{7}}} \times \frac{\overset{7}{\cancel{49}}}{\underset{2}{\cancel{4}}}$

$A = \frac{77}{2}$, or $38\frac{1}{2}$

The area is $38\frac{1}{2}$ square inches, or $38\frac{1}{2}$ sq in.

Find the area of each circle.

Ⓒ **1.**

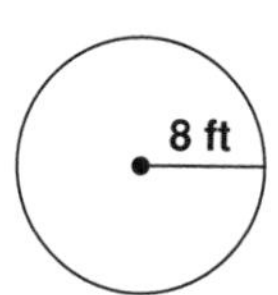

Ⓐ 20.096 sq ft
Ⓑ 20.96 sq ft
Ⓒ 200.96 sq ft
Ⓓ 2,000.96 sq ft

Ⓑ **2.**

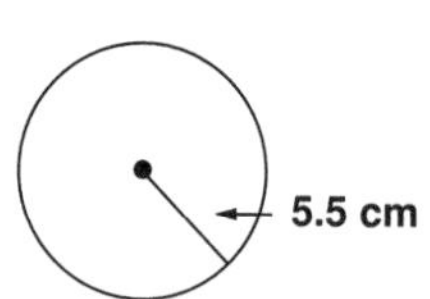

Ⓐ 9.4985 sq cm
Ⓑ 94.985 sq cm
Ⓒ 949.85 sq cm
Ⓓ 9498.5 sq cm

Ⓒ **3.**

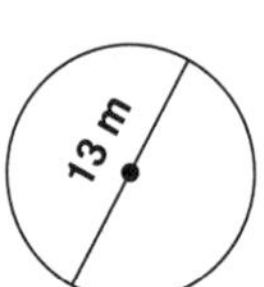

Ⓐ 1.3266 sq m
Ⓑ 13.266 sq m
Ⓒ 132.665 sq m
Ⓓ 1326.65 sq m

Ⓑ **4.**

$4\frac{2}{3}$ ft

Ⓐ $14\frac{1}{3}$ sq ft
Ⓑ $17\frac{1}{9}$ sq ft
Ⓒ $51\frac{1}{3}$ sq ft
Ⓓ $68\frac{4}{9}$ sq ft

Ⓒ **5.** A circle has a radius of 4.1 m. Find its area.

Ⓐ 211.1336 sq m
Ⓑ 105.5668 sq m
Ⓒ 52.7834 sq m
Ⓓ 12.874 sq m

Ⓒ **6.** A circle has a diameter of 10 ft. What is its area?

Ⓐ 15.7 sq ft
Ⓑ 31.4 sq ft
Ⓒ 78.5 sq ft
Ⓓ 314 sq ft

Ⓒ **7.** A sprinkler can water a circular patch of lawn with a diameter of 80 ft. How many square feet can the sprinkler cover?

Ⓐ 125.6 sq ft
Ⓑ 251.259 ft
Ⓒ 5024 sq ft
Ⓓ 20,096 sq ft

Ⓑ **8.** A radio station has a broadcast radius of 60 miles. How large is the area that the station serves?

Ⓐ 45,216 sq mi
Ⓑ 11,304 sq mi
Ⓒ 376.8 sq mi
Ⓓ 188.4 sq mi

Name ______________________ Class __________ Date ______________

8.6 AREA OF IRREGULAR FIGURES

Sometimes you need to use more than one formula and more than one operation to find the area of a figure.

Example 1: Find the area of the shaded portion of the rectangle, given s is the side of the square.

- Find the area of the entire rectangle.

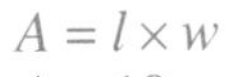

$A = l \times w$
$A = 10 \times 4$
$A = 40$

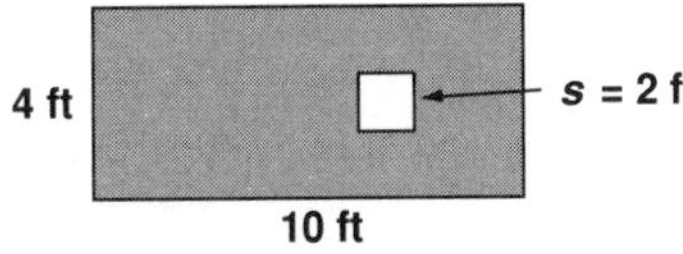

- The unshaded region has the shape of a square. Find the area of the square.

$A = s \times s$
$A = 2 \times 2$
$A = 4$

- To find the area of the shaded area, subtract the area of the square from the area of the rectangle.

40 sq ft	–	4 sq ft	=	36 sq ft
total area		area of unshaded region		area of shaded region

The area of the shaded region is 36 square feet.

Example 2: Find the area of the figure.

- Think of the figure as two rectangles, and label each side.
- Find the area of rectangle X.

$A = l \times w$
$A = 6 \times 4$
$A = 24$

- Find the area of rectangle Y.

$A = l \times w$
$A = 4 \times 2$
$A = 8$

- Add the areas of the two rectangles.

24 sq ft	+	8 sq ft	=	32 sq ft
area of rectangle X		area of rectangle Y		total area

The area of the figure is 32 square feet.

Find the answer.

(B) **1.** Find the area of the shaded portion of the larger rectangle.

Ⓐ 16 sq in
Ⓑ 120 sq in
Ⓒ 360 sq in
Ⓓ 4680 sq in

(D) **2.** Find the area of the shaded portion of the larger square.

Ⓐ 144 sq m
Ⓑ 140 sq m
Ⓒ 136 sq m
Ⓓ 128 sq m

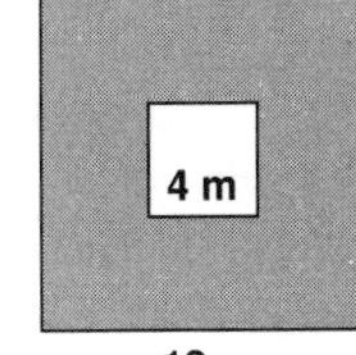

(C) **3.** What is the area of this figure?

Ⓐ 6 sq yd
Ⓑ 7 sq yd
Ⓒ 8 sq yd
Ⓓ 9 sq yd

(B) **4.** Find the area of the figure.

Ⓐ 13 sq mi
Ⓑ $13\frac{1}{4}$ sq mi
Ⓒ $13\frac{1}{2}$ sq mi
Ⓓ $13\frac{3}{4}$ sq mi

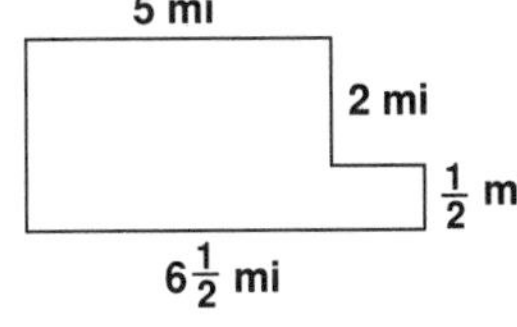

Ⓑ **5.** How many square feet are in the shaded portion of the larger rectangle?

Ⓐ 100 sq ft
Ⓑ 98 sq ft
Ⓒ 84 sq ft
Ⓓ 54 sq ft

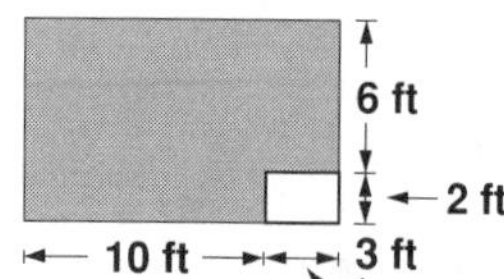

Ⓒ **6.** What is the area of this figure?

Ⓐ 450 sq m
Ⓑ $412\frac{1}{2}$ sq m
Ⓒ 375 sq m
Ⓓ 225 sq m

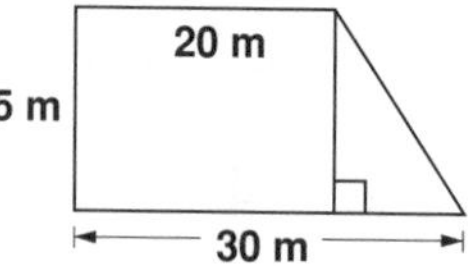

Ⓐ **7.** The outer rim of a deck around a swimming pool has length 18 ft and width 14 ft. The pool is 12 ft by 8 ft. Find the area of the deck.

Ⓐ 156 sq ft　Ⓑ 136 sq ft
Ⓒ 96 sq ft　Ⓓ 36 sq ft

Ⓓ **8.** A room has length of 12 ft and width of 10 ft. The hallway is 6 ft by 3 ft. How much carpet is needed to cover the floor of the room and the hallway?

Ⓐ 102 ft　Ⓑ 102 sq ft
Ⓒ 138 ft　Ⓓ 138 sq ft

Ⓒ **9.** Find the area of this figure.

Ⓐ 225 sq cm
Ⓑ 250 sq cm
Ⓒ 275 sq cm
Ⓓ 300 sq cm

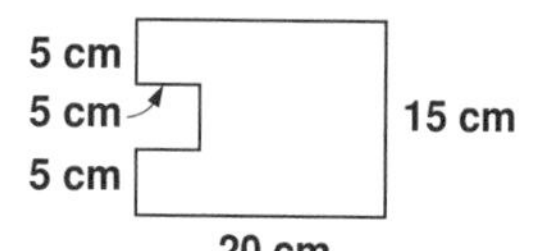

Ⓑ **10.** Find the area of the shaded region.

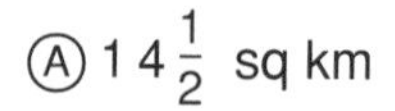

Ⓐ $14\frac{1}{2}$ sq km
Ⓑ 14 sq km
Ⓒ $12\frac{1}{4}$ sq km
Ⓓ $8\frac{3}{4}$ sq km

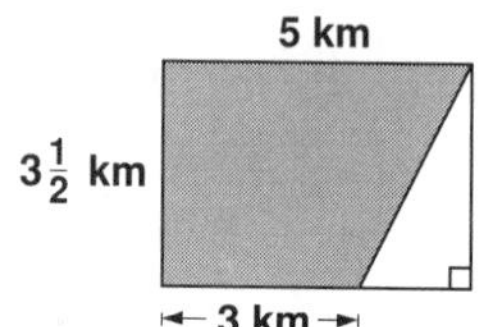

Ⓑ **11.** What is the area of this figure?

Ⓐ 650 sq mi
Ⓑ 6500 sq mi
Ⓒ 700 sq mi
Ⓓ 7000 sq mi

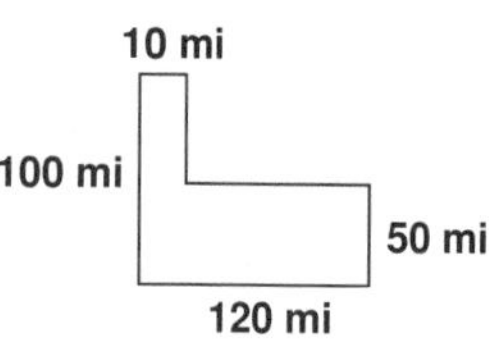

Ⓐ **12.** How many square feet are in the shaded portion of the rectangle? The unshaded region is a square.

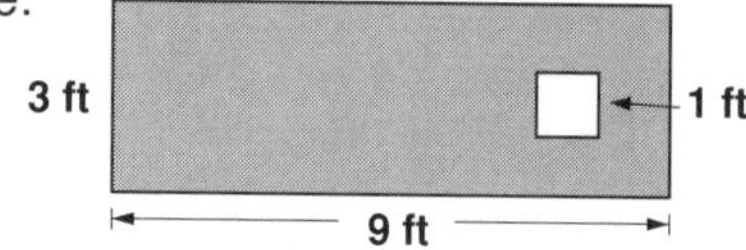

Ⓐ 26 sq ft Ⓑ 27 sq ft Ⓒ 28 sq ft Ⓓ 29 sq ft

Ⓓ **13.** What is the area of the shaded region?

Ⓐ 21.98 sq cm
Ⓑ 43.96 sq cm
Ⓒ 153.86 sq cm
Ⓓ 373.66 sq cm

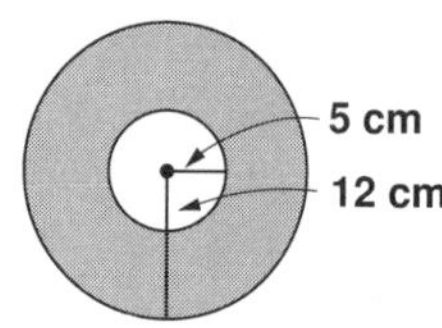

Ⓑ **14.** What is the area of the shaded region? The unshaded region is a circle with a radius of 2 in.

Ⓐ 41.72 sq in
Ⓑ 31.44 sq in
Ⓒ 24 sq in
Ⓓ 15.44 sq in

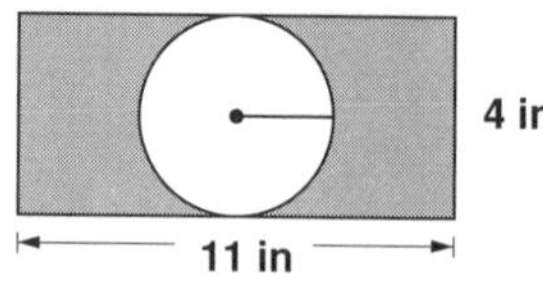

Ⓑ **15.** A rectangular ice-skating rink measures 20 m by 10 m. A 1-m border of snow surrounds the rink. How many square feet of snow surround the rink?

Ⓐ 1 sq m　Ⓑ 64 sq m
Ⓒ 231 sq m　Ⓓ 264 sq m

Ⓒ **16.** One side of a paper record jacket is in the shape of a square with sides of 12 in. In the center of the jacket, there is a circular piece of clear plastic with a radius of 2 in. How many square inches of the jacket are paper?

Ⓐ 6.28 sq in　Ⓑ 17.72 sq in
Ⓒ 131.44 sq in　Ⓓ 137.72 sq in

Name ____________________ Class ________ Date ____________

8.7 SURFACE AREA: RECTANGULAR PRISM AND CUBE

Surface area is the total area of the outer surface of a three-dimensional figure. To find the surface area of a cube or prism, add the areas of its six outer faces.

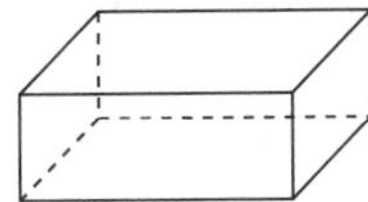

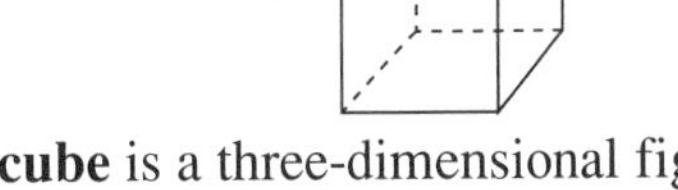

A **rectangular prism** is a three-dimensional figure with rectangles as faces.

A **cube** is a three-dimensional figure with squares as faces.

Example 1: Find the surface area of the rectangular prism.

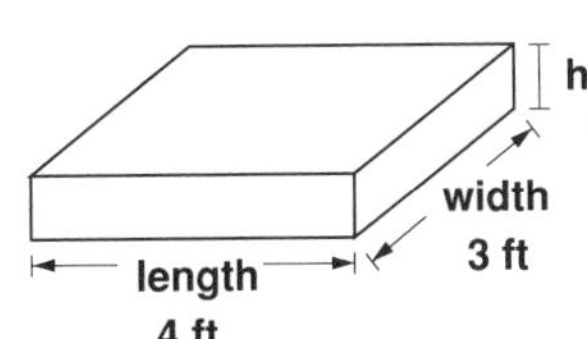

Use the formula:
$A = 2(lw) + 2(wh) + 2(lh)$
(A = surface area, l = length, w = width, h = height)

$A = 2(lw) + 2(wh) + 2(lh)$
$A = 2(4 \times 3) + 2(3 \times 1) + 2(4 \times 1)$
$A = 24 + 6 + 8$
$A = 38$

The surface area is 38 square feet, or 38 sq ft.

Example 2: Find the surface area of the cube.
Use the formula: $A = 6(s \times s)$
A = surface area, s = length of edge

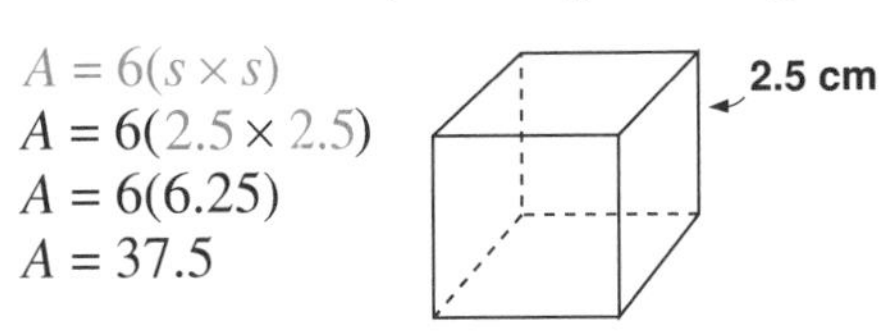

$A = 6(s \times s)$
$A = 6(2.5 \times 2.5)$
$A = 6(6.25)$
$A = 37.5$

The surface area is 37.5 square centimeters, or 37.5 sq cm.

Find the surface area of each prism.

(D) **1.** Rectangular prism

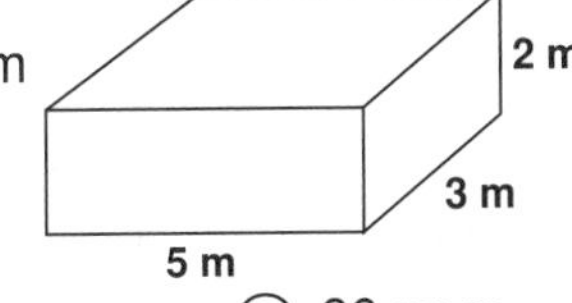

Ⓐ 30 sq m Ⓑ 36 sq m
Ⓒ 56 sq m Ⓓ 62 sq m

(B) **2.** Rectangular prism

10 yd 3 yd 3 yd

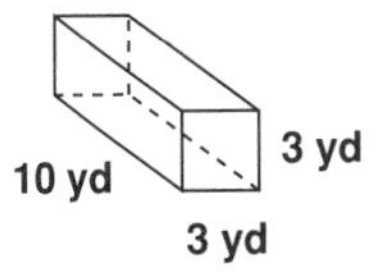

Ⓐ 276 sq yd Ⓑ 138 sq yd
Ⓒ 90 sq yd Ⓓ 48 sq yd

(C) **3.** Cube

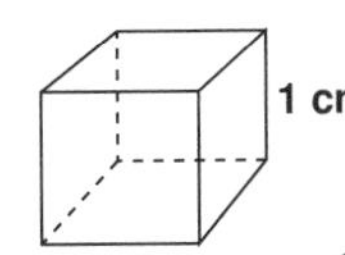

Ⓐ 1 sq cm Ⓑ 4 sq cm
Ⓒ 6 sq cm Ⓓ 8 sq cm

(D) **4.** Cube

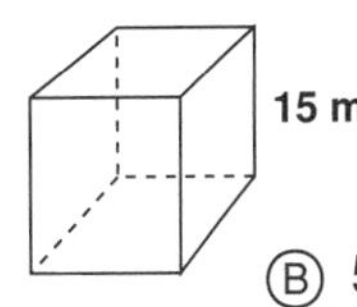

Ⓐ 90 sq mm Ⓑ 540 sq mm
Ⓒ 900 sq mm Ⓓ 1350 sq mm

(A) **5.** Rectangular prism:
$l = 30$ mm, $w = 20$ mm, $h = 100$ mm

Ⓐ 11,200 sq mm Ⓑ 10,120 sq mm
Ⓒ 2200 sq mm Ⓓ 1120 sq mm

(B) **6.** Rectangular prism: $l = 4$ ft, $w = 3$ ft, $h = \frac{1}{2}$ ft

Ⓐ 35 sq ft Ⓑ 31 sq ft
Ⓒ 22 sq ft Ⓓ 6 sq ft

(C) **7.** Cube: $s = \frac{1}{6}$ ft

Ⓐ 36 sq ft Ⓑ 6 sq ft
Ⓒ $\frac{1}{6}$ sq ft Ⓓ $\frac{1}{36}$ sq ft

(C) **8.** Rectangular prism:
$l = 3$ mm, $w = 10$ mm, $h = 1.5$ mm

Ⓐ 45 sq mm Ⓑ 97 sq mm
Ⓒ 99 sq mm Ⓓ 369 sq mm

Name_______________________________ Class __________ Date ______________

8.8 VOLUME: RECTANGULAR PRISM AND CUBE

Volume is the amount of space inside a three-dimensional figure. Volume is measured in cubic units.

Example 1: Find the volume of the rectangular prism.

- Use the formula: $V = l \times w \times h$
  V = volume, l= length, w= width, h = height

$V = l \times w \times h$

$V = 2 \times 6 \times \frac{1}{2}$

$V = 6$

6 ft

2 ft

$\frac{1}{2}$ ft

The volume of the rectangular prism is 6 cubic feet, or 6 cu ft.

Example 2: Find the volume of the cube.

- Use the formula: $V = s \times s \times s$
  (V = Volume, s = length of edge or side)

$V = s \times s \times s$

$V = 5 \times 5 \times 5$

$V = 125$

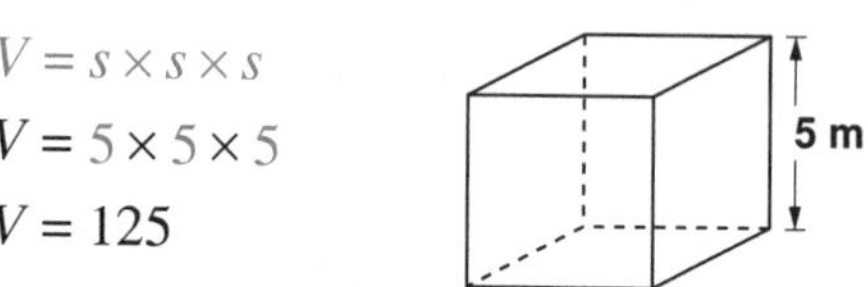

The volume of the cube is 125 cubic meters, or 125 cu m.

Find the volume of each figure.

Ⓑ **1.** Rectangular prism

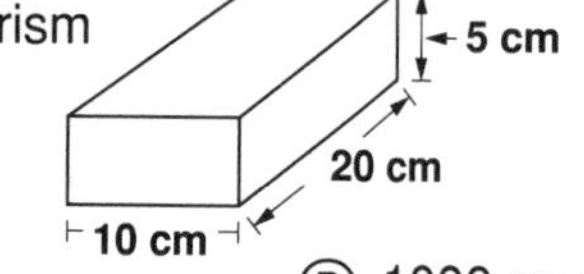

Ⓐ 100 cu cm Ⓑ 1000 cu cm
Ⓒ 10,000 cm Ⓓ 10,000 cu cm

Ⓒ **2.** Rectangular Prism

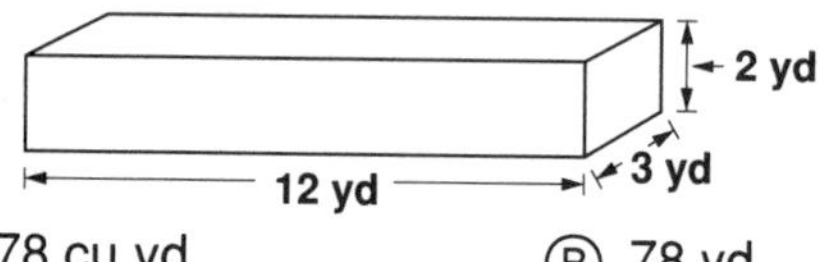

Ⓐ 78 cu yd Ⓑ 78 yd
Ⓒ 72 cu yd Ⓓ 72 yd

Ⓓ **3.** Cube

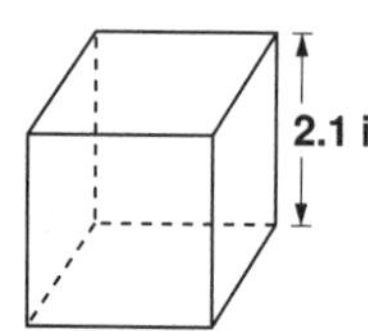

Ⓐ 6.3 cu in Ⓑ 8.1 cu in
Ⓒ 8.82 cu in Ⓓ 9.261 cu in

Ⓐ **4.** Cube

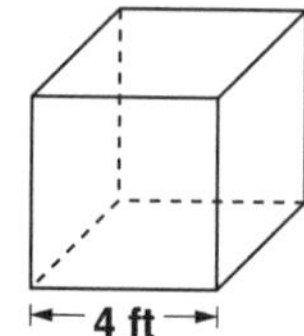

Ⓐ 64 cu ft Ⓑ 64 ft Ⓒ 12 cu ft Ⓓ 12 ft

Ⓑ **5.** Rectangular prism:
l = 14 m, w = 8 m, h = 2 m

Ⓐ 222 cu m Ⓑ 224 cu m
Ⓒ 244 cu m Ⓓ 252 cu m

Ⓓ **6.** Cube: s = 15 mm

Ⓐ 45 cu mm Ⓑ 90 cu mm
Ⓒ 225 cu mm Ⓓ 3375 cu mm

Ⓑ **7.** An aquarium is in the shape of a cube. Each side measures $2\frac{1}{2}$ ft. What is its volume?

Ⓐ $6\frac{1}{4}$ cu ft Ⓑ $15\frac{5}{8}$ cu ft
Ⓒ 25 cu ft Ⓓ 75 cu ft

Ⓒ **8.** The dimensions of a refrigerator are: length = 1 m, width = 1.5 m, height = 2 m. Find the volume.

Ⓐ 1.5 cu m Ⓑ 2 cu m
Ⓒ 3 cu m Ⓓ 12 cu m

Name ______________________ Class __________ Date __________

8.9 SURFACE AREA OF A CYLINDER

REMEMBER: **Surface area** is the total area of the outer surface of a three-dimensional figure.

A **cylinder** is a three-dimensional figure with two bases that are equal circles.

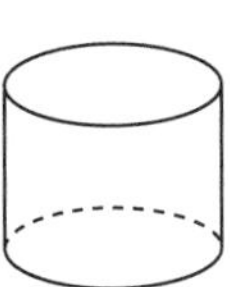

Example 1: Find the surface area of the cylinder.

- Use the formula: $A = 2\pi r^2 + 2\pi r h$ (A = surface area, r = radius, h = height)
- Use 3.14 or $\frac{22}{7}$ for π.

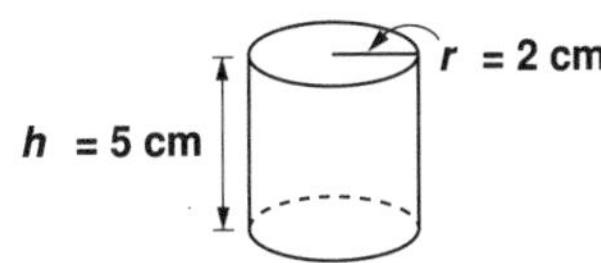

$A = 2\pi r^2 + 2\pi r h$, **or** $A = 2(\pi \times r \times r) + (2 \times \pi \times r \times h)$

$A = (2 \times 3.14 \times 2 \times 2) + (2 \times 3.14 \times 2 \times 5)$

$A = 25.12 + 62.8$

$A = 87.92$

The surface area of the cylinder is 87.92 square centimeters, or 87.92 sq cm.

Find the surface area of each cylinder.

Ⓑ **1.**

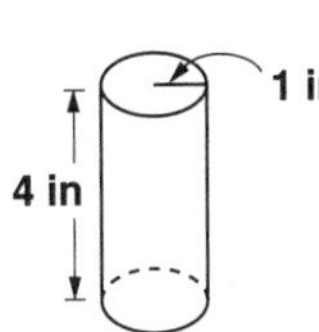

Ⓐ 36.56 sq in Ⓑ 31.4 sq in
Ⓒ 28.26 sq in Ⓓ 12.56 sq in

Ⓑ **2.**

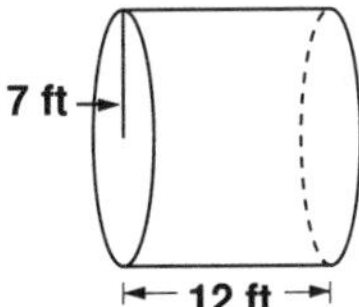

Ⓐ 5,852 sq ft Ⓑ 835.24 sq ft
Ⓒ 682 sq ft Ⓓ 572 sq ft

Ⓒ **3.**

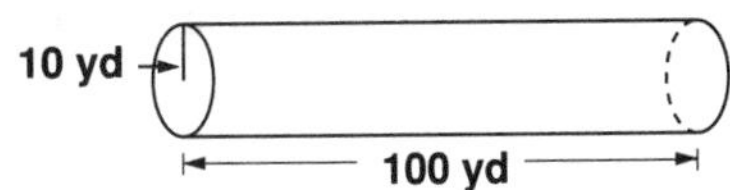

Ⓐ 69.08 sq yd Ⓑ 690.8 sq yd
Ⓒ 6908 sq yd Ⓓ 69,080 sq yd

Ⓑ **4.**

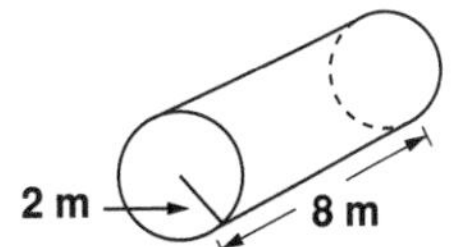

Ⓐ 502.4 sq m Ⓑ 125.6 sq m
Ⓒ 120.36 sq m Ⓓ 75.36 sq m

Ⓑ **5.** radius =14 mm, height = 7 mm

Ⓐ 2772.04 sq mm Ⓑ 1846.32 sq mm
Ⓒ 1320.30 sq mm Ⓓ 924.0 sq mm

Ⓐ **6.** radius = 5 yd, height = 6 yd

Ⓐ 345.4 sq yd Ⓑ 354.5 yd
Ⓒ 414.48 sq yd Ⓓ 441.48 sq yd

Ⓐ **7.** Eric wants to make a cardboard telescope. Each base will have a radius of 2 in. The height will be 12 in. How much cardboard is needed to make this telescope? Round your answer to the nearest square inch.

Ⓐ 176 sq in Ⓑ 163 sq in
Ⓒ 100 sq in Ⓓ 73 sq in

Ⓒ **8.** The ends of a mailing tube are plastic. The tube is cardboard. The radius of each base is 2.5 in. The height of the tube is 24 in. How much cardboard is needed to make the tube? Round your answer to the nearest square inch.

Ⓐ 188 cu in Ⓑ 338 cu in
Ⓒ 377 cu in Ⓓ 416 cu in

Name ____________________ Class ________ Date ________

8.10 VOLUME OF A CYLINDER

REMEMBER: Volume is the amount of space inside a three-dimensional figure.

Example 1: Find the volume of the cylinder.

- Use the formula: $V = \pi r^2 h$ (V = volume, h = height, r = radius)
- Use 3.14 or $\frac{22}{7}$ for π.

$V = \pi r^2 h$, or $V = \pi \times r \times r \times h$
$V = (3.14 \times 6 \times 6) \times 10$
$V = 113.04 \times 10$
$V = 1130.4$
The volume of the cylinder is 1130.4 cubic inches, or 1130.4 cu in.

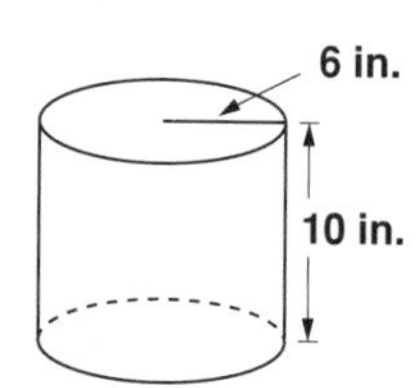

Find the volume of each cylinder.

Ⓐ **1.**

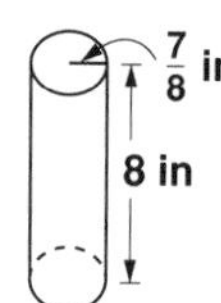

Ⓐ $19\frac{1}{4}$ cu in Ⓑ 19 cu in
Ⓒ $9\frac{5}{8}$ cu in Ⓓ 9 cu in

Ⓒ **2.**

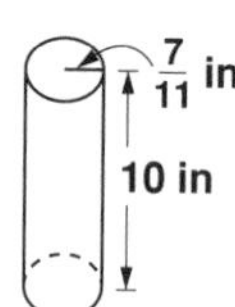

Ⓐ $1\frac{3}{11}$ cu in Ⓑ $11\frac{8}{12}$ cu in
Ⓒ $12\frac{8}{11}$ cu in Ⓓ 140 cu in

Ⓒ **3.**

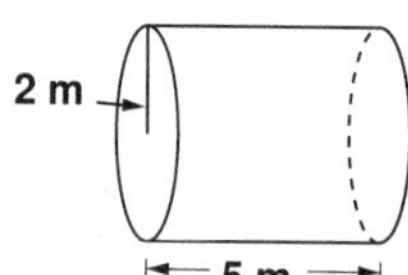

Ⓐ 0.628 cu m Ⓑ 6.28 cu m
Ⓒ 62.8 cu m Ⓓ 628 cu m

Ⓐ **4.**

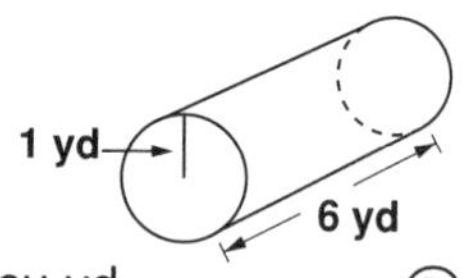

Ⓐ 18.84 cu yd Ⓑ 188.4 cu yd
Ⓒ 113.04 cu yd Ⓓ 11.304 cu yd

Ⓑ **5.**

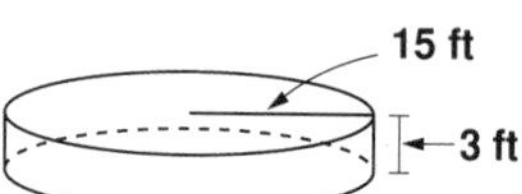

Ⓐ 4239 cu ft Ⓑ 2119.5 cu ft
Ⓒ 847.8 cu ft Ⓓ 423.9 cu ft

Ⓑ **6.**

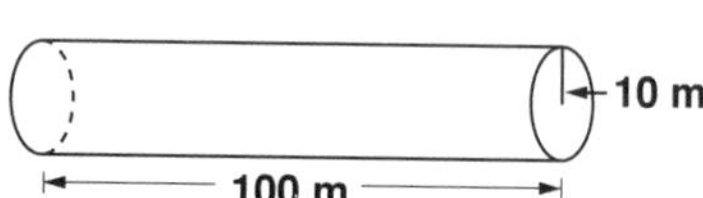

Ⓐ 314,000 cu m Ⓑ 31,400 cu m
Ⓒ 3140 sq m Ⓓ 3140 cu m

Ⓒ **7.** height = 14 in, radius = $3\frac{1}{2}$ in

Ⓐ 154 cu in Ⓑ 308 cu in
Ⓒ 538.51 cu in Ⓓ 2156 cu in

Ⓓ **8.** radius = 5 cm, height = 20.6 cm

Ⓐ 323.42 cu cm Ⓑ 515 cu cm
Ⓒ 646.84 cu cm Ⓓ 1617.1 cu cm

Ⓓ **9.** A cylinder–shaped pool has a radius of 4 ft and a depth of 3 ft. How much water can it hold?

Ⓐ 15.072 sq ft Ⓑ 15.072 cu ft
Ⓒ 150.72 sq ft Ⓓ 150.72 cu ft

Ⓒ **10.** A cylinder–shaped water tank is 10 m tall and has a radius of 4 m. What is its volume?

Ⓐ 50.24 cu m Ⓑ 125.6 cu m
Ⓒ 502.4 cu m Ⓓ 1256 cu m

Name ________________________________ Class __________ Date ______________

CHAPTER 8 TEST

Use the following formulas to help you answer the questions on this test.

Perimeter and Circumference

rectangle: $P = 2l + 2w$
circumference: $C = \pi \times d$, or $C = 2 \times \pi \times r$

Surface area

rectangular prism: $A = 2(lw) + 2(wh) + 2(lh)$
cube: $A = 6(s \times s)$
cylinder: $A = 2(\pi \times r \times r) + (2 \times \pi \times r \times h)$

Area

parallelogram: $A = b \times h$
rectangle: $A = l \times w$
square: $A = s \times s$
triangle: $A = \frac{1}{2} \times b \times h$
circle: $A = \pi \times r \times r$

Volume

rectangular prism: $V = l \times w \times h$
cube: $V = s \times s \times s$
cylinder: $V = \pi \times r \times r \times h$

$\pi = 3.14$, or $\frac{22}{7}$

Find the answer.

(B) **1.** Find the perimeter of the figure.

(A) 61 m (B) 50 m
(C) 39 m (D) 32 m

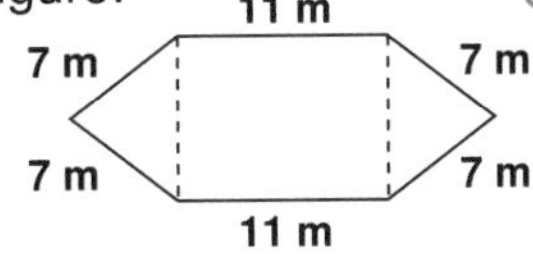

(C) **2.** Find the circumference of the circle.

(A) $\frac{7}{22}$ cm (B) $\frac{7}{11}$ cm
(C) 2 cm (D) 4 cm

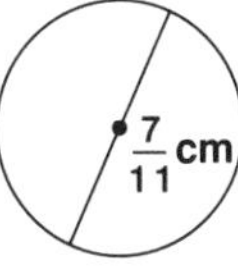

(A) **3.** Find the area of the parallelogram.

(A) 260 sq ft
(B) 130 sq ft
(C) 66 sq ft
(D) 33 sq ft

13 ft
20 ft

(B) **4.** Find the volume of the cube.

(A) 1.21 cu mm
(B) 1.331 cu mm
(C) 3.3 cu mm
(D) 6.6 cu mm

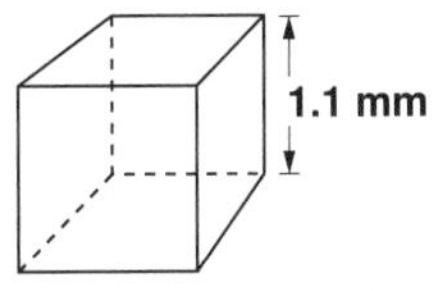

(C) **5.** Find the area of the shaded region.

(A) 2 sq cm
(B) 2.86 sq cm
(C) 5.86 sq cm
(D) 8 sq cm

1 cm
3 cm

(D) **6.** Find the surface area of the rectangular prism.

(A) 7.5 sq mm
(B) 18 sq mm
(C) 33 sq mm
(D) 38 sq mm

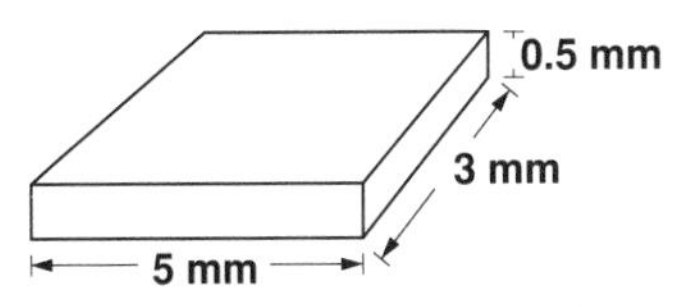

(C) **7.** Find the surface area of the cylinder.

(A) 207.24 sq in
(B) 216.667 sq in
(C) 244.92 sq in
(D) 282.6 sq in

3 in
10 in

(A) **8.** Find the area of the figure.

(A) 45 sq in
(B) 54 sq in
(C) 108 sq in
(D) 324 sq in

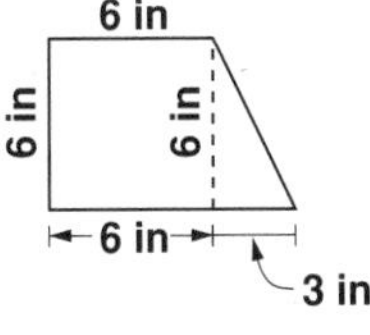

(D) **9.** Find the surface area of the rectangular prism.

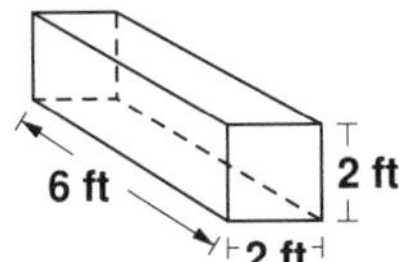

(A) 64 sq ft (B) 24 sq ft (C) 32 sq ft (D) 56 sq ft

(B) **10.** Find the volume of the cylinder.

(A) 6.2 cu m
(B) 38.936 cu m
(C) 64.856 cu m
(D) 77.872 cu m

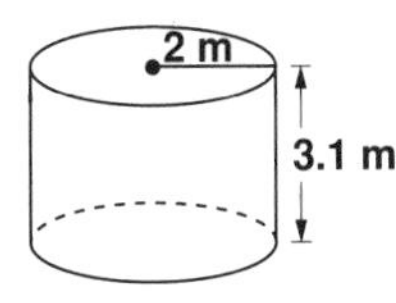

Ⓐ **11.** Find the area of a square with a side of 1.5 cm.

Ⓐ 2.25 sq cm Ⓑ 3 sq cm
Ⓒ 4 sq cm Ⓓ 6 sq cm

Ⓒ **12.** Find the circumference of the circle.

Ⓐ 314 m Ⓑ 78.5 m
Ⓒ 31.4 m Ⓓ 15.7 m

Ⓓ **13.** A triangle has a base of 0.3 cm and a height of 0.5 cm. Find its area.

Ⓐ 7.5 sq cm Ⓑ 1.5 sq cm
Ⓒ 0.15 sq cm Ⓓ 0.075 sq cm

Ⓒ **14.** A circle has a radius of 10 ft. Find its area.

Ⓐ 31.4 sq ft Ⓑ 62.8 sq ft
Ⓒ 314 sq ft Ⓓ 628 sq ft

Ⓑ **15.** Find the area of the figure.

Ⓐ 160 sq ft
Ⓑ 900 sq ft
Ⓒ 1100 sq ft
Ⓓ 1800 sq ft

Ⓑ **16.** Find the area of the circle.

Ⓐ 508.68 sq in
Ⓑ 254.34 sq in
Ⓒ 56.52 sq in
Ⓓ 28.26 sq in

Ⓓ **17.** Find the volume of the cylinder.

Ⓐ 3140 cu ft
Ⓑ 2826 cu ft
Ⓒ 2512 cu ft
Ⓓ 12,560 cu ft

Ⓒ **18.** A circular swimming pool has a radius of 7 ft and a depth of 3 ft. How many cubic feet of water will it hold? Use $\frac{22}{7}$ for π.

Ⓐ 66 cu ft Ⓑ 132 cu ft
Ⓒ 462 cu ft Ⓓ 924 cu ft

Ⓓ **19.** A bedroom wall is 9 ft high by 12 ft wide. There are two windows on the wall, each 4 ft high by $2\frac{1}{2}$ ft wide. How many square feet of wall space is there?

Ⓐ 128 sq ft Ⓑ 108 sq ft
Ⓒ 98 sq ft Ⓓ 88 sq ft

Ⓑ **20.** A rectangular prism is 11 ft long, 3 ft wide, and 3 ft high. Find its volume.

Ⓐ 150 cu ft Ⓑ 99 cu ft
Ⓒ 66 cu ft Ⓓ 17 cu ft

Ⓒ **21.** Find the perimeter of a square with sides of 5 ft.

Ⓐ 10 ft Ⓑ 15 ft
Ⓒ 20 ft Ⓓ 25 ft

Ⓒ **22.** Find the volume of a cylinder with a radius of 3 cm and a height of 20 cm.

Ⓐ 188.4 cu cm Ⓑ 376.8 cu cm
Ⓒ 565.2 cu cm Ⓓ 1130.4 cu cm

Ⓒ **23.** Find the surface area of a cylinder with a radius of 14 m and a height of 4 m. Use $\frac{22}{7}$ for π.

Ⓐ 792 sq m Ⓑ 968 sq m
Ⓒ 1584 sq m Ⓓ 2464 sq m

Ⓒ **24.** Find the area of the triangle.

Ⓐ 43 sq in
Ⓑ 86 sq in
Ⓒ 230 sq in
Ⓓ 460 sq in

Ⓐ **25.** Find the area of the shaded region.

Ⓐ 38 sq yd Ⓑ 68 sq yd
Ⓒ 30 sq yd Ⓓ 10 sq yd

Name ______________________ Class ________ Date ____________

CHAPTER 9: INTEGERS

TEST-TAKING STRATEGY: *Work from the Answers*

Remember that one of the keys to doing well on a standardized test is to use your time efficiently. Sometimes it is faster to work from the answers instead of working the problem. This strategy is very efficient when some answer choices can be eliminated quickly.

It's good to work from the answers when:

1. The numbers are large and using the answers makes estimating easier.
2. You don't know what to do or how to approach the problem directly.
3. The question involves variables.

Example 1: Divide: $628\overline{)25{,}438}$

Ⓐ 4 R318 Ⓑ 40 R318
Ⓒ 50 R318 Ⓓ 400 R318

When working from the answers, always start with an answer that falls near the middle.

Let's begin with choice Ⓒ:
$628 \times 50 = 31{,}400$

Before adding the remainder we see that the product is greater than the dividend: $31{,}400 > 25{,}438$. Therefore, we can eliminate choice Ⓒ.

We can also eliminate choice Ⓓ since $400 > 50$.

Try choice Ⓑ: $628 \times 40 = 25{,}120 + 318 = 25{,}438$

The correct answer is choice Ⓑ.

Example 2: 100 is 40% of what number?

Ⓐ 125 Ⓑ 200
Ⓒ 250 Ⓓ 500

Let's begin with choice Ⓑ because $125 < 200 < 500$.
Find 40% of 200: $0.40 \times 200 = 80$

$80 < 100$, so the correct choice must be greater than 200.

Let's try choice Ⓒ: 250

Find 40% of 250: $0.40 \times 250 = 100$

The correct answer is choice Ⓒ.

Example 3: $\frac{n}{12.5} = \frac{4}{10}$

Ⓐ 4 Ⓑ 4.5
Ⓒ 5 Ⓓ 6

Let's try choice Ⓑ: $\frac{4.5}{12.5} \stackrel{?}{=} \frac{4}{10}$

$4.5 \times 10 \stackrel{?}{=} 12.5 \times 4$

$45 \neq 50$

Choice Ⓑ is incorrect.

Let's try choice Ⓒ: $\frac{5}{12.5} \stackrel{?}{=} \frac{4}{10}$

$5 \times 10 \stackrel{?}{=} 12.5 \times 4$

$50 = 50$

The correct answer is choice Ⓒ.

Example 4: $3x + 17 = 53$

Ⓐ 6 Ⓑ 8 Ⓒ 10 Ⓓ 12

Let's try choice Ⓒ: $3 \times 10 + 17 \stackrel{?}{=} 53$

$30 + 17 \stackrel{?}{=} 53$

$47 \neq 53$

Choice Ⓒ is incorrect. Since $47 < 53$, the answer must be greater than 10.

The only choice greater than 10 is choice Ⓓ.

Let's check choice Ⓓ to be sure:

$3 \times 12 + 17 \stackrel{?}{=} 53$

$36 + 17 \stackrel{?}{=} 53$

$53 = 53$

The correct answer is choice Ⓓ.

Work from the answers to find the correct answer. Remember to begin with an answer choice in the middle.

(A) **1.** $18\overline{)2{,}459}$ = ■

Ⓐ 136 R11 Ⓑ 1,360 R11 Ⓒ 1,460 R11 Ⓓ 13,060 R11

(A) **2.** 564 × ■ = 46,812

Ⓐ 83 Ⓑ 100 Ⓒ 46,248 Ⓓ 26,401,968

(B) **3.** 35% of what number is 24.5?

Ⓐ 50 Ⓑ 70 Ⓒ 100 Ⓓ 200

(C) **4.** Find n: $\frac{2}{n} = \frac{6}{18}$

Ⓐ 3 Ⓑ 4 Ⓒ 6 Ⓓ 8

(A) **5.** Find n: $5n - 1 = 59$

Ⓐ 12 Ⓑ 10 Ⓒ 8 Ⓓ 6

(C) **6.** Find n: $\frac{2n}{17} = 4$

Ⓐ 24 Ⓑ 30 Ⓒ 34 Ⓓ 40

(D) **7.** 17.9 – 3.512 = ■

Ⓐ 200.41 Ⓑ 140.364 Ⓒ 20.412 Ⓓ 14.388

(B) **8.** 224 – 3.415 = ■

Ⓐ 20.585 Ⓑ 220.585 Ⓒ 221.695 Ⓓ 227.415

(C) **9.** $0.002\overline{)0.0018}$ = ■

Ⓐ 0.009 Ⓑ 0.09 Ⓒ 0.9 Ⓓ 9

(B) **10.** Find ■ : $\frac{3}{5} = \frac{■}{10}$

Ⓐ 1 Ⓑ 6 Ⓒ 10 Ⓓ 12

(B) **11.** Find n: $\frac{n}{8.4} = \frac{5}{10}$

Ⓐ 0.42 Ⓑ 4.2 Ⓒ 16.8 Ⓓ 42

(B) **12.** Find n: $\frac{8}{24} = \frac{n}{36}$

Ⓐ 4 Ⓑ 12 Ⓒ 32 Ⓓ 768

(A) **13.** Find x: $2x - 12 = 600$

Ⓐ 306 Ⓑ 312 Ⓒ 606 Ⓓ 612

(D) **14.** 10 is what percent of 400?

Ⓐ 40% Ⓑ 20.5% Ⓒ 4% Ⓓ 2.5%

(D) **15.** The triangles are similar. What is the length of $\overline{SU}$?

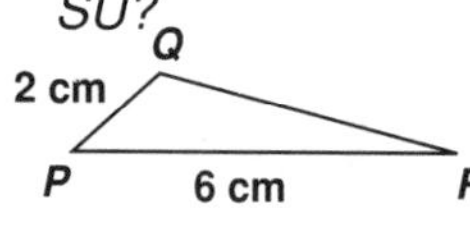

T
5 cm
S
n
U

Ⓐ $\frac{2}{3}$ Ⓑ $2\frac{2}{5}$ Ⓒ 10 cm Ⓓ 15 cm

(B) **16.** Albert has $35.00. He buys as many tickets as he can. Each ticket costs $8.25. How many tickets does he buy?

Ⓐ 3 Ⓑ 4 Ⓒ 5 Ⓓ 6

(C) **17.** $\sqrt{324}$ = ■

Ⓐ 162 Ⓑ 22 Ⓒ 18 Ⓓ 15

(D) **18.** $\sqrt{2025}$ = ■

Ⓐ 20 Ⓑ 30 Ⓒ 40 Ⓓ 45

(D) **19.** $x - 124 = 90$

Ⓐ 34 Ⓑ 114 Ⓒ 204 Ⓓ 214

(B) **20.** 21 added to what number is 184?

Ⓐ 143 Ⓑ 163 Ⓒ 105 Ⓓ 205

Name ______________________ Class __________ Date __________

CHAPTER 9 PRETEST

Fill in the correct circle to answer each question.

Use the number line below to answer questions 1-2.

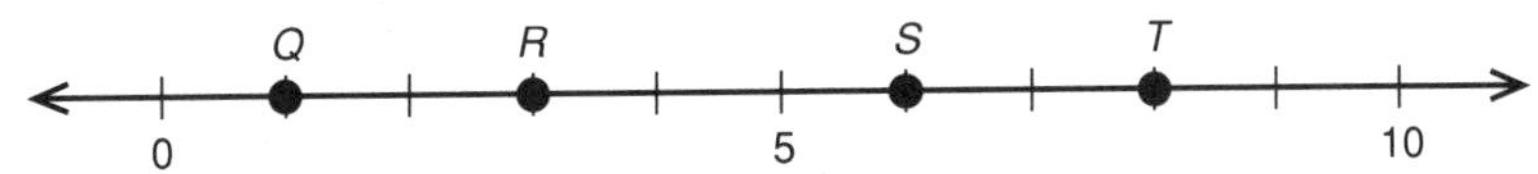

Ⓒ **1.** What letter names the point 6?

Ⓐ *Q* Ⓑ *R* Ⓒ *S* Ⓓ *T*

Ⓓ **2.** What letter names the point 8?

Ⓐ *Q* Ⓑ *R* Ⓒ *S* Ⓓ *T*

Ⓑ **3.** Choose the letter that makes the statement true.

15 ▒ 0

Ⓐ < Ⓑ > Ⓒ =

Ⓐ **4.** Which number has the *least* value?

Ⓐ 11.2 Ⓑ 18.02 Ⓒ 18.2 Ⓓ 12.85

Ⓑ **5.** Choose the list of numbers ordered from *least to greatest.*

Ⓐ 4, 0, 15, 39 Ⓑ 0, 4, 15, 39

Ⓒ 15, 39, 4, 0 Ⓓ 39, 15, 4, 0

Ⓓ **6.** Which set of numbers shows its elements ordered from *greatest to least?*

Ⓐ 0.08, 0.8, 8.08, 10.8 Ⓑ 10.8, 8.08, 0.08, 0.8

Ⓒ 8.08, 0.8, 10.8, 0.08 Ⓓ 10.8, 8.08, 0.8, 0.08

Ⓒ **7.** Add: 42 + 15 + 10

Ⓐ 23 Ⓑ 57 Ⓒ 67 Ⓓ 78

Ⓒ **8.** Find the answer: (31 – 12) + 14

Ⓐ 5 Ⓑ 23 Ⓒ 33 Ⓓ 57

Ⓐ **9.** Subtract: 82 – 14

Ⓐ 68 Ⓑ 74 Ⓒ 78 Ⓓ 96

Ⓒ **10.** Find the answer: (12 + 28) – 6

Ⓐ 10 Ⓑ 24 Ⓒ 34 Ⓓ 46

Ⓒ **11.** Multiply: 14 × 8

Ⓐ 82 Ⓑ 96 Ⓒ 112 Ⓓ 252

Ⓒ **12.** Multiply: 8 × 5 × 4

Ⓐ 44 Ⓑ 150 Ⓒ 160 Ⓓ 1600

Ⓒ **13.** Divide: 3600 ÷ 60

Ⓐ 6 Ⓑ 30 Ⓒ 60 Ⓓ 600

Ⓑ **14.** Find the answer: (64 ÷ 8) × 4

Ⓐ 2 Ⓑ 32 Ⓒ 64 Ⓓ 288

Use the map at the right to answer questions 15-16.

Ⓑ **15.** What landmark is 1 block right and 1 block up from the Meat Market?

Ⓐ Depot Ⓑ Shoe Factory

Ⓒ School Ⓓ Clothes Outlet

Ⓐ **16.** What landmark is 1 block left and 3 blocks up from the Diner?

Ⓐ Depot Ⓑ Shoe Factory

Ⓒ Clothes Outlet Ⓓ Bank

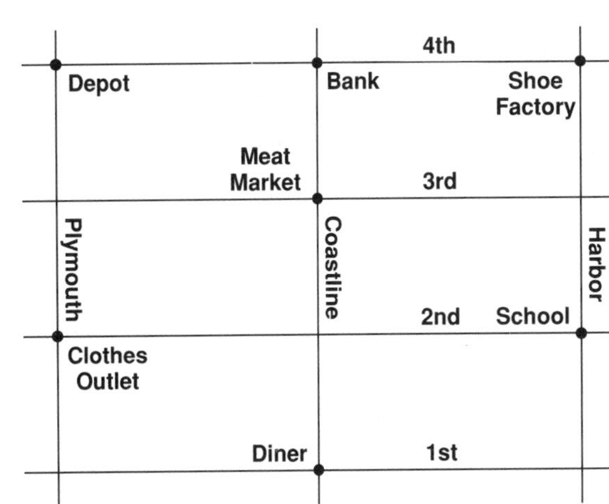

Use the number line below to answer questions 17-18.

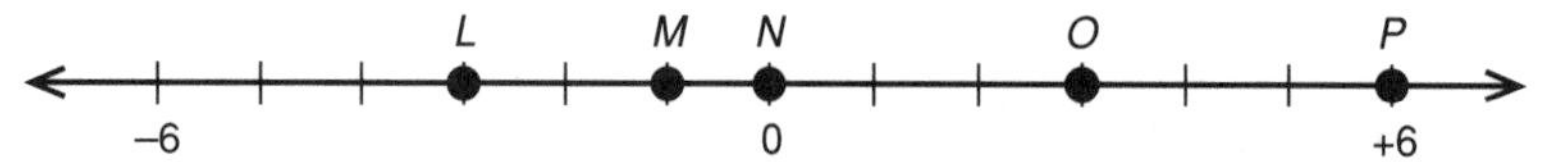

Ⓑ **17.** What letter names the point –1?

Ⓐ *L* Ⓑ *M* Ⓒ *N* Ⓓ *O*

Ⓒ **18.** What number corresponds to the point *N?*

Ⓐ –4 Ⓑ –1 Ⓒ 0 Ⓓ +1

Fill in the correct circle to answer each question.

Ⓑ **19.** Name the opposite of +18.

Ⓐ –81 Ⓑ –18 Ⓒ +18 Ⓓ +81

Ⓓ **20.** Name the opposite of –70.

Ⓐ –70 Ⓑ –7 Ⓒ +7 Ⓓ +70

Ⓑ **21.** +2 ■ –2

Ⓐ < Ⓑ > Ⓒ =

Ⓑ **22.** –5 ■ –7

Ⓐ < Ⓑ > Ⓒ =

Ⓐ **23.** Choose the list of numbers ordered from *least to greatest.*

Ⓐ –10, –4, 0, +2 Ⓑ –4, –10, 0, +2

Ⓒ +2, –4, 0, –10 Ⓓ +2, 0, –4, –10

Ⓒ **24.** Which set of integers shows its elements ordered from *greatest to least?*

Ⓐ –18, –16, –1, +10 Ⓑ –1, –16, –18, +10

Ⓒ +10, –1, –16, –18 Ⓓ +10, –18, –16, –1

Ⓒ **25.** Add: 28 + –12

Ⓐ –40 Ⓑ –16 Ⓒ +16 Ⓓ +40

Ⓒ **26.** Subtract: –14 – –22

Ⓐ –36 Ⓑ –8 Ⓒ +8 Ⓓ +36

Ⓓ **27.** Find the answer: 22 + (–5) – (–8)

Ⓐ –25 Ⓑ +9 Ⓒ +19 Ⓓ +25

Ⓐ **28.** Multiply: –12 × –9

Ⓐ +108 Ⓑ +21 Ⓒ –21 Ⓓ –108

Ⓑ **29.** Divide: 200 ÷ –8

Ⓐ –192 Ⓑ –25 Ⓒ +25 Ⓓ +192

Ⓐ **30.** Find the answer: (–64 ÷ 4) × 2

Ⓐ –32 Ⓑ –8 Ⓒ +8 Ⓓ +32

Use the graph to answer the following questions.

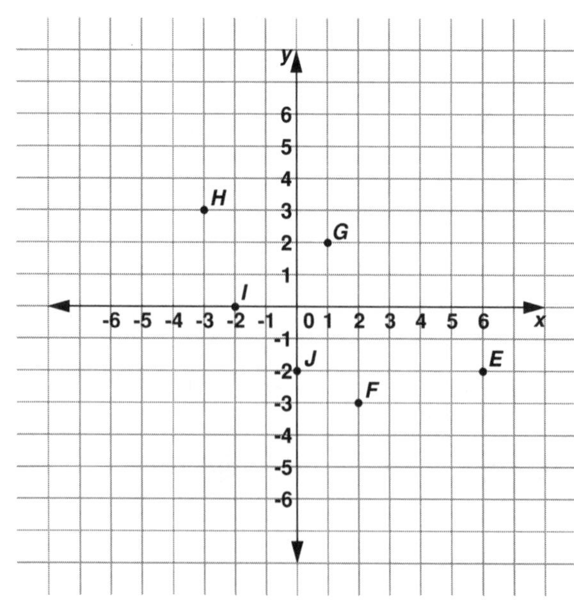

Ⓑ **31.** What are the coordinates of Point *F?*

Ⓐ (–2, –3) Ⓑ (+2, –3)

Ⓒ (–3, +2) Ⓓ (+3, –2)

Ⓑ **32.** Which point has coordinates (–2, 0)?

Ⓐ *G* Ⓑ *I* Ⓒ *F* Ⓓ *J*

Ⓐ **33.** What are the coordinates of Point *E?*

Ⓐ (+6, –2) Ⓑ (–2, +6)

Ⓒ (–6, –2) Ⓓ (–2, –6)

Name ____________ Class ________ Date ________

9.1 INTEGERS

Every positive whole number has an opposite, called a negative number. Positive numbers, negative numbers, and zero make up the set of numbers called **integers**. Integers can be shown on a number line.

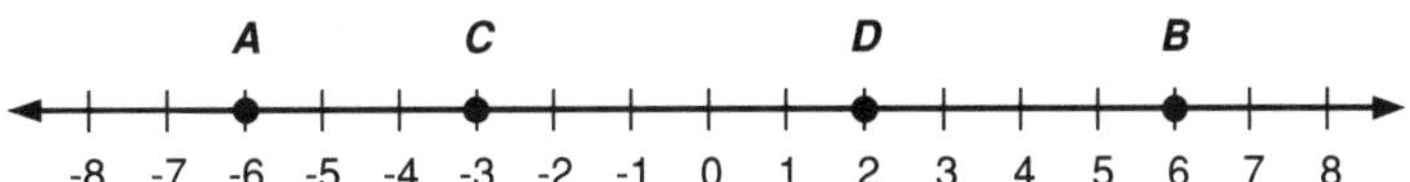

Example 1: Name the opposite of +7.

- +7 is 7 units to the right of 0 on a number line.
- Find the integer that is 7 units to the left of 0.
- –7 is the opposite of +7.

Example 2: A. What letter names the point –3?

- –3 is 3 units to the left of 0.
- Find the letter that names this point.
- *C* names the point –3.

B. What number corresponds to point *B*?

- Find letter *B*.
- Find the number below B.
- The integer 6 corresponds to point *B*.

Example 3: Charles spent \$50 from his savings. Write the integer that describes this amount.

- Charles's savings have decreased by \$50.
- Write –50 to show this amount.

Use the number line below to answer the following questions.

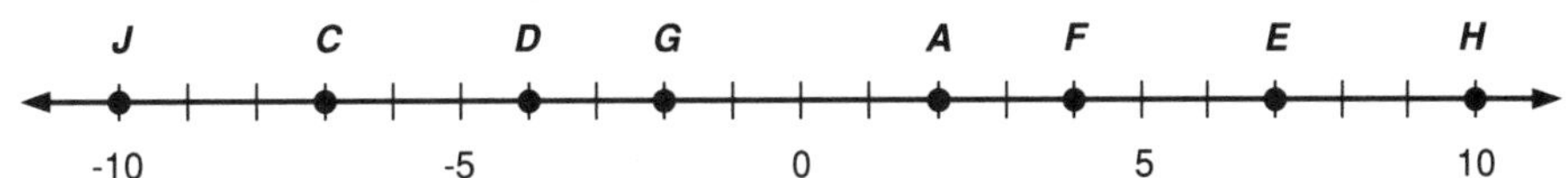

Ⓓ **1.** What letter names the point –2?

Ⓐ A Ⓑ C Ⓒ E Ⓓ G

Ⓒ **2.** What letter names the point +7?

Ⓐ A Ⓑ C Ⓒ E Ⓓ G

Ⓒ **3.** What number corresponds to point *E?*

Ⓐ –8 Ⓑ –7 Ⓒ 7 Ⓓ 8

Ⓑ **4.** What number corresponds to point *D?*

Ⓐ –6 Ⓑ –4 Ⓒ 4 Ⓓ 6

Write the integer that best describes each situation.

Ⓐ **5.** winning by 6 points

Ⓐ +6 Ⓑ +4 Ⓒ –4 Ⓓ –6

Ⓓ **6.** 15 degrees below zero

Ⓐ +15 Ⓑ 0 Ⓒ –6 Ⓓ –15

Ⓒ **7.** a bonus of \$25

Ⓐ –25 Ⓑ +7 Ⓒ +25 Ⓓ +52

Ⓐ **8.** a loss of 12 pounds

Ⓐ –12 Ⓑ –3 Ⓒ –1 Ⓓ +12

Name the opposite of each number.

Ⓑ **9.** –26

Ⓐ +62 Ⓑ +26 Ⓒ –8 Ⓓ –62

Ⓒ **10.** +14

Ⓐ +41 Ⓑ –5 Ⓒ –14 Ⓓ –41

Name________________________________ Class __________ Date ______________

9.2 COMPARING AND ORDERING INTEGERS

A number line shows the order of integers. As you move to the right, the integers increase in value. As you move to the left, the integers decrease in value.

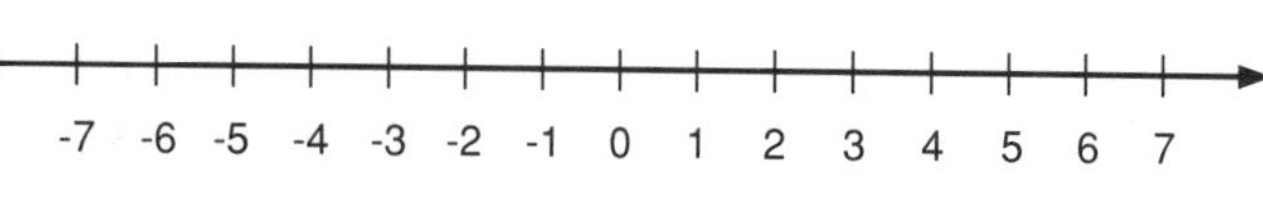

Example 1: Compare the following integers using < or >.

−3 ■ +1
- −3 is to the left of +1, therefore −3 < +1.

Write: −3 < +1

−2 ■ −6
- −2 is to the right of −6, therefore −2 > −6.

Write: −2 > −6

Example 2: Order the following integers from *least to greatest:* −5, 3, 2, −2

- Draw a number line to help you, if needed.
- Then read from left to right to order the integers from *least to greatest:* −5, −2, 2, 3.

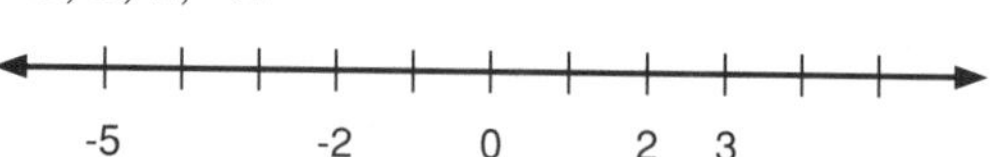

REMEMBER: **Ascending order** means *least to greatest.* **Descending order** means *greatest to least.*

Choose the letter that makes the statement true.

Ⓑ **1.** +5 ■ −7
Ⓐ < Ⓑ > Ⓒ =

Ⓐ **2.** −3 ■ −8
Ⓐ > Ⓑ < Ⓒ =

Ⓑ **3.** −10 ■ +2
Ⓐ = Ⓑ < Ⓒ >

Ⓐ **4.** +5 ■ +18
Ⓐ < Ⓑ = Ⓒ >

Choose the list of numbers ordered from *least to greatest.* Draw a number line to help you, if needed.

Ⓒ **5.** Ⓐ +1, −4, −6, +8 Ⓑ −4, −6, +1, +8
Ⓒ −6, −4, +1, +8 Ⓓ +8, +1, −4, −6

Ⓓ **6.** Ⓐ 15, 7, −1, −14 Ⓑ 15, −14, 7, −1
Ⓒ −1, −14, 7, 15 Ⓓ −14, −1, 7, 15

Which set of integers shows its elements in *descending order?*

Ⓓ **7.** Ⓐ {−3, +9, +4, −12} Ⓑ {−12, +9, +4, −3}
Ⓒ {−12, −3, +4, +9} Ⓓ {9, 4, −3, −12}

Ⓑ **8.** Ⓐ {−25, +1, −32, −19 Ⓑ {+1, −19, −25, −32}
Ⓒ {−32, −25, −19, +1} Ⓓ {−25, −19, +1, −32}

Which integer has the *least* value?

Ⓐ **9.** Ⓐ −12 Ⓑ +4 Ⓒ +11 Ⓓ −3

Ⓓ **10.** Ⓐ −3 Ⓑ +1 Ⓒ +51 Ⓓ −25

Which integer has the *greatest* value?

Ⓐ **11.** Ⓐ 5 Ⓑ −7 Ⓒ −12 Ⓓ −19

Ⓑ **12.** Ⓐ −8 Ⓑ 17 Ⓒ 0 Ⓓ −23

Name ______________________ Class __________ Date __________

9.3 ADDING INTEGERS

Example 1: Add: +2 + 6

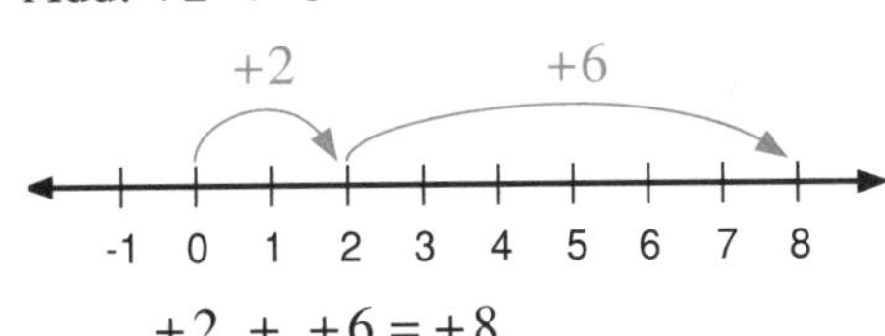

+2 + +6 = +8

Add: –4 + –3

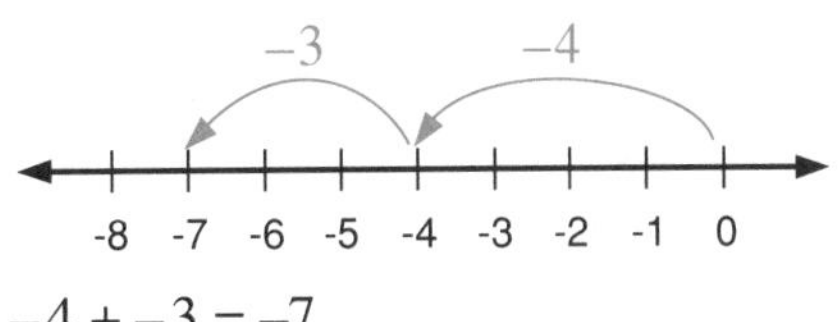

–4 + –3 = –7

Example 2: Use the number line to add –9 and +2.

- Start at 0.
- Move 9 units to the left.
- Move 2 units to the right.

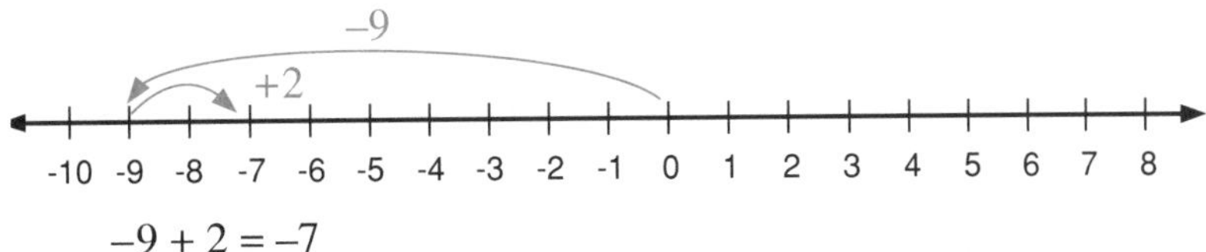

–9 + 2 = –7

The next example shows you how to add a positive integer and a negative integer without using a number line.

Example 3: Add: –6 + 13

- Treat both numbers as if they were positive: 6, 13
- Subtract the smaller number from the larger number: 13 – 6 = 7
- Use the original sign of the larger number for your answer: +

–6 + 13 = +7

REMEMBER: When adding integers with the same sign:

- the sum of the two positive integers is *always* positive.
- the sum of two negative integers is *always* negative.

Add. Draw a number line, if it is helpful to you.

Ⓑ **1.** 2 + –8

Ⓐ –10 Ⓑ –6 Ⓒ +6 Ⓓ +10

Ⓐ **2.** –4 + –5

Ⓐ –9 Ⓑ –1 Ⓒ +1 Ⓓ +9

Ⓐ **3.** –7 + –5

Ⓐ –12 Ⓑ –2 Ⓒ +2 Ⓓ +12

Ⓑ **4.** –14 + 9

Ⓐ –23 Ⓑ –5 Ⓒ +5 Ⓓ +23

Ⓑ **5.** 8 + –6

Ⓐ +14 Ⓑ +2 Ⓒ –2 Ⓓ –14

Ⓒ **6.** –2 + 11

Ⓐ –13 Ⓑ –9 Ⓒ +9 Ⓓ +13

Ⓑ **7.** –4 + (–3) + 6

Ⓐ –13 Ⓑ –1 Ⓒ +5 Ⓓ +7

Ⓒ **8.** 8 + (–2) + 7

Ⓐ +1 Ⓑ +3 Ⓒ +13 Ⓓ +17

Ⓒ **9.** 10 + 4 + (–6)

Ⓐ –20 Ⓑ –8 Ⓒ +8 Ⓓ +20

Ⓑ **10.** –11 + 16 + (–20)

Ⓐ –7 Ⓑ –15 Ⓒ –25 Ⓓ –47

Ⓓ **11.** 17 + 14

Ⓐ –31 Ⓑ –3 Ⓒ +3 Ⓓ +31

Ⓑ **12.** –25 + 16

Ⓐ –41 Ⓑ –9 Ⓒ +9 Ⓓ +41

Ⓐ **13.** –43 + –9

Ⓐ –52 Ⓑ –34 Ⓒ +34 Ⓓ +52

Ⓒ **14.** 21 + (–4) + 7

Ⓐ +10 Ⓑ +18 Ⓒ +24 Ⓓ +32

Ⓑ **15.** 34 + –14

Ⓐ +48 Ⓑ +20 Ⓒ –20 Ⓓ –48

Ⓐ **16.** 7 + 26

Ⓐ +33 Ⓑ +19 Ⓒ –19 Ⓓ –33

Ⓓ **17.** –11 + 4 + (–6)

Ⓐ +1 Ⓑ –1 Ⓒ –9 Ⓓ –13

Ⓐ **18.** –22 + –14

Ⓐ –36 Ⓑ –8 Ⓒ +8 Ⓓ +36

Ⓒ **19.** 45 + –43

Ⓐ –88 Ⓑ –2 Ⓒ +2 Ⓓ +88

Ⓓ **20.** –12 + (–4) + (–9)

Ⓐ –1 Ⓑ –7 Ⓒ –17 Ⓓ –25

Ⓑ **21.** –63 + 14

Ⓐ –77 Ⓑ –49 Ⓒ +49 Ⓓ +77

Ⓑ **22.** 75 + (–18) + (–4)

Ⓐ +61 Ⓑ +53 Ⓒ –53 Ⓓ –61

Ⓐ **23.** –68 + –23

Ⓐ –91 Ⓑ –45 Ⓒ +45 Ⓓ +91

Ⓑ **24.** –36 + (–17) + 8

Ⓐ –61 Ⓑ –45 Ⓒ –27 Ⓓ +45

Ⓒ **25.** (–6) + (–19) + +25

Ⓐ +50 Ⓑ +25 Ⓒ 0 Ⓓ –50

Ⓑ **26.** +15 + (–28) + 3

Ⓐ –46 Ⓑ –10 Ⓒ +10 Ⓓ +46

Ⓐ **27.** 42 + (–8) + (–50)

Ⓐ –16 Ⓑ –8 Ⓒ +16 Ⓓ +100

Ⓓ **28.** (–65) + 37 + (–42)

Ⓐ +70 Ⓑ +14 Ⓒ –14 Ⓓ –70

Solve.

Ⓒ **29.** The Wildcat Football Team was at the 10-yard line. In the next four plays, they lost 4 yards, lost 12 yards, gained 24 yards, and lost 3 yards. At what yard line did the team end up after the four plays?

Ⓐ –18 Ⓑ –15 Ⓒ 15 Ⓓ 27

30. Ⓑ Barry had $345 in his checking account. He wrote a check for $382 to pay for his rent. How much money does he need to deposit into his checking account to cover his rent check?

Ⓐ –$37 Ⓑ $37 Ⓒ $345 Ⓓ 382

Ⓒ **31.** The temperature at 5:00 A.M. one winter morning was –15° F. By 2:00 P.M., the temperature had risen 19 degrees. What was the temperature at 2:00 P.M.?

Ⓐ –34° Ⓑ –4° Ⓒ 4° Ⓓ 34°

32. Ⓑ At the end of the first round of a quiz show, Cheryl's score was –250. During the second round, she scored 475 points. What was her score after the second round?

Ⓐ 475 Ⓑ 225 Ⓒ –225 Ⓓ –725

Name _______________ Class _______ Date _______

9.4 SUBTRACTING INTEGERS

To subtract an integer, add its opposite.

Example 1: Subtract: 4 – 10
4 – +10 = 4 + –10 = –6

Example 2: Subtract: 10 – –4
10 – –4 = 10 + +4 = 14

Example 3: Subtract: –10 – 4
–10 – +4 = –10 + –4 = –14

Example 4: Subtract: –10 – –4
–10 – –4 = –10 + +4 = –6

Subtract.

Ⓒ **1.** 4 – 8
Ⓐ +12 Ⓑ +4 Ⓒ –4 Ⓓ –12

Ⓒ **2.** 10 – 3
Ⓐ –13 Ⓑ –7 Ⓒ +7 Ⓓ +13

Ⓒ **3.** –5 – –2
Ⓐ +7 Ⓑ +3 Ⓒ –3 Ⓓ –7

Ⓑ **4.** –8 – –1
Ⓐ –9 Ⓑ –7 Ⓒ +7 Ⓓ +9

Ⓑ **5.** 13 – 9
Ⓐ +22 Ⓑ +4 Ⓒ –4 Ⓓ –22

Ⓑ **6.** –25 – –11
Ⓐ –36 Ⓑ –14 Ⓒ +14 Ⓓ +36

Ⓐ **7.** 12 – –17
Ⓐ +29 Ⓑ +5 Ⓒ –5 Ⓓ –29

Ⓓ **8.** –36 – 14
Ⓐ +50 Ⓑ +22 Ⓒ –22 Ⓓ –50

Ⓓ **9.** 27 – (–8) – 14
Ⓐ –21 Ⓑ –5 Ⓒ +5 Ⓓ +21

Ⓑ **10.** –18 – 6 – –22
Ⓐ –34 Ⓑ –2 Ⓒ +2 Ⓓ +10

Ⓑ **11.** –26 – –42
Ⓐ +68 Ⓑ +16 Ⓒ –16 Ⓓ –68

Ⓑ **12.** 74 – 28
Ⓐ +102 Ⓑ +46 Ⓒ –46 Ⓓ –102

Ⓐ **13.** –54 – 16
Ⓐ –70 Ⓑ –38 Ⓒ +38 Ⓓ +70

Ⓑ **14.** –27 – (–7) – 4
Ⓐ –38 Ⓑ –24 Ⓒ –16 Ⓓ +24

Ⓓ **15.** 84 – –25
Ⓐ –109 Ⓑ –59 Ⓒ +59 Ⓓ +109

Ⓐ **16.** 65 – 14 – (–10)
Ⓐ +61 Ⓑ +41 Ⓒ –41 Ⓓ –61

Ⓐ **17.** –17 – 43
Ⓐ –60 Ⓑ –26 Ⓒ +26 Ⓓ +60

Ⓑ **18.** –77 – –45
Ⓐ –122 Ⓑ –32 Ⓒ +32 Ⓓ +122

Ⓓ **19.** –14 – 40 – (–2)
Ⓐ +52 Ⓑ +24 Ⓒ –24 Ⓓ –52

Ⓓ **20.** 82 – (–12) – 14
Ⓐ –80 Ⓑ –56 Ⓒ +56 Ⓓ +80

Ⓐ **21.** –50 – 10 – 30
Ⓐ –90 Ⓑ –10 Ⓒ +10 Ⓓ +90

Ⓑ **22.** 96 – 125
Ⓐ –221 Ⓑ –29 Ⓒ +29 Ⓓ +221

Ⓒ **23.** –92 – –100

Ⓐ –192 Ⓑ –8 Ⓒ +8 Ⓓ +192

Ⓓ **24.** 18 – (–40) – –50

Ⓐ –108 Ⓑ –38 Ⓒ +38 Ⓓ +108

Find the answer. Work from left to right. Watch the signs carefully.

Ⓐ **25.** (–8) – 6 + (–4)

Ⓐ –18 Ⓑ –10 Ⓒ –6 Ⓓ –2

Ⓓ **26.** 16 – 7 + (–5)

Ⓐ 28 Ⓑ 18 Ⓒ 14 Ⓓ 4

Ⓐ **27.** (–40) – 6 + (–10)

Ⓐ –56 Ⓑ –44 Ⓒ –36 Ⓓ 44

Ⓒ **28.** 25 + (–8) – (–14)

Ⓐ 3 Ⓑ 19 Ⓒ 31 Ⓓ 47

Ⓑ **29.** 16 – 20 + (–5)

Ⓐ –41 Ⓑ –9 Ⓒ –1 Ⓓ 9

Ⓐ **30.** (–12) –18 + (–14)

Ⓐ –44 Ⓑ –20 Ⓒ –8 Ⓓ 8

Ⓑ **31.** (–4) – (–12) + (–30)

Ⓐ –14 Ⓑ –22 Ⓒ –38 Ⓓ –46

Ⓒ **32.** 35 – 50 + (–85)

Ⓐ 0 Ⓑ –70 Ⓒ –100 Ⓓ –170

Use Table 9.4 below to answer questions 33-38.

Table 9.4

Lowest Recorded Temperatures

Continent	Date	Degrees Fahrenheit
Africa	Feb. 11, 1935	–11
Antarctica	July 21, 1983	–129
Asia	Feb. 6, 1983	–90
Australia	July 22, 1947	–8
Europe	Not available	–67
North America	Feb. 3, 1947	–81
South America	Jan. 1, 1907	–27

Ⓓ **33.** Which continent had the lowest recorded temperature?

Ⓐ North America Ⓑ Asia

Ⓒ Africa Ⓓ Antarctica

Ⓐ **34.** Which two continents recorded their lowest temperatures in 1947?

Ⓐ Australia and North America

Ⓑ Africa and Australia

Ⓒ North America and Antarctica

Ⓓ Antarctica and Europe

Ⓐ **35.** What is the difference between the lowest temperature in Asia and that of South America?

Ⓐ –63° Ⓑ –9° Ⓒ 9° Ⓓ 63°

Ⓑ **36.** How many degrees colder was the coldest day in North America than the coldest day in Australia?

Ⓐ –89° Ⓑ –73° Ⓒ 73° Ⓓ 89°

Ⓒ **37.** How many degrees colder was the coldest day in Europe than the coldest day in Australia?

Ⓐ 75° Ⓑ 59° Ⓒ –59° Ⓓ –75°

Ⓑ **38.** What is the difference between the lowest recorded temperature in Antarctica and that of Africa?

Ⓐ –140° Ⓑ –118° Ⓒ 118° Ⓓ 140°

Name ______________________________ Class __________ Date ______________

9.5 MULTIPLYING INTEGERS

REMEMBER: The product of two integers with the *same sign* is *positive*.
The product of two integers with *unlike signs* is *negative*.
In all other ways, multiplying integers is like multiplying whole numbers.

Example 1: Multiply: -4×-3

- The two integers have the same sign.
- The product is positive.

$-4 \times -3 = +12$

Example 2: Multiply: -5×6

- The two integers have unlike signs.
- The product is negative.

$-5 \times 6 = -30$

When multiplying three or more integers, the product is:

- positive if there are an even number of negative factors.
- negative if there are an odd number of negative factors.

Example 3: Multiply: $-2 \times 6 \times -3 \times 2$

- There are two negative integers.
- The product is a positive integer.

$-2 \times 6 \times -3 \times 2 = +72$

Example 4: Multiply: $-2 \times 6 \times -3 \times -2$

- There are three negative integers.
- The product is a negative integer.

$-2 \times 6 \times -3 \times -2 = -72$

Multiply.

(D) **1.** 6×7

Ⓐ −42 Ⓑ −13 Ⓒ +13 Ⓓ +42

(A) **2.** 9×5

Ⓐ +45 Ⓑ +14 Ⓒ −14 Ⓓ −45

(D) **3.** -4×-11

Ⓐ −44 Ⓑ −15 Ⓒ +15 Ⓓ +44

(A) **4.** -15×-5

Ⓐ +75 Ⓑ +20 Ⓒ −20 Ⓓ −75

(D) **5.** -12×5

Ⓐ +60 Ⓑ +17 Ⓒ −17 Ⓓ −60

(A) **6.** 50×-10

Ⓐ −500 Ⓑ −40 Ⓒ +40 Ⓓ +500

(D) **7.** -26×14

Ⓐ +364 Ⓑ +40 Ⓒ −40 Ⓓ −364

(D) **8.** 15×18

Ⓐ −270 Ⓑ −33 Ⓒ +33 Ⓓ +270

(A) **9.** -16×-30

Ⓐ +480 Ⓑ +48 Ⓒ −48 Ⓓ −480

(C) **10.** -75×50

Ⓐ +3750 Ⓑ +375 Ⓒ −3750 Ⓓ −37,500

(A) **11.** $-2 \times 4 \times (-6)$

Ⓐ +48 Ⓑ +12 Ⓒ −12 Ⓓ −48

(A) **12.** $(-3) \times 5 \times (-2) \times (-1)$

Ⓐ −30 Ⓑ −11 Ⓒ +11 Ⓓ +30

(A) **13.** $7 \times (-4) \times (-8) \times 2$

Ⓐ +448 Ⓑ +21 Ⓒ −21 Ⓓ −448

(A) **14.** $(-9) \times (-2) \times (-6)$

Ⓐ −108 Ⓑ −66 Ⓒ +66 Ⓓ +108

(D) **15.** $(-5) \times (-6) \times 7 \times 5$

Ⓐ −1050 Ⓑ −42 Ⓒ +1 Ⓓ +1050

(B) **16.** $40 \times (-6) \times 0 \times (-8)$

Ⓐ −1920 Ⓑ 0 Ⓒ +26 Ⓓ +1920

Name ______________________ Class __________ Date ______________

9.6 DIVIDING INTEGERS

REMEMBER: The quotient of two integers with the *same sign* is *positive*.
The quotient of two integers with *unlike signs* is *negative*.
In all other ways, dividing integers is like dividing whole numbers.

Example 1: Divide: $-10 \div -2$

- The two integers have the same sign.
- The quotient is positive.

$-10 \div -2 = 5$

Example 2: Divide: $-54 \div 9$

- The two integers have unlike signs.
- The quotient is negative.

$-54 \div 9 = -6$

Example 3: Find the answer: $(-72) \div 9 \times (-4)$

- Work from left to right. Watch the signs carefully: $-72 \div 9 \times (-4) = (-72 \div 9) \times -4$

$$= -8 \times -4$$
$$= 32$$

Divide.

Ⓑ **1.** $12 \div 4$

Ⓐ -3 Ⓑ $+3$ Ⓒ $+8$ Ⓓ $+48$

Ⓒ **2.** $36 \div 6$

Ⓐ $+216$ Ⓑ $+30$ Ⓒ $+6$ Ⓓ -6

Ⓒ **3.** $-14 \div -2$

Ⓐ -12 Ⓑ -7 Ⓒ $+7$ Ⓓ $+12$

Ⓑ **4.** $-48 \div -6$

Ⓐ $+42$ Ⓑ $+8$ Ⓒ -8 Ⓓ -42

Ⓓ **5.** $-75 \div 15$

Ⓐ -60 Ⓑ $+60$ Ⓒ $+5$ Ⓓ -5

Ⓒ **6.** $-78 \div 13$

Ⓐ $+65$ Ⓑ $+6$ Ⓒ -6 Ⓓ -65

Ⓑ **7.** $88 \div -4$

Ⓐ -84 Ⓑ -22 Ⓒ $+22$ Ⓓ $+84$

Ⓐ **8.** $84 \div -7$

Ⓐ -12 Ⓑ -77 Ⓒ $+12$ Ⓓ $+77$

Ⓒ **9.** $-144 \div -8$

Ⓐ -136 Ⓑ -18 Ⓒ $+18$ Ⓓ $+136$

Ⓑ **10.** $192 \div -8$

Ⓐ -184 Ⓑ -24 Ⓒ $+24$ Ⓓ $+184$

Ⓒ **11.** $600 \div 20$

Ⓐ -300 Ⓑ -30 Ⓒ $+30$ Ⓓ $+300$

Ⓐ **12.** $-289 \div 17$

Ⓐ -17 Ⓑ $+17$ Ⓒ $+272$ Ⓓ -272

Ⓑ **13.** $180 \div -15$

Ⓐ -165 Ⓑ -12 Ⓒ $+12$ Ⓓ $+165$

Ⓒ **14.** $-420 \div -30$

Ⓐ -390 Ⓑ -14 Ⓒ $+14$ Ⓓ $+390$

Find the answer. Watch the signs carefully.

Ⓑ **15.** $(-6) \times 8 \div (-4)$

Ⓐ -12 Ⓑ 12 Ⓒ 44 Ⓓ 192

Ⓑ **16.** $(-72) \div 8 \times 3$

Ⓐ -240 Ⓑ -27 Ⓒ -3 Ⓓ 27

Ⓒ **17.** $64 \div (-4) \times (-5)$

Ⓐ -80 Ⓑ -12 Ⓒ 80 Ⓓ 300

Ⓓ **18.** $(-240) \div 4 \times (-20)$

Ⓐ -1200 Ⓑ -3 Ⓒ 80 Ⓓ 1200

Name______________________________ Class__________ Date__________

9.7 COORDINATE GRAPHS

Each point on the graph to the right is named by an ordered pair of numbers called *coordinates.*

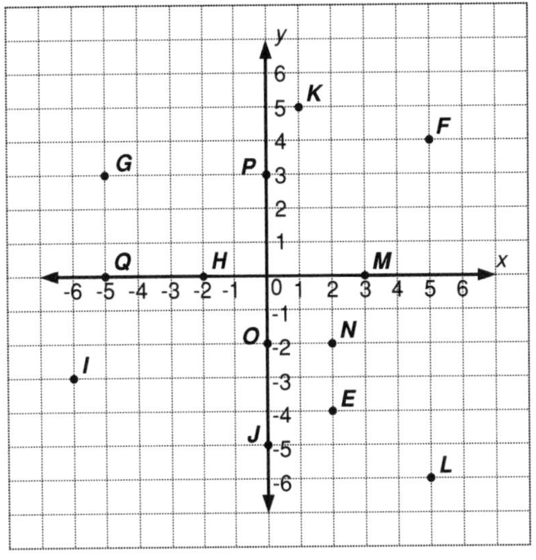

Example 1: Which point has coordinates (–5, 3)?

- Start at the origin (0,0).
- –5 means move left 5 units.
- 3 means move up 3 units.

Point *G* is named by the coordinates (–5, 3).

Example 2: What are the coordinates of Point *E?*

- Find point *E* on the graph.
- The number on the *x*-axis that corresponds to point *E* is 2.
- The number on the *y*-axis that corresponds to point *E* is –4.

The coordinates of point *E* are (2, –4).

REMEMBER: **1.** When the **first** coordinate is *positive*, move *right* on the *x*–axis. When it is *negative*, move *left* on the *x*–axis.

2. When the **second** coordinate is *positive*, move *up* on the *y*–axis. When it is *negative*, move *down* on the *y*–axis.

Use the coordinate graph above to answer the following questions.

Ⓐ **1.** What are the coordinates of Point *K?*
Ⓐ (1, 5) Ⓑ (5, 1) Ⓒ (–1, 5) Ⓓ (1, –5)

Ⓓ **2.** Which point has the coordinates (–6, –3)?
Ⓐ *L* Ⓑ *G* Ⓒ *F* Ⓓ *I*

Ⓒ **3.** Which point has the coordinates (–2, 0)?
Ⓐ *J* Ⓑ *I* Ⓒ *H* Ⓓ *E*

Ⓒ **4.** What are the coordinates of Point *L?*
Ⓐ (–6, 5) Ⓑ (–5, 6) Ⓒ (5, –6) Ⓓ (–5, –6)

Ⓑ **5.** What are the coordinates of Point *F?*
Ⓐ (4, 5) Ⓑ (5, 4) Ⓒ (–5, 4) Ⓓ (–4, –5)

Ⓓ **6.** Which point has the coordinates (3, 0)?
Ⓐ *P* Ⓑ *O* Ⓒ *N* Ⓓ *M*

Ⓒ **7.** What are the coordinates of Point *N?*
Ⓐ (2, 2) Ⓑ (–2, –2) Ⓒ (2, –2) Ⓓ (–2, 2)

Ⓑ **8.** Which point has the coordinates (0, –5)?
Ⓐ *Q* Ⓑ *J* Ⓒ *F* Ⓓ *E*

Ⓒ **9.** Which point has the coordinates (0, –2)?
Ⓐ *M* Ⓑ *P* Ⓒ *O* Ⓓ *A*

Ⓓ **10.** What are the coordinates of Point *J?*
Ⓐ (–5, 0) Ⓑ (1, 5) Ⓒ (–1, –5) Ⓓ (0, –5)

Ⓓ **11.** What are the coordinates of Point *G?*
Ⓐ (–5, –3) Ⓑ (5, –3) Ⓒ (3, –5) Ⓓ (–5, 3)

Ⓐ **12.** Which point has the coordinates (–5, 0)?
Ⓐ *Q* Ⓑ *J* Ⓒ *F* Ⓓ *K*

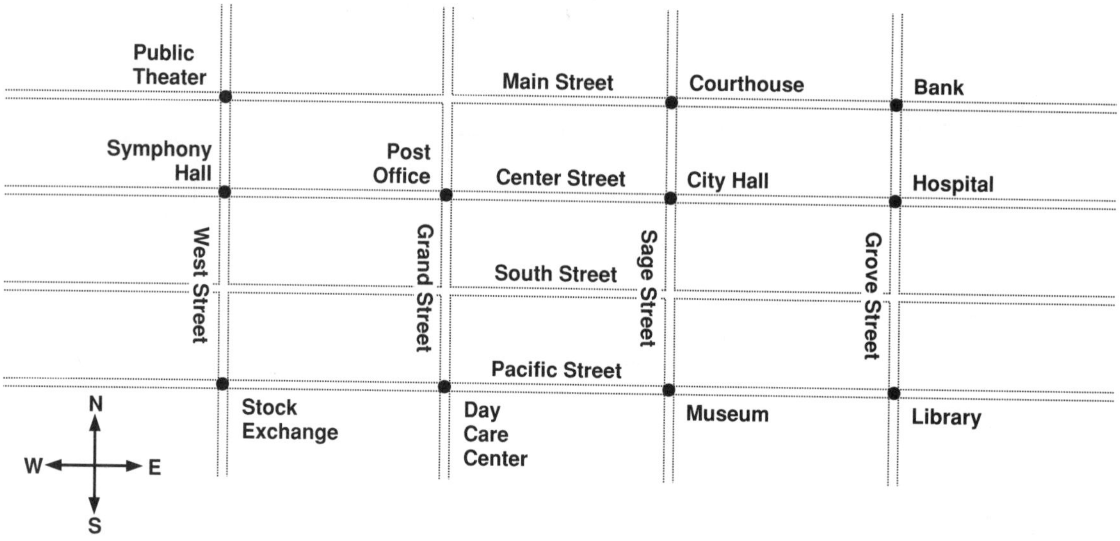

Public Theater
Main Street
Courthouse
Bank
Symphony Hall
Post Office
Center Street
City Hall
Hospital
West Street
Grand Street
South Street
Sage Street
Grove Street
Pacific Street
Stock Exchange
Day Care Center
Museum
Library
N
W
E
S

Use the map above to answer the following questions.

Ⓒ **13.** At what intersection is the Post Office located?

Ⓐ Center and South Ⓑ Center and West
Ⓒ Center and Grand Ⓓ Center and Sage

Ⓑ **14.** What building is located at Pacific and Sage?

Ⓐ Library Ⓑ Museum
Ⓒ City Hall Ⓓ Day Care Center

Ⓒ **15.** What building is located at Center and Grand?

Ⓐ Symphony Hall Ⓑ City Hall
Ⓒ Post Office Ⓓ Courthouse

Ⓐ **16.** At what intersection is the Hospital located?

Ⓐ Grove and Center Ⓑ Grove and Sage
Ⓒ Grand and South Ⓓ Center and Main

Ⓑ **17.** At what intersection is the Public Theater located?

Ⓐ Main and Center Ⓑ Main and West
Ⓒ West and Center Ⓓ West and Grand

Ⓓ **18.** What building is located at Main and Sage?

Ⓐ City Hall Ⓑ Hospital
Ⓒ Post Office Ⓓ Courthouse

Ⓒ **19.** In which direction is City Hall from the Post Office?

Ⓐ North Ⓑ South
Ⓒ East Ⓓ West

Ⓑ **20.** In which direction is the Museum from the Courthouse?

Ⓐ North Ⓑ South
Ⓒ East Ⓓ West

Ⓓ **21.** If you travel 2 blocks north from the Library, which building will you encounter?

Ⓐ Day Care Center Ⓑ Bank
Ⓒ City Hall Ⓓ Hospital

Ⓑ **22.** If you travel 2 blocks west from the Courthouse, which building will you encounter?

Ⓐ Hospital Ⓑ Public Theater
Ⓒ Post Office Ⓓ Museum

Ⓓ **23.** Start at the Stock Exchange. Go 2 blocks east, then 3 blocks north. Which building will you find?

Ⓐ Library Ⓑ Public Theater
Ⓒ Hospital Ⓓ Courthouse

Ⓒ **24.** Start at the Courthouse. Go 1 block south, 1 block east, and then 2 blocks south. Which building will you find?

Ⓐ Day Care Center Ⓑ Stock Exchange
Ⓒ Library Ⓓ Post Office

Name ______________________ Class __________ Date ______________

CHAPTER 9 TEST

Use the number line below to answer the following questions.

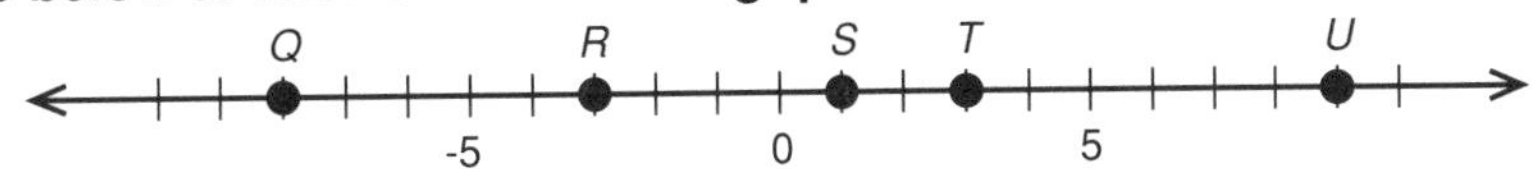

(B) **1.** What letter names the point –3?

(A) *Q* (B) *R* (C) *S* (D) *T*

(C) **2.** What integer corresponds to point *S*?

(A) –3 (B) –1 (C) +1 (D) +3

(D) **3.** Choose the list of numbers ordered from *least to greatest*.

(A) +4, +8, –9, –6 (B) –6, –9, +4, +8
(C) +8, +4, –6, –9 (D) –9, –6, +4, +8

(B) **4.** Which set of numbers shows its elements from *greatest to least?*

(A) +3, –2, +1, +5 (B) +5, +1, –2, –3
(C) –2, –3, +1, +5 (D) +5, +1, –3, –2

(C) **5.** The temperature one winter day in Maine rose from –15° F to –4° F. What is the increase in temperature?

(A) –19° F (B) –11° F
(C) +11° F (D) +19° F

(C) **6.** Over the course of three days, a stock gained 5 points, lost 2 points, then gained 8 points. What was the resulting gain after the 3 days?

(A) –11 points (B) +1 point
(C) +11 points (D) +15 points

(C) **7.** Add: –8 + 48

(A) –56 (B) –40 (C) +40 (D) +56

(D) **8.** Subtract: 98 – (–12)

(A) –110 (B) –86 (C) +86 (D) +110

(D) **9.** Multiply: –4 × 2 × (–6)

(A) –48 (B) –12 (C) +12 (D) +48

(B) **10.** Divide: 204 ÷ –17

(A) –187 (B) –12 (C) +22 (D) +12

Choose the best answer.

(A) **11.** 63 ÷ 9 × (–2) =

(A) –14 (B) –5 (C) +5 (D) +14

(D) **12.** (–18) × (–6) ÷ (–4) =

(A) +27 (B) +12 (C) –12 (D) –27

(C) **13.** (–26) + (–10) – (–4) =

(A) +40 (B) +32 (C) –32 (D) –40

(A) **14.** 18 – 45 + (–5) =

(A) –32 (B) –22 (C) +32 (D) +68

Name the opposite of each number.

(B) **15.** –112

(A) –211 (B) +112 (C) +121 (D) +211

(A) **16.** +543

(A) –543 (B) –453 (C) –345 (D) +345

Choose the letter that makes the statement true.

(A) **17.** –10 ■ –4

(A) < (B) > (C) =

(B) **18.** 0 ■ –2

(A) < (B) > (C) =

(D) **19.** Which integer has the *least* value?

(A) +4 (B) –3 (C) +1 (D) –8

(B) **20.** Which integer has the *greatest* value?

(A) –4 (B) +1 (C) –1 (D) –8

Ⓑ **21.** Ivan had $126 in his checking account. He wrote checks for $51 and $85. How much money does Ivan need to deposit to make sure his checks can be cashed?

Ⓐ –$10 Ⓑ $10 Ⓒ $136 Ⓓ $262

Ⓓ **22.** Start with the number 5. Subtract 10. Add 4. Multiply by –6. What is the result?

Ⓐ –6 Ⓑ –24 Ⓒ –54 Ⓓ +6

Coffee Shop
Sanborn Street
Department Store
Playground
Book Store
Chloe Street
6th Avenue
5th Avenue
4th Avenue
3rd Avenue
Main Street
Card Store
N
W
E
S
Scott Street
Botanic Garden

Use the map to answer the following questions.

Ⓒ **23.** At what intersection is the Playground located?

Ⓐ Main & 6th Ⓑ Chloe & 5th

Ⓒ Chloe & 6th Ⓓ Sanborn & 6th

Ⓒ **24.** What landmark is located at Sanborn & 3rd?

Ⓐ Coffee Shop Ⓑ Card Store

Ⓒ Dept. Store Ⓓ Book Store

Ⓓ **25.** Start at the Botanic Garden. Go 1 block east and 2 blocks north.Which landmark will you find?

Ⓐ Playground Ⓑ Card Store

Ⓒ Coffee Shop Ⓓ Book Store

26. In which direction is the Coffee Shop from the Ⓐ Book Store?

Ⓐ North Ⓑ East

Ⓒ South Ⓓ West

Write the integer that best describes each situation.

Ⓐ **27.** A loss of 18 pounds

Ⓐ –18 Ⓑ –9 Ⓒ –7 Ⓓ +18

Ⓓ **28.** A bonus of $125.00

Ⓐ –$125 Ⓑ $250 Ⓒ +$12.5 Ⓓ +$125

Ⓒ **29.** Add: 89 + –18 + 22

Ⓐ –85 Ⓑ –93 Ⓒ +93 Ⓓ +129

Ⓓ **30.** Subtract: 24 – (–31) – (–19)

Ⓐ –26 Ⓑ –12 Ⓒ +12 Ⓓ +74

Use the graph to answer the following questions.

Ⓑ **31.** What are the coordinates of Point *J?*

Ⓐ (+1, +2) Ⓑ (+2, +1)

Ⓒ (+2, –1) Ⓓ (–2, +1)

Ⓒ **32.** What are the coordinates of Point *K?*

Ⓐ (–5, 0) Ⓑ (0, – 5) Ⓒ (+5, 0) Ⓓ (0, +5)

Ⓐ **33.** Which point is named by the coordinates (–3, +4)?

Ⓐ *G* Ⓑ *P* Ⓒ *N* Ⓓ *L*

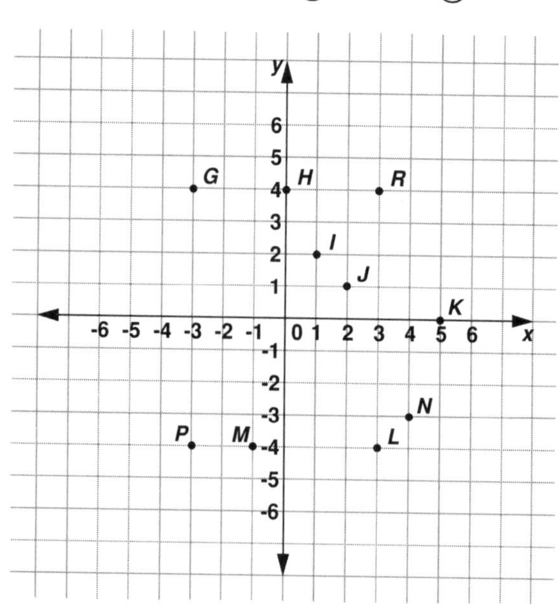

Name ______________________ Class ________ Date ____________

CHAPTERS 1-9 CUMULATIVE REVIEW

Fill in the correct circle to answer each question.

Ⓓ **1.** A circular garden has a radius of 7 feet. Bonnie wants to plant flowers along the border. How long will the border be? Use $\frac{22}{7}$ for π.

Ⓐ 26 ft Ⓑ 22 ft Ⓒ 154 ft Ⓓ 44 ft

Ⓐ **2.** Round 725,503 to the nearest *thousand*.

Ⓐ 726,000 Ⓑ 725,000
Ⓒ 600,000 Ⓓ 700,000

Ⓓ **3.** Which set of integers is in *ascending* order?

Ⓐ +1, +2, –3, +5 Ⓑ +5, +4, +3, +2
Ⓒ +5, –6, +7, –8 Ⓓ –4, –1, +3, +4

Ⓒ **4.** A car leaves Auburn at 10:15 A.M. and arrives in Springfield at 3:30 P.M. How long did the drive take?

Ⓐ 1 hr 45 min Ⓑ 4 hr 15 min
Ⓒ 5 hr 15 min Ⓓ 6 hr 45 min

Ⓑ **5.** Find the surface area of a rectangular prism with sides 6 in long, 5 in high, and 3 in wide. Use the formula: $A = 2(lw) + 2(wh) + 2(lh)$

Ⓐ 180 sq ft Ⓑ 126 sq ft
Ⓒ 90 sq ft Ⓓ 30 cu ft

Ⓐ **6.** What is the quotient of 938 and 14?

Ⓐ 67 Ⓑ 67R1
Ⓒ 938:14 Ⓓ 13,132

Ⓑ **7.** $112 \div -8 = $ ■

Ⓐ –13 Ⓑ –14 Ⓒ +13 Ⓓ +14

Ⓐ **8.** Write $\frac{7}{10}$ as a decimal.

Ⓐ 0.7 Ⓑ 70 Ⓒ 0.07 Ⓓ 0.007

Ⓑ **9.** A circle has a diameter of 6 cm. What is its area? Use the formula: $A = \pi \times r \times r$. Use 3.14 for π.

Ⓐ 37.68 sq cm Ⓑ 28.26 sq cm
Ⓒ 18.84 sq cm Ⓓ 113.04 sq cm

Ⓒ **10.** $573.8 - 0.071 = $ ■

Ⓐ 40.7398 Ⓑ 573.09
Ⓒ 573.729 Ⓓ 573.871

Ⓐ **11.** $-12 \times -3 = $ ■

Ⓐ 36 Ⓑ 27 Ⓒ –36 Ⓓ –15

Ⓐ **12.** Several friends compared their scores on a math test. The scores were 68, 95, 74, 87, 78. What was the range?

Ⓐ 27 Ⓑ 78 Ⓒ 80.4 Ⓓ 72

Ⓑ **13.** Find the area of the rectangle.

Ⓐ 3015 sq ft
Ⓑ 450 sq ft
Ⓒ 90 sq ft
Ⓓ 45 sq ft

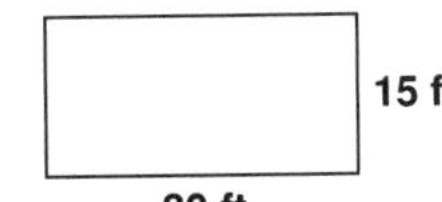

Ⓓ **14.** Name the figure.

Ⓐ parallelogram
Ⓑ rectangle
Ⓒ pentagon
Ⓓ trapezoid

Ⓑ **15.** $7 + -13 = $ ■

Ⓐ –20 Ⓑ –6 Ⓒ +6 Ⓓ +20

Ⓑ **16.** $3 \times$ ■ $= 81$

Ⓐ 78 Ⓑ 27 Ⓒ 4 Ⓓ 3

Ⓒ **17.** Find the perimeter of a regular pentagon if each side is $1\frac{1}{2}$ inches.

Ⓐ $4\frac{5}{7}$ in Ⓑ 6 in Ⓒ $7\frac{1}{2}$ in Ⓓ 12 in

Ⓓ **18.** Add 3 ft 2 in and 1 ft 11 in.

Ⓐ 1 ft 3 in Ⓑ 2 ft 9 in
Ⓒ 2 yds 1 in Ⓓ 5 ft 1 in

Ⓓ **19.** Which of the following describes a loss of $33?

Ⓐ +$33 Ⓑ +30% Ⓒ −3% Ⓓ −$33

Ⓐ **20.** $\frac{25}{56} \times 7 = ■$

Ⓐ $3\frac{1}{8}$ Ⓑ $3\frac{4}{7}$ Ⓒ 7 Ⓓ $8\frac{1}{3}$

Ⓓ **21.** 6 − −4 = ■

Ⓐ −10 Ⓑ −2 Ⓒ +2 Ⓓ +10

Ⓑ **22.** $\frac{2}{3} = \frac{■}{51}$

Ⓐ 33 Ⓑ 34 Ⓒ 48 Ⓓ 102

Ⓑ **23.** Find the volume. Use the formula: $V = l \times w \times h$

Ⓐ 9 cu yd
Ⓑ 20 cu yd
Ⓒ 40 cu yd
Ⓓ 48 cu yd

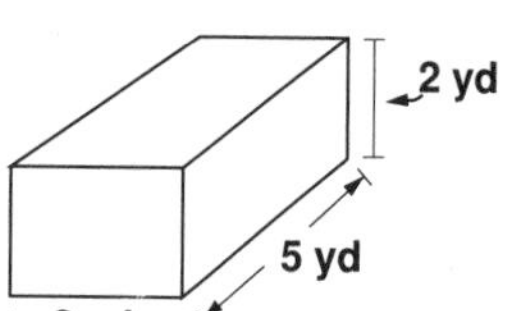

2 yd
5 yd
2 yd

Ⓒ **24.**
$$\begin{array}{r} \frac{7}{8} \\ -\ \frac{1}{3} \\ \hline \end{array}$$

Ⓐ $1\frac{1}{5}$ Ⓑ $\frac{3}{8}$ Ⓒ $\frac{13}{24}$ Ⓓ $\frac{7}{8}$

Use the coordinate graph to answer questions 25-27.

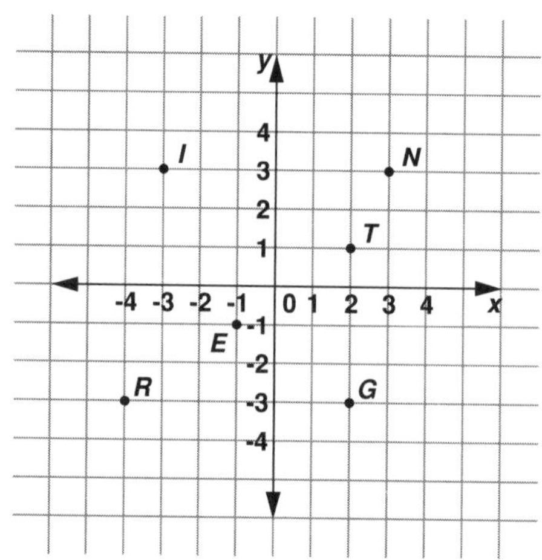

Ⓓ **25.** What are the coordinates of Point *G*?

Ⓐ (−3, +2) Ⓑ (+3, −2)
Ⓒ (+2, +3) Ⓓ (+2, −3)

Ⓒ **26.** Which point has coordinates (+3, +3)?

Ⓐ *R* Ⓑ *I* Ⓒ *N* Ⓓ *G*

Ⓑ **27.** Start at Point T. Go 2 units right, then 3 units down. What are coordinates of the new point?

Ⓐ (+4, +4) Ⓑ (+4, −2)
Ⓒ (−2, +3) Ⓓ (+5, −1)

Complete the table to answer questions 28–30.

Coat Sale			
Coat	Original Price	Sale	Sale Price
A	$100	25% off	
B	$120	1/3 off	
C	$150		$105

Ⓓ **28.** What fraction of the original price is the sale price of Coat A?

Ⓐ $\frac{1}{4}$ Ⓑ $\frac{1}{3}$ Ⓒ $\frac{1}{2}$ Ⓓ $\frac{3}{4}$

Ⓐ **29.** Which statement is true about Coat C on sale?

Ⓐ It offers the greatest total dollar saving.
Ⓑ It offers the greatest percentage saving.
Ⓒ It is twice the sale price of Coat A.
Ⓓ All of the above.

Ⓒ **30.** Carlos has $90 to spend. Which coat can he buy?

Ⓐ A only Ⓑ B only
Ⓒ A or B Ⓓ A and B

Name ______________________ Class __________ Date __________

(C) **31.** Find the area of the triangle below.

(A) 24 sq ft
(B) 15 sq ft
(C) 12 sq ft
(D) 7.5 sq ft

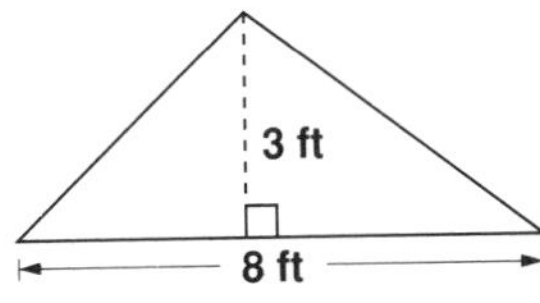

(A) **32.**
$$\begin{array}{r} 275{,}891 \\ 67{,}035 \\ +\,785{,}109 \\ \hline \end{array}$$

(A) 1,128,035 (B) 1,128,030
(C) 1,127,035 (D) 1,028,035

(C) **33.** What is the surface area of a cylinder with a radius of 21 cm and a height of 14 cm? Use the formula: $A = 2\,(\pi \times r \times r) + (2 \times \pi \times r \times h)$. Use $\frac{22}{7}$ for π.

(A) 1848 sq cm (B) 2772 sq cm
(C) 4620 sq cm (D) 6930 sq cm

(D) **34.** $38\overline{)13{,}657}$

(A) 38 R15 (B) 39 R15
(C) 359R5 (D) 359 R15

(A) **35.** –25 ■ –31

(A) > (B) < (C) =

(A) **36.** 25.310 ■ 9.9905

(A) > (B) < (C) =

(D) **37.** Subtract 9 from –16.

(A) +25 (B) +7 (C) –7 (D) –25

(B) **38.** 67 cm = ■ m

(A) 0.067 (B) 0.67 (C) 6700 (D) 6.7

(B) **39.** Find the area of the figure.

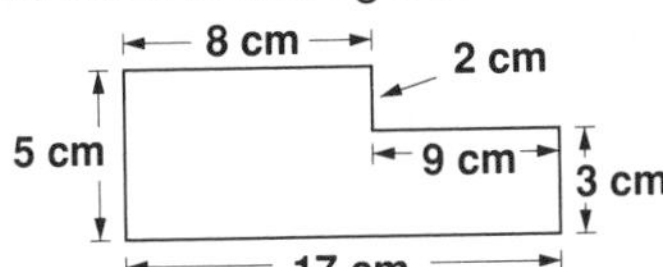

(A) 18 sq cm (B) 67 sq cm
(C) 85 sq cm (D) 44 sq cm

(B) **40.** Classify the triangle.

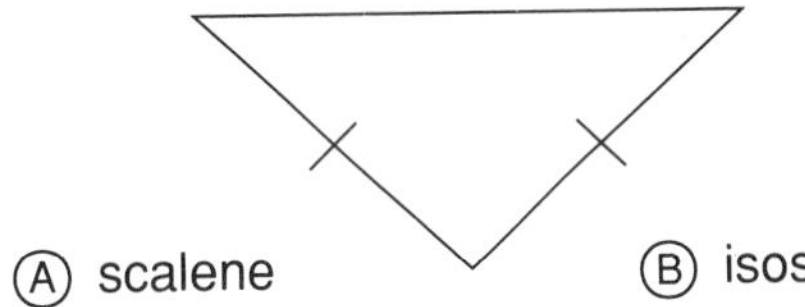

(A) scalene (B) isosceles
(C) acute (D) obtuse

(C) **41.** –25 ÷ 5 = ■

(A) –125 (B) –20 (C) –5 (D) +5

(B) **42.** 0.9715 × 18 = ■

(A) 0.16487 (B) 17.487 (C) 1698.7 (D) 1707.7

(C) **43.** Find the circumference.
Use the formula: $C = \pi \times d$. Use 3.14 for π.

(A) 9874.04 cm
(B) 87.92 cm
(C) 175.84 cm
(D) 2461.76 cm

56 cm

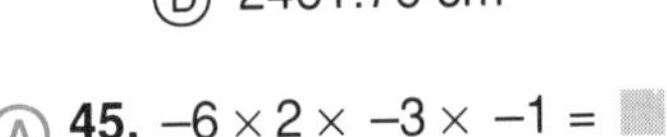

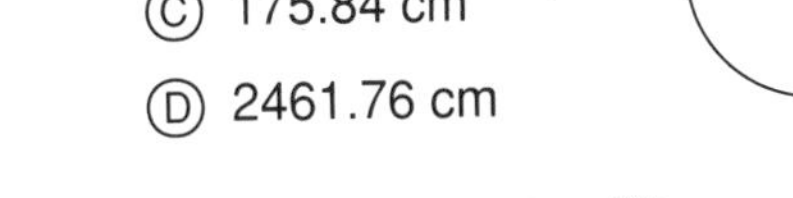

(D) **44.** Intersecting lines

(A) can never be perpendicular.
(B) can never have one point in common.
(C) always intersect ar right angles.
(D) can never be parallel.

(A) **45.** –6 × 2 × –3 × –1 = ■

(A) –36 (B) –15 (C) +35 (D) +36

(A) **46.** Select a fraction that is equivalent to $\frac{22}{7}$.

(A) $\frac{88}{28}$ (B) $\frac{7}{22}$ (C) $\frac{14}{44}$ (D) $\frac{66}{18}$

(C) **47.** A cylindrical oil storage tank has a diameter of 20 ft and a height of 40 ft. How much oil can it hold? Use the formula: $V = \pi \times r \times r \times h$. Use 3.14 for π.

(A) 125.6 cu ft (B) 2512 cu ft
(C) 12,560 cu ft (D) 50,240 cu ft

(B) **48.** $3\frac{1}{2} \div 7 =$ ■

(A) $\frac{3}{7}$ (B) $\frac{1}{2}$ (C) 21 (D) $24\frac{1}{2}$

(C) **49.** Find the surface area of a rectangular prism: $l = 20$ ft, $w = 10$ ft, $h = 15$ ft. Use the formula $A = 2(lw) + 2(wh) + 2(lh)$.

(A) 6000 sq ft (B) 3000 cu ft
(C) 1300 sq ft (D) 90 sq ft

(D) **50.** Write 7.31 as a percent.

(A) 0.0731% (B) 0.731%
(C) 7.31% (D) 731%

(B) **51.** Find the area of the triangle below.

(A) 11 sq m
(B) 15 sq m
(C) 30 sq m
(D) 60 sq m

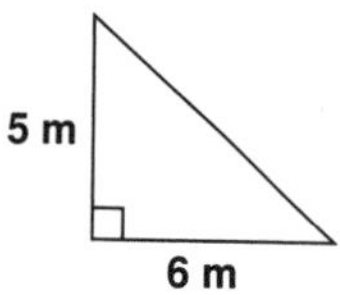

(D) **52.** Find the missing length. Use the Pythagorean Theorem: $a^2 + b^2 = c^2$

(A) 656
(B) 144
(C) $\sqrt{656}$
(D) 12

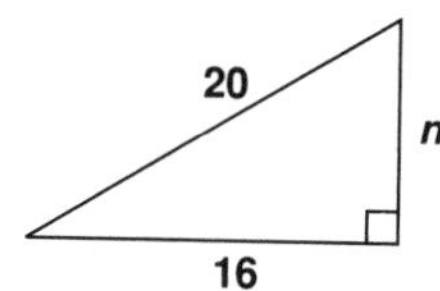

(B) **53.** Find the sum of 9.713, 56.001, 0.0079, and 3.

(A) 65.7219 (B) 68.7219
(C) 68.7309 (D) 68.793

(C) **54.** Choose the number that best describes an increase in pay of 75 cents per hour.

(A) –7.5 (B) –0.75 (C) +0.75 (D) +7.5

(A) **55.** A number cube is labeled with the numbers 1, 2, 3, 4, 5, and 6. What is the probability of rolling an even number?

(A) $\frac{1}{2}$ (B) $\frac{1}{3}$ (C) $\frac{12}{21}$ (D) 3

(A) **56.** A box for storing albums is shaped like a cube. One side measures 13 in. What is the volume of the box ? Use the formula: $V = s \times s \times s$.

(A) 2197 cu ft (B) 1807 cu ft
(C) 169 cu ft (D) 139 cu ft

(D) **57.** The product of $2\frac{2}{3}$ and 6 is ■.

(A) $\frac{4}{9}$ (B) $8\frac{2}{3}$ (C) 14 (D) 16

(B) **58.** Add: +6 + –9

(A) +15 (B) –3 (C) –5 (D) –15

(D) **59.** In a parking lot, there are 12 pick-up trucks and 3 cars. What is the ratio of trucks to cars?

(A) 1:4 (B) 3:12 (C) 12:15 (D) 4:1

(C) **60.** What is the area of a circle with a diameter of 20 in ? Use the formula: $A = \pi \times r \times r$.

(A) 62.8 sq in (B) 125.6 sq in
(C) 314 sq in (D) 1256 sq in

(C) **61.** Add: $5\frac{1}{4} + 7\frac{3}{8} + \frac{5}{6}$

(A) $12\frac{9}{24}$ (B) $13\frac{1}{4}$ (C) $13\frac{11}{24}$ (D) $12\frac{11}{24}$

(D) **62.** Find the area of the parallelogram: base = 18 cm, height =12 cm. Use the formula: $A = b \times h$

(A) 30 sq cm (B) 60 sq cm
(C) 108 sq cm (D) 216 sq cm

(A) **63.** An acute angle has a measure of

(A) more than 0° but less than 90°.
(B) 90°.
(C) more than 90° but less than 180°.
(D) 180°.

(B) **64.** Find the volume of the cylinder: height = 20 m, radius = 7 m. Use the formula: $V = \pi \times r \times r \times h$. Use $\frac{22}{7}$ for π.

(A) 1760 cu m (B) 3080 cu m
(C) 880 cu m (D) 140 cu m

Name ____________________ Class ________ Date ____________

CHAPTER 10: EXPRESSIONS AND EQUATIONS

TEST-TAKING STRATEGY: *Try Numbers*

In the last Test-Taking Strategy lesson you used the "guesses" that were given to find the answer. In this lesson, you will learn what to do when you are not given any guesses. You must find your own "guesses." Try numbers until you "guess" the correct answer. This technique is sometimes called "guess and check."

Example 1: $4x + 56 = 108$

- Try 10 for x.

$$\begin{aligned} 4x + 56 &= 108 \\ 4(10) + 56 &= 108 \\ 40 + 56 &= 108 \\ 96 &\neq 108 \\ 96 &< 108 \end{aligned}$$

When you substitute 10 for x, you get $96 < 108$. So your guess is too low. Try another number greater than 10.

- Let's try 14:

$$\begin{aligned} 4x + 56 &= 108 \\ 4(14) + 46 &= 108 \\ 56 + 56 &= 108 \\ 112 &\neq 108 \\ 112 &> 108 \end{aligned}$$

When you substitute the number 14 for x, you get $112 > 108$. So your guess is too high. Try another number. This time your guess should be between 10 and 14.

- Let's try 13:

$$\begin{aligned} 4x + 56 &= 108 \\ 4(13) + 56 &= 108 \\ 52 + 56 &= 108 \\ 108 &= 108 \end{aligned}$$

The correct answer is $x = 13$.

Example 2: If x is an even integer, which of the following must also be an even integer?

Ⓐ $2x + 1$ Ⓑ $2x - 1$ Ⓒ $\frac{x}{2}$ Ⓓ $x + 2$

- Replace the variable x in each expression with an even integer. Let's let $x = 4$.

Ⓐ $2(4) + 1 = 9$ Ⓑ $2(4) - 1 = 7$ Ⓒ $\frac{4}{2} = 2$ Ⓓ $4 + 2 = 6$

- We can eliminate choice Ⓐ and choice Ⓑ because they both result in an odd integer. Test choice Ⓒ and choice Ⓓ again with another even integer. For example, let $x = 6$.

Ⓒ $\frac{x}{2} = \frac{6}{2} = 3$ Ⓓ $x + 2 = 6 + 2 = 8$

The only expression that always results in an even integer is $x + 2$. The correct answer is choice Ⓓ.

Solve for *x*.

7 **1.** $8x + 7 = 63$

$x =$ ____

8 **2.** $9x - 12 = 60$

$x =$ ____

3 **3.** $16x + 3 = 51$

$x =$ ____

5 **4.** $14x - 8 = 62$

$x =$ ____

Solve each problem by using the strategy of trying numbers. Remember to use simple numbers.

Ⓑ **5.** If *a* and *b* are both positive even integers, then *ab* must be

Ⓐ odd　Ⓑ even　Ⓒ negative　Ⓓ not enough Information

Ⓐ **6.** If a and b are both negative even integers, then *ab* must be

Ⓐ positive　Ⓑ negative　Ⓒ odd　Ⓓ not enough Information

Ⓐ **7.** If *x* is a negative integer, which of the following must also be a negative integer?

Ⓐ $x - 1$　Ⓑ $x + 1$　Ⓒ $\frac{x}{-1}$　Ⓓ $1 - x$

Ⓓ **8.** If *x* is an odd integer, which of the following must also be an odd integer?

Ⓐ $x + 7$　Ⓑ $2x - 2$　Ⓒ $2x + 2$　Ⓓ $x + 8$

Ⓒ **9.** If a is a positive odd number and b is a negative odd number their product is

Ⓐ positive and odd　Ⓑ positive and even　Ⓒ negative and odd　Ⓓ negative and even

Ⓐ **10.** If a and b are both negative odd numbers, their product is

Ⓐ positive and odd　Ⓑ positive and even　Ⓒ negative and odd　Ⓓ negative and even

Ⓒ **11.** If *a* and *b* are consecutive even integers, then the value of *b* is

Ⓐ $a + 4$　Ⓑ $a + b$　Ⓒ $a + 2$　Ⓓ $a + 2b$

Ⓒ **12.** If *a* and *b* are consecutive odd integers, then the value of *b* is

Ⓐ $a + 1$　Ⓑ $a + 3$　Ⓒ $a + 2$　Ⓓ $2a + 1$

Ⓓ **13.** If *e, f,* and *g* are positive integers greater than 1 and $e < f < g$, which of the following is the largest quantity?

Ⓐ $e(f + g)$　Ⓑ $ef + g$　Ⓒ $eg + f$　Ⓓ efg

Ⓐ **14.** A car's empty gas tank is filled up with *g* gallons of gas. It travels *m* miles until the tank is empty. How many miles did it travel per gallon?

Ⓐ $\frac{m}{g}$　Ⓑ $\frac{g}{m}$　Ⓒ $\frac{mg}{m}$　Ⓓ $\frac{m}{mg}$

Ⓓ **15.** If *x, y,* and *z* are all positive integers and $x < y < z$, then which of the following must always be true?

Ⓐ $y + z < x$　Ⓑ $z - y < x$　Ⓒ $yz < x$　Ⓓ $x < yz$

Ⓑ **16.** If *a* and *b* are negative integers and *c* is a positive integer, then the value of *abc* is:

Ⓐ a negative integer　Ⓑ a positive integer　Ⓒ zero　Ⓓ one

Ⓑ **17.** If *x* and *y* are both negative numbers in the expression $\frac{y}{x}$, then its value must be:

Ⓐ a negative number　Ⓑ a positive number　Ⓒ zero　Ⓓ one

Ⓓ **18.** Out of *x* days, y of them were rainy. How many days were not rainy?

Ⓐ $x + y$　Ⓑ xy　Ⓒ $\frac{x}{y}$　Ⓓ $x - y$

Name ______________________ Class __________ Date ______________

CHAPTER 10 PRETEST

Fill in the correct circle to answer each question.

The formula for the area of a circle is: $A = \pi \times r \times r$. Use $\pi = 3.14$ to find the area of:

(D) **1.** a circle with a radius of 4 in.

(A) 12.56 sq in (B) 16 sq in (C) 25.12 sq in (D) 50.24 sq in

(B) **2.** a circle with a radius of 1 m.

(A) 3.14 m (B) 3.14 sq m (C) 4.14 (D) 6.28 sq m

Find the answer.

(D) **3.** 2 ft + 4 ft + 3 in =

(A) 9 ft (B) 9 in (C) 2 ft 7 in (D) 6 ft 3 in

(B) **4.** 5 m + 10 cm – 2 m =

(A) 13 cm (B) 310 cm (C) 710 cm (D) 17 m

(C) **5.** –4 + 12 =

(A) –16 (B) –8 (C) +8 (D) +16

(A) **6.** –15 – 4 =

(A) –19 (B) –11 (C) +11 (D) +19

(B) **7.** 2 – 4 =

(A) –6 (B) –2 (C) +2 (D) +6

(A) **8.** –2 + –8 =

(A) –10 (B) –6 (C) +6 (D) +10

(A) **9.** 6 × –4 =

(A) –24 (B) –10 (C) +10 (D) +24

(B) **10.** –18 × 0 =

(A) –18 (B) 0 (C) +1 (D) +18

(D) **11.** 8(6 + 4) =

(A) 18 (B) 38 (C) 52 (D) 80

(C) **12.** –28 ÷ –7 =

(A) –21 (B) –4 (C) +4 (D) +56

(B) **13.** 64 ÷ –4 =

(A) –68 (B) –16 (C) +16 (D) +60

(B) **14.** 4 + (144 ÷ 12) =

(A) 9 (B) 16 (C) 48 (D) 147

Use the number line below to answer the following questions.

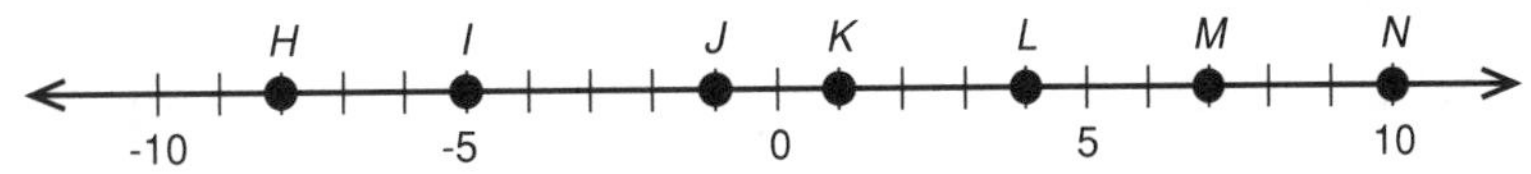

(A) **15.** Which letter names a point less than –6?

(A) *H* (B) *I* (C) *J* (D) *K*

(D) **16.** Which letter names a point greater than +3?

(A) *I* (B) *J* (C) *K* (D) *L*

Find the answer.

(A) **17.** 10 × 2 + 5 × 3 =

(A) 35 (B) 75 (C) 170 (D) 210

(C) **18.** 35 – 7 + 4 × (8 – 4) =

(A) 12 (B) 21 (C) 44 (D) 128

Ⓓ **19.** $\frac{25 - 5}{2 \times 3 + 4} =$

Ⓐ $1\frac{1}{9}$ Ⓑ $1\frac{3}{7}$ Ⓒ $1\frac{9}{11}$ Ⓓ 2

Ⓑ **20.** $\frac{2(12 + 12)}{27 - 3 + 3} =$

Ⓐ $1\frac{5}{9}$ Ⓑ $1\frac{7}{9}$ Ⓒ $\frac{8}{9}$ Ⓓ 12

Evaluate each expression when $x = 4$ and $y = -2$.

Ⓓ **21.** $6x - y =$

Ⓐ -22 Ⓑ -14 Ⓒ $+22$ Ⓓ $+26$

Ⓑ **22.** $\frac{x + y}{-2} =$

Ⓐ -3 Ⓑ -1 Ⓒ $+1$ Ⓓ $+3$

Simplify each expression by combining like terms.

Ⓑ **23.** $12k + 8k - k$

Ⓐ $19k^2$ Ⓑ $19k$

Ⓒ $11k^2 + 8k$ Ⓓ $12 + 8k$

Ⓓ **24.** $4p + 2p - 3r$

Ⓐ $2p + 3r$ Ⓑ $3p$

Ⓒ $3pr$ Ⓓ $6p - 3r$

Write as an equation.

Ⓐ **25.** The sum of a number and 19 is 75.

Ⓐ $n + 19 = 75$ Ⓑ $n - 19 = 75$

Ⓒ $n + 75 = 19$ Ⓓ $19 + 75 + n$

Ⓑ **26.** 22 times a number is 264.

Ⓐ $22n = 264n$ Ⓑ $22n = 264$

Ⓒ $22 \times 264 = n$ Ⓓ $264n = 22$

Solve for the variable.

Ⓑ **27.** $d + 1.5 = 8.8$

Ⓐ 1.5 Ⓑ 7.3 Ⓒ 8.8 Ⓓ 10.3

Ⓓ **28.** $144 = n - 65$

Ⓐ 65 Ⓑ 79 Ⓒ 144 Ⓓ 209

Ⓓ **29.** $\frac{f}{4} + 3 = 12$

Ⓐ 5 Ⓑ 11 Ⓒ 16 Ⓓ 36

Ⓑ **30.** $15w + 10 = 280$

Ⓐ 11.2 Ⓑ 18 Ⓒ 26.5 Ⓓ 255

Choose the equation or inequality that represents each graph.

Ⓐ **31.**

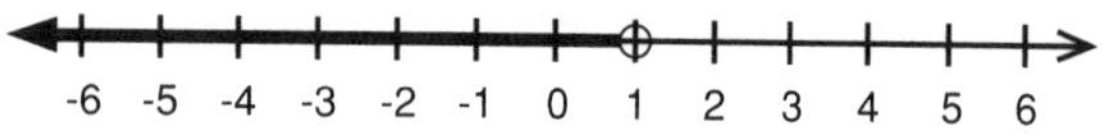

Ⓐ $x < 1$ Ⓑ $x \leq 1$

Ⓒ $x \geq 1$ Ⓓ $x > 1$

Ⓒ **32.**

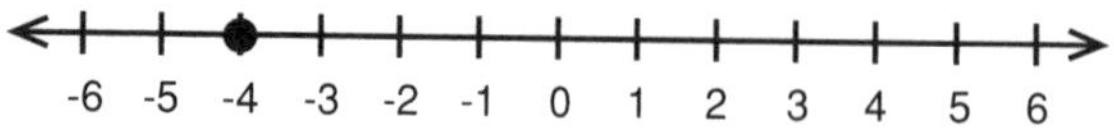

Ⓐ $x < -4$ Ⓑ $x \leq 4$

Ⓒ $x = -4$ Ⓓ $x + 2 = 6$

Ⓒ **33.** What does the diagram show about the relationship between whales and mammals?

Ⓐ All mammals are whales Ⓑ No whales are mammals

Ⓒ All whales are mammals Ⓓ No mammals are whales

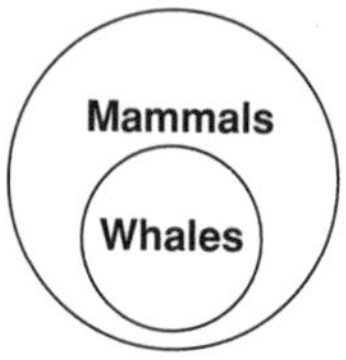

Name ______________________________ Class __________ Date ______________

10.1 ORDER OF OPERATIONS

How would you simplify the following expression: $8 \times 5 + 2$? Would you multiply first, and then add? Or would you add first, and then multiply? To avoid this problem, we follow a set of rules called the **order of operations.**

To use the order of operations, follow these steps:
1. Do all operations within parentheses first.
2. Do all multiplications and divisions from left to right.
3. Do all additions and subtractions from left to right.

Example 1: Simplify: $18 \div 3(8-6)+4$

$18 \div 3(8-6)+4 = 18 \div 3(2)+4$ • Work inside the parentheses first. Then divide.

$= 6(2)+4$ • Multiply.

$= 12+4$ • Add.

$= 16$

$18 \div 3(8-6)+4 = 16$

Example 2: Simplify: $\dfrac{28 \div 7}{14-6 \times 2}$

$\dfrac{28 \div 7}{14-6 \times 2} = \dfrac{4}{14-6 \times 2}$ • Work above the fraction bar. • Work below the fraction bar: multiply.

$= \dfrac{4}{14-12}$ • Then subtract.

$= \dfrac{4}{2}$ • Divide.

$= 2$

$\dfrac{28 \div 7}{14-6 \times 2} = 2$

Simplify. Follow the order of operations.

Ⓒ **1.** $22 - 8 + 6 =$

Ⓐ 36 Ⓑ 24 Ⓒ 20 Ⓓ 8

Ⓒ **2.** $9 + 5 \times 3 =$

Ⓐ 45 Ⓑ 32 Ⓒ 24 Ⓓ 17

Ⓒ **3.** $\frac{1}{2} + \frac{1}{3} \times \frac{2}{5} =$

Ⓐ $\frac{2}{30}$ Ⓑ $\frac{10}{30}$ Ⓒ $\frac{19}{30}$ Ⓓ $1\frac{7}{30}$

Ⓓ **4.** $10 \times (12 + 8) =$

Ⓐ 20 Ⓑ 92 Ⓒ 128 Ⓓ 200

Ⓓ **5.** $\left(\frac{1}{3} + \frac{1}{2}\right) \times \left(\frac{1}{2} - \frac{1}{3}\right) =$

Ⓐ 1 Ⓑ $\frac{5}{6}$ Ⓒ $\frac{2}{3}$ Ⓓ $\frac{5}{36}$

Ⓑ **6.** $(14 + 14) \times (16 - 6) =$

Ⓐ 1960 Ⓑ 280 Ⓒ 38 Ⓓ 10

Ⓒ **7.** $48 \div 4 + (6 \times 7) - 5 =$

Ⓐ 5 Ⓑ 20 Ⓒ 49 Ⓓ 121

Ⓐ **8.** $72 \div 12 + 1 \times 5 - 2 =$

Ⓐ 9 Ⓑ 10 Ⓒ 21 Ⓓ 33

Ⓒ **9.** $\dfrac{18 - 9}{7 + 10 \times 2} =$

Ⓐ 3 Ⓑ $\frac{9}{34}$ Ⓒ $\frac{1}{3}$ Ⓓ $\frac{9}{72}$

Ⓑ **10.** $\dfrac{4 + 6}{18 \div 9 + 3} =$

Ⓐ $\frac{10}{18 \div 12}$ Ⓑ 2 Ⓒ $\frac{10}{6}$ Ⓓ $\frac{10}{15}$

Name________________________________ Class __________ Date ______________

10.2 EVALUATING EXPRESSIONS

An **expression** is a mathematical phrase such as 7, $8 - d$, or $5a$. Sometimes an expression can contain a **variable,** such as d or a that may be replaced by a number or numbers.

To find the value of an expression, first substitute the values given for each variable, and then compute.

Example 1: Find the value of the expression $4x + y - 2$ when $x = 5$ and $y = 3$.

- Substitute the values for x and for y.
  Use the order of operations to help you compute.

$4x + y - 2 = 4(5) + 3 - 2$ Multiply first.

$= 20 + 3 - 2$ Start at the left. Add, then subtract.

$= 23 - 2$

$= 21$

When $x = 5$ and $y = 3$, $4x + y - 2 = 21$.

Find the value of each expression when $x = 3$ and $y = -5$.

Ⓒ **1.** $2x + y$

Ⓐ -11 Ⓑ -1 Ⓒ $+1$ Ⓓ $+11$

Ⓐ **2.** $2y + x - 6$

Ⓐ -13 Ⓑ -5 Ⓒ $+7$ Ⓓ $+13$

Ⓒ **3.** $x + y + 8$

Ⓐ $+16$ Ⓑ $+10$ Ⓒ $+6$ Ⓓ 0

Ⓓ **4.** $\frac{3y}{x}$

Ⓐ $+5$ Ⓑ $+\frac{9}{5}$ Ⓒ $-\frac{9}{5}$ Ⓓ -5

Ⓒ **5.** $\frac{x + y}{5}$

Ⓐ $+3$ Ⓑ $+\frac{8}{5}$ Ⓒ $-\frac{2}{5}$ Ⓓ -3

Ⓐ **6.** $3(x - y)$

Ⓐ $+24$ Ⓑ $+6$ Ⓒ -6 Ⓓ -24

Find the value of each expression when $a = 2.5$, $b = 7$, and $c = 3.4$.

Ⓑ **7.** $2(b - a) + c$

Ⓐ 9.7 Ⓑ 12.4 Ⓒ 15.8 Ⓓ 30.6

Ⓒ **8.** $\frac{2a + b}{5c}$

Ⓐ $\frac{12}{3.4}$ Ⓑ $\frac{16.5}{17}$ Ⓒ $\frac{12}{17}$ Ⓓ $\frac{11.5}{17}$

Ⓑ **9.** $a(b + c)$

Ⓐ 59.5 Ⓑ 26 Ⓒ 20.9 Ⓓ 15.5

Ⓒ **10.** $a + c - b$

Ⓐ $+6.1$ Ⓑ $+1.1$ Ⓒ -1.1 Ⓓ -6.1

Find the value of each expression when $a = 3\frac{3}{4}$, $b = 6$, and $c = 2\frac{1}{2}$.

Ⓒ **11.** $a - 2b$

Ⓐ $15\frac{3}{4}$ Ⓑ $8\frac{1}{4}$ Ⓒ $-8\frac{1}{4}$ Ⓓ $-15\frac{3}{4}$

Ⓐ **12.** $a - c + 3$

Ⓐ $4\frac{1}{4}$ Ⓑ $9\frac{1}{4}$ Ⓒ $11\frac{1}{2}$ Ⓓ $12\frac{3}{4}$

Ⓓ **13.** $4ac - b$

Ⓐ $-31\frac{1}{2}$ Ⓑ $-27\frac{1}{2}$ Ⓒ $27\frac{1}{2}$ Ⓓ $31\frac{1}{2}$

Ⓑ **14.** $b(a + c)$

Ⓐ 75 Ⓑ $37\frac{1}{2}$ Ⓒ $31\frac{7}{8}$ Ⓓ $24\frac{3}{8}$

Name________________________ Class ________ Date ____________

10.3 EVALUATING FORMULAS

A **formula** is a statement of a mathematical rule. For example, the formula for the area of a rectangle is *Area = length × width,* or $A = l \times w$. You **evaluate,** or find the value of, a formula in the same way you evaluate an expression. First substitute the values given for the variables, and then compute.

Example 1: Find the volume of the pyramid.

The formula for the volume of a pyramid is: $V = \frac{1}{3} \times l \times w \times a$

V = Volume, l = length, w = length, a = altitude

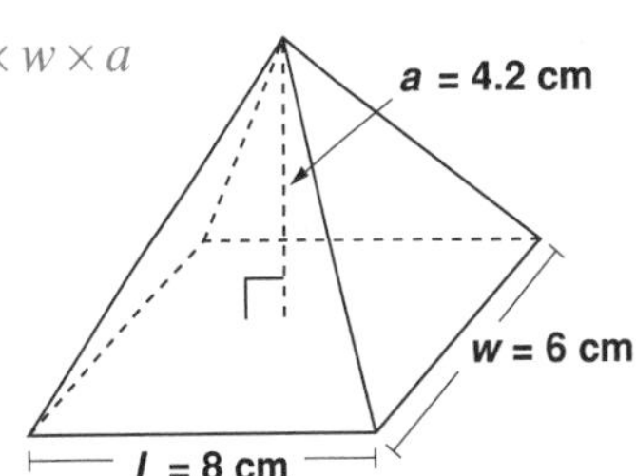

$V = \frac{1}{3} \times l \times w \times a$

$V = \frac{1}{3} \times 8 \times 6 \times 4.2$

$V = 67.2$

The volume of the pyramid is 67.2 cubic centimeters, or 67.2 cu cm.

Use the formula in Example 1 to find the volume of each pyramid.

Ⓑ **1.** l = 10 m, w = 12m, a = 15m

Ⓐ 5400 cu m Ⓑ 600 cu m Ⓒ 540 cu m Ⓓ 60 cu m

Ⓑ **2.** l = 26 in, w = 25 in, a = 18 in

Ⓐ 35,100 cu in Ⓑ 3900 cu in Ⓒ 3510 cu in Ⓓ 390 cu in

Ⓐ **3.** l = 3.6 mm, w = 3.6 mm, a = 5 mm

Ⓐ 21.6 cu mm Ⓑ 194.4 cu mm Ⓒ 216 cu mm Ⓓ 1944 cu mm

Ⓐ **4.** l = 0.7 m, w = 1.8 m, a = 9 m

Ⓐ 3.78 cu m Ⓑ 34.02 cu m Ⓒ 37.8 cu m Ⓓ 340.2 cu m

The formula for the volume of a cone is: $V = \frac{1}{3}\pi r^2 a$, or $V = \frac{1}{3} \times \pi \times r \times r \times a$
(V = Volume, r = radius, a = altitude)

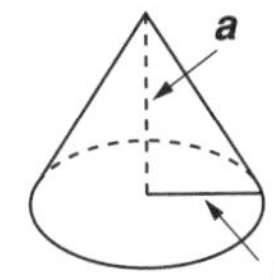

Find the volume of each cone. Use 3.14 for π.

Ⓒ **5.** r = 8 cm, a = 6 cm

Ⓐ 100.48 cu cm Ⓑ 301.44 cu cm Ⓒ 401.92 cu cm Ⓓ 3617.28 cu cm

Ⓑ **6.** r = 1.5 yd, a = 3 yd

Ⓐ 4.71 cu yd Ⓑ 7.065 cu yd Ⓒ 14.13 cu yd Ⓓ 63.585 cu yd

Ⓒ **7.** r = 10 mm, a = 30 mm

Ⓐ 28,260 cu mm Ⓑ 9420 cu m Ⓒ 3140 cu mm Ⓓ 314 cu mm

Ⓒ **8.** r = 4 cm, a = 24 cm

Ⓐ 3617.28 cu cm Ⓑ 2411.52 cu cm Ⓒ 401.92 cu cm Ⓓ 200.48 cu cm

Evaluate the given formula.

Ⓓ **9.** Given $I = PRT$, find the value of I when P =1000, R = 0.08, T = 2.

Ⓐ 8 Ⓑ 16 Ⓒ 80 Ⓓ 160

Ⓓ **10.** Given $d = rt$, find the value of d when r = 55 and $t = 4\frac{1}{2}$.

Ⓐ $220\frac{1}{2}$ Ⓑ $227\frac{1}{2}$ Ⓒ $245\frac{1}{2}$ Ⓓ $247\frac{1}{2}$

Name ____________________ Class ________ Date ____________

10.4 COMBINING LIKE TERMS

In the expression $7a - 6y + 5a$, $7a$ and $5a$ are **like terms** because they have exactly the same variable. You can simplify expressions by combining **like terms**.

Example 1: Simplify: $3c^2 + 8b^2 + 5c - 2b^2 - 3$

- Identify the like terms: $8b^2$ and $2b^2$. Note: $3c^2$ and $5c$ are *not* like terms.
- Regroup the like terms, then combine them.

$$3c^2 + 8b^2 + 5c - 2b^2 - 3 = 3c^2 + 8b^2 - 2b^2 + 5c - 3$$
$$= 3c^2 + 6b^2 + 5c - 3$$

Example 2: Simplify: $3(2x - 3) + 4 - x$

- Use the distributive property* to eliminate parentheses, then combine like terms.

$$3(2x - 3) + 4 - x = 6x - 9 + 4 - x$$
$$= 6x - x - 9 + 4$$
$$= 5x - 5$$

*For a review of the distributive property, see page 11.

Simplify each expression by combining like terms.

Ⓒ **1.** $24d - 18d$

Ⓐ $-6d$ Ⓑ 6 Ⓒ $6d$ Ⓓ $42d$

Ⓑ **2.** $5(5a^2 - 2a^2)$

Ⓐ $15a$ Ⓑ $15a^2$ Ⓒ $23a^2$ Ⓓ $8a^2$

Ⓑ **3.** $18t - 3t - 5t$

Ⓐ 10 Ⓑ $10t$ Ⓒ $10t^2$ Ⓓ $16t$

Ⓐ **4.** $6c + 2 - 2c$

Ⓐ $4c + 2$ Ⓑ $4c^2 + 2$ Ⓒ $6c$ Ⓓ $8c + 2$

Ⓑ **5.** $6x + 2 - (3x - 5)$

Ⓐ $3x - 3$ Ⓑ $3x + 7$ Ⓒ $3x + 3$ Ⓓ $9x + 7$

Ⓒ **6.** $5(4 - 3a) - 2a + 7$

Ⓐ $17a + 27$ Ⓑ $-5a + 27$ Ⓒ $27 - 17a$ Ⓓ $27a - 13a$

Ⓓ **7.** $4(3r - 1) + r$

Ⓐ $13r - 1$ Ⓑ $9r$ Ⓒ $12r - 4$ Ⓓ $13r - 4$

Ⓑ **8.** $2(5g + 2h) - 2g$

Ⓐ $8g + 4$ Ⓑ $8g + 4h$ Ⓒ $8g + 2h$ Ⓓ $8g - 4h$

Ⓑ **9.** $-4y^2 + 5x - 2y^2$

Ⓐ $5x - 6y^4$ Ⓑ $5x - 6y^2$ Ⓒ $5x - 2y^2$ Ⓓ $5x + 6y^2$

Ⓒ **10.** $12m^2 - 4m^2 + 7m^2$

Ⓐ $8m^2 + 7m$ Ⓑ 15 Ⓒ $15m^2$ Ⓓ $19m^2 - 4m$

Ⓒ **11.** $-9xy + 9xy$

Ⓐ $18x^2y^2$ Ⓑ $-18xy$ Ⓒ 0 Ⓓ x^2y^2

Ⓐ **12.** $2(2a + 3b) - (a - 3b)$

Ⓐ $3a + 9b$ Ⓑ $3a + 3b$ Ⓒ $3a$ Ⓒ $6ab$

Ⓓ **13.** $3w^2 + 8wx - 3w^2 + 4wx^2$

Ⓐ $12w^2x^3$ Ⓑ $12wx^2$ Ⓒ $6w^2 + 4wx^2 + 8wx$ Ⓓ $8wx + 4wx^2$

Ⓒ **14.** $2(5fg + 7g^2f) - 8f^2g - 7g^2f$

Ⓐ $18f^3g^2$ Ⓑ $10fg + 21g^2f - 8f^2g$ Ⓒ $10fg + 7g^2f - 8f^2g$ Ⓓ $10fg - 8f^2g$

Name ____________________ Class ________ Date ____________

10.5 READING AND WRITING EQUATIONS

An **equation** is a mathematical sentence stating that two expressions are equal. Examples of equations are $7 + b = 12$ and $3x + 6y = 21$. To write an equation, first choose a letter for the variable. Then translate words into symbols.

Example 1: Write as an equation: Eight more than a number is fifteen.

- Choose a letter for the variable. Let n stand for the number.
- Translate words into symbols.
  Eight more than a number is fifteen.

Example 2: Write as an equation: Twenty-three is six times a number minus seven.

- Let b stand for the number.
- Translate words into symbols.
  Twenty-three is six times a number minus seven.

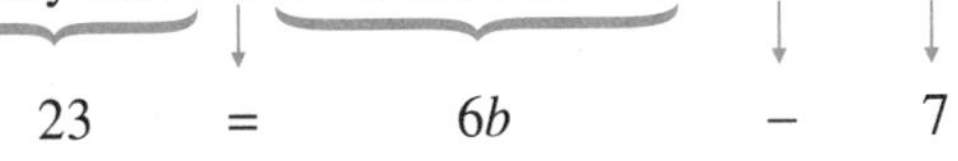

Example 3: Read the equation: $4n + 12 = 28$

- Translate symbols into words.

Four times a number plus twelve is twenty-eight.

Write as an equation.

(B) **1.** The sum of a number and twenty four is fifty-nine.

Ⓐ $n - 24 = 59$ Ⓑ $n + 24 = 59$ Ⓒ $n + 59 = 24$ Ⓓ $24 \div 59 = n$

(C) **2.** Forty-two subtracted from a number is three hundred twenty-eight.

Ⓐ $328 - n = 42$ Ⓑ $42 - n = 328$ Ⓒ $n - 42 = 328$ Ⓓ $n + 42 = 328$

(A) **3.** Eighteen times a number is nine hundred.

Ⓐ $18n = 900$ Ⓑ $18n = 900n$ Ⓒ $18 \times 900 = n$ Ⓓ $900n = 18$

(B) **4.** Twenty-four divided by the sum of a number and three is four.

Ⓐ $\frac{n+3}{24} = 4$ Ⓑ $\frac{24}{n+3} = 4$ Ⓒ $\frac{24}{n+4} = 3$ Ⓓ $\frac{24}{3+4} = n$

Choose the correct sentence for each equation.

(D) **5.** $n + 40 = 50$

Ⓐ The sum of fifty and a number is forty.

Ⓑ Forty more than fifty is a number.

Ⓒ Fifty more than a number is forty.

Ⓓ The sum of forty and a number is fifty.

(B) **6.** $n - 19 = 84$

Ⓐ Eighty-four less than a number is nineteen.

Ⓑ Nineteen less than a number is eighty-four.

Ⓒ Eighty-four subtracted from a number is nineteen.

Ⓓ A number subtracted from nineteen is eighty-four.

Choose the correct equation for each sentence.

Ⓑ **7.** Thirty-two less than a number is fifty-four.

Ⓐ $n - 54 = 32$ Ⓑ $n - 32 = 54$ Ⓒ $32 - n = 54$ Ⓓ $n + 32 = 54$

Ⓐ **8.** Twenty-two times a number is four hundred forty.

Ⓐ $22n = 440$ Ⓑ $22n = 440n$ Ⓒ $22 \times 440 = n$ Ⓓ $440n = 22$

Ⓒ **9.** Seventy-five divided by the sum of five and a number is five.

Ⓐ $\frac{75}{5} + n = 5$ Ⓑ $\frac{75}{5n} = 5$ Ⓒ $\frac{75}{n + 5} = 5$ Ⓓ $\frac{n + 5}{75} = 5$

Ⓒ **10.** Fifteen times the difference of a number and twenty-two is four hundred eighty.

Ⓐ $15n - 22 = 480$ Ⓑ $15(22 - n) = 480$ Ⓒ $15(n - 22) = 480$ Ⓓ $22(n - 15) = 480$

Ⓓ **11.** Eignt less than the sum of a number and twenty-six is forty-two.

Ⓐ $8 - (n + 26) = 42$ Ⓑ $(n - 8) + 26 = 42$ Ⓒ $(26 - n) + 8 = 42$ Ⓓ $(26 + n) - 8 = 42$

Choose the correct sentence for each equation.

Ⓓ **12.** $\frac{108}{n} = 27$

Ⓐ Twenty-seven divided by a number is one hundred eight.

Ⓑ The quotient of twenty-seven and a number is one hundred eight.

Ⓒ A number divided by one hundred eight is twenty-seven.

Ⓓ One hundred eight divided by a number is twenty-seven.

Ⓑ **13.** $3n - 5 = 16$

Ⓐ Three times a number minus sixteen is five.

Ⓑ Five subtracted from three times a number is sixteen.

Ⓒ A number subtracted from three times five is sixteen.

Ⓓ Three subtracted from five times a number is sixteen.

Ⓒ **14.** $53 = 28 + \frac{1}{2} n$

Ⓐ One half of twenty-eight plus a number is fifty-three.

Ⓑ One half of a number minus twenty-eight is fifty-three.

Ⓒ Fifty-three is twenty-eight plus one half a number.

Ⓓ Fifty-three plus twenty-eight is one half a number.

Ⓑ **15.** $\frac{50}{n} - 7 = 18$

Ⓐ Seven subtracted from a number divided by fifty is eighteen.

Ⓑ Seven subtracted from the quotient of fifty and a number is eighteen.

Ⓒ Eighteen is seven less than a number and fifty.

Ⓓ The quotient of fifty minus seven and a number is eighteen.

Name________________________ Class ________ Date ____________

10.6 VENN DIAGRAMS

A **set** is a collection of elements or things.

We can use a **Venn Diagram** to show the relationship between two or more sets.

Example 1: A set is a subset of a second set if every element of the first set is an element of the second set.

In the diagram on the right, set A is a **subset** of set B.

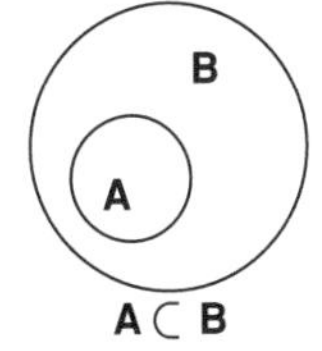

$A \subset B$

Additional Examples

$\{1, 2\} \subset \{1, 2, 3\}$

Example 2: The **intersection** of two sets is the set of elements that are in *both* sets.

In the diagram on the right, the **intersection** of set A and set B is shaded.

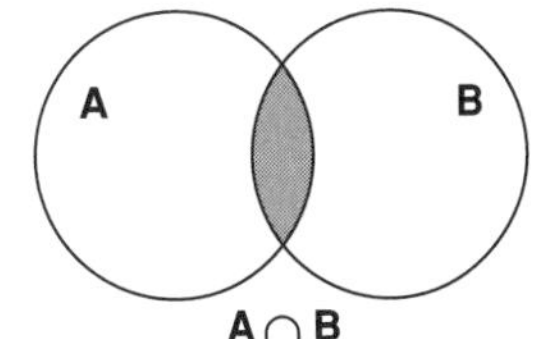

$A \cap B$

$\{1, 2\} \cap \{1, 2, 3\} = \{1, 2\}$

Example 3: The **union** of two sets is the set of all elements that belong to *either* set.

In the diagram on the right, the **union** of set A and set B is shaded.

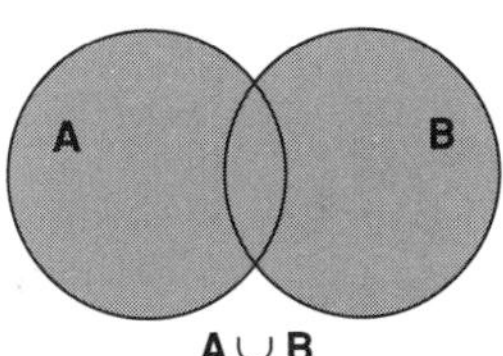

$A \cup B$

$\{1, 2\} \cup \{1, 2, 3\} = \{1, 2, 3\}$

REMEMBER: $\varnothing$ and { } are the mathematical symbols used to represent the **empty set**. For example, $\{1, 2\} \cap \{5, 6\} = \varnothing$.

Let A = {1, 2, 3} and B = {2, 3, 4}. Find each set.

(D) **1.** $A \cap B =$

- (A) {1, 4}
- (B) {1, 2, 3, 4}
- (C) {2, 3, 4}
- (D) {2, 3}

(B) **2.** $A \cup B =$

- (A) {1, 4}
- (B) {1, 2, 3, 4}
- (C) {1, 2, 3}
- (D) {2, 3, 4}

Use Figure 10.6A to answer questions 3-5.

Figure 10.6A

A: 15, 5, 25 | A ∩ B: 10, 20, 30 | B: 40, 60, 50

(C) **3.** Which of the following sets is a subset of set A?

- (A) {5, 15, 60}
- (B) {10, 20, 50}
- (C) {5, 10, 20}
- (D) {15, 30, 60}

(D) **4.** Which of the following sets is a subset of set B?

- (A) {15, 30, 40}
- (B) {5, 20, 30, 50}
- (C) {10, 20, 25}
- (D) {10, 20, 30}

(A) **5.** Which of the following sets is $A \cap B$?

- (A) {10, 20, 30}
- (B) {20, 30, 40}
- (C) {5, 15, 25}
- (D) {40, 50, 60}

Use Figure 10.6B to answer questions 6-8.

Figure 10.6B

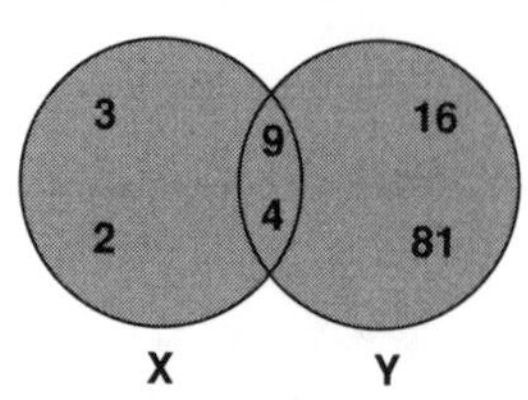

Ⓓ **6.** Which of the following sets is a subset of set X?

Ⓐ {4, 9, 16} Ⓑ {2, 4, 16}
Ⓒ {3, 4, 81} Ⓓ {2, 3, 9}

Ⓐ **7.** Which of the following sets is $X \cap Y$?

Ⓐ {4, 9} Ⓑ {2, 3, 4, 9, 16, 81}
Ⓒ {2, 3, 4, 9} Ⓓ {4, 9, 16, 81}

Ⓑ **8.** Which of the following sets is $X \cup Y$?

Ⓐ {4, 9} Ⓑ {2, 3, 4, 9, 16, 81}
Ⓒ {2, 3, 4, 9} Ⓓ {4, 9, 16, 81}

Use Figure 10.6C to answer questions 9-11.

Figure 10.6C

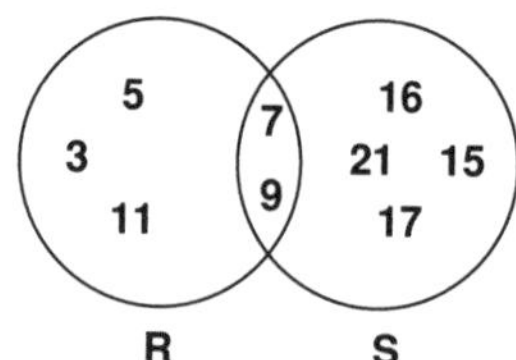

Ⓐ **9.** Which of the following sets is $S \cap R$?

Ⓐ {7, 9} Ⓑ {7, 9, 17}
Ⓒ {17} Ⓓ {3, 7, 9, 17}

Ⓑ **10.** Which of the following sets is a subset of set S?

Ⓐ {5, 7, 9} Ⓑ {17, 21}
Ⓒ {7, 9, 11} Ⓓ {9, 11, 13}

Ⓒ **11.** Which of the following sets is a subset of set R?

Ⓐ {3, 5, 17} Ⓑ {5, 9, 11, 13}
Ⓒ {7, 9, 11} Ⓓ {11, 17}

Use Figure 10.6D to answer questions 12-15.

Figure 10.6D

C
3 15
2 5 9 10
7 8
A B

Ⓓ **12.** Find $A \cap C$.

Ⓐ ∅ Ⓑ {2, 3, 5, 7}
Ⓒ {9, 15} Ⓓ {3, 5}

Ⓐ **13.** Find B.

Ⓐ {8, 9, 10, 15} Ⓑ {9, 15}
Ⓒ {8, 10} Ⓓ ∅

Ⓓ **14.** Which set is a subset of set C?

Ⓐ {8, 9, 15} Ⓑ {3, 5, 7}
Ⓒ {2, 7, 8, 10} Ⓓ {5, 9}

Ⓒ **15.** Find $A \cap B$.

Ⓐ {2, 7, 8, 10} Ⓑ {3, 5, 9, 15}
Ⓒ ∅ Ⓓ {2, 3, 5, 7, 8, 9, 15}

Ⓓ **16.** What does the diagram show about the relationship between animals with tusks and elephants?

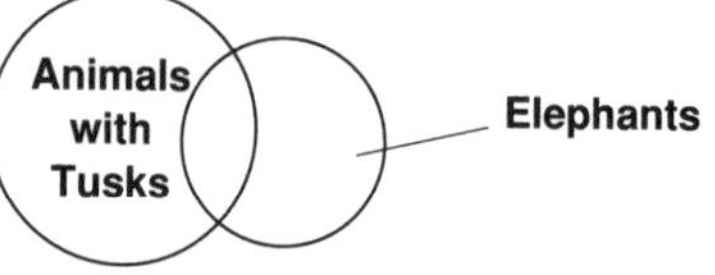

Ⓐ All elephants have tusks.
Ⓑ All animals with tusks are elephants.
Ⓒ No elephants have tusks.
Ⓓ Some elephants have tusks.

Name______________________ Class ________ Date ____________

10.7 SOLVING EQUATIONS: ADDITION AND SUBTRACTION

To solve an equation using addition or subtraction, isolate the variable on one side of the equal sign.

REMEMBER: An equation must balance. If you add to or subtract from one side, you must do the same on the other side to keep the equation in balance.

Example 1: Solve: $n - 7 = 6$

$n - 7 = 6$
$n - 7 + 7 = 6 + 7$ • Add 7 to both sides of the equation. $-7 + 7 = 0$
$n - 0 = 13$
$n = 13$

Check: $n - 7 = 6$
$13 - 7 \stackrel{?}{=} 6$ • Substitute 13 for n in the original equation.
$6 = 6$ ✓

Example 2: Solve: $20 = e + 12$

$20 = e + 12$
$20 - 12 = e + 12 - 12$ • Subtract 12 from both sides of the equation. $+12 - 12 = 0$
$8 = e + 0$
$8 = e$

Check: $20 = e + 12$
$20 \stackrel{?}{=} 8 + 12$ • Substitute 8 for e in the original equation.
$20 = 20$ ✓

Solve.

Ⓓ **1.** $a - 10 = 62$
Ⓐ $a = 10$ Ⓑ $a = 52$ Ⓒ $a = 62$ Ⓓ $a = 72$

Ⓓ **2.** $24 = r - 17$
Ⓐ $r = -17$ Ⓑ $r = +17$ Ⓒ $r = +24$ Ⓓ $r = +41$

Ⓓ **3.** $s - 4.8 = 19.3$
Ⓐ $s = 4.8$ Ⓑ $s = 14.5$ Ⓒ $s = 19.3$ Ⓓ $s = 24.1$

Ⓓ **4.** $42.4 = y - 8.7$
Ⓐ $y = 8.7$ Ⓑ $y = 33.7$ Ⓒ $y = 42.4$ Ⓓ $y = 51.1$

Ⓓ **5.** $x - 3\frac{1}{4} = 5\frac{1}{2}$
Ⓐ $x = 2\frac{1}{4}$ Ⓑ $x = 3\frac{1}{4}$ Ⓒ $x = 5\frac{1}{2}$ Ⓓ $x = 8\frac{3}{4}$

Ⓐ **6.** $r + 402 = 566$
Ⓐ $r = 164$ Ⓑ $r = 402$ Ⓒ $r = 566$ Ⓓ $r = 968$

Ⓑ **7.** $12.7 = 2.4 + f$
Ⓐ $f = 2.4$ Ⓑ $f = 10.3$ Ⓒ $f = 12.7$ Ⓓ $f = 15.1$

Ⓑ **8.** $x - \frac{3}{8} = \frac{3}{4}$
Ⓐ $x = 1\frac{1}{4}$ Ⓑ $x = 1\frac{1}{8}$ Ⓒ $x = \frac{3}{4}$ Ⓓ $x = \frac{3}{8}$

Ⓐ **9.** $p + 28.9 = 50.1$
Ⓐ $p = 21.2$ Ⓑ $p = 28.9$
Ⓒ $p = 50.1$ Ⓓ $p = 79$

Ⓑ **10.** $108.8 = k + 24.4$
Ⓐ $k = 24.4$ Ⓑ $k = 84.4$
Ⓒ $k = 108.8$ Ⓓ $k = 133.2$

Ⓑ **11.** $p + 33 = 92$
Ⓐ $p = 33$ Ⓑ $p = 59$ Ⓒ $p = 92$ Ⓓ $p = 125$

Ⓐ **12.** $1 = t + \frac{2}{3}$
Ⓐ $t = \frac{1}{3}$ Ⓑ $t = \frac{2}{3}$ Ⓒ $t = 1\frac{1}{3}$ Ⓓ $t = 1\frac{2}{3}$

Solve.

Ⓑ **13.** $712 = b + 100$

Ⓐ $b = 100$ Ⓑ $b = 612$ Ⓒ $b = 712$ Ⓓ $b = 812$

Ⓓ **14.** $d - 82 = 401$

Ⓐ $d = 82$ Ⓑ $d = 319$ Ⓒ $d = 401$ Ⓓ $d = 483$

Ⓒ **15.** $c + 2.6 = 5.9$

Ⓐ $c = 8.5$ Ⓑ $c = 5.9$ Ⓒ $c = 3.3$ Ⓓ $c = 2.6$

Ⓐ **16.** $62.4 = y - 12.8$

Ⓐ $y = 75.2$ Ⓑ $y = 62.4$ Ⓒ $y = 49.6$ Ⓓ $y = 12.8$

Ⓐ **17.** $102.2 = m - 19.4$

Ⓐ $m = 121.6$ Ⓑ $m = 102.2$ Ⓒ $m = 82.8$ Ⓓ $m = 19.4$

Ⓒ **18.** $78 = p + 31$

Ⓐ $p = 109$ Ⓑ $p = 78$ Ⓒ $p = 47$ Ⓓ $p = 31$

Ⓓ **19.** $\frac{2}{3} + j = \frac{3}{4}$

Ⓐ $j = \frac{5}{12}$ Ⓑ $j = \frac{3}{4}$ Ⓒ $j = \frac{2}{3}$ Ⓓ $j = \frac{1}{12}$

Ⓐ **20.** $x + 1.4 = 2.7$

Ⓐ $x = 1.3$ Ⓑ $x = 1.4$ Ⓒ $x = 2.7$ Ⓓ $x = 4.1$

Ⓐ **21.** $e - 98 = 100$

Ⓐ $e = 198$ Ⓑ $e = 100$ Ⓒ $e = 98$ Ⓓ $e = 2$

Ⓓ **22.** $x - 3\frac{1}{2} = 8\frac{1}{2}$

Ⓐ $x = 8\frac{1}{2}$ Ⓑ $x = 5$ Ⓒ $x = 3\frac{1}{2}$ Ⓓ $x = 12$

Ⓐ **23.** $r + \frac{5}{9} = \frac{7}{9}$

Ⓐ $r = \frac{2}{9}$ Ⓑ $r = \frac{5}{9}$ Ⓒ $r = \frac{7}{9}$ Ⓓ $r = 1\frac{1}{3}$

Ⓐ **24.** Solve for s: $s - 1464 = 582$

Ⓐ $s = 2046$ Ⓑ $s = 1464$ Ⓒ $s = 582$ Ⓓ $s = -880$

Ⓓ **25.** What is the value of h in the equation $176.6 = h - 13.2$?

Ⓐ $h = 13.2$ Ⓑ $h = 163.4$ Ⓒ $h = 176.6$ Ⓓ $h = 189.8$

Ⓑ **26.** What is the value of y in the equation $y + 297 = 601$?

Ⓐ $y = 297$ Ⓑ $y = 304$ Ⓒ $y = 601$ Ⓓ $y = 898$

Ⓓ **27.** Dan Burns spent \$22.50. He had \$42.50 left over. How much money did he start with?

Ⓐ \$20.00 Ⓑ \$22.50 Ⓒ \$42.50 Ⓓ \$65.00

Ⓑ **28.** Zach Taylor is 175 cm tall. He is 15 cm taller than Sheila Marco. How tall is Sheila?

Ⓐ 15 cm Ⓑ 160 cm Ⓒ 175 cm Ⓓ 190 cm

Ⓑ **29.** When a restaurant opened, there was \$236.00 in the cash register. When the restaurant closed, there was \$1451.96 in the register. How much money did the restaurant take in?

Ⓐ \$236.00 Ⓑ \$1215.96 Ⓒ \$1451.96 Ⓓ \$1687.96

Ⓐ **30.** There were 685 people at a concert before the curtain opened. By intermission there were 989 people. How many people came after the curtain opened?

Ⓐ 304 Ⓑ 685 Ⓒ 989 Ⓓ 1293

Ⓓ **31.** Sam sold $11\frac{1}{2}$ qt of lemonade. He had 2 qt left over. How many quarts did he start with?

Ⓐ 2 qt Ⓑ $9\frac{1}{2}$ qt Ⓒ $11\frac{1}{2}$ qt Ⓓ $13\frac{1}{2}$ qt

Ⓓ **32.** Jennie is 8 years younger than Kenji. If Kenji is 12 years old, how old was Jennie 2 years ago?

Ⓐ 12 years old Ⓑ 8 years old Ⓒ 4 years old Ⓓ 2 years old

Name ______________________ Class __________ Date __________

10.8 SOLVING EQUATIONS: MULTIPLICATION AND DIVISION

To solve equations using multiplication or division, isolate the variable on one side of the equation.

REMEMBER: An equation must balance. If you multiply or divide on one side, you must do the same on the other side to keep the equation in balance.

Example 1: Solve: $8k = 200$

$8k = 200$

$\frac{8k}{8} = \frac{200}{8}$ • Divide both sides of the equation by 8. $\frac{8}{8} = 1$

$k = 25$

Check: $8k = 200$

$8 \times 25 \stackrel{?}{=} 200$ • Substitute 25 for k in the original equation.

$200 = 200$ ✓

Example 2: Solve: $\frac{a}{9} = 10$

$\frac{a}{9} = 10$

$\frac{a}{9} \times 9 = 10 \times 9$ • Multiply both sides of the equation by 9. $\frac{1}{9} \times 9 = 1$

$a = 90$

Check: $\frac{a}{9} = 10$

$\frac{90}{9} \stackrel{?}{=} 10$ • Substitute 90 for a in the original equation.

$10 = 10$ ✓

Solve.

Ⓐ **1.** $5z = 40$

Ⓐ $z = 8$ Ⓑ $z = 35$ Ⓒ $z = 40$ Ⓓ $z = 320$

Ⓑ **2.** $8m = 72$

Ⓐ $m = \frac{1}{9}$ Ⓑ $m = 9$ Ⓒ $m = 72$ Ⓓ $m = 648$

Ⓒ **3.** $7e = 42$

Ⓐ $e = 294$ Ⓑ $e = 42$ Ⓒ $e = 6$ Ⓓ $e = \frac{1}{6}$

Ⓑ **4.** $90 = 5s$

Ⓐ $s = 5$ Ⓑ $s = 18$ Ⓒ $s = 90$ Ⓓ $s = 450$

Ⓑ **5.** $12f = 180$

Ⓐ $f = 12$ Ⓑ $f = 15$ Ⓒ $f = 180$ Ⓓ $f = 2160$

Ⓓ **6.** $48p = 576$

Ⓐ $p = 27{,}648$ Ⓑ $p = 576$ Ⓒ $p = 48$ Ⓓ $p = 12$

Ⓒ **7.** $\frac{w}{4} = 8$

Ⓐ $w = 2$ Ⓑ $w = 8$ Ⓒ $w = 32$ Ⓓ $w = 64$

Ⓓ **8.** $\frac{n}{6} = 4$

Ⓐ $n = \frac{2}{3}$ Ⓑ $n = 4$ Ⓒ $n = 16$ Ⓓ $n = 24$

Ⓑ **9.** $\frac{r}{6} = 9$

Ⓐ $r = 81$ Ⓑ $r = 54$ Ⓒ $r = 9$ Ⓓ $r = \frac{2}{3}$

Ⓐ **10.** $\frac{1}{4}t = 52$

Ⓐ $t = 208$ Ⓑ $t = 52$ Ⓒ $t = 13$ Ⓓ $t = 4$

Ⓓ **11.** $84 = \frac{v}{12}$

Ⓐ $v = 7$ Ⓑ $v = 12$ Ⓒ $v = 84$ Ⓓ $v = 1008$

Ⓓ **12.** $\frac{h}{4.2} = 21$

Ⓐ $h = 4.2$ Ⓑ $h = 5$ Ⓒ $h = 21$ Ⓓ $h = 88.2$

Ⓓ **13.** $\frac{k}{15} = 8$

Ⓐ $k = \frac{8}{15}$ Ⓑ $k = 8$ Ⓒ $k = 64$ Ⓓ $k = 120$

Ⓑ **14.** $1.4x = 6.3$

Ⓐ $x = 1.4$ Ⓑ $x = 4.5$ Ⓒ $x = 6.3$ Ⓓ $x = 8.82$

Ⓐ **15.** $28t = 616$

Ⓐ $t = 22$ Ⓑ $t = 588$

Ⓒ $t = 616$ Ⓓ $t = 17{,}248$

Ⓓ **16.** $\frac{n}{9} = 288$

Ⓐ $n = 9$ Ⓑ $n = 32$

Ⓒ $n = 288$ Ⓓ $n = 2592$

Ⓒ **17.** $2.4 = \frac{s}{0.4}$

Ⓐ $s = 6$ Ⓑ $s = 2.4$

Ⓒ $s = 0.96$ Ⓓ $s = 0.4$

Ⓓ **18.** $3.1r = 21.7$

Ⓐ $r = 67.27$ Ⓑ $r = 21.7$

Ⓒ $r = 18.6$ Ⓓ $r = 7$

Ⓐ **19.** $561 = 51t$

Ⓐ $t = 11$ Ⓑ $t = 510$

Ⓒ $t = 561$ Ⓓ $t = 28{,}611$

Ⓓ **20.** $\frac{x}{3} = 39.9$

Ⓐ $x = 3$ Ⓑ $x = 13.3$

Ⓒ $x = 39.9$ Ⓓ $x = 119.7$

Ⓓ **21.** $37.8 = \frac{f}{4.2}$

Ⓐ $f = 4.2$ Ⓑ $f = 9$

Ⓒ $f = 37.8$ Ⓓ $f = 158.76$

Ⓓ **22.** $720 = 40k$

Ⓐ $k = 28{,}800$ Ⓑ $k = 720$

Ⓒ $k = 680$ Ⓓ $k = 18$

Ⓑ **23.** $\frac{2}{3}x = 12$

Ⓐ $x = 24$ Ⓑ $x = 18$

Ⓒ $x = 12$ Ⓓ $x = 8$

Ⓒ **24.** $\frac{3}{5}y = 21$

Ⓐ $y = 12\frac{3}{5}$ Ⓑ $y = 21$

Ⓒ $y = 35$ Ⓓ $y = 63$

Ⓓ **25.** Ricardo paid \$38.40 for 12.8 lb of cheese. How much did he pay per pound?

Ⓐ \$491.51 Ⓑ \$38.40

Ⓒ \$12.80 Ⓓ \$3.00

Ⓓ **26.** Jessica drove $7\frac{1}{4}$ hours at a speed of 58 mph. How many miles did she travel?

Ⓐ 8 mi Ⓑ 58 mi

Ⓒ 406 mi Ⓓ $420\frac{1}{2}$ mi

Ⓓ **27.** Rob was packing a dozen eggs into each carton that he had. He had 132 eggs in all. How many cartons did he pack?

Ⓐ 1584 Ⓑ 132

Ⓒ 12 Ⓓ 11

Ⓑ **28.** Joanie had a certain amount of money in coins. She divided it into 3 equal piles. Each pile had \$7.50 in it. How much money did she have?

Ⓐ \$35.15 Ⓑ \$22.50

Ⓒ \$21.15 Ⓓ \$2.50

Name________________________ Class ________ Date ____________

10.9 SOLVING TWO-STEP EQUATIONS

To solve two-step equations, first add or subtract. Then multiply or divide.

Example 1: Solve: $14r - 40 = 58$

$$14r - 40 = 58$$
$$14r - 40 + 40 = 58 + 40$$
• Add 40 to both sides of the equation. $-40 + 40 = 0$
$$14r = 98$$
$$\frac{14r}{14} = \frac{98}{14}$$
• Divide both sides of the equation by 14. $\frac{14}{14} = 1$
$$r = 7$$

Check: $14r - 40 = 58$
$$14(7) - 40 \stackrel{?}{=} 58$$
• Substitute 7 for r in the original equation.
$$98 - 40 \stackrel{?}{=} 58$$
$$58 = 58 \checkmark$$

Example 2: Solve: $\frac{y}{6} + 9 = 17$

$$\frac{y}{6} + 9 = 17$$
$$\frac{y}{6} + 9 - 9 = 17 - 9$$
• Subtract 9 from both sides of the equation. $+9 - 9 = 0$
$$\frac{y}{6} = 8$$
$$\frac{y}{6} \times 6 = 8 \times 6$$
• Multiply both sides of the equation by 6. $\frac{1}{6} \times 6 = 1$
$$y = 48$$

Check: $\frac{y}{6} + 9 = 17$
$$\frac{48}{6} + 9 \stackrel{?}{=} 17$$
• Substitute 48 for y in the original equation.
$$8 + 9 \stackrel{?}{=} 17$$
$$17 = 17 \checkmark$$

Solve.

Ⓓ **1.** $9r + 10 = 64$

Ⓐ $r = 486$ Ⓑ $r = 54$ Ⓒ $r = 45$ Ⓓ $r = 6$

Ⓑ **2.** $2m + 3.2 = 6$

Ⓐ $m = 0.2$ Ⓑ $m = 1.4$ Ⓒ $m = 2.8$ Ⓓ $m = 5.6$

Ⓓ **3.** $15z - 14 = 136$

Ⓐ $z = 2250$ Ⓑ $z = 150$ Ⓒ $z = 135$ Ⓓ $z = 10$

Ⓓ **4.** $6.2w - 1.08 = 20$

Ⓐ $w = 130.696$ Ⓑ $w = 25.12$ Ⓒ $w = 21.08$ Ⓓ $w = 3.4$

Ⓒ **5.** $1.2x + 0.4 = 10.6$

Ⓐ $x = 6.625$ Ⓑ $x = 8.43$ Ⓒ $x = 8.5$ Ⓓ $x = 12.24$

Ⓒ **6.** $\frac{k}{3} + 10 = 25$

Ⓐ $k = 5$ Ⓑ $k = 15$ Ⓒ $k = 45$ Ⓓ $k = 75$

Ⓐ **7.** $\frac{g}{30} - 2 = 3$

Ⓐ $g = 150$ Ⓑ $g = 30$ Ⓒ $g = \frac{1}{6}$ Ⓓ $g = \frac{1}{30}$

Ⓒ **8.** $\frac{p}{4.8} + 3 = 7$

Ⓐ $p = 0.8$ Ⓑ $p = 2.08$ Ⓒ $p = 19.2$ Ⓓ $p = 48$

Solve.

Ⓐ **9.** $\frac{h}{2.5} - 30 = 10$

Ⓐ $h = 100$ Ⓑ $h = 42.5$ Ⓒ $h = 37.5$ Ⓓ $h = 16$

Ⓒ **10.** $\frac{e}{49} + 3 = 19$

Ⓐ $e = 8$ Ⓑ $e = 33$ Ⓒ $e = 784$ Ⓓ $e = 928$

Ⓑ **11.** $3n + 15 = 30$

Ⓐ $n = 15$ Ⓑ $n = 5$ Ⓒ $n = 1$ Ⓓ $n = \frac{1}{5}$

Ⓓ **12.** $\frac{w}{6} + 10 = 22$

Ⓐ $w = 144$ Ⓑ $w = 132$ Ⓒ $w = 122$ Ⓓ $w = 72$

Ⓐ **13.** $\frac{z}{26} - 5 = 5$

Ⓐ $z = 260$ Ⓑ $z = 135$ Ⓒ $z = 100$ Ⓓ $z = 0$

Ⓒ **14.** $12h - 36 = 36$

Ⓐ $h = \frac{1}{6}$ Ⓑ $h = 0$ Ⓒ $h = 6$ Ⓓ $h = 39$

Ⓓ **15.** $\frac{2}{3}x + 8 = 14$

Ⓐ $x = 24$ Ⓑ $x = 18$ Ⓒ $x = 12$ Ⓓ $x = 9$

Ⓐ **16.** $\frac{3}{4}z + 8 = 14$

Ⓐ $z = 8$ Ⓑ $z = 9$ Ⓒ $z = 14$ Ⓓ $z = 16$

Ⓐ **17.** $10k + 12 = 62$

Ⓐ $k = 5$ Ⓑ $k = 5.8$ Ⓒ $k = 40$ Ⓓ $k = 50$

Ⓓ **18.** $\frac{r}{18} - 8 = 42$

Ⓐ $r = 32$ Ⓑ $r = 420$ Ⓒ $r = 764$ Ⓓ $r = 900$

Ⓓ **19.** $9x + 0.5 = 7.7$

Ⓐ $x = 64.8$ Ⓑ $x = 7.2$
Ⓒ $x = 1.8$ Ⓓ $x = 0.8$

Ⓑ **20.** $\frac{t}{2.1} + 4 = 55$

Ⓐ $t = 111.15$ Ⓑ $t = 107.1$
Ⓒ $t = 51$ Ⓓ $t = 48.9$

Ⓓ **21.** $\frac{y}{70} - 5 = 5$

Ⓐ $y = 60$ Ⓑ $y = 70$ Ⓒ $y = 355$ Ⓓ $y = 700$

Ⓐ **22.** $11e - 20 = 90$

Ⓐ $e = 10$ Ⓑ $e = 59$ Ⓒ $e = 81$ Ⓓ $e = 99$

Ⓑ **23.** $8.9f + 1 = 63.3$

Ⓐ $f = 53.4$ Ⓑ $f = 7$ Ⓒ $f = 6.39$ Ⓓ $f = 6.11$

Ⓑ **24.** $\frac{h}{0.5} + 5 = 35$

Ⓐ $h = 29.5$ Ⓑ $h = 15$ Ⓒ $h = 12.5$ Ⓓ $h = 6.36$

Ⓒ **25.** Only $\frac{1}{2}$ of the students enrolled in a math class were present on time. Ten students came late. Then there were 26 students in the room. How many students are enrolled in the class?

Ⓐ 16 Ⓑ 18 Ⓒ 32 Ⓓ 52

Ⓑ **26.** A class of 28 students was allotted \$5.00 each for a class trip. They had some money in the class treasury which they added to this amount giving them a total of \$204.00. How much money was in the class treasury?

Ⓐ \$12.80 Ⓑ \$64.00 Ⓒ \$198.40 Ⓓ \$344.00

Ⓒ **27.** There was enough juice for everyone to have 2 glasses. Maria spilled 6 glasses, leaving 34 glasses of juice. How many people were there?

Ⓐ 40 Ⓑ 28 Ⓒ 20 Ⓓ 14

Ⓓ **28.** A water tank was only $\frac{2}{3}$ full. Then, three gallons were used, leaving 7 gallons in the tank. How many gallons does a full tank hold?

Ⓐ 6 Ⓑ 10 Ⓒ $10\frac{2}{3}$ Ⓓ 15

Ⓑ **29.** Clark paid \$8.40 for each T-shirt. Then he paid \$22.90 for a pair of shorts. His bill was \$48.10. How many T-shirts did he buy ?

Ⓐ 2 Ⓑ 3 Ⓒ 4 Ⓓ 5

Ⓑ **30.** Greg bought 5 books, each at the same price. Then he bought a magazine for \$1.95, making his bill \$16.60. How much was each book?

Ⓐ \$1.95 Ⓑ \$2.93 Ⓒ \$3.32 Ⓓ \$3.71

Name____ Class ____________ Date ________________

10.10 GRAPHING EQUATIONS AND INEQUALITIES

You can graph the solution set to an equation or inequality on a number line.

Example 1: Graph the solution of $x + 2 = 5$.

- Solve for x.
  $x + 2 = 5$
  $x + 2 - 2 = 5 - 2$
  $x = 3$

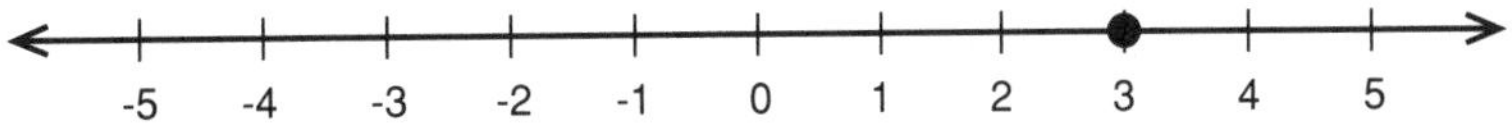

- Graph the solution on a number line.

An **inequality** is a statement that uses the symbol >, <, ≥ (greater than or equal to), or ≤ (less than or equal to) to compare two expressions.

Example 2: Graph the solution of $x + 8 < 12$.

$x + 8 < 12$
$x + 8 - 8 < 12 - 8$
$x + 0 < 4$
$x < 4$

- $x < 4$ means that x is any number less than 4.
- An open circle at 4 means 4 *is not* in the solution set.

Example 3: Graph the solution of $x \geq -2$.

- $x \geq -2$ means that $x = -2$ or $x > -2$

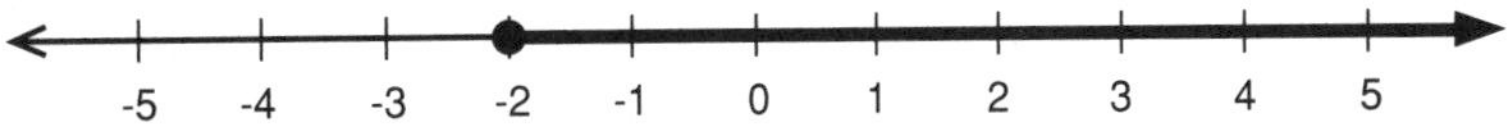

- A filled-in circle at –2 means –2 *is* in the solution set.

Solve.

(D) **1.** Which graph represents the equation $x + 4 = 8$?

(A) 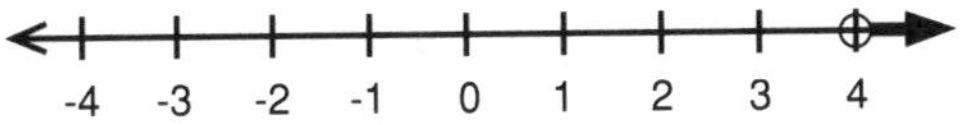

(B) 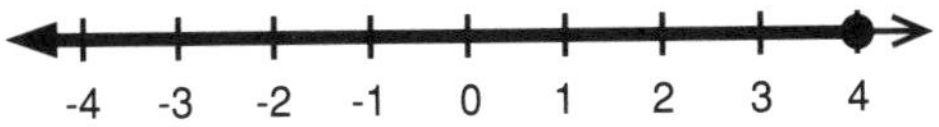

(C) 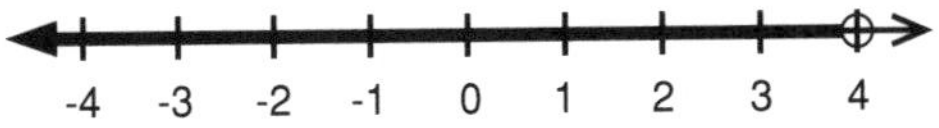

(D) 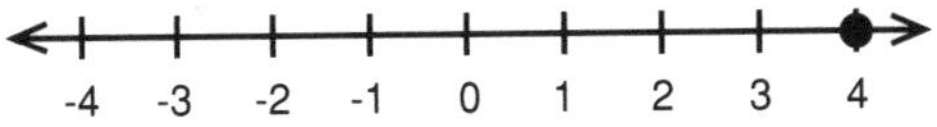

(B) **2.** Which graph represents the inequality $x > 1$?

(A) 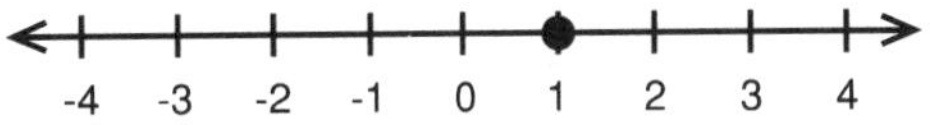

(B) 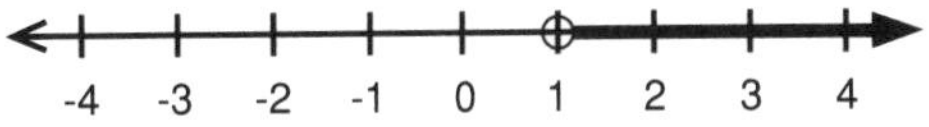

(C) 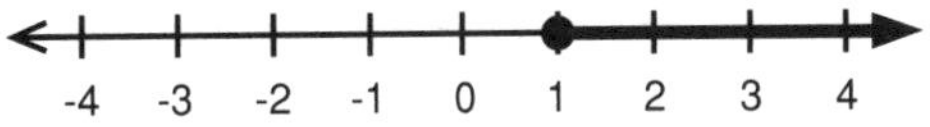

(D) 

Choose the equation or inequality that represents each graph.

(B) **3.** 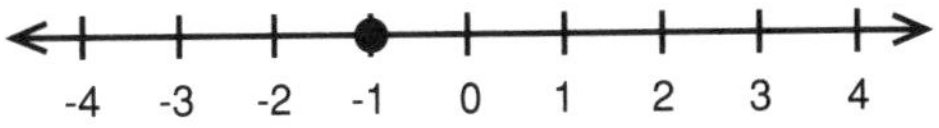

(A) $x < -1$ (B) $x = -1$ (C) $x > -1$ (D) $x < 1$

(D) **4.** 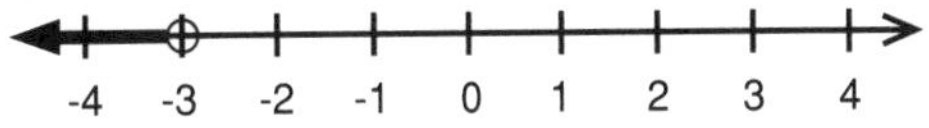

(A) $x > -3$ (B) $x \leq -3$ (C) $x = -3$ (D) $x < -3$

(D) **5.**

Ⓐ $x \geq 1$ Ⓑ $x \leq 1$ Ⓒ $x < 1$ Ⓓ $x > 1$

(C) **6.**

Ⓐ $x \geq -2$ Ⓑ $x \leq -2$ Ⓒ $x > -2$ Ⓓ $x < -2$

(B) **7.** Which graph represents the inequality $x + 4 < 7$?

Ⓐ 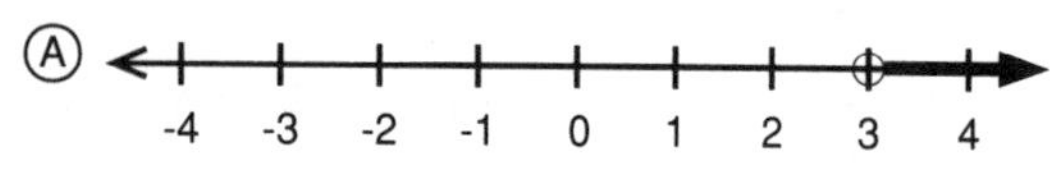

Ⓑ

Ⓒ

Ⓓ

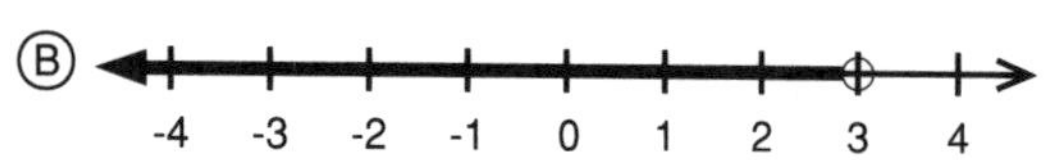

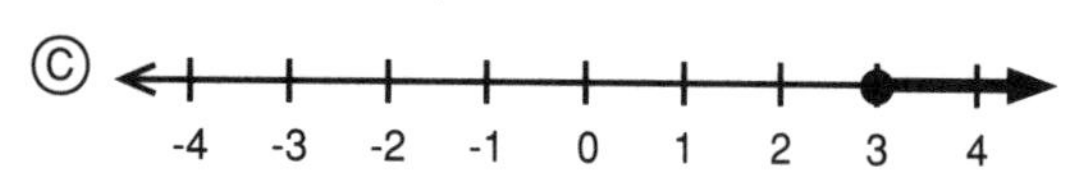

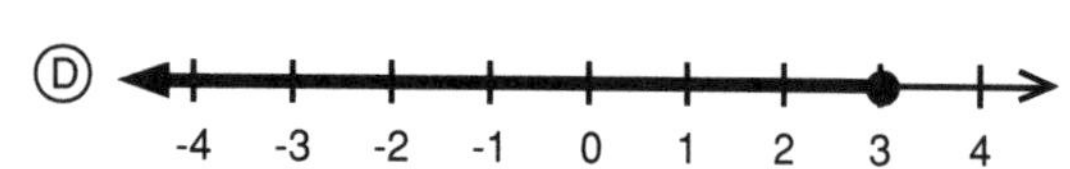

(A) **8.** Which graph represents the inequality $x + 9 \geq 5$?

Ⓐ 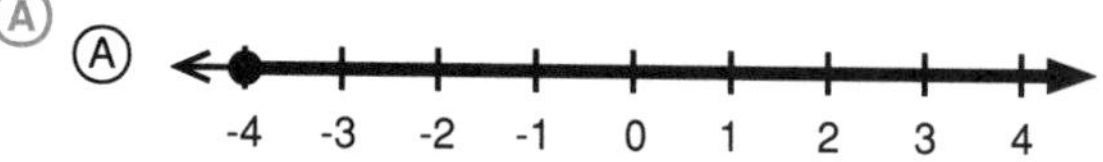

Ⓑ

Ⓒ

Ⓓ

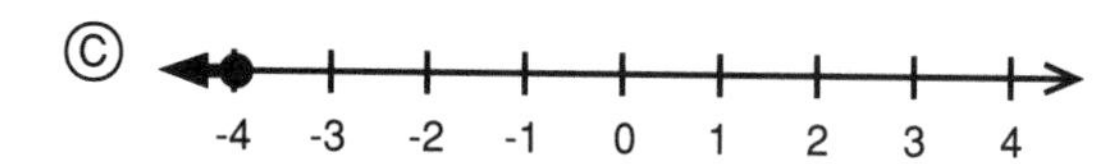

(C) **9.** Which graph represents the equation $x - 2 = 0$?

Ⓐ 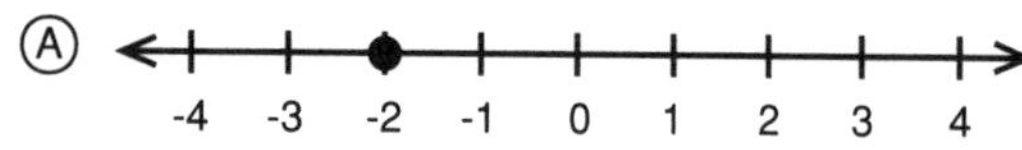

Ⓑ

Ⓒ

Ⓓ

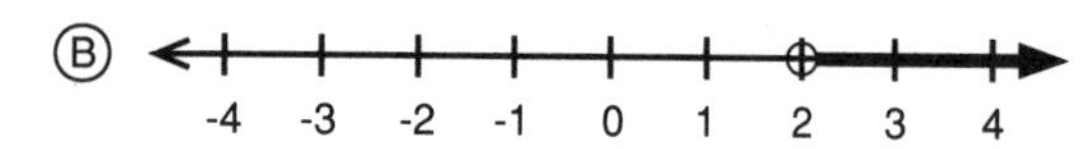

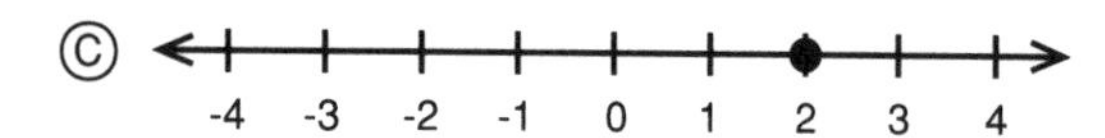

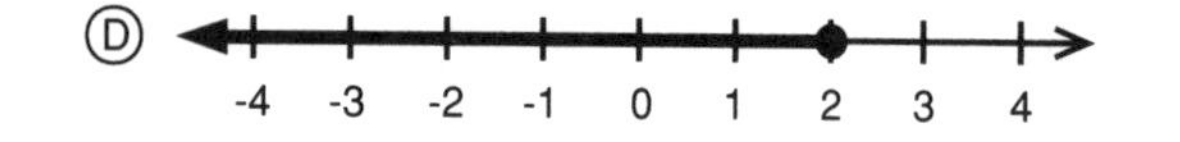

(D) **10.** Which graph represents the inequality $x + 3 \leq 2$?

Ⓐ 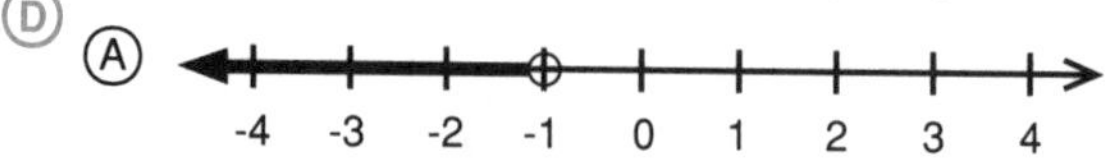

Ⓑ

Ⓒ

Ⓓ

Choose the equation or inequality that represents each graph.

(D) **11.**

Ⓐ $x = -1$ Ⓑ $x < -1$ Ⓒ $x > -1$ Ⓓ $x \geq -1$

(A) **12.**

Ⓐ $x = 0$ Ⓑ $x < 0$ Ⓒ $x > 0$ Ⓓ $x \geq 0$

(B) **13.**

Ⓐ $x < 1$ Ⓑ $x > 1$ Ⓒ $x = 1$ Ⓓ $x \leq 1$

(C) **14.**

Ⓐ $x = -4$ Ⓑ $x \geq -4$ Ⓒ $x \leq -4$ Ⓓ $x > -4$

(B) **15.**

Ⓐ $x > 4$ Ⓑ $x = 4$ Ⓒ $x \leq 4$ Ⓓ $x \geq 4$

(A) **16.**

Ⓐ $x \leq -2$ Ⓑ $x > -2$ Ⓒ $x \geq -2$ Ⓓ $x < -2$

Name ______________________ Class __________ Date __________

CHAPTER 10 TEST

Fill in the correct circle to answer each question.

The formula for the volume of a pyramid is: $V = \frac{1}{3} \times l \times w \times a$ (V = volume, l = length, w = width, a = altitude). Find the volume of each pyramid.

Ⓑ **1.** l = 8m, w = 15m, a = 25m

Ⓐ 1000 sq m Ⓑ 1000 cu m Ⓒ 3000 cu m Ⓓ 9000 cu m

Ⓐ **2.** l = 2 ft, w = 7 ft, a = 12 ft

Ⓐ 56 cu ft Ⓑ 168 cu ft Ⓒ 504 cu ft Ⓓ 560 cu ft

Simplify each expression by combining like terms.

Ⓐ **3.** $9t + 1 - 3t$

Ⓐ $6t + 1$ Ⓑ $7t$ Ⓒ $10t - 3$ Ⓓ $12t - 1$

Ⓑ **4.** $7b + 3c - 6b - c$

Ⓐ $4c + b$ Ⓑ $b + 2c$ Ⓒ $13b - 2c$ Ⓓ $c + b$

Simplify. Follow the order of operations.

Ⓑ **5.** $63 - 28 \div 7 + (3 \times 5) =$

Ⓐ 75 Ⓑ 74 Ⓒ 40 Ⓓ 20

Ⓒ **6.** $\frac{11 + 9}{30 - 5 \times 4} =$

Ⓐ $\frac{1}{5}$ Ⓑ $\frac{7}{10}$ Ⓒ 2 Ⓓ 10

Solve for the variable.

Ⓒ **7.** $18.4 = b - 5.3$

Ⓐ 3.47 Ⓑ 13.1 Ⓒ 23.7 Ⓓ 97.52

Ⓑ **8.** $z + 305 = 799$

Ⓐ 2.62 Ⓑ 494 Ⓒ 1104 Ⓓ 243,695

Ⓐ **9.** $19e = 342$

Ⓐ 18 Ⓑ 323 Ⓒ 361 Ⓓ 6498

Ⓓ **10.** $15.6 = \frac{d}{3.9}$

Ⓐ 4 Ⓑ 11.7 Ⓒ 0.25 Ⓓ 60.84

Ⓐ **11.** $10t + 1.8 = 9$

Ⓐ 0.72 Ⓑ 1.08 Ⓒ 2.8 Ⓓ 7.2

Ⓓ **12.** $\frac{k}{2} - 6 = 38$

Ⓐ 22 Ⓑ 32 Ⓒ 64 Ⓓ 88

Choose the correct sentence for each equation.

Ⓑ **13.** $2n - 4 = 212$

Ⓐ Two times a number minus two hundred twelve is four.

Ⓑ Four subtracted from two times a number is two hundred twelve.

Ⓒ Two times a number less than four is two hundred twelve.

Ⓓ Four subtracted from a number and two is two hundred twelve.

Ⓐ **14.** $\frac{n}{25} - 2 = 9$

Ⓐ Two subtracted from a number divided by twenty-five is nine.

Ⓑ Two subtracted from twenty-five divided by a number is nine.

Ⓒ Nine is two less than the product of twenty-five and a number.

Ⓓ A number divided by twenty-five less than two is nine.

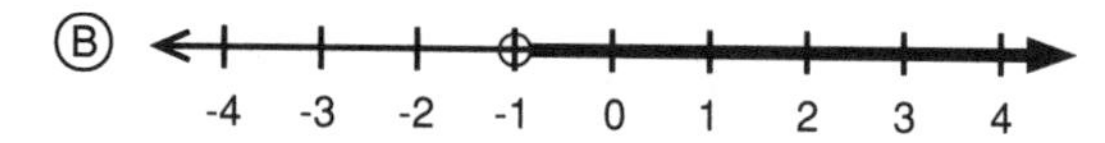

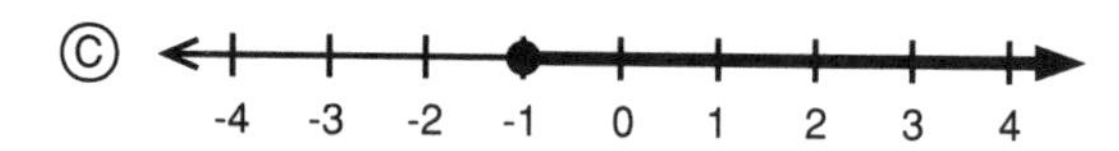

Which equation represents the statement below?

(B) **15.** Twenty-five divided by the difference of a number and ten is four.

Ⓐ $\frac{25}{4} = n - 10$ Ⓑ $\frac{25}{n-10} = 4$

Ⓒ $\frac{n-10}{25} = 4$ Ⓓ $\frac{n-25}{10} = 4$

(D) **16.** Eight times the sum of a number and six is forty-four.

Ⓐ $8n + 6 = 44$ Ⓑ $6(n + 8) = 44$

Ⓒ $n(8 + 6) = 44$ Ⓓ $8(n + 6) = 44$

Write an equation first, then solve the problem.

(C) **17.** If you divide Ken's father's age by 11 and add 7, you get Ken's age, 12. How old is Ken's father?

Ⓐ 16 Ⓑ 31 Ⓒ 55 Ⓓ 77

(C) **18.** Yolanda is 9 inches taller than three times the height she was when she was born. If she is 60 inches tall now, how tall was she when she was born?

Ⓐ 11 in Ⓑ 13 in Ⓒ 17 in Ⓓ 49 in

Find the value of each expression.

(B) **19.** $5t + 4$ when $t = -3$

Ⓐ −9 Ⓑ −11 Ⓒ +11 Ⓓ +19

(C) **20.** $\frac{4d}{-2} + d$ when $d = -3$

Ⓐ −6 Ⓑ −3 Ⓒ +3 Ⓓ +6

Choose the equation or inequality that represents each graph.

(D) **21.** -6 -5 -4 -3 -2 -1 0 1 2 3 4 5 6

Ⓐ $x \geq 0$ Ⓑ $x \leq 0$ Ⓒ $x > 0$ Ⓓ $x < 0$

(A) **22.** -6 -5 -4 -3 -2 -1 0 1 2 3 4 5 6

Ⓐ $x \geq 4$ Ⓑ $x > 4$ Ⓒ $x \leq -4$ Ⓓ $x < 4$

(D) **23.**

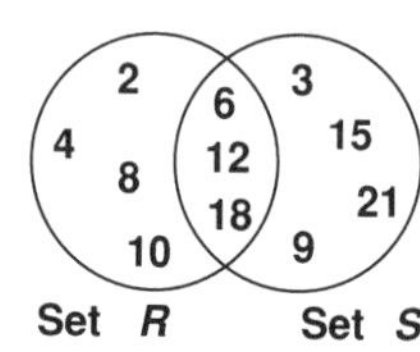

What is $R \cap S$?

Ⓐ {2,4,8,10}

Ⓑ {3,9,15,21}

Ⓒ {2,3,4,6,8,9,10,12,15,18,21}

Ⓓ {6,12,18}

(B) **24.**

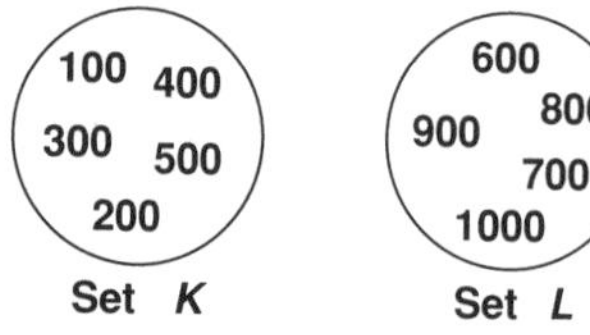

What is $K \cup L$?

Ⓐ Ø

Ⓑ {100,200,300,400,500,600,700,800,900,1000}

Ⓒ {600,700,800,900,1000}

Ⓓ {100,200,300,400,500}

(C) **25.** Which graph represents the equation $x + 9 = 14$?

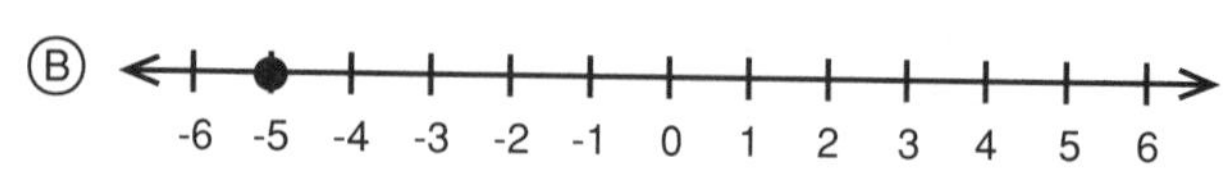

Ⓐ

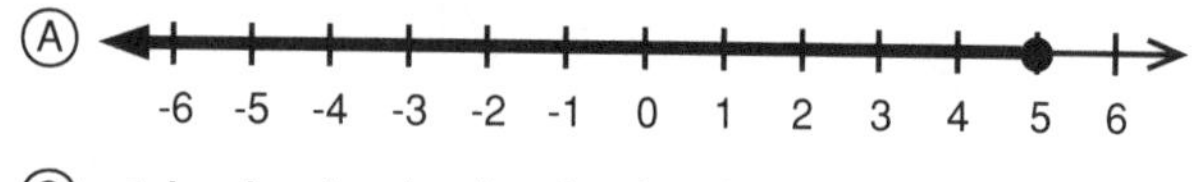

Ⓑ -6 -5 -4 -3 -2 -1 0 1 2 3 4 5 6

Ⓒ

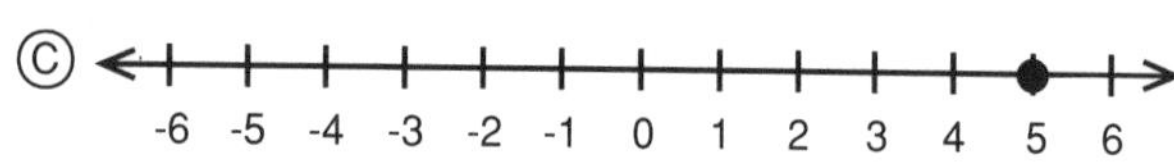

Ⓓ

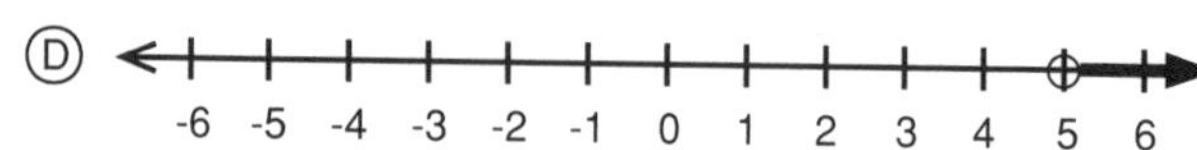

Name ______________________ Class __________ Date __________

CHAPTER 11: CONSUMER TOPICS

TEST-TAKING STRATEGY: *A Review*

In previous chapters, you have learned the following strategies to help you do well on standardized tests.

Test-Taking Strategies

1 Look for Key Words	**2** Use Estimation	**3** Should You Guess?
4 Use Your Time Efficiently	**5** Pull Out Information	**6** Compare Numbers
7 Think On Paper	**8** Mark or Draw a Diagram	**9** Work From the Answers
10 Try Numbers		

The first step in answering any test question is to decide which strategy to use.

Example 1: One leg of a right triangle measures 12 units. The hypotenuse measures 13 units. Find the length of the other leg. (Use the Pythagorean Theorem, $a^2 + b^2 = c^2$.)

- Draw a diagram to help you understand the problem.
- Substitute the given values into the equation and solve.

$a^2 + b^2 = c^2$
$a^2 + 12^2 = 13^2$
$a^2 + 144 = 169$
$a^2 = 25$
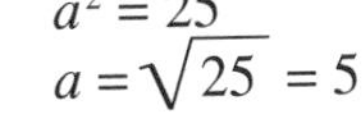
$a = \sqrt{25} = 5$

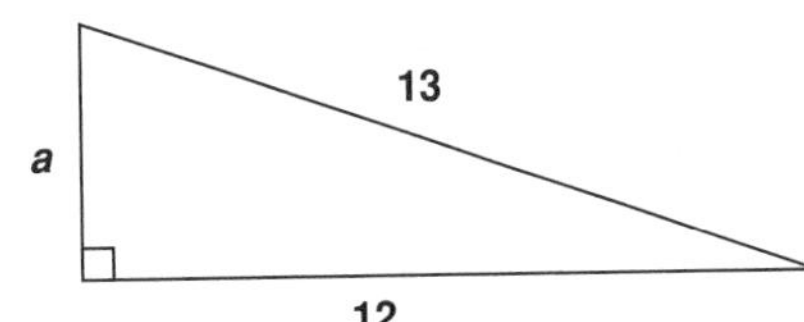

The length of leg a is 5 units.

Sometimes more than one strategy can be used to find the answer.

Example 2: $89\overline{)70,723}$

Ⓐ 75 R48 Ⓑ 794 R57 Ⓒ 794 R63 Ⓓ 7946 R36

You could first estimate the answer by rounding.

$90\overline{)70,000}$ is about 800, which eliminates choices Ⓐ and Ⓓ immediately.

Now work from the answers. Since the estimated quotient is 800, try answer Ⓑ.

Multiply: $89 \times 794 = 70,666$ Add the remainder: $70,666 + 57 = 70,723$

The correct answer is choice Ⓑ.

Find the answer by using the strategy you find most helpful.

Ⓐ **1.** Paul turned 16 in 1988. In what year was he born?

Ⓐ 1972 Ⓑ 1982
Ⓒ 2004 Ⓓ not enough information

Ⓓ **2.** A good estimate of 42×373 would be:

Ⓐ 50×400 Ⓑ 40×300
Ⓒ 50×300 Ⓓ 40×400

Ⓒ **3.** Find n: $\frac{8}{10} = \frac{n}{25}$

Ⓐ 27 Ⓑ 23 Ⓒ 20 Ⓓ 10

Ⓒ **4.** Which decimal is between 0.42 and 0.438?

Ⓐ 0.043 Ⓑ 0.4 Ⓒ 0.426 Ⓓ 0.439

Ⓑ **5.** If x is a positive integer and y is a negative integer, then the value of xy is:

Ⓐ a positive integer Ⓑ a negative integer

Ⓒ zero Ⓓ one

Ⓐ **6.** Estimate the answer. Use your estimate to help you select the correct answer.

$3886 \div 58$

Ⓐ 67 Ⓑ 74 R14 Ⓒ 670 Ⓓ 3944

Ⓑ **7.** Arrange in *descending* order:

$\frac{3}{10}$, 0.697, 0.83, $\frac{3}{4}$

Ⓐ $\frac{3}{10}, \frac{3}{4}$, 0.697, 0.83 Ⓑ 0.83, $\frac{3}{4}$, 0.697, $\frac{3}{10}$

Ⓒ 0.83, 0.697, $\frac{3}{4}, \frac{3}{10}$ Ⓓ $\frac{3}{10}$, 0.697, $\frac{3}{4}$, 0.83

Ⓓ **8.** A 90-minute test has 60 items. How much time should you spend on each test item?

Ⓐ 40 seconds Ⓑ 1 minute

Ⓒ $1\frac{1}{4}$ minutes Ⓓ $1\frac{1}{2}$ minutes

Ⓒ **9.** Find: $\sqrt{784}$

Ⓐ 10 Ⓑ 22 Ⓒ 28 Ⓓ 392

Ⓓ **10.** In the number 9583.461, which digit is in the hundredths place?

Ⓐ 1 Ⓑ 3 Ⓒ 5 Ⓓ 6

Ⓐ **11.** A playground will be built on a plot of ground in the shape of an isosceles triangle. The base of the triangle measures 50 ft. Each of the other sides measures one-half the length of the base. What is the perimeter of the playground?

Ⓐ 100 ft Ⓑ 75 ft Ⓒ 250 ft Ⓓ 180 ft

Ⓒ **12.** The ratio of the corresponding sides of two similar triangles is 1 to 4. If the sides of the smaller triangle measure 2 cm, 4 cm, and 20 cm, what is the perimeter of the larger triangle?

Ⓐ 26 cm Ⓑ 52 cm Ⓒ 104 cm Ⓓ 208 cm

Ⓑ **13.** Solve for y: $7y - 5 = 100$

Ⓐ 5 Ⓑ 15 Ⓒ 20 Ⓓ 50

Ⓒ **14.** Add: 16,848 + 25,389 + 38,483

Ⓐ 50,720 Ⓑ 60,720 Ⓒ 80,720 Ⓓ 110,720

Ⓓ **15.** Joyce leaves her home and walks 2 blocks south and 1 block west. At which place does she arrive?

Ⓐ Pet Shop

Ⓑ Supermarket

Ⓒ School

Ⓓ Record Store

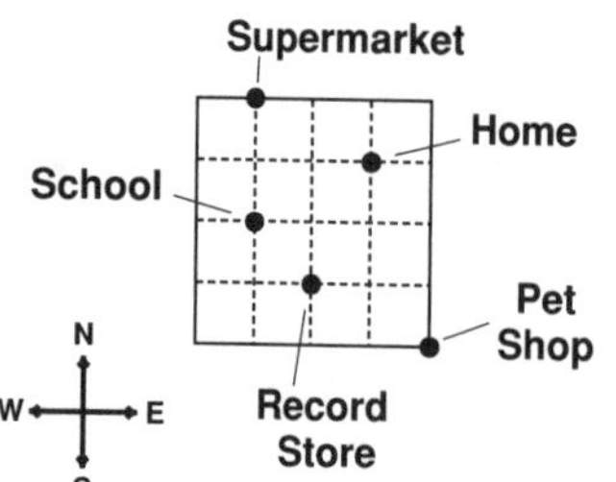

Ⓐ **16.** Find the pattern in the diagram below. How many dots will appear in the next arrangement?

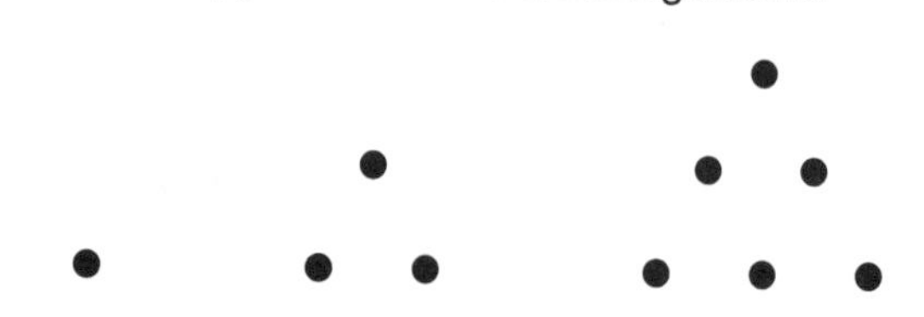

Ⓐ 10 Ⓑ 24 Ⓒ 6 Ⓓ 4

Name ______________________ Class __________ Date __________

CHAPTER 11 PRETEST

Fill in the correct circle to answer each question.

Ⓐ **1.** Add: –30 + –40

Ⓐ –70 Ⓑ –10 Ⓒ +10 Ⓓ +70

Ⓑ **2.** Add: 10 + –4

Ⓐ –14 Ⓑ +6 Ⓒ –6 Ⓓ +14

Ⓒ **3.** Subtract: –5 – –6

Ⓐ –11 Ⓑ –1 Ⓒ +1 Ⓓ +11

Ⓑ **4.** Subtract: 17 – 42

Ⓐ –59 Ⓑ –25 Ⓒ +25 Ⓓ +59

Ⓒ **5.** Multiply: $225 \times \$0.08$

Ⓐ $0.18 Ⓑ $1.80

Ⓒ $18.00 Ⓓ $1800.00

Ⓑ **6.** Multiply: 403×0.025

Ⓐ 1.0075 Ⓑ 10.075

Ⓒ 10,075 Ⓓ 100.75

Write each percent as a decimal.

Ⓒ **7.** 45%

Ⓐ 0.0045 Ⓑ 0.045 Ⓒ 0.45 Ⓓ 4500

Ⓓ **8.** 15%

Ⓐ 0.0015 Ⓑ 0.015 Ⓒ 1500 Ⓓ 0.15

Find the percent of the number.

Ⓒ **9.** 60% of 40

Ⓐ 2.4 Ⓑ 15 Ⓒ 24 Ⓓ 2400

Ⓐ **10.** 20% of $15.00

Ⓐ $3.00 Ⓑ $0.75 Ⓒ $0.30 Ⓓ $300.00

Find the missing number.

Ⓒ **11.** 56 days = ■ weeks

Ⓐ 6 Ⓑ 7 Ⓒ 8 Ⓓ 9

Ⓓ **12.** 14 days = ■ hours

Ⓐ 168 Ⓑ 200 Ⓒ 98 Ⓓ 336

Choose the correct temperature.

Ⓑ **13.**

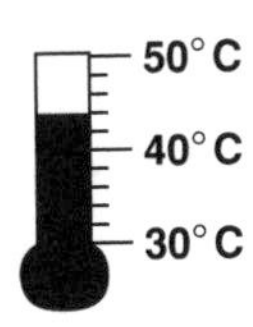

Ⓐ 42° C Ⓑ 44° C Ⓒ 46° C Ⓓ 48° C

Ⓒ **14.**

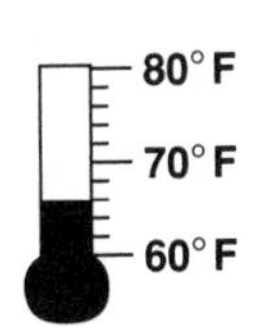

Ⓐ 62° F Ⓑ 63° F Ⓒ 66° F Ⓓ 74° F

Use the rate schedule to determine the usage charge for the following kWh of usage.

ABC Electric Co. Rate Schedule	
First 500 kWh	$0.10 per kWh
Over 500 kWh	$0.09 per kWh

Ⓒ **15.** 2350 kWh

Ⓐ $21.65 Ⓑ $211.50
Ⓒ $216.50 Ⓓ $235.00

Ⓑ **16.** 620 kWh

Ⓐ $55.80 Ⓑ $60.80 Ⓒ $62.00 Ⓓ $608.00

Choose the correct sale price.

Ⓐ **17.** List price: $30 Percent of discount: 15%

Ⓐ $25.50 Ⓑ $4.50 Ⓒ $29.55 Ⓓ $34.50

Ⓑ **18.** List price: $385 Percent of discount: 25%

Ⓐ $96.25 Ⓑ $288.75
Ⓒ $360.00 Ⓓ $481.25

Ⓒ **19.** List price: $75 Percent of discount: 20%

Ⓐ $15.00 Ⓑ $55.00
Ⓒ $60.00 Ⓓ $90.00

Ⓑ **20.** List price: $560 Percent of discount: 30%

Ⓐ $168.00 Ⓑ $392.00
Ⓒ $500.30 Ⓓ $720.00

Solve.

Ⓑ **21.** Find the amount of sales tax on the following purchases: $19.75, $4.25. Tax rate is 6%.

Ⓐ $0.44 Ⓑ $1.44 Ⓒ $24.44 Ⓓ $25.44

Ⓓ **22.** Find the total cost of the following purchases: $55.00, $29.95. Tax rate is 5%.

Ⓐ $4.25 Ⓑ $80.70 Ⓒ $84.95 Ⓓ $89.20

Ⓒ **23.** Compute the interest due on this loan.
Principal: $250.00 Time: 18 months
Annual simple interest rate: 9%

Ⓐ $3.38 Ⓑ $288.75
Ⓒ $33.75 Ⓓ $40,500.00

Ⓒ **24.** Calculate the total amount of the loan.
Principal: $1,500.00 Time: 3 years
Annual simple interest rate: 5%

Ⓐ $225.00 Ⓑ $1,522.50
Ⓒ $1,725.00 Ⓓ $22,500.00

Compute the tip for each service below.

Ⓑ **25.** $20 dinner and a 15% tip

Ⓐ $2.00 Ⓑ $3.00 Ⓒ $20.15 Ⓓ $23.00

Ⓑ **26.** $12 haircut and a 20% tip

Ⓐ $14.40 Ⓑ $2.40 Ⓒ $1.20 Ⓓ $0.20

Ⓓ **27.** $12 cab ride and a 10% tip

Ⓐ $0.10 Ⓑ $13.20 Ⓒ $12.10 Ⓓ $1.20

Ⓒ **28.** $15 lunch and a 15% tip

Ⓐ $17.25 Ⓑ $15.15 Ⓒ $2.25 Ⓓ $0.15

Find the total cost of the meal.

Ⓑ **29.** The bill shows $28. You want to leave a 20% tip.

Ⓐ $48.00 Ⓑ $33.60 Ⓒ $28.20 Ⓓ $5.60

Ⓓ **30.** The bill shows $42. You want to leave a 15% tip.

Ⓐ $0.15 Ⓑ $6.30 Ⓒ $42.15 Ⓓ $48.30

Name ______________________ Class ________ Date ____________

11.1 READING A MAP

Maps are scale drawings. They can be used to estimate distances. Here is a partial map of Maryland. The scale is 1 inch = 6 miles.

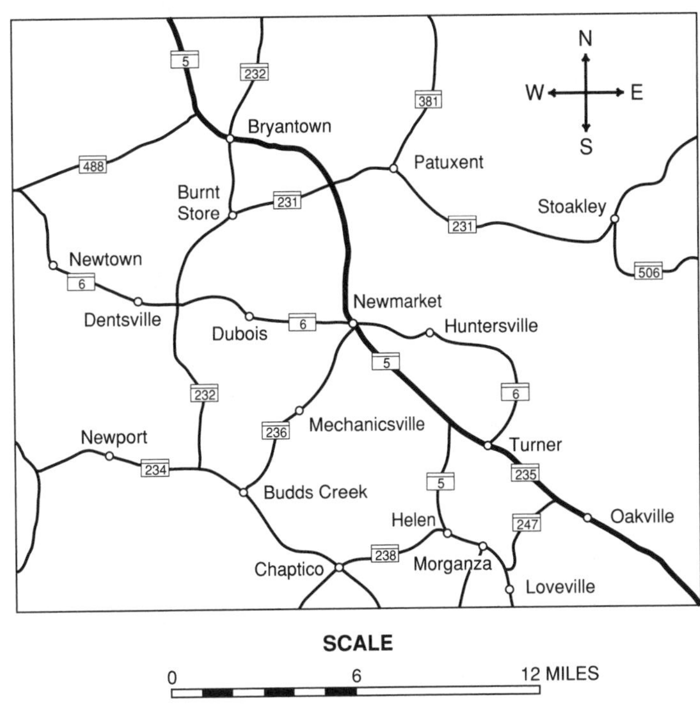

Example 1: What is the best route to take from Huntersville to Mechanicsville?

- Locate the two towns on the map.
- Follow the possible routes from one town to another.
- Choose the shortest route.

The best route is west on Route 6, then south on Route 236. This can be expressed as "Rte. 6 to Rte. 236," or "6 to 236."

Example 2: What is the approximate distance between Budds Creek and Mechanicsville?

- Locate the towns on the map.
- Estimate the distance between the two towns. The distance is about $\frac{1}{2}$ inch.
- Use the scale to find the distance in miles.

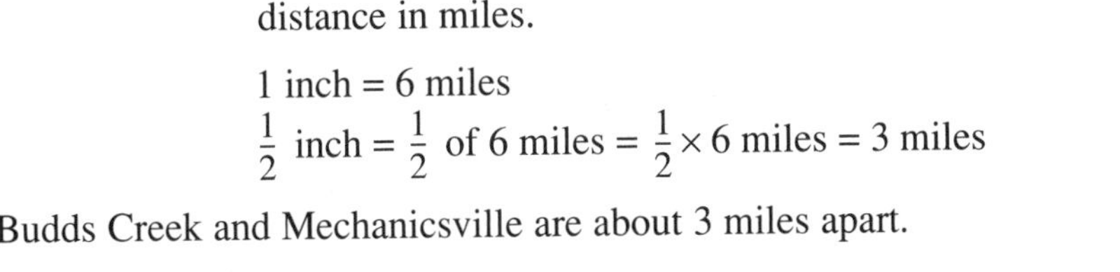

1 inch = 6 miles

$\frac{1}{2}$ inch = $\frac{1}{2}$ of 6 miles = $\frac{1}{2} \times 6$ miles = 3 miles

Budds Creek and Mechanicsville are about 3 miles apart.

Use the map above to determine the shortest distance or best route to take from:

(B) **1.** Newport to Mechanicsville

Ⓐ 234 to 6 Ⓑ 234 to 236
Ⓒ 234 to 232 Ⓓ 234 to 238

(A) **2.** Huntersville to Oakville

Ⓐ 6 to 235 Ⓑ 6 to 5
Ⓒ 6 to 472 Ⓓ 6 to 236

(A) **3.** Morganza to Mechanicsville

Ⓐ 238 to 234 to 236 Ⓑ 238 to 5 to 236
Ⓒ 238 to 234 to 232 Ⓓ 238 to 5

(D) **4.** Mechanicsville to Bryantown

Ⓐ 5 to 232 Ⓑ 236 to 5 to 231 to 232
Ⓒ 236 to 234 to 232 Ⓓ 236 to 5

(D) **5.** Dentsville to Mechanicsville

Ⓐ 6 to 5 Ⓑ 6 to 232
Ⓒ 6 to 232 to 234 to 236 Ⓓ 6 to 236

(A) **6.** Budds Creek to Turner

Ⓐ 236 to 5 to 235 Ⓑ 236 to 6
Ⓒ 236 to 234 to 238 to 247 to 235 Ⓓ 236 to 234 to 238 to 5

Use the map on page 229 to estimate the distance between:

Ⓓ **7.** Newtown and Huntersville

Ⓐ 3 miles Ⓑ 6 miles
Ⓒ 9 miles Ⓓ 15 miles

Ⓒ **8.** Oakville and Turner

Ⓐ 1 mile Ⓑ 2 miles
Ⓒ 4 miles Ⓓ 12 miles

Ⓑ **9.** Newmarket and Huntersville

Ⓐ 1 mile Ⓑ 3 miles
Ⓒ 6 miles Ⓓ 12 miles

Ⓓ **10.** Oakville and Newtown

Ⓐ 3 miles Ⓑ 6 miles
Ⓒ 12 miles Ⓓ 18 miles

Use the map below to determine the shortest distance or best route to take from:

Ⓒ **11.** Ashbox to Cheltenham

Ⓐ 381 to 5 to 301 Ⓑ 301 to 5 to 381
Ⓒ 381 to 301 Ⓓ 381 to 382 to 301

Ⓐ **12.** Naylor to Cheltenham

Ⓐ 382 to 301 Ⓑ 301 to 382
Ⓒ 382 to 381 to 301 Ⓓ 301 to 381 to 382

Ⓓ **13.** Brandywine to Tippett

Ⓐ 381 to 301 to 5 to 223 Ⓑ 381 to 5 to 373 to 223
Ⓒ 381 to 373 to 223 Ⓓ 381 to 5 to 223

Ⓓ **14.** Croom to Brandywine

Ⓐ 382 to 381 Ⓑ 381 to 382
Ⓒ 381 to 301 to 382 Ⓓ 382 to 301 to 381

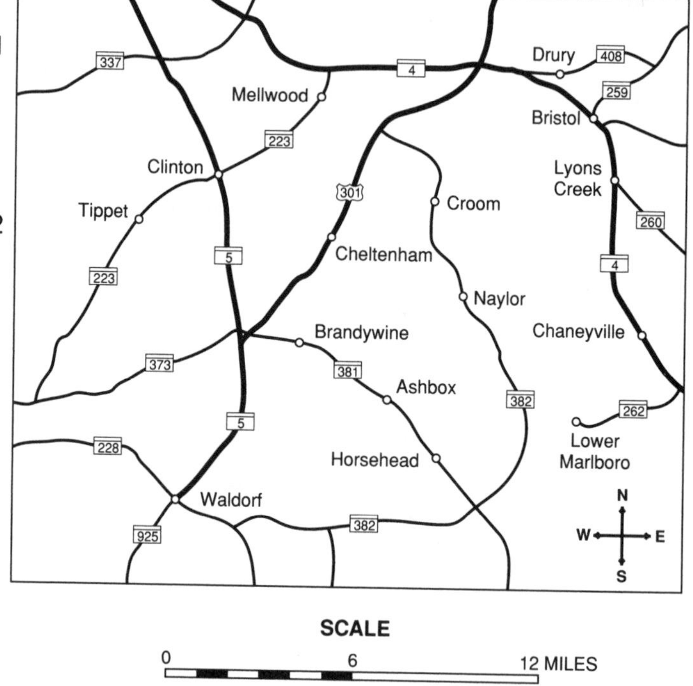

Use the map above to estimate the distance between:

Ⓑ **15.** Brandywine and Horsehead

Ⓐ 1 mile Ⓑ 6 miles
Ⓒ 12 miles Ⓓ 24 miles

Ⓒ **16.** Waldorf and Drury

Ⓐ 3 miles Ⓑ 6 miles
Ⓒ 20 miles Ⓓ 36 miles

Ⓑ **17.** Brandywine and Ashbox

Ⓐ $\frac{1}{2}$ mile Ⓑ 3 miles
Ⓒ 12 miles Ⓓ 24 miles

Ⓑ **18.** Chaneyville and Bristol

Ⓐ 6 miles Ⓑ 8 miles
Ⓒ 12 miles Ⓓ 18 miles

Name _______________ Class _______ Date _______

11.2 TEMPERATURE

A **thermometer** is used to measure temperature. Temperature can be measured on the **Celsius** scale or on the **Fahrenheit** scale.

On the Celsius scale, the freezing point of water is 0°, and the boiling point of water is 100°.

On the Fahrenheit scale, the freezing point of water is 32°, and the boiling point of water is 212°.

Most temperatures in the United States are given in degrees Fahrenheit.

Example 1: What is the temperature?

- Each mark on the thermometer shown stands for 2°, since there are 5 marks from 0° to 10° .
- Start at 10°. Count forward by twos to 14°.

The temperature is 14° C.

Choose the correct temperature or the correct thermometer.

Ⓒ **1.** 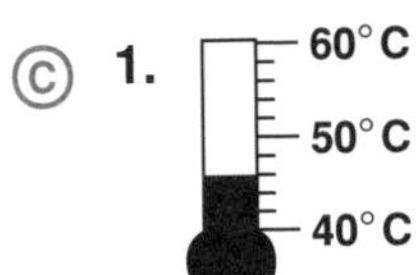

Ⓐ 43° C Ⓑ 44° C Ⓒ 46° C Ⓓ 48° C

Ⓑ **2.** 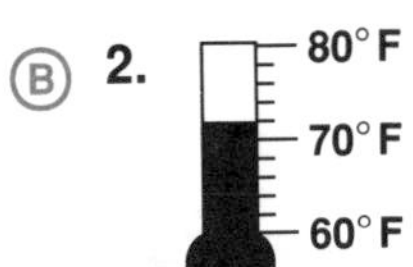

Ⓐ 74° F Ⓑ 72° F Ⓒ 71° F Ⓓ 70° F

Ⓒ **3.** 36° C

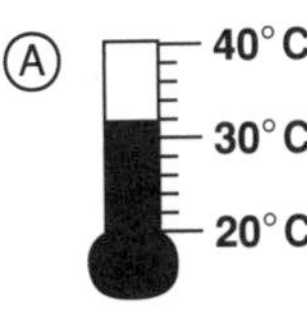

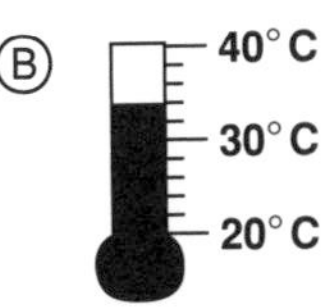

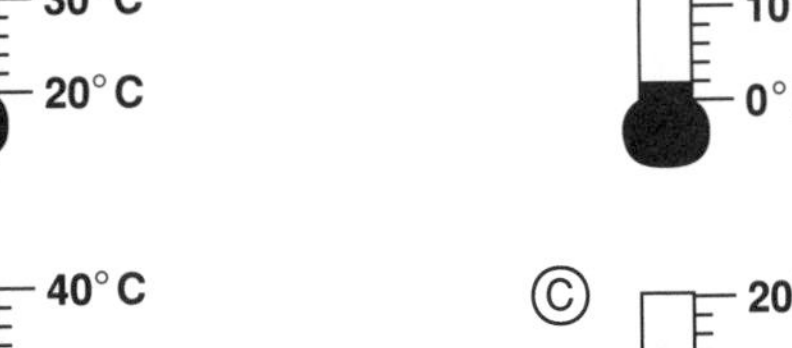

Ⓑ **4.** 12° F

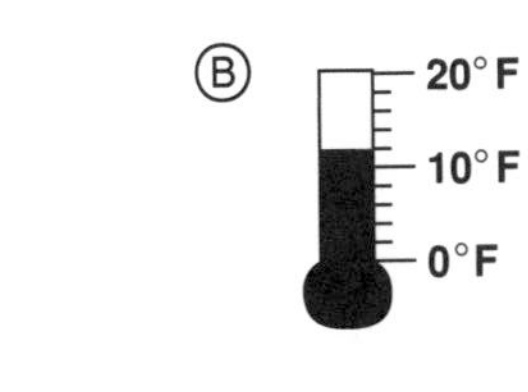

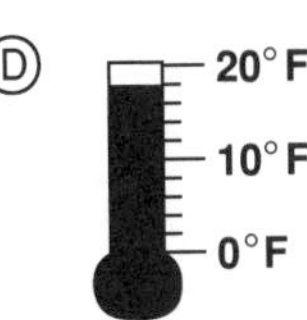

Solve.

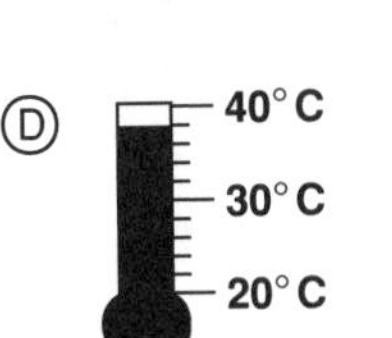

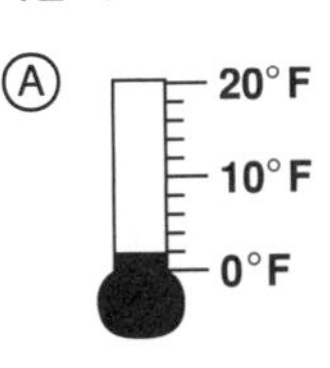

Ⓑ **5.** The temperature was recorded at six different times during one day. The temperatures were 60° F, 66° F, 70° F, 78° F, 74° F, 72° F. What was the average temperature?

Ⓐ 60° F Ⓑ 70° F Ⓒ 72° F Ⓓ 78° F

Ⓓ **6.** One day in Seattle, the low temperature was –3° C. The high temperature was 7° C. What was the difference between the high temperature and the low temperature?

Ⓐ –10° C Ⓑ –4°C Ⓒ +4° C Ⓓ +10° C

Ⓒ **7.** The temperature at 9:00 A.M. was –2° C. By 4:00 P.M. the temperature rose 14 degrees. What was the temperature at 4:00 P.M.?

Ⓐ –16° C Ⓑ –12° C Ⓒ 12° C Ⓓ 16° C

Ⓒ **8.** The temperature at 10:00 P.M. was 53° F. By 5:00 A.M. the temperature dropped 17 degrees. What was the temperature at 5:00 A.M.?

Ⓐ 70° F Ⓑ 44°F Ⓒ 36° F Ⓓ –36° F

Name ______________________ Class ________ Date ____________

11.3 UTILITIES

We use **utilities** such as electricity, gas, water, and the telephone in our homes. Companies that provide these utilities set up rate schedules.

Example 1: The amount of electricity used in a home is measured in **kilowatt hours (kWh).** In June, Jaime Ruiz used 810 kWh of electricity. How much was his bill from the Omega Electric Company?

- Compute the charge for electricity usage. Use the rate table below.

OMEGA ELECTRIC CO. RATE SCHEDULE	
First 500 kWh	$0.12 per kWh
Over 500 kWh	$0.11 per kWh

Charge for first 500 kWh	500 kWh x $0.12 =	$60.00
Charge for amount over 500 kWh	310 kWh x $0.11 =	$34.10
Total Usage Charge		$94.10

Jaime Ruiz's bill from the Omega Electric Company was $94.10.

Use the rate schedule above to determine the usage charge in questions 1-6.

Ⓓ **1.** 1230 kWh

Ⓐ $80.30 Ⓑ $147.60
Ⓒ $135.30 Ⓓ $140.30

Ⓐ **2.** 502 kWh

Ⓐ $60.22 Ⓑ $60.24
Ⓒ $55.22 Ⓓ $50.20

Ⓐ **3.** 714 kWh

Ⓐ $83.54 Ⓑ $78.54
Ⓒ $85.68 Ⓓ $71.40

Ⓒ **4.** 1605 kWh

Ⓐ $176.55 Ⓑ $192.60
Ⓒ $181.55 Ⓓ $160.50

Ⓓ **5.** Sam Robbins runs a record and video store. Last month his store used 23,870 kWh of electricity. What was his bill for that month?

Ⓐ $2387.00 Ⓑ $2864.40
Ⓒ $2625.70 Ⓓ $2630.70

Ⓐ **6.** Kitty Bronski was away on vacation last month. She used only 68.3 kWh of electricity instead of her usual 600 kWh. What was her bill for that month?

Ⓐ $8.20 Ⓑ $6.83
Ⓒ $7.50 Ⓓ $8.01

Ⓐ **7.** A television set uses 0.225 kilowatts of electricity in one hour. The cost of electricity is $0.15 per kilowatt hour. How much does it cost to watch the television for 8 hours?

Ⓐ $0.27 Ⓑ $1.20
Ⓒ $1.80 Ⓓ $2.70

Ⓓ **8.** A clothes dryer uses 3.750 kilowatts of electricity in one hour. The cost of electricity is $.12 per kilowatt hour. How much does it cost to use the dryer for two hours?

Ⓐ $90 Ⓑ $7.50
Ⓒ $1.08 Ⓓ $.90

Name ______________________ Class __________ Date __________

11.4 DISCOUNTS

A **discount** is the amount an item is reduced from its original price. Discounts are often indicated as a percent of the original (or list) price.

SALE
20% OFF ALL KITCHENWARE

Example 1: Ted Wilson wants to buy a blender with a list price of \$175. The store is offering a 20% discount. What is the sale price?

- Find the amount of discount.

  Calculate 20% of \$175.

  Write 20% as 0.20.

  $0.20 \times \$175 = \$35$

- Find the sale price.

  Sale price = Original price − discount

  = \$175 − \$35

  = \$140

The sale price of the blender is \$140.

Example 2: Robin Orantes bought a hand mixer for \$21. The original price was \$25. What was the percent of discount?

- Find the amount of discount.

  \$25 − \$21 = \$4

- Find the percent of discount.

  $$\text{Percent of discount} = \frac{\text{Amount of Discount}}{\text{Original price}} = \frac{\$4}{\$25} = 0.16 = 16\%$$

The percent of discount was 16%.

Choose the correct sale price.

(B) **1.** List price: \$400 Percent of discount: 30%

Ⓐ \$120.00 Ⓑ \$280.00 Ⓒ \$387.00 Ⓓ \$388.00

(D) **2.** List price: \$190 Percent of discount: 5%

Ⓐ \$9.50 Ⓑ \$95.00 Ⓒ \$152.00 Ⓓ \$180.50

Choose the correct percent of discount.

(B) **3.** Original price: \$200 Sale price: \$160

Ⓐ 5% Ⓑ 20% Ⓒ 25% Ⓓ 80%

(D) **4.** Original price: \$525 Sale price: \$105

Ⓐ 20% Ⓑ 25% Ⓒ 50% Ⓓ 80%

Solve.

(D) **5.** A pair of sneakers usually costs \$38. They are on sale for 20% off. What is the sale price?

Ⓐ \$7.60 Ⓑ \$18 Ⓒ \$20 Ⓓ \$30.40

(C) **6.** The regular price of a shirt is \$45. The sale price is \$33.75. What is the percent of discount?

Ⓐ 4% Ⓑ 11.25% Ⓒ 25% Ⓓ 75%

(A) **7.** A ring regularly sells for \$700. The sale price is \$420. What is the percent of discount?

Ⓐ 40% Ⓑ 60% Ⓒ 66% Ⓓ 280%

(D) **8.** The list price of a dress is \$48. It is on sale for 25% off. What is the sale price?

Ⓐ \$12 Ⓑ \$23 Ⓒ \$25 Ⓓ \$36

Name________________________________ Class __________ Date ______________

11.5 SALES TAX

Many cities and states charge a **sales tax** on purchased items. The money from taxes is used for roads, bridges, schools, and other services. Sales tax is expressed as a percent. To find the sales tax on a group of items, multiply the cost of the items by the sales tax rate.

Example 1: Elaine Goldberg bought a notebook for $12.60, a box of pencils for $3.65, and a box of paper clips for $1.75. Sales tax is 6%. How much sales tax does she have to pay?

- Find the total price of the purchases.
  $12.60 + $3.65 + $1.75 = $18.00
- Multiply the sales tax rate by the total price of the purchases.
  Calculate 6% of $18.00.
  $0.06 \times \$18.00 = \$1.08$

Elaine Goldberg has to pay $1.08 in sales tax.

Example 2: Tom O'Brien bought a pair of sneakers for $42.00 and a pair of socks for $8.95. Sales tax is 4%. What is the total cost of his purchases?

- Find the total price of the purchases: $42.00 + $8.95 = $50.95
- Find the amount of sales tax. Round up to the nearest cent: $\$50.95 \times 0.04 = \$2.038 \approx \$2.04$
- Add the amount of sales tax to the total price: $50.95 + $2.04 = $52.99

The total cost of Tom O'Brien's purchases is $52.99.

Find the total sales tax on the following purchases.

Ⓑ **1.** $25.95, $16.02, $1.50 tax rate: 4%
Ⓐ $0.17 Ⓑ $1.74 Ⓒ $4.35 Ⓓ $43.47

Ⓑ **2.** $12.50, $8.60, $4.00 tax rate: 8%
Ⓐ $0.20 Ⓑ $2.01 Ⓒ $2.50 Ⓓ $25.10

Ⓓ **3.** $1.95, $2.50, $1.99 tax rate: 3%
Ⓐ $6.44 Ⓑ $2.00 Ⓒ $0.64 Ⓓ $0.19

Ⓓ **4.** $109.95, $29.95 tax rate: 4.5%
Ⓐ $139.90 Ⓑ $62.95
Ⓒ $13.90 Ⓓ $6.30

Find the total cost of the following purchases.

Ⓓ **5.** $10.95, $5.50 tax rate: 4.5%
Ⓐ $0.74 Ⓑ $15.71 Ⓒ $16.45 Ⓓ $17.19

Ⓐ **6.** $2.50, $1.25 tax rate: 8.25%
Ⓐ $4.06 Ⓑ $3.75 Ⓒ $3.44 Ⓓ $0.31

Ⓒ **7.** $0.89, $1.09, $0.75 tax rate 5%
Ⓐ $.14 Ⓑ $2.73 Ⓒ $2.87 Ⓓ $4.09

Ⓑ **8.** $4.00, $6.25, $8.50 tax rate: 3.5%
Ⓐ $18.09 Ⓑ $19.41 Ⓒ $18.75 Ⓓ $.0.66

Ⓒ **9.** Carmen Esposito bought a pair of earrings for $27.50 and a bottle of nailpolish for $6.95. The rate of sales tax is 8%. How much sales tax will she pay?
Ⓐ $27.56 Ⓑ $2.80 Ⓒ $2.76 Ⓓ $37.21

Ⓒ **10.** Paul Chantal bought a cassette tape for $7.99 and a headset for $29.95. The rate of sales tax is 7%. What is the total cost (including sales tax) of his purchases?
Ⓐ $2.66 Ⓑ $37.94 Ⓒ $40.60 Ⓓ $64.50

Name__________ Class __________ Date __________

11.6 INTEREST

Interest is the amount charged for use of money.

Simple Interest is calculated based upon the amount borrowed, called **principal**. To compute simple interest, use the formula $i = p \times r \times t$, where i = interest, p = principal, r = rate, and t = time.

Example 1: Calculate the simple interest Joe Morgan owes on a 6-month loan if the annual interest rate is 8.25% and the amount borrowed is $1000.

- $p = \$1000$, $r = 8.25\%$, $t = 6$ months

REMEMBER: Write the rate of interest as a decimal. $r = 8.25\%$ or 0.0825

Since there are 12 months in 1 year, $t = 6 \text{ months} = \frac{1}{2}$ year.

- Use the formula: $i = p \times r \times t$

$$i = \$1000 \times 0.0825 \times \frac{1}{2}$$

$$i = \$41.25$$

Example 2: What is the total amount of Joe Morgan's loan?

- Add the interest to the princpal.

$\$1000 + \$41.25 = \$1041.25$

The total amount of Joe Morgan's loan is $1041.25.

Compute the simple interest due on each loan.

(A) **1.** Principal: $350 Annual interest rate: 6.25% Time: 3 months

Ⓐ $5.47 Ⓑ $21.88 Ⓒ $55.00 Ⓓ $65.63

(C) **2.** Principal: $605 Annual interest rate: 8% Time: 12 months

Ⓐ $580.80 Ⓑ $403.33
Ⓒ $48.40 Ⓓ $4.84

(A) **3.** Principal: $924.35 Annual interest rate: 7.5% Time: 18 months

Ⓐ $103.99 Ⓑ $69.33
Ⓒ $46.22 Ⓓ $10.40

(B) **4.** Principal: $1,254.25 Annual interest rate: 5% Time: 3 years

Ⓐ $209.04 Ⓑ $188.14
Ⓒ $20.90 Ⓓ $15.68

Calculate the total amount due on each loan. (Assume the loan is a simple interest loan.)

(D) **5.** Principal: $500.00 Annual interest rate: 5% Time: 3 years

Ⓐ $6.25 Ⓑ $75.00
Ⓒ $525.00 Ⓓ $575.00

(D) **6.** Principal: $1,200.50 Annual interest rate: 5.5% Time: 3 months

Ⓐ $16.51 Ⓑ $1365.57
Ⓒ $1266.33 Ⓓ $1217.01

(B) **7.** Janet Kingsley borrowed $15,000 from a bank. She has 4 years to repay the loan. The annual interest rate is 8.5%. Calculate the simple interest due.

Ⓐ $20,100 Ⓑ $5100
Ⓒ $1275 Ⓓ $16,275

(C) **8.** Pete Skirchak obtained a $1500 simple interest loan for 9 months. The annual interest rate is 10%. Calculate the total amount of the loan.

Ⓐ $112.50 Ⓑ $1350
Ⓒ $1612.50 Ⓓ $1650

Name ______________________ Class ________ Date ____________

11.7 TIPS

Tips are given in this country and in others countries for many different services such as meals served by waiters, haircuts, and taxi rides. Usually tips are computed as a percentage of the total cost.

Example 1: The Oleski family had dinner at a restaurant. The bill was \$35. Mrs. Oleski wanted to leave a 15% tip. How much change would she have from a \$50 bill?

- Compute the tip.

$15\% \times \$35 = 0.15 \times \$35$
$= \$5.25$

- Add the tip to the bill to find the total cost of the meal.

$\$35 + \$5.25 = \$40.25$

- Subtract the total cost from \$50.

$\$50 - \$40.25 = \$9.75$

Mrs. Oleski should receive \$9.75 in change.

Compute the tip for each service below.

Ⓑ **1.** \$10 dinner and a 16% tip

Ⓐ \$0.16 Ⓑ \$1.60 Ⓒ \$10.16 Ⓓ \$11.60

Ⓒ **2.** \$20 haircut and a 10% tip

Ⓐ \$0.10 Ⓑ \$0.20 Ⓒ \$2.00 Ⓓ \$20.00

Ⓒ **3.** \$24 cab ride and a 15% tip

Ⓐ \$27.60 Ⓑ \$24.15 Ⓒ \$3.60 Ⓓ \$0.18

Ⓑ **4.** \$90 dinner and a 20% tip

Ⓐ \$0.20 Ⓑ \$18.00 Ⓒ \$20.00 Ⓓ \$90.20

Compute the tip for each service below. Round your answer to the nearest dollar.

Ⓓ **5.** Dinner costs \$103.98 for a group of 4. You leave a 15% tip.

Ⓐ \$15.00 Ⓑ \$15.50 Ⓒ \$15.60 Ⓓ \$16.00

Ⓐ **6.** A cab ride costs \$23.60. You give the driver a 20% tip.

Ⓐ \$5.00 Ⓑ \$4.72 Ⓒ \$4.70 Ⓓ \$4.00

Ⓐ **7.** A haircut costs \$15.45. You give a tip of 15%.

Ⓐ \$2.00 Ⓑ \$2.31 Ⓒ \$2.40 Ⓓ \$3.00

Ⓓ **8.** Lunch costs \$18.67. You leave a 20% tip.

Ⓐ \$3.00 Ⓑ \$3.70 Ⓒ \$3.73 Ⓓ \$4.00

Find the total cost of the dinner.

Ⓓ **9.** The bill shows \$16. You want to leave a 15% tip.

Ⓐ \$2.40 Ⓑ \$16.15 Ⓒ \$16.24 Ⓓ \$18.40

Ⓒ **10.** The bill shows \$102. You want to leave a 25% tip.

Ⓐ \$102.25 Ⓑ \$127.00 Ⓒ \$127.50 Ⓓ \$25.50

Ⓑ **11.** The bill shows \$57. You want to leave tip of 10%.

Ⓐ \$67.00 Ⓑ \$62.70 Ⓒ \$60.00 Ⓓ \$57.57

Ⓒ **12.** The bill shows \$88. You want to leave a tip of 20%.

Ⓐ \$88.20 Ⓑ \$108.00 Ⓒ \$105.60 Ⓓ \$17.60

Name ____________________ Class ________ Date ____________

CHAPTER 11 TEST

Fill in the correct circle to answer each question.

Ⓑ **1.** Choose the correct sale price.
List price: $390 Discount: 30%

Ⓐ $117.00 Ⓑ $273.00
Ⓒ $360.00 Ⓓ $507.30

Ⓒ **2.** Choose the correct percent of discount.
Original price: $290 Sale Price: $261

Ⓐ 0.1% Ⓑ 11.1%
Ⓒ 10% Ⓓ 90%

Ⓒ **3.** A bicycle usually costs $195. It is on sale for $126.75. What is the percent of discount?

Ⓐ 65% Ⓑ 53.85% Ⓒ 35% Ⓓ 68.25%

Ⓑ **4.** A dress costs $85. It is on sale for 20% off. What is the sale price?

Ⓐ $17.00 Ⓑ $68.00 Ⓒ $65.00 Ⓓ $102.00

Compute the simple interest due on each loan.

Ⓐ **5.** Principal: $785 Time: 9 months
Annual interest rate: 7.5%

Ⓐ $44.16 Ⓑ $58.88
Ⓒ $529.88 Ⓓ $829.16

Ⓒ **6.** Principal: $1,075 Time: 3 years
Annual interest rate: 5%

Ⓐ $16.13 Ⓑ $1236.25
Ⓒ $161.25 Ⓓ $16,125.00

Find the answers.

Ⓑ **7.** What is the temperature?

Ⓐ 15°F Ⓑ 14°F
Ⓒ 12°F Ⓓ 23°F

Ⓒ **8.** The temperature at 5 P.M. was 38°F. In three hours, the temperature dropped to 23°F. What was the difference in temperature?

Ⓐ −61°F Ⓑ −15°F Ⓒ +15°F Ⓓ +61°F

Use the rate schedule to determine the usage charge for the following kWh of usage.

Ⓑ **9.** 629 kWh

Ⓐ $50.32 Ⓑ $55.32
Ⓒ $56.61 Ⓓ $90.32

Rapid Power & Electric Company Rate Schedule	
First 500 kWh	$0.09 per kWh
Over 500 kWh	$0.08 per kWh

Ⓑ **10.** A dryer uses 5.89 kilowatts of electricity in one hour. The cost of electricity is $0.18 per kilowatt hour. How much does it cost to use the dryer for $1\frac{1}{2}$ hours?

Ⓐ $0.71 Ⓑ $1.59 Ⓒ $15.90 Ⓓ $49.08

Ⓑ **11.** Sophia Gucci borrowed $8,450. The annual simple interest rate is 6.5%. She has $2\frac{1}{2}$ years to repay the loan. Calculate the interest due.

Ⓐ $549.25 Ⓑ $1,373.13
Ⓒ $9,823.13 Ⓓ $137,312.50

Find the total amount of sales tax on the following purchases.

(A) **12.** \$18.50, \$4.50, \$2.00; tax rate: 6%

Ⓐ \$1.50 Ⓑ \$15.00 Ⓒ \$25.00 Ⓓ \$26.50

(A) **13.** \$155.45, \$49.95; tax rate: 4.5%

Ⓐ \$9.24 Ⓑ \$20.54 Ⓒ \$214.64 Ⓓ \$205.40

Find the total cost of the following purchases.

(C) **14.** \$12.95, \$22.50, \$3.95; tax rate: 8%

Ⓐ \$3.15 Ⓑ \$39.40 Ⓒ \$42.55 Ⓓ \$70.92

(C) **15.** \$5.50, \$6.25, \$1.50; tax rate: 6%

Ⓐ \$0.80 Ⓑ \$13.25 Ⓒ \$14.05 Ⓓ \$21.20

Compute the tip for each service below.

(C) **16.** \$16 cab ride and a 15% tip

Ⓐ \$0.15 Ⓑ \$1.00 Ⓒ \$2.40 Ⓓ \$18.40

(C) **17.** \$23 haircut and a 20% tip

Ⓐ \$0.20 Ⓑ \$0.46 Ⓒ \$4.60 Ⓓ \$27.60

Find the total cost of the dinner.

(D) **18.** The bill shows \$34. You leave a tip of 20%.

Ⓐ \$6.80 Ⓑ \$34.20 Ⓒ \$36.00 Ⓓ \$40.80

(B) **19.** The bill shows \$78. You leave a tip of 15%.

Ⓐ \$93.00 Ⓑ \$89.70 Ⓒ \$78.15 Ⓓ \$11.70

Solve.

(C)

(B) **21.** The Money Bank has loaned Maryanne Baker \$7500 for 2.5 years. The annual simple interest rate is 11%. Calculate the interest due.

Ⓐ \$9562.50 Ⓑ \$2062.50

Ⓒ \$18,750 Ⓓ \$206,250

Use the map to answer questions 22–25.

(C) **22.** Kim took Routes 99 and 80 from Modesto to Reno. She arrived in 4 hours. Her average speed was about:

Ⓐ 35 mph. Ⓑ 40 mph.

Ⓒ 50 mph. Ⓓ 65 mph.

(B) **23.** The town nearest Angels Camp is:

Ⓐ Modesto. Ⓑ Buck Meadows.

Ⓒ Lodi. Ⓓ Dardanelle.

(D) **24.** What is the shortest route from Buck Meadows to Modesto?

Ⓐ 120 to 99 Ⓑ 132 to 120

Ⓒ 132 to 149 to 120 Ⓓ 120 to 49 to 132

(A) **25.** How many numbered roads does Route 49 intersect?

Ⓐ Five Ⓑ Four Ⓒ Three Ⓓ Two

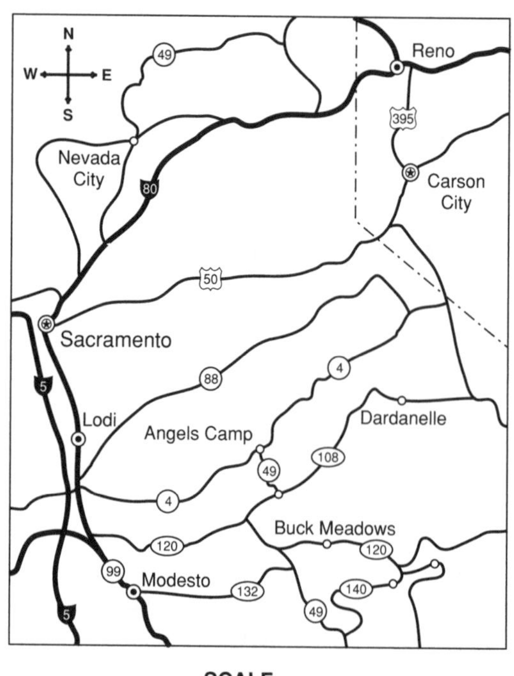

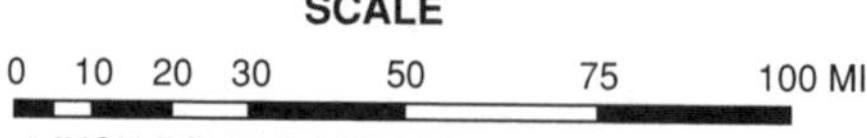

Name ____________________ Class ________ Date ____________

CHAPTERS 1-11 CUMULATIVE REVIEW

Fill in the correct circle to answer each question.

Ⓓ **1.** $12 \times 8 - 6 =$ ■

Ⓐ 14 Ⓑ 24 Ⓒ 80 Ⓓ 90

Ⓑ **2.** What is the sum of 4035 and 269?

Ⓐ 1,085,415 Ⓑ 4304
Ⓒ 3766 Ⓓ 15

Ⓐ **3.** What is the total cost including sales tax of a calculator priced at $69.95? Sales tax is 6%.

Ⓐ $74.15 Ⓑ $65.75 Ⓒ $65.15 Ⓓ $4.20

Ⓓ **4.** Which set of integers shows its elements in *descending* order?

Ⓐ –80, 40, –5, 3 Ⓑ –80, –5, 3, 40
Ⓒ 40, –5, 3, –80 Ⓓ 40, 3, –5, –80

Ⓒ **5.** What is the temperature shown on the thermometer?

Ⓐ 11° F Ⓑ 12° F
Ⓒ 14° F Ⓓ 15° F

Ⓑ **6.** What is the area of the triangle?

Ⓐ $2\frac{1}{2}$ Ⓑ 6 sq in
Ⓒ $7\frac{7}{12}$ Ⓓ 12 sq in

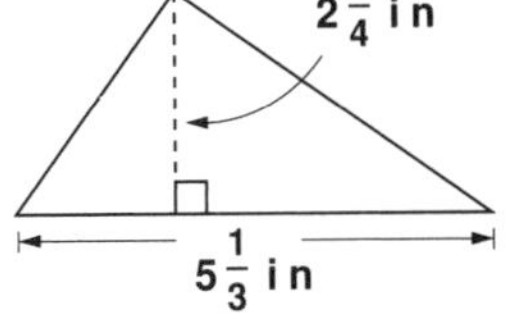

Ⓒ **7.** Which equation matches the following statement? Three times a number minus seventeen equals forty–four.

Ⓐ 3 (n – 17) = 44 Ⓑ 3n – 7 = 44
Ⓒ 3n – 17 = 44 Ⓓ 3n = 17 – 44

Ⓒ **8.**
$$\begin{array}{r} 378 \\ \times 934 \\ \hline \end{array}$$

Ⓐ 46,842 Ⓑ 353,022
Ⓒ 353,052 Ⓓ 363,042

Ⓓ **9.** Solve for *g*: $2g - 6 = 10$

Ⓐ 2 Ⓑ 3 Ⓒ 7 Ⓓ 8

Ⓑ **10.** Write $\frac{7}{20}$ as a percent.

Ⓐ 286% Ⓑ 35% Ⓒ 3.5% Ⓓ 2.86%

Ⓒ **11.** Combine like terms: $7b + 8a - b$

Ⓐ $16ab$ Ⓑ $-b + 8a$
Ⓒ $6b + 8a$ Ⓓ $8(b + a)$

Ⓓ **12.** What is the volume of a cube with one side that measures 12 inches? Use the formula: $V = s \times s \times s$.

Ⓐ 72 cu in Ⓑ 432 cu in
Ⓒ 864 cu in Ⓓ 1728 cu in

Ⓒ **13.** The regular price of a bicycle is $160.00. It is on sale for 25% off. What is the sale price?

Ⓐ $200 Ⓑ $135 Ⓒ $120 Ⓓ $40

Ⓓ **14.**
$$\begin{array}{r} 27.93 \\ 999.01 \\ 0.009 \\ +888.8 \\ \hline \end{array}$$

Ⓐ 19,167.49 Ⓑ 9915.849
Ⓒ 1915.83 Ⓓ 1915.749

Ⓑ **15.** Subtract –4 from –17.

Ⓐ –21 Ⓑ –13 Ⓒ +13 Ⓓ +21

Ⓐ **16.** What percent is 12 of 120?

Ⓐ 10% Ⓑ 144% Ⓒ 1000% Ⓓ 12%

Ⓓ **17.** Compute the simple interest due on the following loan. Principal: $4000; Annual Interest Rate: 6.5%; Time: 3 years

Ⓐ $4780 Ⓑ $87 Ⓒ $680 Ⓓ $780

Ⓑ **18.** Find the value of the expression $2a + b \times c$ when $a = 7$, $b = 3$, and $c = 1$.

Ⓐ 13 Ⓑ 17 Ⓒ 18 Ⓓ 42

Ⓒ **19.** Solve for k: $18 - k = 8$

Ⓐ 26 Ⓑ 12 Ⓒ 10 Ⓓ –10

Ⓐ **20.** 29,750 ÷ 3.4 = ■

Ⓐ 8750 Ⓑ 8600 Ⓒ 875 Ⓓ 860

Ⓑ **21.** A long distance call costs $1.17 for the first 3 minutes and $0.25 for each additional minute. Lisa spoke for 12 minutes. How much did her long distance call cost?

Ⓐ $3.92 Ⓑ $3.42 Ⓒ $4.17 Ⓓ $10.78

Ⓑ **22.** If you toss a coin, what is the probability that it will land on tails?

Ⓐ 2 Ⓑ $\frac{1}{2}$ Ⓒ $\frac{1}{6}$ Ⓓ $\frac{1}{3}$

Ⓐ **23.** Evaluate the formula $d = r \times t$ when $t = 24$ and $r = 50$.

Ⓐ 1200 Ⓑ $2\frac{1}{12}$ Ⓒ $\frac{12}{25}$ Ⓓ 74

Ⓑ **24.** Solve for w: $9.6w - 1.2 = 6$

Ⓐ 0.1875 Ⓑ 0.75 Ⓒ 46.08 Ⓓ 69.12

Ⓓ **25.** A stereo uses 0.15 kilowatt hours of electricity in one hour. The cost of electricity is $0.11 per kilowatt hour. Estimate how much it costs to play the stereo for 5 hours.

Ⓐ $6.82 Ⓑ $3.67 Ⓒ $0.02 Ⓓ $0.08

Ⓐ **26.** Find the perimeter of a rectangle with sides 12 cm and 15 cm. Use the formula: $P = 2l + 2w$.

Ⓐ 54 cm Ⓑ 54 sq cm

Ⓒ 108 cm Ⓓ 108 sq cm

Ⓓ **27.** Sales tax is 6.5%. What is the total cost of a bicycle priced at $350.00?

Ⓐ $22.75 Ⓑ $327.25

Ⓒ $367.50 Ⓓ $372.75

Ⓓ **28.** Which of the following statements is true based on the diagram?

Grey Horses

Arabian Horses

Fast Horses

Ⓐ All Arabian horses are fast.

Ⓑ Some grey horses are fast.

Ⓒ All grey horses are Arabian.

Ⓓ All fast horses are Arabian.

Ⓒ **29.** What is the radius of a circle with a circumference of 31.4 in ?
Use the formula: $C = \pi \times d$.

Ⓐ 0.5 Ⓑ 98.596 Ⓒ 5 Ⓓ 10

Ⓐ **30.** Some quadrilaterals are ■ .

Ⓐ trapezoids Ⓑ pentagons

Ⓒ complementary Ⓓ perpendicular

Ⓓ **31.** -13×6 = ■

Ⓐ +78 Ⓑ –18 Ⓒ –7 Ⓓ –78

Ⓑ **32.** Determine the amount of simple interest:
Principle = $2500, Rate = 12.5% per year,
Time = 18 months.

Ⓐ $17.36 Ⓑ $468.75

Ⓒ $562.50 Ⓓ $2968.75

Name ______________________________ Class __________ Date ______________

(D) **33.** A trapezoid

Ⓐ has 4 congruent sides.

Ⓑ has 4 right angles.

Ⓒ never has sides parallel.

Ⓓ has exactly one pair of parallel sides.

(A) **34.** What does the diagram show about the relationship between jugglers and men?

Ⓐ Some jugglers are men.

Ⓑ All men are jugglers.

Ⓒ No men are jugglers.

Ⓓ All jugglers are men.

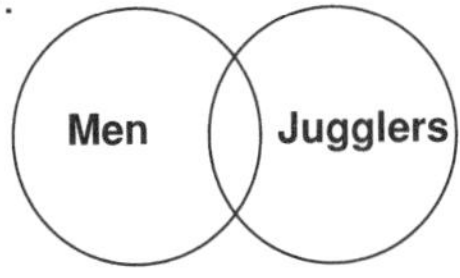

(C) **35.** Divide $\frac{2}{7}$ by $\frac{7}{28}$.

Ⓐ $\frac{1}{28}$ Ⓑ $\frac{1}{14}$ Ⓒ $1\frac{1}{7}$ Ⓓ $2\frac{1}{7}$

(D) **36.** $2\frac{1}{4} + \frac{2}{7} - \frac{3}{8} = \blacksquare$

Ⓐ $\frac{24}{56}$ Ⓑ $1\frac{25}{28}$ Ⓒ $2\frac{1}{7}$ Ⓓ $2\frac{9}{56}$

(D) **37.** What is the volume of the cylinder? Use the formula: $V = \pi \times r \times r \times h$. Use 3.14 for π.

Ⓐ 19.468 sq m

Ⓑ 19.468 cu m

Ⓒ 38.936 sq m

Ⓓ 38.936 cu m

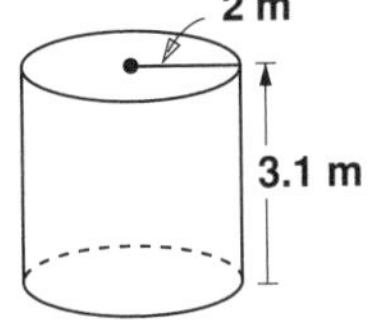

(A) **38.** What is the temperature?

Ⓐ –4° C

Ⓑ –2° C

Ⓒ –16° C

Ⓓ –13° C

(D) **39.** Which set of lengths gives a right triangle? Use the Pythagorean Theorem: $a^2 + b^2 = c^2$.

Ⓐ 1, 2, 3 Ⓑ 6, 7, 9

Ⓒ 4, 5, $\sqrt{40}$ Ⓓ 1, 2, $\sqrt{5}$

(B) **40.** A bill for dinner is $33.00. You leave a 15% tip. What is the total cost of the meal?

Ⓐ $82.50 Ⓑ $37.95 Ⓒ $28.05 Ⓓ $4.95

(D) **41.** Select the numeral for seventy billion three hundred thousand five hundred eighteen.

Ⓐ 17,300,518 Ⓑ 70,300,518

Ⓒ 17,300,518,000 Ⓓ 70,000,300,518

(A) **42.** If r and s are negative integers and t is a positive integer, then $r \times s \times t$ is:

Ⓐ a positive integer Ⓑ 1

Ⓒ a negative integer Ⓓ 0

(B) **43.** Divide: –27 ÷ –3

Ⓐ +81 Ⓑ +9 Ⓒ –81 Ⓓ –9

(A) **44.** Solve for x: $\frac{51.6}{x} = 3$

Ⓐ 17.2 Ⓑ 48.6 Ⓒ 54.6 Ⓓ 154.8

(B) **45.** A train departs at 7:30 P.M. and arrives at 1:45 A.M. How long did the trip take?

Ⓐ 7h 15 min Ⓑ 6h 15 min

Ⓒ 4h 15 min Ⓓ 5h 45 min

(C) **46.** $\frac{6 + 2 \times 8}{2 \times 4 + 4} = \blacksquare$

Ⓐ $\frac{4}{5}$ Ⓑ $1\frac{2}{9}$ Ⓒ $1\frac{5}{6}$ Ⓓ $5\frac{1}{3}$

(C) **47.** Find the quotient of 11,567 and 43.

Ⓐ 29 R10 Ⓑ 268 R33

Ⓒ 269 Ⓓ 369

(D) **48.** A new pair of running shoes cost $39.95. Sales tax is 4.5%. What is the total cost?

Ⓐ $1.80 Ⓑ $38.15 Ⓒ $40.75 Ⓓ $41.75

Ⓒ **49.** Find the area of the parallelogram. Use the formula: $A = b \times h$.

Ⓐ 14.4 sq ft
Ⓑ 20.6 sq ft
Ⓒ 21.6 sq ft
Ⓓ 22.3 sq ft

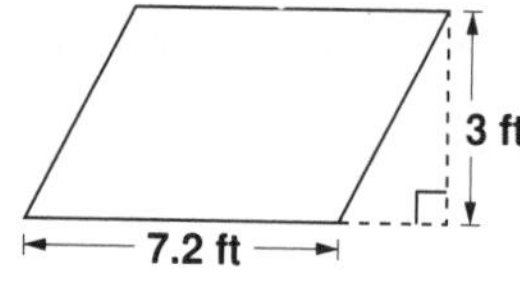

Ⓓ **50.** Combine like terms.
$25a + 16a - ab + 3a - 15ab$

Ⓐ $44a - 16b$
Ⓑ $44a + 15b$
Ⓒ $28ab$
Ⓓ $44a - 16ab$

Ⓒ **51.** 270 is 30% of what number?

Ⓐ 9000 Ⓑ 8100 Ⓒ 900 Ⓓ 81

Ⓐ **52.** Solve for w: $\frac{w}{5} = 325$

Ⓐ 1625 Ⓑ 320 Ⓒ 85 Ⓓ 65

Ⓑ **53.** Solve for d: $37.8 + d = 17.5$

Ⓐ –55.3 Ⓑ –20.3 Ⓒ 2.16 Ⓓ 19.3

Ⓓ **54.** Solve for x: $3x + 2 = 6$

Ⓐ 24 Ⓑ 12 Ⓒ $6\frac{2}{3}$ Ⓓ $1\frac{1}{3}$

Ⓑ **55.** Round 27,581 to the nearest *thousand*.

Ⓐ 30,000 Ⓑ 28,000
Ⓒ 27,600 Ⓓ 27,000

Ⓐ **56.** Maria borrows $5000 from a bank. She has 3 years to pay the loan at the simple interest rate of 8%. Calculate the total amount of Maria's loan.

Ⓐ $6200 Ⓑ $5400 Ⓒ $16,200 Ⓓ $1200

Ⓑ **57.** What is the surface area of a cylinder with diameter of 6 meters and a height of 5 meters? Use the formula: $A = (2 \times \pi \times r \times r) + (2 \times \pi \times r \times h)$. Use 3.14 for π.

Ⓐ 226.08 sq m Ⓑ 150.72 sq m
Ⓒ 131.88 sq m Ⓓ 414.48 sq m

Ⓒ **58.** Find the volume of the pyramid below. The formula for the volume of a pyramid is: $V = \frac{1}{3} \times l \times w \times a$.

Ⓐ 21 cu cm
Ⓑ 203 sq cm
Ⓒ 210 cu cm
Ⓓ 315 cu cm

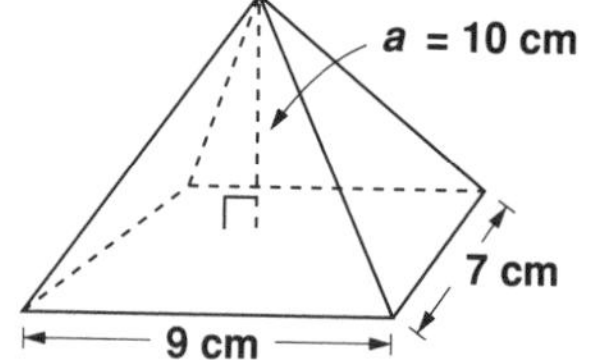

Ⓐ **59.** The distance between Evergreen and Pine Valley is 200 miles. On a map, this distance measures 5 inches. What is the scale?

Ⓐ 1 in = 40 mi Ⓑ 4 in = 1 mi
Ⓒ 200 in = 5 mi Ⓓ 40 in = 1 mi

Ⓐ **60.** $5.43 \times 10^6 =$ ▇

Ⓐ 5,430,000 Ⓑ 543,000
Ⓒ 543,000,000 Ⓓ 0.00000543

Ⓒ **61.** A jacket is regularly priced $59.95. It is on sale for 30% off. What is the sale price?

Ⓐ $17.99 Ⓑ $40.98 Ⓒ $41.97 Ⓓ $77.94

Ⓐ **62.** A haircut costs $12. You want to leave a tip of 10%. How much will you leave?

Ⓐ $1.20 Ⓑ $1.50 Ⓒ $10.00 Ⓓ $13.20

Ⓑ **63.** Compute the mean of 627.8, 37.9, 800, and, 555.5.

Ⓐ 500.3 Ⓑ 505.3
Ⓒ 590.575 Ⓓ 675.73

Ⓓ **64.** A triangle with 3 unequal sides is ▇ .

Ⓐ isoceles Ⓑ right
Ⓒ equilateral Ⓓ scalene

Ⓑ **65.** $6 + -12 + 20 =$ ▇

Ⓐ –26 Ⓑ +14 Ⓒ –14 Ⓓ +26

Ⓒ **66.** Evaluate $4y - 6x + xy$ when $x = 3$ and $y = 10$.

Ⓐ –18 Ⓑ –8 Ⓒ 52 Ⓓ 88

SCORING CHART

Number Correct

No. of Questions	0	1	2	3	4	5	6	7	8	9	10	11	12	13	14	15	16	17	18	19	20	21	22	23	24	25	26	27	28	29	30	31	32	33	34	35	36	37	38	39	40 --------
5	0	20	40	60	80	100																																			
6	0	17	34	50	67	84	100																																		
7	0	15	29	43	58	72	86	100																																	
8	0	13	25	38	50	63	75	88	100																																
9	0	12	23	34	45	56	67	78	89	100																															
10	0	10	20	30	40	50	60	70	80	90	100																														
11	0	10	19	28	37	46	55	64	73	82	91	100																													
12	0	9	17	25	34	42	50	59	67	75	84	92	100																												
13	0	8	16	24	31	39	47	54	62	70	77	85	93	100																											
14	0	8	15	22	29	36	43	50	58	65	72	79	86	93	100																										
15	0	7	14	20	27	34	40	47	54	60	67	74	80	87	94	100																									
16	0	7	13	19	25	32	38	44	50	57	63	69	75	82	88	94	100																								
17	0	6	12	18	24	30	36	42	48	53	59	65	71	77	83	89	95	100																							
18	0	6	12	17	23	28	34	39	45	50	56	62	67	73	78	84	89	95	100																						
19	0	6	11	16	22	27	32	37	43	48	53	58	64	67	74	79	85	90	95	100																					
20	0	5	10	15	20	25	30	35	40	45	50	55	60	65	70	75	80	85	90	95	100																				
21	0	5	10	15	20	24	29	34	39	43	48	53	58	62	67	72	77	81	86	91	96	100																			
22	0	5	10	14	19	23	28	32	37	41	46	50	55	60	64	69	73	78	82	87	91	96	100																		
23	0	5	9	14	18	22	27	31	35	40	44	48	53	57	61	66	70	74	79	83	87	92	96	100																	
24	0	5	9	13	17	21	25	30	34	38	42	46	50	55	59	63	67	71	75	80	84	88	92	96	100																
25	0	4	8	12	16	20	24	28	32	36	40	44	48	52	56	60	64	68	72	76	80	84	88	92	96	100															
26	0	4	8	12	16	20	24	27	31	35	39	43	47	50	54	58	62	66	70	74	77	81	85	89	93	97	100														
27	0	4	8	12	15	19	23	26	30	34	38	41	45	49	52	56	60	63	67	71	75	78	82	86	89	93	97	100													
28	0	4	8	11	15	18	22	25	29	33	36	40	43	47	50	54	58	61	65	68	72	75	79	83	86	90	93	97	100												
29	0	4	7	11	14	18	21	25	28	32	35	38	42	45	49	52	56	59	63	66	69	73	76	80	83	87	90	94	97	100											
30	0	4	7	10	14	17	20	24	27	30	34	37	40	44	47	50	54	57	60	64	67	70	74	77	80	84	87	90	94	97	100										
31	0	4	7	10	13	17	20	23	26	30	33	36	39	42	46	49	52	55	59	62	65	68	71	75	78	81	84	88	91	94	97	100									
32	0	4	7	10	13	16	19	22	25	29	32	35	38	41	44	47	50	54	57	60	63	66	69	72	75	79	82	85	88	91	94	97	100								
33	0	4	7	10	13	16	19	22	25	28	31	34	37	40	43	46	49	52	55	58	61	64	67	70	73	76	79	82	85	88	91	94	97	100							
34	0	3	6	9	12	15	18	21	24	27	30	33	36	39	42	45	48	50	53	56	59	62	65	68	71	74	77	80	83	86	89	92	95	98	100						
35	0	3	6	9	12	15	18	20	23	26	29	32	35	38	40	43	46	49	52	55	58	60	63	66	69	72	75	78	80	83	86	89	92	95	98	100					
36	0	3	6	9	12	14	17	20	23	25	28	31	34	37	39	42	45	48	50	53	56	59	62	64	67	70	73	75	78	81	84	87	89	92	95	98	100				
37	0	3	6	9	11	14	17	19	22	25	28	30	33	36	38	41	44	46	49	52	55	57	60	63	65	68	71	73	76	79	82	84	87	90	92	95	98	100			
38	0	3	6	8	11	14	16	19	22	24	27	29	32	35	37	40	43	45	48	50	53	56	58	61	64	66	69	72	74	77	79	82	85	87	90	93	95	98	100		
39	0	3	6	8	11	13	16	18	21	24	26	29	31	34	36	39	42	44	47	49	52	54	57	59	62	65	67	70	72	75	77	80	83	85	88	90	93	95	98	100	
40	0	3	5	8	10	13	15	18	20	23	25	28	30	33	35	38	40	43	45	48	50	53	55	58	60	63	65	68	70	73	75	78	80	83	85	88	90	93	95	98	100 --------

Note: All non-whole number scores have been rounded up.

INDEX